KALIMANTAN & REGION

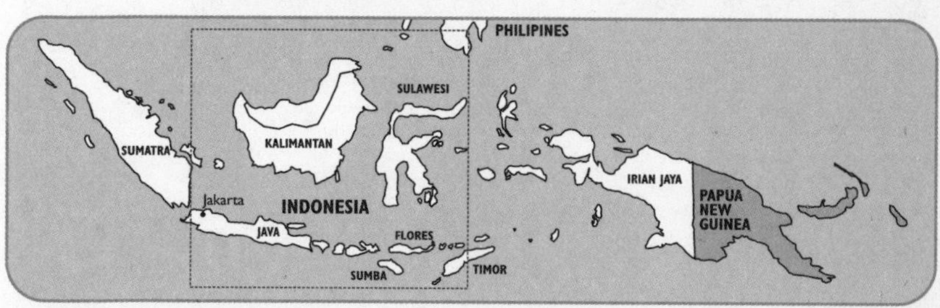

Published by: Sid Harta Publishers

P.O. Box 1042
Hartwell Victoria Australia 3124
email: author@sidharta.com.au

Internet sites:
http://www.sidharta.com.au
http://www.publisher-guidelines.com
http://www.temple-house.com

First Published: January 2002
Copyright: Kerry B. Collison
Design, Typesetting, Graphics: Alias Design
Cover Design: Mario Cicivelli

Editing: Robert N. Stephenson
Proofreading: A. J. Stephenson

© This book is copyright. Apart from any fair dealing for the purpose of private study, research, criticism or review, as permitted under the Copyright Act, no part may be reproduced by any person without the written permission of the copyright owner.

Collison, Kerry B.
ISBN: 0 957870 93 0
Printed by: Shannon Books

INDONESIAN GOLD

©

Kerry B. Collison

Also by Kerry Collison

Non Fiction

The Happy Warrior – an anthology of Australian Military Poetry
Co-edited by: Kerry B. Collison & Warrant Officer Paul Barrett

In Search of Recognition – the Leo Stach Story
(Biographical)

Fact-based Fiction

The Fifth Season

Indonesian Gold

The Asian Trilogy
consisting of:

Jakarta

Merdeka Square (Freedom Square)
(book of the month, Singapore)

The Timor Man
(book of the month, Singapore, Hong Kong, Australia)

Screenplays

Co-author – *The Golden Flux*

Kerry B. Collison followed a distinguished period of service in Indonesia as a member of the Australian military and government intelligence services during the turbulent period known as 'The Years of Living Dangerously'. This was followed by a successful business career spanning thirty years throughout Asia.

Recognized for his chilling predictions in relation to Asia's evolving political and economic climate through his books, he brings unique qualifications to his historically-based vignettes and intriguing accounts of power-politics and the shadowy world of governments' clandestine activities.

Further information is available on the
Internet site: http://www.sidharta.com.au

Photo: Courtesy of Dominion Newspapers, N.Z.

Indonesian Gold

Author's Note

For those readers who are new to Indonesia, The Philippines and the Malay Archipelago, or unfamiliar with Australian slang, there is a glossary at the back of this book, following the Postscript.

The use of italicised dialogue is deliberate – this indicates that the characters are, in fact, conversing in their own tongues.

This story is a work of fiction. The inspiration for this novel was based on events surrounding the infamous, billion-dollar BRE-X gold fraud, and the determined few who recklessly destroyed so many lives and severely impacted on indigenous cultures with their all-consuming quest for gold, in Kalimantan, Indonesian Borneo.

The characters as depicted in Indonesian Gold and the events recorded in this book are not intended to reflect any association with any real person in any way, with the exception of those characters whose names are accurately recorded.

'Be not penny-wise; riches have wings,
and sometimes they fly away by themselves,
sometimes they must be set flying to bring in more.'

FRANCIS BACON (1561 – 1620)
Essays: *Of Riches*

Part One

Fire, Water, Earth and Wind

Prologue

The pilot's grip on the cyclic control firmed instinctively as an abrupt wind change challenged the hovering helicopter, lateral stability maintained as he manipulated the collective and foot pedals to position the helicopter directly above the deserted stretch of exposed, river sand.

Droplets rolled down the pilot's brow momentarily blinding, and he cursed loudly, wiping sweat-stung eyes with the back of his torn flying suit as he struggled to identify movement through the thick, jungle canopy, along the river's edge.

Where the hell were they?

His concern growing, the pilot permitted the chopper to drift as he continued to search for signs of his party, relief sweeping across his face when he spotted the men breaking from the dense jungle, dragging their unwilling companion towards a narrow, treeless strip near the water's edge. Without hesitation, the pilot decreased the main rotor's lift, the hasty descent resulting in his approaching passengers' near decapitation as whirling blades drove the placid, silicon-laden carpet below into a maelstrom of stinging, blinding river-sand.

Camouflage-battle-dressed soldiers dragged their gagged captive across the shallow water and onto the sandbank, the soft, dry surface tugging at their boots and she pleaded, begging for mercy, her cries drowned by the helicopter's blades as these chopped furiously through the thick tropical air.

The pilot signaled, impatiently, observing as the men bundled their prisoner on board. He then drove the Bell 205 to five thousand feet, before navigating his way visually to the drop zone. There, he hovered steadily, cursing the two men as they struggled to untie their hysterical victim's hands while she kicked and screamed.

Her captors punched her repeatedly – savagely. When her limp frame offered no further resistance, the killers removed the cloth covering her face and tossed her, unconscious into space, watching in silence, as she tumbled earthwards towards the slashed and burned forest floor, below.

★ ★ ★ ★

The young woman's death would be recorded as a suicide. Two months later North American stock markets would reel in shock when it was discovered that the Kalimantan gold mine, once touted as the world's richest deposit, was indeed, worthless.

Chapter One

MAY 1989

KALIMANTAN TIMUR

(INDONESIAN EAST BORNEO)

To the unskilled, the suggestion of change in the still, suffocating, humid forest air might have gone unnoticed. As the momentary breath of wind passed by ever so gently, Jonathan Dau paused, conscious of the shift in the natural balance of his immediate environment. The shaman cocked his head to one side and listened. Somewhere, amongst the trees, a wild pig snorted and the shaman stiffened – identifying the deception; and one so often played by the spirits. Encumbered by this thought, the Dayak chief's hand unconsciously moved to the gold amulet hanging on a simple thread around his neck, and he whispered an appropriate chant.

Deep in the sun-hidden canopy above, where wild, black-speckled orchids hung unnoticed, protected from man's curious hand, *proboscis* monkeys engaged in dispute or play squealed – their occasional engagements of no importance to the *Penehing* leader, Jonathan Dau. With brow creased and a perceptive eye, he searched his timeless surrounds, finding reassurance when the hornbill came into view; satisfied that she would watch over him. Equipped with the cautionary signals his instincts and empiric knowledge had taught him to respect, the shaman exhaled slowly and paused. Then, with rehearsed motion he drew deeply, his chest swelling, as he inhaled the forest's air. His senses questioned the scents and movements within his immediate environment. Becoming one with the forest and its demanding spirits, he remained motionless, as time moved slowly forward. Then the shaman's eyes glazed and he stood silently centered on the gently swaying bridge; a giant butterfly flapping across his vision unseen, but recognized by its presence as the chief remained in trance-like state.

The squawk of a hornbill shattered the moment. A puff of wind caressed his cheeks and he turned and looked downstream; his eyes followed the black hornbill's flight along the narrow river's course, before her form blurred amongst the towering, giant forest trees. The *dukun* remained paused, alert, and when he recognized the hornbill's familiar cry, he knew then that the interlopers were near.

Jonathan Dau offered a brief chant before he cautiously lifted one foot then another, moving at surreptitious pace while proceeding across the rickety, twisted, ageing twine-and-bamboo suspension bridge strung perilously across the narrow gorge, and over the cascading falls far below. Suspecting that wandering forest ghosts, those lost souls known to roam the misty, upper-river reaches remained in observance he decided that it would not be prudent to linger there. Jonathan Dau quickened his pace and, with determined steps, soon left the dangling bridge well behind. He entered deep into the forest where in compatible blend, his image fused with the sun-blocked landscape. Now in perfect harmony with the surrounding spirits, Jonathan Dau, chief shaman to the *Aoheng, Penehing* tribe made his way downstream to where the reported sighting had been made.

* * * *

Eric Baird accepted that swatting the mosquito would be a waste of energy. By the time the insect's blood-drawing presence was obvious, the damage would already have been done. He raised his hand perfunctorily, missed, sighed then moved his body forward to restore circulation to a now bruised, near-calloused backside.

The expedition had, without doubt, been the most disastrous he had ever undertaken in his years spent dragging his frail, thin frame through Indonesian leech-infested, swamps and jungles. He sighed, again, his despondency due more to the absence of his companion, Mardidi, than the overwhelming obstacles encountered since leaving the young and ailing Javanese, two days downstream. Mardidi had succumbed to yet another malaria bout just days before and Baird, albeit reluctantly, was obliged to leave his personal assistant behind. Baird pushed ahead to maintain the punishing survey schedule. An experienced expatriate geologist, Baird valued the advice and experience of field assistants, wishing now he had not acted so hastily in moving this far upstream without reliable guidance.

He listened to the longboat crew's mumblings and, although unable to understand their dialect, their mood reflected their misgivings at having ventured into unfamiliar territory. The three-man crew consisted of *Modang* river-Dayaks, whose temperament had become visibly hostile as their party progressed upstream, following un-chartered tributary systems that fed the great Mahakam River. They were now in P*enehing* territory, the Dayak tribal group known for their mystical powers, derived from decapitating their foes. Baird, questioning his own judgment at having undertaken this expedition without his partner, drifted off into a troubled review of events which had brought him to this relatively unexplored place.

★ ★ ★ ★

Baird's survey party had left the provincial capital, Samarinda, a week before where he had made final arrangements for the expedition, sending Mardidi on errands to purchase supplies from the city's well-stocked stores. They had flown from Jakarta to Balikpapan, and then traveled by minibus between these two coastal cities, which served as communications and business centers for the wealthy province.

Borneo's diverse cultures and local economies were well known to Eric Baird. East Kalimantan exports exceeded four billion American dollars annually, ninety percent of which being generated from oil and natural gas products. Huge plywood factories, owned and operated by presidential palace cronies, dotted the landscape, while diminishing forests were grave evidence of their success. Baird, who had conducted surveys across the greater part of Central and East Kalimantan, had trudged through snake-filled swamps, found Samarinda's crossroads environment, a city where Chinese millionaires conducted business on mobile phones and carpetbaggers lined the streets, dull and uninviting.

Founded by *Bugis* warrior-merchants who had sailed their *perahus* across the straits from southern Sulawesi in the early 18th Century, Samarinda's isolated population had since exploded as a result of oil and gas discoveries, exceeding a quarter of a million by the 1990s. As the point of departure for all river travel inland, the city's merchants maintained a generous flow of goods, their small stores boasting the latest in electrical equipment smuggled from neighboring Singapore and Hong Kong. Here, where the Mahakam River Bridge splits the capital in half, huge log rafts heading for nearby mills exacerbate conditions amongst the dangerously congested river traffic as ships of all sizes maneuver their way through precarious lanes. Fiberglass, aluminum and timber speedboats crashed over each other's wakes as they streaked across the brown, choppy waters, their overpowered outboard engines screaming warning of approach. Downstream, where the river opened into a wide delta before flowing into the strait of Makasar, smaller craft hauled huge, succulent river-shrimp from nets strung across the myriad of channels crisscrossing the delta area.

Baird has been sent out to reconnoiter an area identified by airborne geological surveys as promising, an area yet to be taken up by any mining interests. His mission was to walk over the target area taking samples for analysis, make a general assessment of the geology and attempt to establish dialogue with local tribesmen regarding their concessions. His brief included identifying properties with gold potential, both alluvial and hard rock deposits – areas that could easily be acquired from traditional owners, and would withstand an independent geological survey inspection. The expatriate geologist's knowledge of Indonesia's mineral opportunities was unique, having spent almost twenty years plodding across the country's fields, valleys and swamps, checking terrain and examining deposits as a freelance geologist. With the surge in general exploration over recent years, his services had remained in demand, his fortunes improving beyond expectation until he had become involved with Alexander Kremenchug, a flamboyant expatriate would-be-mining entrepreneur. Now, as he approached his fortieth birthday, Baird was desperate to recover from his financial slump, determined now to rebuild the fortune lost through his association with Kremenchug.

Being *au fait* with the methodology devised by many of these investors, Baird had been closely associated in a number of speculative arrangements with Canadian and Australian interests. A plethora of less viable, foreign mining companies had swamped Indonesia over the past decade, eager to participate in the country's growing mineral boom. Baird had acted as consulting geologist to a number of these entities many of which, he discovered, could barely pay for his services let alone establish a *bona fide* mining operation. Nevertheless, he needed to recover his losses, and accepted whatever work came his way.

His role as geologist often required his participation in negotiating with all levels of Indonesia's mining fraternity, from village peasant to senior government bureaucrats. He would venture into relatively unknown areas believed to bear significant gold or other precious mineral deposits, conduct a general survey, and then submit his report to the client. Practice dictated that in the event Baird's report was in any way promising, negotiations with the traditional rights' owners would be concluded, followed by a formal application being processed with the Department of Mines. The foreign participant would then make announcements to their own Exchanges hoping that the Indonesian gold frenzy would drive their shares up and beyond par value. Depending on the viability of the find, Baird would often instruct his stockbroker to buy into the relevant miner's stock before any announcement could be made, selling whenever he acquired advance information relating to drilling results.

In 1988, the year following his disastrous losses, desperate, Baird had agreed to support Alexander Kremenchug's proposal to acquire a number of local, Kalimantan gold leases, and offer these as equity in future, Canadian public company floats. Apart from identifying prospects based on geological formations, Baird was also responsible for convincing the traditional owners to surrender their concessions in exchange for future payment, once mining had commenced.

Baird had set out, surveying available areas around Palangkaraya in Indonesian-Borneo's southernmost province and, after some months, having secured a number of interesting sites for future investigation, moved around the east coast to the Mahakam River. He rested for two weeks in Samarinda, the sores on his arms and legs the result of mosquitoes, leeches and rashes that inevitably accompanied surveys into such remote parts, not yet healed from incessant scratching. When his companion and assistant, Mardidi, had suffered a reoccurring malaria attack, Baird had been tempted to postpone the Mahakam survey and return to Jakarta for a number of months, to recuperate. But the urgency in Kremenchug's voice when Baird had phoned from Samarinda suggesting the delay had put an end to that.

★ ★ ★ ★

The Australian geologist had taken a room in the river port's Mesra Hotel, an oasis by Borneo standards and one that could never have survived without expatriates and Indonesia's timber tycoons. In contrast, Mardidi's accommodations in the local *losmen* were, however, far from luxurious. Although Baird insisted that they share his tent when out in the field, the geologist remained distant, even aloof towards the younger man when in the presence of other foreigners. Baird had explained the social parameters that required their relationship remain covert, and Mardidi abided by these.

After a number of days resting, Mardidi had been able to rejoin Baird. Provisions and equipment loaded, the two men had boarded a speedboat before sunrise and headed upstream at speed, the powerful outboard engines weaving through the perilous path, blocked at many points by half-submerged logs.

This first leg of their journey lasted until dusk, leaving the men with tired, and aching bodies. Their arrival at the Long Bagun, *losmen*-styled rest station had been expected, the staff there had been alerted by radio. Here, the river's conditions required a change in carrier and, as it would have been foolhardy to attempt the rapids in darkness, the group remained overnight, retiring early in preparation of yet another pre-dawn start. The following morning the two men watched as their provisions and other precious cargo were loaded into a cigar shaped longboat, Baird satisfied that the two-hundred-horsepower outboards hanging over the stern, would get them to Tiong Ohang before nightfall.

Following the river's meandering course throughout another monotonous day, they reached the river station and Mardidi suffered another relapse. Baird decided to leave him there to recuperate – electing to complete the survey alone, promising to return within the week. He left sufficient supplies and cash with the villagers to cover Mardidi's needs, then addressed the problem of whether to retain the *Modang* boatmen, or call for others from further upstream.

He was now in a quandary. Changing crews, which also meant vessels, without his assistant to oversee the transition might result in equipment essential for the survey either being damaged, or even disappearing altogether. He decided to continue with the longboat-men already on hand, and offered them bonuses to transport him to where he intended establishing the isolated base camp. The *Modang* crewmen had reluctantly agreed. Baird spoke to the headman and, assured of their commitment to care for Mardidi, left his companion and his first aid kit, in their care. Now, alone with the disgruntled crew, his concerns grew as their mood became openly aggressive, and he regretted his hasty decision to move ahead without his Javanese assistant.

★ ★ ★ ★

Leaving the Mahakam, they ventured deeper into the reaches of the secondary tributary system, and the *Modang* crew became increasingly agitated, as they were reminded of the *Penehing-Dayak's* past penchant for taking heads. Many downstream-river dwellers maintained that the practice was still evident amongst the more isolated groups that dwelled in the Mount Batubrok foothills, not far from where Baird was determined to visit.

Needles of dancing sunlight pierced the heavy-foliaged jungle canopy whilst unfamiliar sounds tricked their ears. Swept with fear, the lead boatman whispered in his own dialect to the crewman aft, possibly suggesting they abandon the foreigner, and leave this dark place. Baird sensed a change in the air – a chill touched his spine as he caught a glimpse of the navigating crewman's stony features when he turned and signaled his co-conspirator. The longboat's engines were immediately stifled in response to the navigator's gesture. Alarmed by the sudden quiet and the guide's obvious concern, Eric Baird fought familiar bowel-tugging dread of the unknown, the jungle rushed to envelop their surrounds and his mind raced, and conjured up non-existent dangers. A shrill call permeated the choking stillness and all reared back as a low-flying, black, rhinoceros hornbill struck out from a nearby bank, startled by their presence. Baird heard a loud grunt followed by movement along the muddy riverbank as camouflaged predators rose in readiness, then something slid from the shadows into the water nearby.

'*Ada apa, sih?*' – 'What is it?' Baird asked, his voice a hoarse whisper, a raised palm in response, silencing him immediately. He tucked his arms inside the boat's hull, and his nervousness grew when the forward crewman's hand went to the sheathed, razor-sharp *parang* hanging at his waist.

'*Babi*,' the man announced, and turned with a wide grin across his face. A wild pig broke through the thick undergrowth, raised its snout, sniffed, then turned and fled.

The Australian's eyes raced along the shadowy riverbank reaches, every log a frame in his mind depicting a crocodile waiting to feast on his carcass. He shivered, reached up to brush aside hanging vines partially blocking his vision and froze; a well-camouflaged but deadly poisonous snake coiled within inches of his outstretched fingers. Baird was momentarily lost in the screaming quiet that only a jungle environment can deliver; he recovered from his lapse once the danger had passed. Shaken, he reached for a cigarette, fumbled when he attempted to open the silver cigarette case which then slipped from his hands into the partially, water-filled, and now drifting longboat. Soon, he would be all out of cigarettes and he looked at the intimidating navigator, wondering where the man had secreted the dozen or more cartons that had so mysteriously disappeared during the previous night's camp.

Mutely, Baird observed as both men extracted paddles, secured inside the hull, and guided the long, wooden vessel on a course parallel to the embankment, bending low to avoid being snared by the thick, clinging vines. Drawn by the current the longboat continued to drift, entering a much narrower flow, separated now from the larger stream by a series of broken mud banks. Less than ten meters to either side decaying jungle growth blanketed the forest floor. The dank surrounds were spotted with wild, and highly toxic mushrooms, spawned under intermittent sunlight, and offering instant death to the foolish. Baird checked his compass then squinted up through the canopy at the fading light, anxious to reach his destination and establish camp before nightfall.

Before he embarked on this expedition Baird had examined Mines Department data and Dutch records covering the Upper Mahakam reaches. He decided to survey a relatively un-chartered area where a number of minor tributaries entered the main river system.

'*Start the engines,*' Baird ordered in *Bahasa Indonesia*, the national *lingua franca*. His voice carried more bravado than he felt. The boatmen glanced at each other, their unspoken words clearly understood.

'*Come on,*' he urged, '*we need to find somewhere to camp, before dark.*'

'*Tidak mau terus, Tuan,*' the man crouched forward announced, refusing to go on. '*Kami mau pulang,*' he added, suggesting that they return to their village downstream.

They had been contracted to ferry the geologist upstream, clear a site for his base camp then return. Baird had originally planned on spending two weeks surveying the area and was counting on the local villagers to provide river transport back to the transit station. But now, with Mardidi not at his side, and having not seen any semblance of village life in over two hours, he accepted that his plan lay flawed.

'*Okay,*' Baird sighed, tapping the wallet they knew he kept in the jacket's pocket. '*I will pay you an extra five day's charter if you continue for another day,*' but the men immediately started shaking their heads.

'*This is a bad place, Tuan. We don't wish to continue,*' one complained.

'*Alright*,' Baird's experience warned him that now was the time to be generous. '*I'll pay you for an additional ten days if you continue*.'

While the two men discussed the situation, heatedly, Baird waited anxiously for the expected counter offer, annoyed that he could not understand the *Modang* dialect, his anxiety growing with each passing minute.

'*We could drown him in the river and take all his money*,' the more confident of the two suggested.

'*Why don't we just leave him after making camp?*' the boatman aft responded.

'*No*,' the other argued, '*if we take his money, we can't leave him alive*.' They had observed the geologist's billfold when advance payment had been made for the longboat. The local currency, Rupiah, was far too bulky. Baird was carrying American dollars which were easily exchanged even in the most remote corners of this vast country.

The second man appeared unconvinced. '*It would be better that someone finds an empty camp*,' he insisted. '*We will surely be questioned. If remains of a camp are found, we will be believed. We could say that he sent us back*.'

Baird's uneasiness increased. He knew they were discussing him; their furtive looks a clear signal that trouble lay ahead.

'*Start the engines!*' he demanded, concern now evident in his voice. '*I will pay you an extra fourteen days and no more*.' He hesitated, looking over his shoulder first at the man aft, then forward to the more belligerent of the two. '*Okay?*'

The *Modang* boatmen exchanged glances, considering their options. If they *were* to throw the foreigner into the river, it would be unlikely that his body would be discovered. The suggestion of establishing camp before killing the man made sense. They could poison him, take his money, then return to their village. The *Penehing Dayaks* would be blamed. The boatman nodded slowly, Baird interpreted this as acceptance whilst, in reality, the other was contemplating how he would remove the foreigner's head to lay blame on the local inhabitants.

'*Boleh juga!*' The boatman answered, feigning acceptance. The foreigner nodded, and the outboard engines roared into life.

An hour later Baird called for the longboat to slow when they came upon a clearing that reached down to the riverbank. Baird gave the setting a cursory inspection, before ordering the boatmen to land. The area was roughly half the size of a soccer field surrounded by thick forest and, to the geologist, the absence of tall timbers suggested that this site had been cleared at some earlier time. When he stepped ashore he could see that the strip was actually a small promontory, and decided that this would be a suitable location for his primary base. And, fearing creatures that crawled in the night, the men immediately set about having a grassy area cleared for the camp.

★ ★ ★ ★

As Baird and his reluctant team unloaded the longboat, their efforts were hampered by slippery conditions, shoulder-high grass, and fading light. As they worked, they were keenly observed. The *Penehing Dayak* shaman remained motionless, his almost invisible form woven into the intricate, rain-forest imagery as he leaned against the towering ironwood tree, contempt for the shadows that moved before him staining his face. Directly above, orchids of rare and dazzling beauty stood scattered amongst clusters of staghorns clinging effortlessly to the giant tree, whilst crimson-breasted wood partridges courted amongst the highest branches.

Jonathan Dau scrutinized the trespassers' movements as they established camp, more concerned with the white intruder and what his presence might mean, than the *Modang* boatmen with their Twin-Yamaha powered riverboat. The shaman was surprised that the *Modang* had accompanied the foreigner this deep into *Penehing* territory. A cruel smile crossed his lips – not so many years before these men would have been swiftly dealt with, their heads left as a warning to others.

There was no doubt in his mind that the white man and his two *Modang* companions were there to investigate gold deposit potential, within his community's territory. Angered at the intrusion, the shaman's jaw clenched as he continued to observe the men clear an area and establish their camp. Darkness threatened, and he observed closely as one of the boatmen slipped away from the others, momentarily disappearing from view. Then the shaman caught another glimpse of the man again, as he continued along the river's edge – and suddenly he was gone.

Jonathan Dau moved closer to the camp where he could see that the foreigner would sleep alone in the erected tent. He watched the fair-headed man eat from cans whilst preparing for the rapidly approaching night. Then one of the boatmen reappeared, standing half-crouched, directly within the shaman's view. In his right hand, grasped between thumb and forefinger, a *krait*, the highly venomous snake's striking, black and white banded body coiled around the man's arm. The shaman watched closely when Baird entered his tent and the boatman moved cautiously along the riverbank until reaching the longboat where he bagged the snake, then waited with his co-conspirator.

An eddy of air gently touched the shaman's face mimicking the caress of a woman's soft breath. Jonathan Dau sensed the spirit's presence and became even more alert, his eyes searching through the dim jungle light for evidence of its intentions. He spotted the black hornbill perched, almost within reach, overlooking the campsite. And, as Dayaks firmly believed the hornbill transported souls to heaven, the shaman's eyes narrowed, considering the scene before him – and contemplated which of the three men was about to die. Then, with measured patience the shaman settled down to wait, the green hue that concealed his presence turning to dark, confused shadows as the remaining sunlight blinked, before disappearing under the onset of night.

★ ★ ★ ★

Eric Baird sprayed insect repellent over his hands, neck and face, then sealed the two-man tent before climbing into his sleeping bag. He reached up and adjusted the Petromax light, then settled down to record the events of the day as the jungle's darkness swallowed the camp. The two *Modang* boatmen stretched out comfortably inside their longboat smoking the foreigner's cigarettes, and waited impatiently for him to go to sleep.

Having completed his notes, Baird placed them in a waterproof case then opened a small bottle and spilled the contents into the palm of his hand, swallowing several pills in succession. He looked over at the empty space alongside, admitting that, had Mardidi been there, the sleeping pills may not have been necessary. He then turned the Petromax lamp down, permitting the light to fade into darkness, his body slowly relaxing as his system reacted to the drug. Soon, Baird had drifted away and, by the time the boatmen approached with their deadly gift, he was asleep, the sound of the tent's zipper being carefully opened going unheard.

★ ★ ★ ★

Overhead, a brilliant moon sent scattered, blinking messages of light, the ghostly effect surreal as the silhouetted figure lifted the deadly *krait*. His hand moved towards the half-opened flap, the air still as a tiny, poisonous, Dayak dart, hit his neck. Instinctively, his free hand reached to where he had been stung, his heart ceasing to pump before the boatman collapsed to the ground. Startled, his companion jumped back to avoid being bitten by the now released snake.

Jonathan Dau raised the blowpipe he carried when hunting wild boar and aimed at the second boatman. He drew deeply, poised but for a moment then blew, the escaping air lost as the would-be-killer's eyes opened wide in shock, the deadly dart killing the man instantly.

★ ★ ★ ★

With the arrival of morning Eric Baird rolled to one side, the sleeping bag restricting his movement. A cramp in his lower, right leg jerked him awake from some convoluted dream. He winced, raised his leg and massaged the calf muscle trying to restore circulation, his head still groggy from the sleeping pills. He turned to wake Mardidi, frowning when he discovered that he was alone. Slowly, Baird dragged his body into a sitting position, reached for a cigarette and lit the clove *kretek*, burning his fingers as he struck the match. He swore as blood rushed to his brain, and succeeded in lighting the cigarette the second time around. He drew heavily on the unfiltered *Gudang Garam*, filling his lungs with the clove-scented aroma, the smoke bringing tears to his eyes and he coughed, then went in search for coffee. Baird wrapped a sarong around his waist and climbed out of his tent, surprised to discover that he had not sealed the zip properly. He wandered down to the bank to pee, yawning as he overlooked the stream, casting an occasional glance towards the longboat, relieved that the crew had not abandoned him during the night.

The geologist strolled lazily back to his tent, changed into field clothes then went down to the longboat, mystified by the absence of the boatmen. Assuming they had wandered off in search of game, he prepared breakfast for himself, demolishing a can of corned beef whilst he waited. With coffee on his mind, he lit the portable primus then sat on his haunches waiting for the water to boil. Half an hour passed before Baird concluded, that for the boatmen to leave their vessel unattended this long, something had to be amiss. Aware that it would be foolhardy for him to leave the camp until they had returned, the invitation for them to steal everything in his absence too great, he strolled back down to the longboat, calling out as he approached. There was no answer. Annoyed, Baird climbed down into the boat and went searching for the missing cartons of cigarettes. He flicked the loose cover tarpaulin to one side and froze.

Both crewmen lay stretched out, their faces grim evidence of how they had died. Baird leapt backwards, stunned, and fell overboard. Desperate, he groped his way up the muddy bank tearing nails from flesh as he slipped and slid, finally making it to his feet and ran towards his tent, terrified that whoever had murdered these men might still be lurking close by. Realizing that was no place to hide Baird stopped in his tracks, and stared around. Fear gripped his heart; in moments he was shaking with shock.

★ ★ ★ ★

The shaman had followed Eric Baird's movements fascinated with the foreigner's behavior. He had removed the deadly darts and placed his victims' bodies in the vessel, expecting Baird would decamp immediately upon discovering the dead crewman. The Dayak chief had considered killing the foreigner, but reasoned that an expatriate death would only bring grave consequences, for all. That he had taken the lives of the two boatmen in no way troubled the chief; the *Modang* had brought the white man to a sacred site and desecrated the soil by establishing camp there. He was deeply distressed that the outsiders had selected this location, and his concern that others would follow and disturb ancestral spirits in their quest for gold, prompted his next step. The shaman removed his clothing and extracted his father's *golok* from its leather sheath. With the machete raised in one hand and the blowpipe in the other for effect, he let forth a most terrifying call, and started running towards Baird.

The Australian heard the blood-curdling scream, and his jaw fell. When he realized that this savage looking creature meant danger, he snapped alert and ran back towards the river, slipping and sliding down the embankment. He scrambled on board the longboat, released the lines then climbed over the boatmen's bodies in his haste to get to the engines. He hit the starter – dismayed when the engine coughed and died. He punched the button hard, again, with the palm of his hand, a wave of relief flooding through his body as the outboards caught, and roared into life.

Standing further along the riverbank Jonathan Dau continued with his show, dancing around like the proverbial wild man of Borneo, yelling and cursing in his native dialect, waving the intimidating machete in the most menacing manner until Baird disappeared from view. Satisfied that the intruders were done with, he strolled back to where he had disrobed, dressed quickly then commenced the two-hour journey back to his village, through the densely timbered forest.

★ ★ ★ ★

The shaman moved with stealth along familiar paths, arriving at a point overlooking the most idyllic of river-island settings, where he took a moment to rest. From his vantage point on the ridge, he could clearly see across the waterfall-fed streams to his Longhouse village, a complex community building perched high on tall stilts, half-encircled by a limestone ridge. Spray rising from the waterfall on his left painted a welcoming rainbow across the sky, and the shaman offered a prayer of thanks to the mid-morning. Villagers tendered fields towards the center of the island, while children played at their heels and, downstream, where the river rejoined to become one again, a pocket of thick forest remained, untouched. In the distance he could see a longboat approaching, carrying supplies to the isolated tribe.

The chief moved down the path to the river's edge, passing through a naturally carved cavern hidden behind the waterfall, to emerge on the other side unseen. He crossed a rope and bamboo suspension bridge, acknowledging the guardian statues on either side. They had been placed there at the entrance to the longhouse by his forefathers to protect those inside against evil spirits. He stepped onto the boardwalk that followed the riverbank – the Perkins diesel's steady thump, thump, thump drifting up the gorge informing him that the elders were watching television, inside.

Jonathan entered the long, carefully planned dwelling unbuckling the *golok* in his stride, and was greeted by a chorus of voices acknowledging his return. He smiled, and joined his extended family, taking the privileged position reserved for the shaman in the communal room. There, he sat, comfortably cross-legged on a *tikar* mat, with the others, watching a European soccer match final via satellite, the parabolic dish mounted conspicuously outside.

★ ★ ★ ★

Eric Baird managed his way back to the transit station, but not before finding the courage to dump the two bodies overboard not far from where they had been murdered. Any investigation would not only complicate matters with respect to his client's acquisition of the general exploration area, but might possibly require his returning to the site. With an image of the wild, screaming bushman fresh in his mind, Baird opted to disguise the truth. He would fabricate a story that would be credible.

The authorities accepted his well-rehearsed and convincing story of how the boatmen had died. He remained at the transit station until Mardidi was well enough to travel, taking advantage of the delay to prepare a fictitious report for survey work he did not complete. The pair returned to Samarinda where Baird paid one thousand dollars compensation to the boatmen's families, the money gratefully received, the widow of one kissing his right hand in gratitude as her oldest child looked on, in bewildered grief – the boy's chest filling with pride when Baird explained that his father had died courageously, whilst attempting to save his drowning companion from the mighty Mahakam's currents, when a overhanging branch had knocked the man into the river.

Baird never revealed the true events to anyone; not even to Mardidi. Upon his return to Jakarta the following week, he submitted a copy of his report to the Indonesian Mines Department with recommendations that the area further east might be deserving of further exploration activity. Baird had no wish to ever return to the scene of his wild encounter, deciding then, that in the event Alexander Kremenchug *was* successful in putting a deal together with the Canadians, he would find a reason not to return to this site. Baird had copied an earlier report from his files; the data compiled some years before during a survey of terrain, relatively similar to the target area. He understood that Kremenchug needed a positive result from this initial survey, and he was only too happy to provide one. Baird collected twenty-five thousand dollars for his efforts and an undertaking from Kremenchug that he would be included in any vendor's share issues, once an investor had acquired the property.

By an accident of bureaucratic blunder and Baird's misleading submission to the Mines Department, Jonathan Dau's spiritual grounds remained untouched for another two years, when a group of Samarinda businessmen discovered that the stretch of river land had not been assigned to any of the mining companies. Nine months after these local entrepreneurs acquired the exploration rights, they, too, abandoned the prospect, when a number of calamitous survey expeditions earned the area a fierce reputation, and was then considered taboo.

And along the Upper Mahakam reaches identified as Longdamai, this isolated pocket of land became known as Longdamai *Sial* – a place cursed, even in tranquility.

★ ★ ★ ★

Chapter Two

November 1989

Jakarta

The instant the traffic slowed to a grinding halt, deformed children, the maimed and crippled, lepers and blind beggars all appeared as if by command. Many were guided, pushed or dragged between rows of stagnated vehicles by their helpers, most seemingly oblivious to the choking exhaust fumes that consistently blanketed the capital's congested arterial roads. Street urchins swarmed through the grid locked traffic, skirting amidst the carcinogenic-pumping machines, hands outstretched to the privileged within their chauffeured, air-conditioned cocoons.

Screaming horns added to the cacophonous moment as a child knocked hopefully against a Mercedes window offering an assortment of cigarettes, chewing gum, and Chiclets, intimidated in no way by the driver's obvious anger as he waved her away with clenched fist. She raised her eyebrows, mockingly, as if surprised or even afraid, then tapped with greater determination as the foggy image behind the heavily tinted glass moved. The ragged child tossed a glance further down through the midday traffic and observed that there was movement ahead. Recognizing the intermittent brake-light flashes as the traffic commenced to flow, she knew she would have to be swift.

'*Tuan!*' the child called with muffled voice. Billowing, ugly black clouds of fumes spilling from an adjacent bus' broken exhaust caused her to cough, and she tapped impatiently on the passenger door window with even more vigor, painfully conscious of the motorbikes that maneuvered their way between these near-stagnated rows of city traffic. Injury went with the territory; her scarred limbs carrying fresh scabs over old wounds, evidence of frequent encounters. A Suzuki squeezed past, the motorbike's burning exhaust within touch of her legs, extended rear-vision mirrors grazing her skinny shoulders scoring the flesh painfully and she wheeled, her eyes filled with venom as she spat, hitting the unsuspecting rider square on the back. Then she turned her attention to the car's obviously wealthy occupant.

★ ★ ★ ★

Amused, Stewart Campbell observed the child's antics with ambivalence, tempted to lower the window and drop a hundred *Rupiah* into her tiny hands. The driver, sensing the Tuan's mood, eased the Mercedes forward to discourage the girl but, ignoring the danger, she remained clinging to the door handle, undeterred. Swayed by her persistence, Campbell activated the electric windows creating an opening through which he held a crisp, newly printed one thousand Rupiah note, the money snatched from his well-manicured fingers as several discolored packets of gum appeared in an outstretched hand.

'*Terima kasih*,' he heard the scrawny peddler thank him as the window closed, the expatriate simply nodding as the sedan moved forward, his thoughts returning to the day ahead. Campbell glanced at his white gold, Patek Philippe watch and exhaled heavily, in obvious annoyance with the traffic congestion. He leaned back against the leather-upholstered seats and, with closed eyes, gently rubbed his temples. An earlier headache, legacy from the previous evening's overindulgences, threatened to revisit and he recalled the Saint Andrew's black-tie ball, thankful now he had resisted following the diehards to the Chieftain's home, for the traditional follow-on breakfast.

Campbell's mind roamed, occasionally glancing at familiar landmarks as the Mercedes crawled towards the congested, outer roundabout. The driver jockeyed for position amongst the other vehicles, skillfully avoiding a converted, smog-belching private minibus that had cut dangerously across their path, near spilling its load of standing passengers whilst they clung precariously to the overcrowded Toyota's rusty frame.

As the city's skyline became more visible through the smog, the impressive number of construction cranes evidencing Indonesia's apparent never-ending growth momentarily distracted Campbell, and he recalled how significantly the capital had mushroomed since his arrival, ten years before. A tight smile creased his face as he was also reminded of how little he had known, back then, about this sprawling, Moslem-dominated, fractious archipelago of two hundred million, and how much more there was to learn.

Although his professional background had given him some prior knowledge with respect to the republic's vast mineral, oil and gas wealth, Campbell quickly learned that the nation's real wealth lay in its diversity, and the depth of culture so apparent within the republic's multi-faceted society.

During his first years in-country, he had been contracted by Baron Mining, a North-American-based mining conglomerate, to conduct onsite geological field surveys throughout the republic. Campbell had trudged across areas in Indonesia never before visited by Europeans, slept amongst isolated villagers of West Papua and squatted around evening fires in Borneo's cloud-cloaked, highland communities – often listening to elders boast of not-so-distant times, when they were still feared for their headhunting, or cannibalistic practices.

Stewart Campbell's love affair with the island nation and its people had not been immediate – his initial reaction, when witness to the poverty-stricken peoples of the more neglected provinces in Eastern Indonesia, had cast its own, negative spell. Before completing his first year in-country, he had already decided not to extend his time in Indonesia. The corruption and tyranny of the Suharto regime, the debasement of many of the minority groups within the Republic, and the incredible environmental impact the former general's vested interest groups had throughout the islands convinced the American geologist that Indonesia could not survive under such corrupt and immoral practices. As the time for his departure approached, Campbell's position had mellowed, his attitude with respect to the 'Indonesian Way' tempered by exposure and opportunity. Before he realized how it happened, Stewart Campbell had become inextricably enmeshed in the gold and diamond potential of Kalimantan, as Indonesia's territories in southern Borneo were known.

In 1982, and in response to President Suharto's directive to accelerate the transmigration process that annually deposited tens of thousands of Javanese and Madurese families in outlying and difficult-to-control provinces, the Indonesian Department of Mines announced revised, new-generation operating contracts for foreign mining investment in all *Kalimantan* provinces. Campbell, who was virtually in the process of packing to leave and return to his parents' home in Washington State, was immediately galvanized into action. The enormity of such a push into Indonesian Borneo was a geologist's dream come true. Without hesitation, he cancelled his flight and went about securing documentation that would enable him to remain in the country legally. Campbell then approached the Indonesian Institute of Mines in Bandung and offered his services on the basis that they provided him with the necessary permits, the *quid pro quo* being that he would make himself available as an unpaid, consulting geologist for a few hours each month. The Bandung director agreed, and the American established his offices in Jakarta the following week.

Stewart Campbell could not have made his move at a more appropriate time. Indonesia's reputation as a viable, resource-rich destination for international, general exploration companies exploded onto the world mining stage with Freeport's staggering copper and gold discoveries, in *Irian Jaya.* Jakarta's hotels were overrun with waves of Canadian, American and Australian-based carpetbaggers touting offers to ignorant concession holders, often securing valuable mining rights from unwitting, indigenous owners in exchange for worthless paper scrip issued by nickel-and-dime, foreign, publicly listed companies. Although there were many genuine foreign operators prospecting areas throughout the archipelago, their numbers were heavily peppered with 'Second Board' entrepreneurs whose capital base could barely cover the costs of their overseas visits, let alone support any commitment to mine viable projects. Word spread across the nation to isolated communities in Sulawesi, Irian, Kalimantan, and Sumatra, from Sabang to Merauke and a flood of hopeful, provincial concession holders poured into the capital in eager search of foreign partners. Most held simple, thumbprint-signed documentation issued only at village level asserting their claim over small, traditional plots whilst others, working in conjunction with local officials, carried letters from higher up the food chain, often signed by provincial governors.

At the time, Campbell had been vociferous in his concerns with the gold-rush mentality and the central government's ambitious agenda to attract foreign miners at almost any cost. His condemnation of the system that stripped traditional owners of their rights by transferring these through a maze of middlemen, corrupt government officials and influential military groups only to be surrendered to foreign brokers, made Stewart Campbell unpopular amongst his expatriate peers. Not-so-disguised threats filtered down through the Mines Department suggesting that his appointment to the Institute should be revoked. The Director immediately instructed Campbell to refrain from making further statements and the American agreed, acknowledging that his tenure and legal residency were dependent on the institute's goodwill.

Thereafter, he observed in dismay as large tracts of land were resumed for direct investment leaving traditional owners sidelined with little, if any, compensation. Tens of thousands of square kilometers were contracted to foreign miners, whose financial standing was obviously questionable, the necessary due diligence checks easily avoided in an environment where corruption ruled. Flamboyant directors steered their stockholders into relationships and commitments that would have attracted considerable rebuke by their own country's monitoring authorities, had such activities been undertaken at home. Around Jakarta's mushrooming bars such as the *George and Dragon* and *The Eastern Promise* language changed, adapting new terminology to expatriates' lexicons. 'Farm In' and 'Farm Out', 'Contracts of Work', 'Diamond' and 'Core Drilling' virtually became mandatory vocabulary for one to participate in any bar dialogue as the number of opportunists grew, and deals were struck in the smoke-filled drinking holes.

Although unpopular with the brokers, Stewart Campbell's consultancy grew exponentially to the surge in mining activity, his clients, mainly American interests, keen to evaluate leases on offer by smaller, and under-capitalized corporations, clearly incapable of developing the concessions they had acquired.

⋆ ⋆ ⋆ ⋆

Campbell's driver pulled to an abrupt halt with an apologetic look, his concerned eyes scanning the internal rear-vision mirror for his *Tuan's* response. Unexpectedly, a military convoy had punched through the mid-morning traffic, lead motorcycles' sirens signaling their intrusion, demanding passage and access to the Senayan Sports Complex where elements of TNI, the Indonesian Armed Forces, were assembling in preparation for the Heroes' Day parade. On his left, he could see lines of light tanks, AMX-13s, PT-76s and Scorpions. Saladin and Ferret reconnaissance vehicles were scattered amongst a large number of the Army's APCs – Saracens, Commando Rangers and Stormers were prominent. And, above the Asian Games Complex, a squadron of BO-105 helicopters practised maneuvers for the big day.

Campbell sat in quiet repose as his vehicle continued down the main protocol road, *Jalan Jenderal Sudirman*, reflecting on how Indonesia's brutal, military-controlled government had so firmly ensconced itself under President Suharto's guardianship. He had learned that, in order to succeed in this country, one required access to all echelons within the TNI military and political machine, as the armed forces had developed extensive business interests across the nation, penetrating all sectors of the economy – the mining sector amongst the more recent to attract the generals' interest. Once General Suharto had assumed power in a *coup d'etat* in 1966, the Javanese and Sumatran generals had set about monopolizing the Indonesian economy, forging working relationships with Chinese *cukongs* who were only too eager to share in the spoils. Using foundations as their guise, senior officers accumulated great wealth, the stars on their shoulders guaranteeing their fortunes.

Stewart Campbell accepted that the country *had* benefited under Suharto. Literacy had climbed dramatically, longevity increased, family planning programs had been implemented and infrastructure projects all provided a standard of living unknown during the Soekarno years. Nevertheless, the increased levels of disposable income had come at a price. The dictatorial president's family's domination of all commercial activity resulted in project cost being inflated to compensate for massive commission payments to the First Family, their wealth estimated in the tens of billions of dollars as the national debt spiraled out of control. The First Lady was irreverently referred to as *Madame Ten Percent*, and not because her given name was Tien. Charities and foundations chaired by Madame Tien played an integral role in the gathering processes, collecting fees and siphoning off funds for vested-interest projects. Suharto's sons and daughters led the charge in gutting the economy, their greed only exceeded by their arrogance as their power and wealth grew to incredible proportions. Nepotism was alive and well in Indonesia and Campbell accepted that, to survive, it was essential that he address the situation pragmatically, as had the Chinese.

He was reminded that the Chinese had been targeted during the 1965-66 anti-communist sweeps across the nation when more than half a million Indonesians died, surprised how the collective memory of those murderous times failed to identify current trends. Campbell, conscious of the growing groundswell of indigenous anti-Chinese sentiment, believed it inevitable that history would repeat itself. The disparity between rich and poor was growing at an alarming rate, the powerful, *pribumi* Islamic parties becoming more outspoken in the mosques.

Under the New Order's patronage, new dynasties were created, *cukong* families such as the Lims and Riyadis enjoying a meteoric rise in their fortunes and global influence; Mochtar Riyadi's son James, a frequent visitor to Governor Clinton's offices where he assisted to fill the future president's coffers with re-election campaign funds. Ranches, banks, condominiums, hotels and casinos in Australia, New Zealand, Singapore and the United States felt the hand of Jakarta's *nouvea riche* Chinese as they galloped down the international acquisition trail. And, within Indonesia, steel and flourmills, cement plants, television broadcast licenses, timber concessions, textile factories, car assembly and even electric power plants were delivered to those favored by the family living in *Jalan Cendana*.

★ ★ ★ ★

Campbell's cell-phone dragged him out of his reverie.

'Thought you might have overslept,' the caller admonished. Campbell checked his wristwatch again, shrugging at being only half an hour late.

'Just about there, Phil,' he responded, with warmth. The men had attended the same campus, their friendship often tested by professional considerations. It had been Samuels who had been instrumental in Campbell's securing work with Baron Mining over the years, Stewart often acting as the other's local consultant to the multinational.

'Okay. I'm in Mina's Restaurant,' Samuels advised, just as Campbell's driver pulled into the hotel's driveway. Campbell hung up and then climbed out, nodding at the doorman who had opened the car's door.

'*Selamat datang, Tuan*,' the attendant welcomed.

'*Selamat siang*,' Campbell responded, entering the Sahid Jaya Hotel with leisurely stride, waving at the barrage of beautiful Indonesian receptionists.

'*Hallo, Mister Stewart*.' One of the staff, a Menadonese girl who had dated the foreigner occasionally, smiled, emphasizing the 'mister' in playful manner. Campbell stopped for a few moments to exchange pleasantries, enjoying the customary banter.

'*Where's your new girlfriend, Tuan?*' she challenged, hopefully, her body language obvious to all present.

'*Waiting at home with the others,*' he lied, enjoying the feigned looks of disgust and surprise as he wheeled and strode off towards the restaurant. The *maitre d'* greeted Campbell warmly, escorting him to a corner table where his client waited.

'Sorry I'm running a little late,' he apologized, permitting the waiter to unfold his serviette and place this across his lap. 'Usual traffic problems,' he added, casting a glance around the magnificent décor. Mina's specialized in Chinese seafood; the softly lit surrounds were decorated to resemble an outdoor, provincial fishing village. Fishing nets strung from a main mast pole centered amongst the buffet selections added to the ambience, whilst miniature, thatched roofs built above tables added the finishing touches.

Campbell surveyed the clientele, acknowledging an occasional wave from some, ignoring others. In the far corner he spotted a group deep in conversation, recognizing two of the men as Alex Kremenchug and Eric Baird. Kremenchug spotted Campbell, the forced smile and raised-glass requiring Stewart to respond.

'You know those guys?' Samuels asked, glancing over his shoulder.

'Sure,' Campbell replied. 'Permanent expats. Been around for years.'

'And the one in the suit?' Campbell glanced over again.

'The one sitting facing the others?' He took a brief moment to examine the man in question then shook his head. 'No,' he answered slowly and with some uncertainty. 'Can't say that I do.' Again he glanced over at the tall, middle-aged foreigner whose cheeks were partially covered with long, untidy, gray sideburns. Then Campbell frowned – something triggered his memory suggesting that he had seen the face before. 'I'm not sure.' He glanced over again, then shook his head, 'Should I?'

Phil looked at Stewart with raised eyebrows. 'I'm surprised,' he said, fidgeting with the silver cutlery unconsciously. 'Thought all you 'geos' knew each other.' The statement required no answer but Campbell's curiosity had been aroused.

'Well?' he pressed, annoyance creeping into his voice. 'Who is it?'

The other man smiled smugly, leaned back as the waiter reappeared and reset the cutlery. 'It's Christopher Fielding, for Chrissakes,' he revealed, *sotto voce*, watching for his consultant's reaction. Campbell frowned again, snapped a quick look at the man then nodded, as if deep in thought.

'Well, I'll be...' The words fell from his lips, softly, quite taken by surprise. 'Now what would *he* be doing in Jakarta?' he asked, rhetorically, his mind switching into gear as he recalled reading of the internationally renowned geologist's recent skirmishes with the Canadian courts. He could not resist glancing over again, his eyes locking with Alex Kremenchug's as he did so. Campbell smiled weakly and turned to his client. 'Oh to be a fly on *that* wall,' he suggested, lightly.

'Who are the others?' Samuels asked. Campbell shrugged his shoulders and sampled the mineral water as their attentive waiter withdrew.

'The short one with the anemic complexion is Eric Baird. Been around since the mining boom started. He's Australian. The tall guy with the permanent suntan and safari jacket is Alex Kremenchug. Not sure of his origins but is quite thick with Baird. They've had their fingers in a number of small mining ventures but nothing of any significance.' Campbell hesitated before continuing, reluctant to give all. 'Word is, Baird is not overly fond of the ladies, if you get my drift. He drinks far too much but knows his stuff. As for Kremenchug, he's suave, intelligent, but bullshits about his credentials too much for me. Rumor has it that he was asked to resign a directorship in some Aussie mining firm for dumping his shares without advising the exchange. He left the country not long after that and appeared here, sniffing around for leases. His knowledge of geology is purely empiric. A couple of years back he encouraged a group to invest in an alluvial deposit in Sulawesi based on surveys carried out by that little guy sitting alongside him.' Campbell nodded with a tilt of his head in Eric Baird's direction. 'I saw the initial sampling reports and later ran across one of the drillers who had worked on the survey. Kremenchug had given one of his drinking buddies the nod to build percussion rigs for the job. Of course, every time the hammer drove the pipe stem down, whatever gold may have been in the sample kept on falling to the bottom. There was very little recovered, Baird furious with Kremenchug at the time. The driller also revealed that they were pulled out of the field, and sent back to Jakarta. Seems that Kremenchug and Baird then used local tribesmen to complete the sampling procedures. The next thing we know is that the value of the foreign partner's shares had multiplied fourfold, based on those results.'

Samuels considered this and again lowered his voice. 'Well, they're in good company,' a thin crease suggesting a smile crossed his lips, before breaking to a smirk. 'Fielding's broke,' he claimed, breaking a hot bread roll in half. 'After that ball-breaking wife of his had finished working him over there wasn't much left to cover his debts.' Campbell watched as his client smothered the bread rolls with peppered pate and stuffed these in mouth, sucking the ends of his fingers as he related events leading up to Fielding's demise. 'A receiver was appointed and, the way I heard it, he entered into some sort of arrangement with his creditors. Considering his finances, I'm surprised he's over here. Who would ever have thought it possible? A guy discovers one of the greatest minerals finds in history and ends up with nothing! Just goes to show you…'

* * * *

Across the restaurant, Fielding leaned closer to his colleagues so as not to be overheard. 'How much work-up will be required?' he asked, pointedly, directing the question to Eric Baird. The Australian geologist had anticipated the question and was well prepared to defend the report.

'Not a great deal,' Baird replied. 'I've walked the property extensively and the initial sampling results are very encouraging.' Baird then went on discussing the geological aspects of the concession that both he and Kremenchug had offered the Canadian.

* * * *

Kremenchug sat back permitting the two geologists to communicate without any further input from him, pleased with Christopher

Fielding's response so far. Kremenchug was banking on Fielding's international reputation as a geologist to raise capital for the venture. Kremenchug had paid the Canadian's fares and related costs, bringing him over to Indonesia to meet with Baird and discuss how they might use the recently acquired gold acreage to float a new mining entity on the Vancouver Exchange. Kremenchug had been motivated by the growing Canadian interest in Indonesian prospects, wishing to cash in when this escalated, as he believed it would, once production commenced at the larger Kalimantan sites being operated by multi-nationals.

Kremenchug looked over in Stewart Campbell's direction. Although the envy he felt was not evident in his Slavic, expressionless face, nevertheless, it was there. Unconsciously, his hand ran over the gray, thinning scalp that once boasted a thick crop of black hair, his thoughts roaming as he heard Baird's voice drone on. There had been no real confrontation with the American, Campbell – Kremenchug's annoyance occasioned by the younger man's 'watchdog' mentality, with respect to foreign prospecting activities in Indonesia. That, and the fact Campbell had been negative when assessing a number of gold concessions Kremenchug had offered to one of the American's clients. The deal had fallen through, with Alexander Kremenchug taking Campbell's recommendations as a personal attack on his integrity. Subsequently, whenever the two crossed paths their exchanges were generally brief, but polite; Kremenchug's comments behind the other man's back, caustic, and often vitriolic. He signaled a waitress by raising his now empty glass.

'Gin and tonic, *Tuan*?' she asked, smiling warmly. Kremenchug nodded, twirling his index finger in the air to indicate a round.

'No, leave me out, Alex,' Fielding interrupted Baird's monologue. 'Still have a lot to do here.'

'Just these two, then,' Kremenchug pointed at his associate's empty tumbler, then settled back to listen to Baird's glowing report supporting the concession's viability to produce tonnes of gold.

★ ★ ★ ★

Kremenchug was confident that Baird's presentation would be convincing. The men were jointly responsible for delivering the government-approved concession. Under a prior arrangement, reached before inviting Fielding to Jakarta, they had agreed to equally split whatever vendors' shareholding might be negotiated in the proposed Kalimantan gold exploration company. Fielding had jumped at the offer to visit, Kremenchug's confidence that the company would be floated on the Canadian Exchange growing as Fielding warmed to the concession's potential.

All three men would receive a substantial allocation of fully paid vendors' shares in the Canadian company. Obviously, these shares would be placed in escrow, as required by law. Kremenchug had already established dialogue with Scott Walters, a Vancouver-based promoter cum financier. Walters had been receptive to providing whatever mezzanine capital might be required to take the deal public, as Indonesia had recently become 'flavor of the month' with Calgary and Vancouver stockbrokers. The list of Canadian mining companies vying for Indonesian properties was extensive, the huge volume of shares traded encouraging non-Canadian interests to establish new or subsidiary interests there.

Walters' offer to provide initial funding had been conditional, requiring Fielding to place his name on the concession as senior geologist, his stamp of approval sufficient to guarantee a successful capital raising. Although Christopher Fielding's private life had all but left the man broken, his reputation as a geologist remained intact. As a sweetener, both Kremenchug and Baird had suggested that Fielding take a position on the new company's board. They, in turn, would not seek any directorships, content to wait until their shares could be traded once the escrow period had expired – at which time they would sell and move on.

Baird and Fielding continued to discuss the merits of the concession throughout their lunch of chili crab, steamed prawns, rice and deep-fried grouper, Kremenchug content to listen, sipping his way through a constant flow of gin tonics before the geologists concluded their meeting. Fielding dipped the fingers of both hands in a lemon-scented bowl of water, dried his hands, picked up the documents then nodded in affirmation.

'Well, I'm in,' he smiled weakly. The Cathay Pacific flight from Vancouver to Jakarta via Hong Kong had taken more than twenty hours, the jetlag beginning to show.

Kremenchug was ecstatic, his alcohol-charged response over-enthusiastic, attracting the attention of other Mina guests.

'That's great news!' he gushed. 'You won't regret coming in with us, Chris.' He snapped his fingers summoning a waiter and, when the young man approached, ordered in a voice for all to hear. 'Get us a bottle of Moet Chandon!'

The champagne arrived, the inexperienced waiter's attempts to uncork the bottle ending with Kremenchug grabbing the wine impatiently, dismissing the embarrassed waiter and completing the task himself. With the champagne poured, he raised his glass. 'To the Kalimantan venture,' he offered the toast. Fielding and Baird raised their glasses together, their celebratory gesture not lost on those around.

'And to precious, precious gold,' Baird added, somewhat relieved and surprised that Fielding had accepted his evaluations so readily.

Their spirits lifted, all three men relaxed, the tone of their conversation tempered with newfound camaraderie as they exchanged stories, Kremenchug throwing in an occasional joke as the accumulative effects of alcohol took hold. Kremenchug peered over at Stewart Campbell's table, flashed an insincere smile, waved, then after some hesitation rose and sauntered over to where the Americans were sitting.

'Stewart!' he started, a glass in one hand, the other extended. 'Come and join us?'

Caught off guard, Campbell looked to Samuels for assistance while Kremenchug pumped his hand. 'We were about to leave,' Campbell offered, somewhat lamely.

'No, don't go yet.' Kremenchug had taken Campbell's guest's hand, expecting to be introduced. 'Come over and meet Chris Fielding. I'm Alex Kremenchug,' and after a pause, 'and you would be?'

His annoyance well disguised, Campbell smiled and introduced Phil Samuels. Kremenchug was visibly impressed. 'Ah!' he exclaimed. 'Baron Mining, no doubt? The heavies have finally arrived!' with which he turned, took hold of the man's arm and led him across to where Baird and Fielding were again engrossed in conversation. Campbell followed, gesturing for the *maitre d'* to bring their check. Chairs were hastily added to the table, the geologists rising to their feet as Kremenchug introduced the Americans. 'You already know Eric?' Stewart nodded. 'And this is Chris Fielding,' Kremenchug turned to Campbell's client and completed the formalities. 'Now, gentlemen, please join us for a glass of champagne?' He then realized that the bottle had been drained and called for another, whilst indicating that his guests should be seated.

'Alex, another time if you don't mind,' Campbell stepped in. 'We have appointments to keep.'

'Nonsense,' Kremenchug was insistent, 'sit down for a few minutes and help us celebrate.'

'Celebrate?' Campbell responded. Although not keen to be dragged into a session with these men, his curiosity got the better of him. 'What's the occasion?'

'Sit down, and join us first,' Kremenchug persisted. Campbell looked at the time and reluctantly accepted.

'Just one,' he warned, nodding to Samuels. They waited uncomfortably until the champagne was delivered to the table and uncorked.

'To our senior geologist,' Kremenchug announced, indicating Christopher Fielding, enjoying the look spreading across Campbell's face. 'And to gold mining in Kalimantan,' with which Kremenchug drained and refilled his glass in one motion.

Although pressed for time, Campbell appeared gracious. 'Congratulations seem in order,' he offered. Then, directing his question to Baird, asked, 'What areas are you holding?'

Eric Baird did not hesitate, now in effervescent mood. 'There are a number of sites,' he revealed, with great animation, 'one up in Palangkaraya and a couple more further north in *Kalimantan Timur*.'

'Alluvial?' Campbell asked.

'Not all of it.' Baird was enjoying this, his smug demeanor more than partially fuelled by the alcohol.

'Done any drilling yet?' Campbell pressed, observing the other man's eyes closely.

'Enough to convince us that we have a winner,' Baird bragged.

'Are you able to disclose your findings?'

'Guess that's up to our senior geologist here,' Baird replied, passing the buck.

Fielding shot a warning look at his associates, uncomfortable with revealing too much before corporate structure and funding procedures had been finalized in Canada. Deciding enough had been said, he straightened his shoulders and started to rise. 'It's been a long trip. If you gentlemen don't mind, I'm going to catch up on some sleep. When it's opportune, I'd be delighted to send you something more regarding the Palangkaraya site.' With that, he left the group hastily, having undertaken to call his associates, once he had rested.

Following Fielding's abrupt departure, Campbell and Samuels seized the opportunity to withdraw, leaving their unfinished drinks and a miffed Kremenchug for Baird to console.

'Campbell's right up himself,' Baird sneered at the American's departing back.

'Yeah, he can be a real prick at times,' Kremenchug said.

'Did you see his face when I mentioned Fielding's appointment?' Baird's cackle was more of a titter.

'Wouldn't be wise to wind him up too much. We don't want too much attention from the likes of him.'

'He's full of it!' Baird said, a little too loudly, attracting further looks of disapproval from a number of other guests in their proximity.

'You should be careful of what you say in front of Campbell,' Kremenchug was critical.

'Why, what can he do?' Baird lit a cigarette and blew a cloud of smoke over the table.

'He's well connected.'

'If you feel that way, why'd you bring him over?'

'I wanted to establish contact with the guy who was with him.'

'Don't know why you're jittery about Campbell. He doesn't have that many friends in the industry.'

'He has enough,' Kremenchug warned.

'Sure, okay.' Baird seemed miffed. 'I'll play it cool.'

'I'm glad to hear you say that, Eric. We've got a great opportunity here and I wouldn't want you to screw it up – for either of us.'

'I won't,' Baird promised, leaning back and permitting the waiter to give Kremenchug the bill.

★ ★ ★ ★

P.T. Subroto & Associates

'You seem to be in high spirits.' Air Vice Marshal (retired) Subroto waddled back into his office, expecting the Australian, Eric Baird, to follow.

'Looks like I'll be able to meet those outstanding payments, Pak,' Baird replied, respectfully.

'*What's happened?*' The Air Vice Marshal dropped his one hundred and twenty kilos heavily into the specially designed, reinforced leather and teak seat.

'*I've signed with a Canadian group, Pak. You remember Kremenchug?*'

Air Vice Marshal Subroto snorted with apparent distaste. '*That lintah-darah?*'

Baird disguised his annoyance with Subroto's response referring to Kremenchug as 'that bloodsucker'. '*Something beneficial will come of it,*' Baird tried to placate.

'*He is a parasite – Indonesia doesn't need people like him.*'

'*Kremenchug has given us a great opportunity, Pak.*' Baird was apprehensive with the retired officer's mood. He opened a fresh packet of cigarettes, flicked the bottom of the box, and offered the extended *rokok* to his sponsor. At first, Subroto ignored the offer then poked a chubby hand outwards, taking one of the clove sticks and holding it, ready for Baird to light.

'Really, Eric, you should look for others to assist you with our business.'

Baird felt the familiar tug to his stomach – the uncertainty of operating in this country with quasi-legitimate status had a severe downside. Foreign investment laws required substantial capital contribution, the benefits, enormous in terms of tax holidays and other considerations; for those who were limited financially but could bring the necessary expertise, there were but few options. Even marrying an Indonesian woman could not guarantee legitimate status, for Islamic Code influenced the laws. Regulations prohibited Indonesian women married to foreigners from holding directorships and acquiring trading licenses; and, there was no guarantee that foreign men married to local women would have the right of residency, let alone citizenship. As for acquiring the latter, he was aware that only one Westerner had been awarded this privilege under the Suharto regime, not that he wished to emulate the colorful Stephen Coleman, who had long since distanced himself from these shores.

Years before, Baird had taken the path so many of his fellow expatriates had chosen, establishing an Indonesian nominee company to provide legitimacy to their presence. Now, as others had discovered, there was a price to pay.

'*You are right, Pak,*' Baird deferred to the white-haired Air Vice Marshal, '*as soon as this contract is finished, I will not accept any more work from him.*'

'*It would be better for all of us,*' Subroto advised. '*The government is only interested in those who are serious about investing in Indonesia – and your friend does not fall into that description. He makes money from us without producing results for our people.*' He looked over expensive bifocals that had slipped down his near bridgeless-nose. '*And, I know for a fact that Immigrasi has been keeping a close eye on his activities here.*'

The mere suggestion that Immigration was monitoring Kremenchug twisted the knot in Baird's stomach even more, the inevitable panic attack sending his hands searching for an inhaler.

'*Why are the authorities so interested in Alex?*'

The General deflected the question. '*Because of your association, they could have you under surveillance, as well,*' Subroto suggested, '*and that makes me unhappy, Eric. I shouldn't have to remind you that whatever you do, whom you associate with, all reflects on me. When I first joined AURI...'*

Baird remained standing, as Subroto launched into one of his all-too-familiar harangues that would, predictably, revisit most of the Air Force General's career, reminding himself that this was a small price to pay for the revered, Javanese officer's sponsorship.

★ ★ ★ ★

Baird had come to understand that Subroto's early career had been tied, indirectly, to that of the country's president. In 1962, when Indonesia waged war over the Netherlands' last remaining outpost in Asia, West Papua, Subroto was there, serving under the *Mandela* Campaign commander, Suharto. It was a bittersweet time for the young General Suharto who had returned to the field, having been banished by the former C-in-C, General Nasution, accused of smuggling activities with the Chinese *cukong*, Lim Sioe Liong. At that time, Lieutenant Colonel Subroto and his fellow pilots had played a central role in the campaign, flying missions in their Soviet-supplied Tu-2, and Il-28 light, tactical bombers. Subroto had been more fortunate than many of his comrades during this confrontation, as the Dutch accounted for many of the inexperienced pilots during aerial engagements. Nevertheless, President Soekarno had heaped praises and medals upon all involved, when the future province fell to the Indonesians. And, as Subroto's name was linked with Suharto's with respect to the outcome, the AURI General was spared during the ignominious period that followed the coups of 1965, when the Indonesian Air Force was cleansed of its communist elements.

The AVM's star had then remained in limbo up until the AURI 1985 reorganization, when a large number of the country's senior ranking officers were either made redundant, or encouraged to enter Parliament, where the military maintained a controlling block of seats. Subroto had elected to move into private enterprise and was placed on the semi-retirement list, along with some fifty others of general rank, to assist with their transition from military to civilian roles.

It was because of Subroto's close links with the Indonesian Ministry of Mines, that Baird first approached the retired officer seeking sponsorship. That, and the fact Subroto had worked closely with the Australians during the early Seventies, when the RAAF gave AURI a squadron of Sabres to assist rehabilitate operational air-defence training. When Subroto learned that Baird had the capacity to introduce foreign mining companies, the Air Vice Marshal agreed to provide legitimate shelter for the geologist's activities.

At first, their arrangement had prospered. Baird, true to his word, succeeded in introducing a number of mining investment opportunities to Subroto who, in return, showed his gratitude by accepting the geologist into his family circle. But, when Baird's reputation had later been sullied over his dealings with Kremenchug, their relationship had slowly deteriorated, further exacerbated by Subroto's discovery of Baird's deviate sexual preferences which, in turn, led to Mardidi being removed from the office staff, and the appearance of Subroto's niece, Pipi Suhartono.

★ ★ ★ ★

Baird remained politely interested, relieved that Subroto was nearing the end of his often-repeated tale.

'And, when the Sabre flew over the rich rice paddies in Central Java, the pilot experienced a flameout, and ejected.'

Although Baird had heard this story before, he was always at odds as how best to respond to what happened next. As usual, he decided to appear quietly introspective.

'*Who would not believe in 'adjal*', Eric?' the General asked, rhetorically, referring to the belief that all death is predestined. '*A simple farmer, tilling the soil, who has most likely never strayed more than a few kilometers from his village and land since birth, suddenly hears the rush of wind and looks up and, in that moment, is killed by this strange object falling from the heavens.*'

It was normally at this point in the telling, that Baird would put on his serious face, feigning interest.

'*To die from old age or even disease is one thing. But, to be killed by an ejection seat when one has never even seen an aeroplane, surely must demonstrate that Allah planned for this to happen?*'

This, Baird knew, was his signal to nod his acceptance. '*It would certainly seem that way, Pak.*'

'*Yes, that is precisely my point!*'

Baird was surprised by Subroto's deviation from previous closings.

'*If someone dropped something on you, Eric,*' the Javanese's eyes danced mischievously, '*then we would be obliged to accept that such a mishap was, undoubtedly, by Allah's design.*'

Eric Baird experienced a familiar, sinking sensation in his stomach. During his years living in this country, he had learned that opinions were regularly offered, disguised in the most oblique forms. Javanese disliked confrontation – and, even when addressing foreigners, rarely came directly to the point. However, Baird clearly understood the underlying threat Subroto had made.

'*Pak 'Broto,*' he opened, reverently, '*this time, Kremenchug has agreed to give us shares in the Kalimantan venture.*'

'*You cannot trust this man,*' Subroto replied, obstinately.

Baird quickly calculated the value of his quarter of a million dollars in stock. '*We will be given almost half a billion Rupiah worth of stocks in the Canadian company.*'

Subroto removed his glasses, looked directly into Baird's eyes, and started tapping the desk with a ball pen. The US dollar equivalent was around two hundred thousand, the sum far more meaningful in light of recent losses. After some moments of deliberation, he reached across and, waving the pen in the air, asked, '*When?*'

Baird was swept with relief. '*Within the next months, Pak.*'

'*You will keep my share in your name,*' Subroto ordered, '*I don't want any dealings with Kremenchug directly. Is that clear?*'

That his sponsor had failed to thank him for the generous gift was of no consequence to Baird. Subroto could now be counted upon to support the Canadian venture, whenever obstacles appeared, as Baird knew they inevitably would. The mining industry had become an investment nightmare for the unsuspecting investor, the bureaucratic quagmire deliberately created by officialdom, a means for extracting payments from foreign participants.

'*I'll make the necessary arrangements, Pak,*' Baird promised.

Subroto's face turned friendly. '*Speaking of arrangements, Eric, how are things progressing between you and my niece?*'

Baird visibly trembled at the mention of Pipi Suhartono, unable to control his discomfort as he looked towards the closed door for escape.

'*I have been very busy with Kremenchug,*' he explained.

'*You shouldn't neglect her,*' Subroto's face suddenly became serious. '*Pipi is very fond of you, Eric, and you are fortunate to have a woman of her quality and education as a companion.*'

Baird felt his blood begin to freeze. Several months had transpired since Pipi had been introduced to him and, since that first meeting, Subroto had insisted that Baird accompany his niece to a number of formal functions, the most recent, a family wedding. Subroto's intentions were frighteningly clear to Baird, his dilemma, how to avoid involvement with Pipi without offending his sponsor. At Subroto's insistence, he had escorted Pipi to the movies once, and attended an outing to the Bogor gardens with members of her immediate family. Stunned when he discovered that it was assumed they were to become engaged, Baird had seriously considered leaving the country altogether, and had remained only because of Mardidi's ineligibility to obtain a visa for Australia. '*Pak 'Broto,*' Baird's hands were clasped in anxiety, '*I have the greatest respect for Pipi, but I am not ready for another commitment just yet.*'

Subroto's eyes narrowed considerably. '*Are you still involved with that banci?*'

Baird's stomach squeezed with the word. '*Mardidi is not a banci, Pak.*'

'*I am very disappointed, Eric,*' Subroto's voice dropped so staff eavesdropping could not hear. '*I thought I'd made it quite clear how I felt about that relationship?*'

Bereft of an answer, Baird's shoulders slumped, and he looked down at his feet, submissively.

'*He is just my very good friend, Pak,*' he said, knowing that he was on dangerous ground.

'*Is he the reason you don't like Pipi?*' Subroto challenged.

'No!' Baird worried where this was leading. '*I really do have deep feelings for Pipi, Pak, but I don't want to take on any additional responsibilities until I know that I can handle these, financially.*' A wave of nausea threatened, and again Baird looked to the door for escape.

Subroto accepted the compromise. '*Then don't leave it too long, Eric,*' he admonished, '*ladies like Pipi don't grow on trees!*'

'*I know, Pak, I know.*' Baird then mumbled something as he rubbed his stomach and grimaced, apologizing that he was not feeling well, and fled the office before Subroto could further advance their conversation.

★ ★ ★ ★

Subroto squeezed into the Mercedes' rear seat and instructed the driver to take him home. Fine, German engineering groaned underneath as the vehicle made its way through the congested city, heading south through Kebayoran Baru, through Kemang, and onwards to Cilandak. In pensive mood, the retired air force General leaned back into the deeply indented, leather seat and closed his eyes, pondering the import of Baird's future involvement in terms of their consultancy arrangement.

When Baird had first come to him more than five years before, he had not hesitated in offering the young Australian geologist sponsorship, and the corporate structure to facilitate his business dealings in Indonesia. Subroto recalled that time of great excitement and promise, as the New Order, under President Suharto, forged ahead, dragging the country up to competitive speed with the emerging tiger economies of Singapore and Malaysia.

In the years following Suharto's 1966 successful coup, Subroto had watched as many of the four hundred generals appointed under the Soekarno regime were either retrenched, or shifted to inconsequential positions. Fortunately, at the time of the bloodbath, he had been seconded to the AURI rocket program that had successfully launched the *Kartika 1* the year before. The Air Force's "*Project Prima*", Indonesia's rocket research project had been conceived with the intention of developing commercial and military rockets together with the Institute of Technology in Bandung, and *P.T. Pindad*, the Army weapons' factory. Subroto had been instrumental in arranging for the Japanese cooperation which had seen the *Kappa 8* rocket launched, also in the year preceding the turbulent period, predicted by one Indonesian Minister as becoming '*The Years of Living Dangerously*.'

Suharto's armed forces had inherited a number of quasi, commercial structures put more into place out of expediency than sound planning, and dated back to the time of Soekarno's *Guided Democracy* when regional commanders were forced to find their own means of funding operations and meeting personnel costs. As each of the Indonesian military arms vied for control over plantations, government owned hotels, sugar mills, banks, mining and timber concessions it soon became apparent that, without the necessary capital and management skills, these ventures would collapse. Even the Army's Strategic Forces, *Kostrad*, which had been awarded the Volkswagen assembly and marketing agency in the early Sixties, benefited little from this opportunity.

After the Hughes Corporation had overseen the launch of Indonesia's first series of satellites under the *Palapa Program*, Subroto became concerned with his future again, as contemporaries exited the armed forces en masse, many achieving civilian posts within the Suharto Cabinet, or appointments as governors, ambassadors and CEOs of Palace-controlled and TNI foundations.

Subroto had followed, apprehensively, as retiring air force generals were not in such great demand amongst the private sector. His one-off, lump sum pension payment was insufficient to maintain any reasonable norm of lifestyle, and certainly not one he had grown accustomed to whilst still a serving general. Consequently, he had turned to *Kosgoro*, one of the military-controlled cooperatives for a position, and was appointed as one of the many *Komisaris* advisors, to the Board of Directors. However, when (Danny) Dewanto Danusubroto, the *Kosgoro President Komisaris* was jailed for having the military murder his mistress not months after Subroto had joined the organization, Subroto wisely chose to move out on his own, where he met Eric Baird – and his fortunes instantly improved.

At first, their relationship had grown from strength to strength, Baird instrumental in delivering a number of substantial retainers that provided the former air force general with the wherewithal to re-establish his credentials. Within the year, Subroto had acquired a fully imported 450 Mercedes saloon (smuggled into the country by a Chinese expedition agent) and paid a nominal sum through the Veterans' Association, to secure ownership of a Dutch Colonial home in Jalan Serang, Menteng. He renovated the residence and contracted the magnificent dwelling to one of his foreign clients, receiving a five-year, advance rental payment of three hundred thousand dollars, which he invested in property around the growing, expatriate suburbs of Kemang and Cilandak. But, influenced by Baird and his associate Kremenchug, Subroto had lunged into the stock market prior to the Independence celebrations on 17th August 1987, borrowing heavily to acquire mining stocks which Kremenchug claimed would double within the year. The following week, the markets peaked, and eight weeks later Subroto discovered that he had lost all that he had borrowed from the Asian Pacific Commercial Bank.

With cap in hand, he had approached the powerful Salima Family who maintained controlling interest in the APC Bank, and requested a two-year grace period before recommencing loan repayments. He was introduced to James Salima, the effective CEO of APC, and a deal was struck. Unbeknown to Eric Baird, his forty percent share in P. T. Subroto & Associates (which his sponsor had previously been held in trust) was surrendered to the wealthy Chinese, *cukong* family, and Subroto's debt was forgiven.

Although his borrowings greatly exceeded the value of Baird's stock in the company, the Salima group made it quite clear that Subroto could be called upon, at any time, to assist their family should the need arise. Subroto blamed his predicament on Kremenchug and would have arranged for the man's visa to be cancelled had Baird not appealed, arguing that they were close to closing a deal which would recover all their losses. Against his better judgment, Subroto had agreed, now pleased that he had done so as Baird's advice of that day seemed to support this decision.

Now, the only outstanding issue was having Eric Baird marry Pipi, which would not only satisfy his favorite niece, but would keep her mother off his back. With the Australian married into the family, the question of Baird's shareholding in P.T. Subroto & Associates could be easily addressed. When the question arose, as he expected it would, Subroto would explain that Baird's stock was then held in trust for his wife, Pipi, *and who could argue with that*?

Subroto knew that there had been no offspring from Baird's former marriage, suspecting that neither would there be from his union with Pipi. This in no way offended the retired General – in fact, having the foreigner marry his sister's daughter and not produce children resolved another family dilemma. Genetics had not been kind to Pipi's father's line; the incidence of Albino children running through that side of the family unusually high. All in all, Subroto thought, having Baird involved in business and the family, could only be a positive factor for all.

* * * *

As Baird lay quietly contemplating his disastrous state of affairs, he recalled not having explained to Subroto that their stock in the new Canadian mining company would be held in escrow.

* * * *

In the months that followed, the Borneo Gold Corporation (BGC) was launched in Canada, the shares rising meteorically as public relations' rhetoric grossly exaggerated results from work carried out around the Palangkaraya concession. Air Vice Marshal (retired) Subroto, Kremenchug and Baird all waited with great expectations as their stock in BGC rose to more than double their par value then hovered, filling their futures with promise. When drilling of the Palangkaraya leases failed to produce the predicted results, the company moved operations further afield to the East Kalimantan areas. There, independent geologists oversaw a costly drilling program designed to substantiate earlier claims that the BGC acreage was amongst the most promising gold fields in Indonesia. The results proved otherwise, and before the first year of operations had come to a close and the Baird-Kremenchug-Subroto stockholders could offload their stock, Borneo Gold Corporation all but collapsed.

★ ★ ★ ★

Chapter Three

DECEMBER 1990

DAYAK LONGHOUSE VILLAGE – INDONESIAN EAST BORNEO (KALIMANTAN TIMUR)

Jonathan Dau watched silently, observing the young child's fascination with the spider's clever weaving, the web drifting occasionally with the wind, as an insect struggled to escape the gossamer trap. The child raised a long, thin stalk, intent on teasing the captured prey and prodded the tiny grasshopper several times; annoyed when it failed to move. She then turned her attention to a column of ants, creating chaos within their ranks as she twirled the stalk amongst fallen leaves. She quickly lost interest with this game when a giant butterfly winged its way past in majestic fashion and settled, just out of reach. She rose slowly, enraptured by the *kupu-kupu's* magnificence, the soft-beating wings casting their mesmerizing spell over the child and she cried out in delight, calling for anyone who might hear, to come and see.

Away from the forest's edge, villagers toiled in dry fields, tilling the *ladang* in preparation for the rice seedlings. While younger children played, their older siblings, bent to the knee, assisted parents with the arduous task of turning soil and removing weed as the elderly looked on, reminiscing of more youthful times.

The child called again, startled when Jonathan Dau swept her off her feet and playfully tossed her into the air. She shrieked with surprise then, as the chief caught her midair, giggled with glee. Jonathan smothered her playfully, pretending to crush her to his powerful chest, gradually releasing his hold permitting the child to slip gently to the ground. Not wishing an end to the game, she refused to let go, winding her arms and legs around his ankles as a monkey would a pole. With strong, but loving hands, Jonathan tugged her loose, lifting her once again into the air, placing her astride his shoulders. The girl wrapped her arms around his head, her world from upon this perch reaching out and across the fields from where she had strayed. Jonathan's graceful strides returned the child to her grateful mother, the unspoken words of gratitude delivered with a fleeting smile. No sooner had the girl been reunited with the group, she was off and running again with the other children, in pursuit of an overly inquisitive chicken that had strayed into their midst. Jonathan stepped back allowing the children room to run past, encouraging the lagging child as she ran breathless in her attempt to keep up with the others. Satisfied that the girl might now remain within safer confines the shaman returned to the Longhouse to attend to matters that required his attention as village-head.

★ ★ ★ ★

Nestled amongst towering coconut palms, overlooking one of the many tributaries that flowed into the Mahakam, Jonathan's *Aoheng-Penehing* community setting had not changed greatly since he was a child. Apart from the three-meter, parabolic dish mounted like some great saucer atop the water tower, and the cables running from the recently constructed generator block, the village remained much the same as it was when his great-grandfather had hunted clouded leopard along *Bukit Batubrok's* slopes.

Jonathan's forefathers had migrated in nomadic fashion, down from the mountainous northwest, Kayan River headwaters more than two hundred years before. These *Kayan* tribes, which included the *Bahau,* the *Modang*, the *Long Gelat* and *Busang,* had left the *Apokayan,* invading the upper Mahakam, displacing and, in some cases enslaving the original inhabitants, the *Ot Danum* and *Tunjung* people. A century of headhunting raids throughout Borneo's east left a legacy of lingering hostility, the surviving ethnic groups never hesitant in declaring their loathing for each other, at any given opportunity.

Jonathan had been more fortunate than most. Born in the year the Japanese invaded Balikpapan, three hundred kilometers to the east, he was to be seven years of age before sighting another being that was not of Dayak blood.

★ ★ ★ ★

Although it may have been considered unusual for a hereditary chief to simultaneously hold the highly respected position of chief *and* that of the spiritual *dukun,* commencing with Jonathan's great-grandfather, the powers for both had been passed unbroken, from father to son. Even as a young child, Jonathan's unique talents had become apparent, the special gift he had inherited being first manifested whilst he was still a child, and for all who witnessed the event, confirmation that Jonathan Dau was, indeed, a blessed phenomenon.

The incident had occurred when the villagers were fare-welling a young woman who had died during childbirth. In his role as *dukun,* or shaman, Jonathan's father was not only the village healer and its priest, but also the psycho pomp responsible for the long and skillful prayers offered to accompany the deceased's soul on its journey to the 'other' world. The village girl's body had been prepared for burial, and final, protracted prayers were being offered when Jonathan approached the corpse, reached up and touched her lifeless body. Then he fell into a trancelike state, reciting the entire prayer sequence all over again, verbatim.

At that time, Jonathan was just five years of age and had never been instructed in such verse, nor had he previously attended a funeral. Elders, the village council and even his family were filled with awe when, suddenly, Jonathan extended his small hands skywards and became still, a loving smile settling across his lips as a black hornbill swooped down under the thatched shelter and landed, ominously, at the dead girl's feet. Moments passed, the stunned villagers gripped in awe as Jonathan's hand moved slowly towards the bird and stroked it ever so gently, before it took flight, carrying, they all believed, the deceased's soul away. From that moment, Jonathan's father commenced instructing his son in the ways of the 'good' or 'white' *dukun,* revealing the secrets that were passed down to him.

As the most important function of the 'white' shaman is healing, Jonathan remained at his father's side when he administered the sick; accompanying his father into the jungle in search of ingredients required for potions and cures, becoming the chief's small, but dedicated shadow. He observed, as nature surrendered her secrets during those excursions and listened, intently, whenever his father explained the magic of each wild herb he'd gathered, or the medicinal value of specific plants, roots and even wild, river lilies. He watched his father prepare salves, cast spells and exorcise the possessed; memorizing the appropriate chants, whilst remaining obediently solemn, or sitting in awe as his father described the techniques used by the 'black' or 'evil' *dukuns.*

Jonathan Dau learned that it would not be wise to underestimate the power of the much-sought-after 'black' *dukuns,* who for a fee, would cast spells and provide potions mixed with dried, menstrual blood or ear wax for the scorned and lovelorn, poisons for the covetous and ambitious and curses for any occasion.

⋆ ⋆ ⋆ ⋆

Jonathan's father had wisely determined that his gifted and only child would receive an outside education. In 1949 when news that the great *Dayak* nation had been absorbed into what was to be known as the Republic of Indonesia, Jonathan was transported, first by canoe, then diesel-driven riverboat to the river-port township of Samarinda where he was placed in the care of a Chinese family. Before the age of ten, Jonathan Dau was fluent in not only his own dialect, but could converse fluently in Malay-Indonesian and comprehend most of what transpired within the Chinese household. An avid reader by twelve, Jonathan excelled at the Catholic missionary-run school, his religious teachers delighted when he could quote chapter and verse from both Testaments in the *Kitab Suci.*

As a teenager, Jonathan was moved to the larger port city of Balikpapan, where he completed high school, curtailing the frequency of his home visits. It was there that the young Dayak's first glimpse of an aircraft so captivated his imagination he became determined that, one day, he too would fly. As fate would have it, Indonesia's founding president, Soekarno, in delivering his country to the communists, signed pacts with Ho Chi Minh, Mao Tse Tung and the Soviets, resulting in the Indonesian Armed Forces receiving massive military aid from Moscow. Soviet and Chinese aircraft were added to existing squadrons of American B-25s and 26s, P-51 Mustangs and Canadian Catalinas and, whilst the world's attention was focused on what was happening across the short distance to Vietnam, Indonesia suddenly emerged as a most threatening power.

Jonathan was selected for pilot training. Upon graduation, he was sent to Soviet-occupied Czechoslovakia along with scores of others to learn yet another language, and undertake conversion training on MiG aircraft.

When he returned to Indonesia, his country already boasted the third largest communist party in the world and was engaged in war with Malaysia, Singapore and, secretly, Australia. These were proud times for the Republic's young pilots, the more fortunate assigned to fly the recently acquired, TU-16 long-range Soviet bombers. Jonathan was impressed with this huge aircraft, the USSR's equivalent of the American B-52, which his comrades regularly flew from their airfields in Java, to points provocatively close to British Vulcan bomber bases in Singapore. Jonathan watched, proudly, as his country's defense forces grew to threatening proportions, amassing half a million servicemen by the close of 1964, supported by an array of soviet tanks, missiles, warships and, by the close of that year, several squadrons of MiG fighters.

At twenty-three, Captain Jonathan Dau was posted to Number 14 Squadron, located at the Kemayoran Air Force Base in Jakarta where he flew MiG21s. Increasingly disillusioned with President Soekarno's all-embracing, political philosophies, and his failure to make payments for the arsenal Moscow provided, the Soviets ceased supplying spare parts. Within six months, even with cannibalizing most of their aircraft inventory, all but four of AURI's fighter fleet had been grounded, and Jonathan's dream to remain airborne came crashing down. Across the nation, morale fell to an all-time low. In Borneo, Australian and British SAS successful deep-penetration operations across the Sarawak-Kalimantan borders, had brought the Indonesian Army to a standstill. British Vulcan bombers now flew regular missions over AURI bases threatening to drop atomic warheads on Indonesian cities in the event the Soviet supplied TU-16 bombers reappeared on RAF, Singapore or Darwin-based radar screens.

Bitter with the country's rapidly deteriorating military position, one of Jonathan's fellow MiG squadron pilots decided that Soekarno should be removed from the nation's helm. The officer waited for his chance and, when a Palace informant phoned advising that the President would attend a formal reception that evening, the pilot climbed into his MiG and went charging into the capital. He flew south and around Kebayoran, along Jalan Jenderal Sudirman, the jet's engine screaming above the *Selamat Datang* statue outside the Hotel Indonesia as he tore along Jalan Thamrin, before lining up on Merdeka Barat. With the Palace directly in his sights, he commenced firing his canons into the well-lit structure, and continued to do so until exhausting his ammunition. Inside, guests screamed and fell to highly-polished, marble floors, the MiG's cannons piercing the former Dutch Governor's colonial offices' solid walls, showering diplomats and other dignitaries with debris and shattered chandeliers.

Unbeknown to the young officer, the President was not present when the attack was executed, Soekarno finding humor in the fist-sized holes throughout the Palace when he finally strutted into the reception, half an hour late, surviving what was to be the first of six assassination attempts on his charmed life.

The pilot returned to base where word of his transgression had yet to reach his fellow pilots' ears but, when it did, each in turn was equally devastated by the news that their comrade had failed. Stigmatized by the assassination attempt, the squadron's other pilots accepted that their careers would, undoubtedly, take an abrupt turn, and most resigned their commissions.

The following year, General Suharto successfully effected his own *coup d'etat* and turned Indonesia upside down. During the bloody aftermath, Suharto's brutal co-conspirators, Sarwo Eddhie, Ali Murtopo and Amir Machmud specifically targeted the air force – the cleansing process implemented reducing the officer corps by more than eighty percent. The Chief of Air Staff, Air Marshal Omar Dhani, was arrested and tried, his replacement, the thirty-seven year old Rusmin Nuryadin who, the year before, had leaped from colonel to become the country's youngest four star general, and Minister for Air. With a pro-West Suharto undertaking to not only rid the country of communism, but to also break off political ties with the Moscow and Beijing, Jonathan knew that his Soviet training would always be held against him and so, he too resigned, returning home to his Mahakam village, consumed with loathing for everything Javanese. The following year he married a girl selected by the elders and settled down within his own community to reinvent himself, delving once again into the mysteries of the *Dayak Kaharingan,* spiritualist world. When his father died, the mantel of chief passed, unopposed, to Jonathan.

Then, the first wave of Javanese trans-migrants arrived, backed by the might of the Indonesian Army. At first, Dayak communities had welcomed the increase in trade along the Mahakam River, and the employment opportunities created with the explosion of logging activity and the introduction of plywood factories. But, the Dayaks soon realized that they were not to be the final beneficiaries of the enormous wealth generated by Jakarta-sponsored logging operations, plantations and industrial timber estates. Dismayed, they watched as their rattan industry was monopolized, and angered to the point of rebellion when their land was arbitrarily assigned to foreign investors, without compensation. Bulldozers appeared in the most unlikely areas, stripping virgin forests, the giant *meranti* and ironwood trees hauled away to meet Java's insatiable demand for construction materials, the cultural, social and environmental damage devastating in their effect. Where once there were cemeteries and sacred places, palm oil trees now flourished. Land was stripped and cleared, colonies of Javanese migrants taking root, their customs, language and religion abhorred by the many Dayak indigenous groups as a new era of colonialism, through capitalism, started to take shape.

Bloody confrontations, hidden from the International and domestic Press through severe censorship and well-rehearsed, intimidation tactics, resulted in the Javanese-dominated military rethinking its strategies in support of transmigration in the Kalimantan provinces. Department of Defense signaled that Suharto Family interests, and those of their close associates, were to be protected at all costs. Additional troops were sent to areas where vested interest groups were in open conflict with the traditional landowners, their orders to deal swiftly and firmly with the local inhabitants.

Jonathan had witnessed evidence of the brutal *RPKAD's* Special Forces in action. Word had spread through the upper Mahakam reaches that an isolated village had been razed to the ground by army elements. When he arrived at the scene, Jonathan no longer harbored any doubts that the Dayak peoples were not only in grave danger of losing their land and culture to the Javanese, but their lives as well. Amongst the still-smoldering Longhouse embers he counted more than two hundred bodies, the majority belonging to children who had obeyed their parents pleas to remain hidden inside, when the soldiers came. The *RPKAD* Special Forces had surrounded the raised village in crescent formation and opened fire with their automatic weapons, their bullets easily ripping through the timber-clad dwellings, killing or wounding all within. Then they torched the dry, wooden structure, the cries of their victims ignored as thatched roofs ignited spontaneously under intense heat then imploded, destroying the entire complex within minutes.

★ ★ ★ ★

Throughout the following two decades Jonathan Dau conducted his own, secret war against the Javanese. He never involved others in his deadly game; neither did he reveal the real purpose of the frequent excursions that took him away from the village, often for days at a time. Jonathan was cautiously selective in his targets, killing soldiers who had strayed or become lost in the jungle. His actions were entirely covert in nature and, although he enjoyed limited success, the weight of numbers and the constant threat of discovery, finally convinced him to cease what had become a futile action. Although the government's repressive actions continued to fuel anti-Javanese sentiment and calls for a cessation to the transmigration process, the flood continued. Jonathan sadly accepted that the Dayak people would remain subjects of their new colonial masters, the Javanese, but he still prayed that the time would come when Borneo would be returned to its original inhabitants, and the Moslems all sent home.

This was to be Jonathan Dau's impossible dream.

The chief understood that the main impediment towards building a Dayak nation was that the Kalimantan indigenes had never been unified. Borneo's indigenous peoples were comprised of scores of tribes, whose varied cultures and dialects had placed them poles apart, some developing from a highly stratified society with classes of aristocrats, freemen and slaves, whilst others, such as the northern *Ibans,* enjoyed a more egalitarian society.

Political lines now divided the great island, with Malaysia and Brunei to the north, and Indonesian-held Kalimantan to the south. Jonathan accepted that in order for the *Penehing-Dayak* to survive they would have to be guaranteed their own land, the question of how to achieve this aim, forever foremost in his mind. His people were but few in number and, alone, armed but with the most primitive of weapons, the possibility of a successful military confrontation never entered his mind. A pragmatist, Jonathan believed that only with great wealth could the *Penehing-Dayaks'* future be secured, his conundrum, the improbability of such a dream coming to fruition. He had thought of seeking outside help to have their lands declared part of some world heritage trust, abandoning the idea when he discovered that this might very well deliver his people even sooner into Jakarta's brutal hands. Then he embarked on a mission to have the entire area given special status, similar to that of Jogyakarta and Greater, Metropolitan Jakarta, but without central government support, this too failed. When the entire island was divided into concession areas covering minerals, oil and gas, Jonathan accepted that even the great wealth that lay below the surface would never be theirs. Now, approaching his fiftieth year, Jonathan had not mellowed, the strength of his convictions still evident in his dealings with government officials – most of whom being Javanese, or their local lackeys.

When Jonathan was elected village head, out of respect, none of his fellow villagers had challenged Jonathan's right to lead. Out of bloody-mindedness, the East Kalimantan Governor had issued instructions for the military to identify pro-Jakarta candidates from within the local, river communities to run against the powerful spiritualist, but these efforts failed, causing an embarrassing retreat by the Javanese-appointed official.

Jonathan Dau continued to dedicate much of his time to the welfare of the *Penehing* people, counseling, administering cures and complying with the many, bureaucratic requests that flowed unceasingly from the Governor's office in Samarinda. He still ventured out into the relatively unknown forests, sometimes spending days alone on the slopes of *Bukit Batubrok* meditating, occasionally climbing the two-thousand-meter plateau in search of the evasive plants needed for his medicinal potions. On occasion, Jonathan would take one of the village children with him, teaching the child some of the rudiments of jungle lore. The Longhouse children competed for this privilege, their parents delighted to surrender their sons to his care, for their chief had no male heir of his own. And, the possibility that their child might be the one chosen to succeed Jonathan Dau was not lost on their number. Jonathan's wife had never fully recovered from her debilitating liver disease, surrendering to her condition, finally, when their daughter, Angela, was barely three. Jonathan did not seek another mate – such was his sense of loss. Now, he was to be alone, again. Jonathan's daughter, Angela, was to leave to attend the Institute of Technology in Bandung.

As the day for departure neared Jonathan became heavy of heart, the impending void her absence would undoubtedly create sent him aimlessly into the fields where village women bent tirelessly, preparing the *ladang* for planting, their pre-school age children playing in close proximity. There, he had observed a small girl wander off unnoticed, and had retrieved the child, returning her to a grateful mother before strolling back through the naturally protected river island, and the Longhouse. It was time to take his daughter, Angela, up into the mountains.

As Jonathan Dau approached his village, he passed between guardian figures strategically placed along all paths leading to the Longhouse, to deflect evil spirits that might bring sickness to the isolated community. These sentinels took the form of both human and animal shapes, many carved deliberately displaying grotesque eyes and teeth, to intimidate intruders, and repel malevolent spirits. In this land overlooked by modern civilizations, Gods and spirits continued to play important roles in Dayak societies – the rivers and forests revered as hosts to these.

Gargoyle-like images stared down from the thatched roof as Jonathan climbed the steps leading up to the timber structure, a communal village raised three meters above the ground and more than a hundred and fifty meters in length, held together by massive, ornately carved, wooden beams. The elongated building housed more than a hundred families, each living in their own, separate apartment, joined to their neighbors' by a central, wooden corridor, which served as the village 'street'. Jonathan's family quarters, and unofficial office, lay centered amongst this maze adjacent to the community meeting room. The traditional 'gallery' that once housed the most sacred of artifacts and enemy skulls, relics of another time, lay discreetly hidden from any visitor's view.

Jonathan made his way through the Longhouse, stopping briefly to converse with other men, most preoccupied with their own chores, whilst the women tended the fields. He entered his quarters and changed into more appropriate attire, then summoned his daughter, Angela, who had been waiting eagerly for the moment to arrive.

★ ★ ★ ★

Angela's constant companion, a two-year old *orang-utan* by the name of Yuh-Yuh, held her long, reddish-brown arms open wide demanding she be lifted.

'No, Yuh-Yuh, not now!'

Rejected, Yuh-Yuh rolled on the wooden planked floor and clucked.

'Best you leave her behind, this time,' Jonathan recommended. *'We must leave now. The first full moon will soon cross the horizon, chasing the sun's tail through the sky.'*

Angela understood. That month would both commence and close with full moons, auspicious signs, that could not be ignored. She called for a friend to restrain Yuh-Yuh until they were well out of sight then followed her father outside.

Angela had little difficulty in maintaining her father's grueling pace as they followed familiar trails through the emerald rain forest. Since her mother died, Angela had been a frequent visitor to this magic realm and, under Jonathan Dau's doting eyes and patient guidance she had learned to embrace this magnificent environment. As a child, she learned to share her father's attention with other village children on outings, collecting wild honey, or in search of medicinal herbs, and never felt the need to compete – for Angela knew how deeply Jonathan Dau loved her and she understood that her father's responsibilities demanded that he be fair.

Angela had excelled in her primary studies, the Longhouse schoolteacher incapable of accommodating the girl's thirst for knowledge. Before the age of twelve, Angela had revisited every book in their meager library at least twice, and when she was not studying the written word, she dedicated hours listening to short-wave radio broadcasts, even when it was obvious that she did not understand the many languages that filled the air. Within time, she mastered the rudiments of English; her stilted attempts to communicate in that medium encouraged by her father, whose own knowledge of the language had remained reasonably intact. At fourteen, Angela was given even greater advantage over her peers when she was sent to further her studies in the provincial capital, Samarinda.

Angela's attendance at high school provided her with access not only to the capital's limited libraries, but an abundance of magazines and newspapers, which fed both the domestic and foreign readership base, resident in Samarinda. She learned to appreciate the extent of natural wealth that was being exploited across Dayak lands. She saw, first hand, the harvest from Dayak, traditional forests when these were seized and surrendered to powerful timber groups, the tens of thousands of huge rafts of precious timber creating unbelievable log jams along the Mahakam River. Her understanding of how the real world revolved became painfully apparent as she became increasingly aware of the Indonesia's thuggish, ruling elite, and Jakarta-based tycoons who enriched themselves, at the Dayak population's expense.

And, as Angela became older and more venturesome, so, too, did her horizons grow. She visited government offices under guise of seeking information for school projects, devouring material across a wide spectrum covering commerce, politics and the environment, her knowledge of social and ethnic issues profound, in her mind. She ventured into the city's growing slums where young, Dayak women, many still in their early teens, wandered the squalid streets soliciting, and she was shocked that this could be so, concerned, even at her tender age, that she was looking through a window in her people's future. By the time graduation arrived, Angela Dau had blossomed into a mature, intelligent, and very determined young woman, convinced that unless the Dayak people could achieve some semblance of autonomy within the near future, they were doomed. She returned to her village and appealed to her father for the opportunity to study at the Institute of Technology, in Bandung, arguing that it was imperative she advance her studies there – Jonathan, at first, uncertain that sending her to Java would be the correct choice. When the villagers learned of her wish they gathered to support Angela, pledging as a community to provide the funding to enable her to attend. Reluctantly, the chief finally agreed, insisting that his daughter remain under the care of an old friend in Bandung, his approval also conditional on the understanding that she undertake the shaman initiation ceremony before departing. Few amongst the Longhouse community had even considered that Jonathan Dau might be contemplating passing his mantle to Angela. Although there were some whose hopes were dashed when it became apparent that he would do so, none begrudged her right to succeed their chief, particularly as she had so clearly demonstrated that she had inherited at least some of her father's powers.

With only two days remaining, Jonathan and Angela embarked on their demanding trek to the secluded, ancestral cave. Now, as she followed her father's footsteps up the difficult terrain, Angela's excitement grew, for this day she would realize her dream – the right of succession, a claim, which until that time, had only been granted to the male line in her family.

⋆ ⋆ ⋆ ⋆

Angela followed her father's footsteps as they ventured deeper and deeper into the virgin forest, stopping upon silent command to view long-tailed parakeets, or the occasional macaque gobbling leaves high in a canopy draped with creeping lianas and fern. They made their way through the jungle environment, as the land continued to rise. Five hours into their journey Jonathan finally stopped and pointed towards a rocky outcrop a few meters further up the slope. *'We'll enter through there.'*

Angela squinted, unable to identify anything against the late afternoon sun's rapidly fading light, and was virtually upon the natural, limestone caverns before the entrance became apparent.

'Come, Angela, follow me.' Responding to her father's encouragement, she stepped inside, her eyes adjusting to the cavern's dark and cold interior and her pulse rose, reminded that it was here, in this setting, where generations of shamans had conducted similar initiation rites, bestowing powers on an heir apparent.

Angela remained standing while Jonathan unpacked his haversack, the cave coming alive when he lit a circle of candles placed at the base of a heavily carved, altar-shaped rock. Stalactite-formed, candle flows attached to the rock evidenced past visits, Angela's thoughts on those who had gone before her wondering if they, too, had been as apprehensive at what lay ahead. Her eyes wandered the cave's irregular walls, curious as to which of her ancestors had been responsible for the art forms depicting forest creatures and game. Angela accepted that her ancestors originally came to earth from the Seventh Heaven, in the form of hornbills, and also believed that life was continuously controlled by the spirits of her ancestors, and that these spirits were often reincarnated in all living forms, such as deer, the beloved hornbill and even snakes and frogs – all of which were depicted here.

Deeper into the cave where the shadows fell darkest Angela detected a narrow passage. *'Papa. Where does that lead to?'*

Jonathan lifted one of the candles, level with his head, his features severe in the half-light. *'You will learn what lies there, later. Come, kneel with me – we shall offer a prayer then go outside to wait for the moon to rise.'*

She moved to his side where Jonathan sprinkled drops of fragrant water into her hands then his own, each touching their faces gently, in a gesture of cleansing. Then, together, they crouched before the stone altar to join in the familiar chant asking for divine protection, whilst expressing their gratitude to the spirits.

★ ★ ★ ★

Father and daughter stood in harmonious awe as the moon reached the fullness of its white gold, nocturnal bloom, casting a spell across the verdant landscape, giving life to the soft layers of mist, blanketing rivers and valleys, far below.

'It's time.' Jonathan's voice brought Angela back from the hypnotic panorama.

Filled with a reassuring calm, she smiled peacefully. *'I'm ready, Papa.'*

The shaman took Angela and held her lovingly, by the shoulders. *'You must always remember, my daughter, that your soul is your inner guide, and that you are a manifestation of your soul in the physical and material sense. During the indoctrination process, you will become aware of a powerful light, at which time your soul will disconnect from its physical form and take you to the Supreme Being. Do not fight against this light, but relax and merge with it. Do not be frightened – you will think that you are alone, but this will not be so. Your guardian will be at your side.'*

'Is that you, Papa?'

'No, my child, your guardian, or spiritual guide was selected back in time, and takes the form of the hornbill. Once you are fully committed to the latihan trance, the scenes of your life will unfold and you will be transported through these images to places of extreme horror, as a test. The hornbill will carry you through safely. Do not be afraid. You are about to commence the most enlightening experience of your life.'

'Thank you, Papa.'

Jonathan Dau's arms dropped to his side. *'Then we should proceed.'*

Angela closed her eyes, drawing the crisp mountain air into her lungs, then followed her father slowly into the candle-lit cave where the ritual would be held. She knelt on her knees, head bowed and hands clasped together, senses heightened as flickering shadows danced against stone-carved walls and incense drifted through their sacred surrounds.

'Are you ready, my daughter?' And with Angela's response, the shaman sprinkled sacred dust he had gathered, over her head.

'Say as I say,' he directed, shifting his role to that of *dukun* and the young woman obeyed, repeating the words her father articulated, the rhythmic hum of their mantra resonating throughout the chamber as the initiation process began, carrying both into trancelike state, through the door of the spirit world.

Angela floated, her mind filled with promise as she parted with her physical presence. Unburdened by weightlessness and enveloped by a climate of well being, Angela soared into the heavens through space and time until her spirit was touched by the Supreme Being and endowed with the powers of a *Kaharingan dukun*. Then, escorted by guardian spirits, she was taken to the holiest of shrines where her head was taken from her body and her eyes washed, so that she could see her own death – the process of being dismembered and born again. Angela witnessed her skeleton being dismantled with her flesh cut up into pieces and thrown to the four corners of the world, to be eaten by the demons of sickness, so she would know these diseases and have the power to combat them, her dismemberment strengthening the right to cure. When the spirits rebuilt her body one small bone was deliberately discarded, to reflect her human imperfection.

Finally, she fell, descending into the depths of hell where she came face to face with the master of the Deep Worlds, so she would recognize this challenger when confronted in future battles for the souls of the dead, in determining their final dwelling place. She summoned her inner strength and called upon her guardian, the divine bird spirit to carry her away from the evil abode, the giant hornbill answering her call, transporting Angela back to rejoin her earthly presence, as the initiation was done.

Angela returned from the induced state, accompanied by her father's reassuring chants, filled with wonderment at the passage she had made – and the gift that had been bestowed upon her.

'You have been blessed, my child,' she heard Jonathan Dau say, *'from this day on you will carry with you, the shaman's secrets.'*

She peered outside and, to her amazement, was greeted by the morning sun's first rays spilling over distant crests, lighting the new day. Angela gazed up at her father and smiled, understanding now what it was that he saw, that others could not. And, in reverent gesture, she lifted his right hand to her lips, to thank him.

★ ★ ★ ★

Angela had reminded her father of his promise to reveal what lay further into the cave. Now, part of her wished she had not, the reason for her taciturn behavior as they retraced their steps through the forest.

'Even if your mother were alive, you could not reveal what lies here before you,' Jonathan had warned her. Angela had been led through the naturally disguised passage, their way lit by hand-held candles as they advanced through the rocky corridor, twisting and turning for more than twenty meters, before entering yet another large, naturally formed cavern. Her father had turned and blocked her view as she entered the inner sanctum, reminding Angela that she was the first of her gender ever to set foot in this most sacred place. *'Until the time arrives for you to initiate your own son or daughter, you may not reveal this location to any other.'* He had then stepped away and, hold-

ing burning candles high above his head, proudly revealed the gallery lined with skulls. Angela eyes absorbed the scene, struck by the enormity of what lay before her.

'Are they…?' Angela's mouth became suddenly dry as her eyes darted along the rows of skulls, carefully arranged in some sort of order. *'Are they… very old?'* she managed to ask.

'Most,' her father replied, approaching one fine fellow, whose skull enjoyed a place of pride, resting atop a pole. *'This one was a white man,'* Angela detected a touch of mirth in her father's voice, *'but, you wouldn't know it now!'*

'Who…?' She struggled to ask, the Dayak chief coming to her aid. *'Your great-great grandfather started this collection, and our family has maintained the practice, ever since.'*

'Headhunting?' Angela's voice was close to breaking.

'Yes, almost as far back as time reaches,' he answered solemnly. *'Many of these were moved to this location when the Dutch missionaries commenced sweeping through our communities, seizing such trophies.'*

'Papa, please tell me. Have…have you…?' the words spilled from her mouth. She dreaded his response.

'When it's been necessary, 'Gela,' he said, unemotionally, using the diminutive form of her name.

'Recently?' she pressed, apprehensively.

'When the situation demanded.'

'But, why?' she asked, unable to take her eyes off the staggering number of skulls, some of which were stacked in one corner, the pile more than a meter high.

'Retribution, retaliation, revenge, honor, prestige…all of those things.'

'But we're almost in the Twenty-first Century!'

'That won't change the way men feel towards each other. People will continue to kill each other. The manner in which they extract satisfaction is of no consequence.'

'Papa, do you intend to continue with this practice?' she desperately wished to know, her shaky voice signally Jonathan that it was time to leave.

'If I do, Angela, it will be ordained by the spirits.' The mild reproof

was sufficient caution, Angela immediately recognizing that she had gone too far.

Confounded by his revelations, Angela knew then that she would never be able to look at her father again without wondering how many of the hollowed skeletal trophies had arrived there by his hand. Then, as they made their way back through the forest Angela gradually convinced herself that it was not her role to lament the perversity of her father and their ancestors' acts – that, although her father's display of the darker side of her heritage had been unsettling, he had shown that there would be no secrets between them and, for that, she should be grateful. The further they moved away from the mountain, the more relaxed Angela became with the discovery that her own father had hunted heads, troubled only by the question, *would he do it again?*

★ ★ ★ ★

Jonathan Dau was in no way concerned with his daughter's self-imposed silence as they retraced their steps through the dense forest. Angela was still young and had much to learn. He recalled his own reaction to the secret repository when he had been indoctrinated by his father and shown the inner cave. As this memory came to mind the shaman's hand dropped to his waist, reassured when his fingers touched the *golok's* carved handle, the machete handed down from his father. Jonathan knew that this weapon had accounted for a number of heads; his father had proudly imparted this knowledge on numerous occasions, during community gatherings in their village longhouse when ageing warriors boasted of their kills.

The *Penehing* villagers had kept their twenty-five year secret, the withered, white man's skull never displayed openly. His father had removed the helicopter pilot's head after the Bell clipped the forest's treetops and crashed. Incredibly, the pilot had staggered away from the wreckage only to be slain by the Dayak chief who, along with the others in their isolated community, had never seen such an aircraft, let alone had one drop from the sky. Terrified, the village chief had bravely slain the white spirit, the decapitation evidence of the *dukun's* power over evil. The story had not been embellished in any way, nor revealed to any outsiders for fear of reprisals.

As Jonathan's generation had emerged and assumed leadership over the village community, with the exception of the occasional, isolated incident that inevitably arose because of territorial or inter-tribal disputes, headhunting had become a thing of the past; the stories cherished and passed down from father to son. The *Penehing, Modang* and other Dayak groups had been absorbed into the greater Republic of Indonesia, with many of their number accepting Christianity or the *Kaharingan* beliefs. And, without exception, Jonathan Dau's community, all professed.

The shaman recalled a time when the presence of a European attracted great curiosity along the Mahakam's upper reaches. The first to come were the fair haired Dutch explorers followed by missionaries, but their mark had not been felt until the delta communities commenced trading further upstream, bringing Western religions and cultures to the untamed hinterland. For centuries, accounts of cannibalism carried back to civilization discouraged visitors, leaving the greater part of plateau-dwelling communities without any real change until the quest for gold drove the more adventurous deeper into the mountains. When the Japanese occupied Borneo, even they had hesitated in venturing too far into the wild jungle and, of those who did, some remained for decades after the war had come to a close, without realizing that hostilities had ceased.

But now, Jonathan's people, their land and culture were under threat with an increase of mining activity over recent years, the impact upon the downstream-Dayaks, devastating. His concerns had grown with reports of wild game, fish and, occasionally, humans dying from pollution associated with the foreign controlled, mining operations throughout East, Central and Southern Kalimantan. Recently, he had traveled downstream and witnessed the devastation brought to one community, where the streams were severely polluted with mercury, the water fouled forever as a result of unsupervised gold extraction.

Jonathan firmly believed that if the Dayak communities failed to form a common front to combat the spread of migrant settlements, then it would soon be too late, and they would be overrun by Madurese and Javanese settlers.

★ ★ ★ ★

Angela Dau fought back the tears as she pulled away from her father, his powerful hands holding her firmly by the shoulders. *'Thank you again, Papa,'* was all that was left to muster. The *orang-utan* at her feet knew, instinctively, that she was about to be abandoned, and wrapped her disproportionate arms around Angela's thighs.

Jonathan shook her gently. *'If your mother could only see you now...'*

'But, she can, Papa, she can.' Stoically, Angela suppressed the threatening tide of tears.

'Goodbye, 'Gela.' Everyone from the Longhouse had gathered to farewell the chief's daughter. A chorus of children now spilled from the raised, wooden verandah overlooking the village jetty and called her name. Angela had left many times before, but that was only for schooling downriver in Samarinda. Now, she would be gone for an extended spell – and, to live amongst the Javanese.

For the women of this village, Angela's success represented a major breakthrough, providing hope for others who wished to further their educations. Angela's scholarship had been awarded based on political considerations, yet none harbored animosity in any form towards the intelligent, attractive young woman whose achievements were proudly perceived as a reflection on the entire female community. They expected that Angela Dau would be the first of their number to achieve a degree.

'Send us photos, 'Gela!' one teenager pleaded, then shrieked, turning to pinch her friend alongside for pushing.

'Write, and tell us about the boys,' another called, deliberately teasing the adolescent lads who idolized Angela.

'Don't fall in love over there!' This, from one of her many admirers amongst the young village men, the hint of sarcasm lost in the moment. Angela looked up into her father's misty eyes.

'When we have re-installed the radio, you will be able to send messages via the provincial affairs office, in Samarinda,' Jonathan reminded her and, for the umpteenth time, *'so don't forget to telephone us regularly.'*

'I won't, Papa,' she responded, looking around anxiously at the longboat as engines coughed into life, signaling the boatmen's impatience. Water levels had dropped over recent weeks and they wished to cross the rapids while light permitted. Jonathan scowled at the men then released his grip and stepped back with the broadest smile he could stage.

'Go,' the chief ordered, *'and make us even prouder than we are today.'* Angela kissed her father's hand respectfully and turned before tears could flow. She stepped down from the raised boardwalk and with one final wave stepped into the longboat and settled down for the long, monotonous voyage to the provincial capital.

Jonathan Dau looked on in silence as the boat gained speed, the villagers still waving and shouting in festive mood until Angela disappeared from view. Then, he returned to his office where he slumped into his grandfather's rattan chair, sighed heavily at the paperwork he'd neglected and attacked the pile of correspondence with forced enthusiasm. The Central Government was to implement yet another of Jakarta's grandiose development schemes, designed to drag so-called primitive, tribal groups into their world. Questionnaires, directives, communications relating to the general plans had inundated his office over past weeks, Jonathan unwilling to address the outstanding correspondence, distracted by his daughter's departure. He let the pen slide from between his fingers, clasped his head between his hands, leaned forward and stared vacantly into space.

Ageing black and white photographs of a younger Jonathan standing proudly amongst a group of graduating MiG pilots lined one wall of the leader's inner sanctum, amidst these, a much-cherished portrait of Angela. His eyes locked with hers and he smiled, lovingly, the moment again filled his chest with pride. She had completed the *dukun* initiation ceremony – and he could now derive some comfort from the fact that she was now better prepared to go out into the world alone. Excluding any visits Jonathan might now make to

Bandung, he accepted that it would be unlikely that he would see too much more of his daughter whilst she was away, studying. It had been difficult enough, he admitted, even when she had been placed downriver in Samarinda for her secondary schooling, and lodged with the same Chinese family that had cared for her father a generation before. Now she was to attend the Institute of Technology in Bandung, more than two thousand kilometers across the Java Sea.

Jonathan reflected on his own life at twenty-one, his forehead slowly creasing into a weathered-frown, the images of those times still seared into his consciousness. He closed his eyes and, inhaling deeply, shifted the imagery of those times, blanketing the past, permitting his mind to drift. With practised skill the *dukun* willed his body to relax, the tension dissipating effortlessly as taught muscles succumbed, transporting Jonathan to a floating, near comatose state.

Later that day, when Jonathan Dau informed senior members of his council that he would be absent for some days, the villagers understood – and went about their ways as the shaman trudged off into the jungle.

* * * *

Angela arrived in Samarinda at the end of her third day, rested overnight, then proceeded to Balikpapan by minibus where she boarded a Garuda flight to Jakarta. Once in the nation's bustling capital, Angela continued her long journey by train to Bandung, where she would commence her first year studying at the Institute of Technology, founding President Soekarno's *alma mater.*

* * * *

The Philippines

Sharon Ducay removed her shoes and tiptoed along the corridor, entering General Narciso Dominguez's room without making a sound.

'How is he?' she asked the attending nurse, her voice but a whisper.

'He rests,' the middle-aged woman replied, *'the doctor says that he was lucky – this time.'*

Sharon moved to the side of the bed, leaned down and kissed her uncle on the forehead, then took a seat alongside to wait for him to regain consciousness. She settled back into the deep, cushioned chair, resting tired eyes after the long, anxiety-filled journey back from London. The General had suffered his second stroke.

Her eyes drifted around the all too familiar room with its rich furnishings, the presence of cigar smoke still evident in the air and, when she recognized the photograph which had been moved closer to her uncle's side, she shed a tear. Sharon knew that this would have been Alfredo's handiwork, and she muttered a silent prayer of thanks that Dominguez's trusted aide had been present when her uncle had collapsed. Suddenly, she felt cold, the threat of Narciso Dominguez dying gripped her with the reality that the ageing General lying there was her only remaining family, and that with his passing, apart from Alfredo, she would be completely alone.

* * * *

Sharon's parents, along with her two brothers and a sister, had died when the Hercules transport carrying them to Hong Kong had crashed over the ocean, ten years before. Sharon had been devastated at the time, returning home immediately to attend to matters of estate. Since the tragic incident, Sharon had become the daughter General Narciso Dominguez could never have. Now, the old man and his niece were the sole, remaining members of what was once a most influential, Filipino family.

Although her parents had not been overly wealthy Sharon's inheritance provided her with the capacity to travel freely for two years, by which time the therapeutic journey had not only diminished her funds, but had given her a greater appreciation of the power of money.

Whilst touring South Africa she managed to secure a position with Anglovest Reef Mines in Johannesburg, during which time she acquired considerable, practical field training under the guidance of more experienced geologists. Sharon learned quickly, enjoying the frequent field survey trips, the magnificent country and its flora and fauna. But, after three years, she yearned for a change of scenery and, touched by an occasional bout of homesickness, wrote to her uncle advising that she wished to come home. She had returned to the Philippines and accepted the General's offer to live in his sprawling, Manila mansion, grateful for his support and introductions to the wealthy and influential powerbrokers that ate off President Marcos' table in *Malacanang Palace*.

Sharon's most recent visit to London had been to investigate avenues whereby some of the General's associates', illicitly acquired wealth, might be converted into American dollars. She had been unsuccessful, and had been preparing to fly to New York to meet with a number of brokers when Alfredo had called, summoning her home to Manila.

Now, as she rested alongside her uncle, Sharon prayed for his recovery.

* * * *

Jakarta – Indonesia

Heavily armed, blue-beret soldiers stood guard on both sides of Jalan Cendana preventing access to the well known address, those permitted to pass through the heavily cordoned street were either members of the First Family, or those closely associated with the Suharto regime.

A red Lamborghini roared around the corner from Jalan Waringin, the driver laughing as he drove the Italian racer directly at the guards, forcing them to leap sideways, and away from his path. With a squeal of burning rubber, the car turned into a driveway, the air suddenly quiet as the President's son killed the engine and climbed out of his machine, then strutted arrogantly past a black Mercedes-Benz limousine with its 'RI-1' plates, into his father's principal residence.

Inside, he paid his respects to his mother, before wandering through to the rear of the well-fortified compound, where he found a number of his siblings holding court.

'*It could only have been you, with that noisy car!*' an older sister complained.

'*You should be grateful that I get to use the city's roads as much as I do,*' he retorted, referring to the fact that this sister had managed to convince their father to place tolls on the capital's highways, the company appointed to collect the revenue, one of hers.

'*What's wrong with them?*' he asked, nodding in the direction of his two brothers who appeared to be in heated discussion.

'*Same problem as before,*' she replied, clucking as their mother would whenever her children fought. Acrimonious, behind-the-scene battles for power were becoming increasingly frequent in this household. Their first public dispute, almost a decade before, over who should be given the LNG shipping monopoly, severely embarrassed Palace circles. The President had finally decided in favor of one, offering the other an additional monopoly with the *cukong,* Liem Sioe Liong who never failed to contribute considerably to the family's collective coffers.

★ ★ ★ ★

The children were all well versed in the importance of the *cukongs* – their father, Suharto, had been instrumental in paving the way for the Chinese to take control over the country's economy, through which the First Family greatly benefited.

Suharto and Liem Sioe Liong had been financial companions dating back to the days when the former general commanded the *Diponegoro* Divisions in Central Java. Since ascending to the Presidency, the first major deals the partnership produced were the Bogasari flourmills in Surabaya and Jakarta in 1972, to mill US PL-480, foreign aid wheat. Now, after thirty-two years at the nation's helm, the First Family controlled more than twenty foundations which owned stakes in a plethora of large corporations such as cement factories, timber concessions, oil palm plantations, fertilizer factories and even the country's largest private bank. And, this was still not enough.

The President controlled the Judiciary, Parliament, and the Military. He personally appointed the Central Bank Governor, the

Chairman of the Security and Exchange Commission and the CEOs of state-owned companies. And he wanted more.

Such was the power and extent of the Suharto Empire, the children entered adulthood distanced from reality, oblivious to the groundswell building against their family, unaware that their country had become a tinder-box of poverty and bitterness, ready to erupt.

More recently, the family had consolidated its interests in Timor, determined to control the oil and gas resources in the Timor Sea, and in Natuna's gigantic gas fields in the South China Sea. Now, after thirty years of Suharto rule, they had accumulated tens of billions of American dollars in wealth, owned a sprawling array of businesses from satellite communications to airlines, plantations, vehicle assembly plants and even public utilities. The children had acquired luxurious mansions, ranches and hotels in Britain, Bermuda, Hawaii, Germany, Australia and Singapore, their lifestyles a far cry from that of Indonesia's landless peasants and slum dwellers, who, even if they were successful in finding work, would be forced to survive on as little as a dollar per day. With numbered bank accounts in Switzerland, Austria and Singapore, to hide their billions, the First Family went on the international acquisition trail purchasing fine art, golf courses, condominiums, yachts and private jets, the latter used to ferry the sons to casinos in Australia. And still, this was not enough. With his eyes firmly fixed on the mining sector, the younger Suharto had decided to ask for his father's intervention, to enable him to acquire holdings in foreign mining joint ventures that had commenced production in Indonesia.

And, when this was granted, the son went after Kalimantan's gold.

★ ★ ★ ★

Chapter Four

1992

SINGAPORE

Stewart Campbell shuffled through the committee welcoming line, past an array of flowers that were shaped more like the traditional, Western funeral wreaths than celebratory or welcoming arrangements, and entered the Grand Hyatt's Sir Stamford Room function venue on the first floor. He accepted a cocktail from one of the many waiters weaving through the assembly, smiled, acknowledged a number of associates and friends, then eased his way through the sea of locally tailored, black-tie dinner jackets and cocktail dresses to join a group of Asian engineers he had met earlier that day.

A banner dominating one wall welcomed delegates to the 14th South East Asian Mining Conference, the elegant setting and surrounds standing in contradiction to the theme-decorated ballroom, the three meter, black and white photographs depicting mining scenes on the opposing wall in brutal contrast to the original designer's perception, of a fine-dining venue.

Campbell leaned closer to the young woman offering an opinion as to why Singapore had achieved recognition as the only, real safe-banking haven in Asia, the crowded room's chatter reaching deafening levels with inhibition-reduced, alcohol levels loosening tongues and raising self-import. Waiters glided past carrying silver *hors d'oeuvre* trays laden with smoked salmon *coque au vain*, pickled quail eggs dotted with neon-green *Tobilko* caviar, butterfly prawns, and miniature spring rolls, the guests washing these down with generous swills of *Clos des Goisses* champagne with little, if any understanding of the gift offered by the preciously-nurtured grape. Campbell continued to listen, politely, to the soft-spoken Singaporean delegate as she struggled to be heard above the competing rabble.

'...and, added to which, the incredible inflow of funds from Indonesia contributed greatly to Singapore's prosperity,' she paused, losing the opportunity to another and more verbose government type, whose dominance over the conversation had already driven others away.

'In my opinion, ...' the bureaucrat started. Campbell, feigning having caught the attention of a familiar face across the room, used this pretext as an excuse to move away. He edged his way through the gathering, now determined to touch base with a number of colleagues then escape to a lesser-congested environment. He squeezed through the throng towards a more subdued group, the noise level abating considerably as he distanced himself from the bar service area.

A hand touched the small of his back and he turned, the tall and long-waisted woman confronting him so breathtakingly beautiful that, for an uncomfortable moment, Stewart Campbell was struck speechless.

'Mister Campbell?' Stewart's surprise turned to acute embarrassment when his tongue failed to respond, so stunned was he with the stunningly, graceful creature standing before him. 'I'm Sharon Ducay. You *are* Stewart Campbell?' the woman challenged, the suggestion of her beguiling perfume momentarily confusing Campbell even further.

'Yes.' He managed an awkward smile then, near apoplectic when a guest behind stepped back inadvertently nudging him forward, causing Campbell to spill his cocktail onto the Filipino beauty's full-length, pink, beaded cocktail dress.

'Oh, God, I'm so sorry!' he exclaimed, weakly, the damp patch spreading down the woman's front from breast to thigh. For a moment he imagined her eyes on fire, the ever-so-brief flash of anger evident, before misinterpreted dismay transposed to grievous surprise.

'Mister Campbell!' Sharon Ducay raised her hands, palms opened as if in religious gesture, first looking down at her stained, *Javier Larrainzar* gown, then up into his eyes as if he had committed the most heinous of crimes.

'I'm so sorry,' Campbell offered, lamely, conscious of having attracted the attention of other guests in close proximity, 'but I was bumped.' And to substantiate his claim, Stewart turned and glared at the responsible but inebriated guest alongside, hoping to apportion blame. Then, 'I'm deeply embarrassed,' he offered, truly distressed at his clumsiness, even though responsibility for the accident lay elsewhere.

Sharon Ducay accepted a napkin from a concerned waiter. She dabbed directly below her breasts in what Campbell's mind were translated as soft, sensuous movements.

'I'll have to go and change,' she said. Campbell, detecting no trace of malice in her voice, moved to make amends.

'Please accept my apology?' he asked, determined not to let her go, or at least accompany her if she were to leave. 'I'm normally not this clumsy.' She was obviously Asian – possibly Indonesian; perhaps from northern Sulawesi, he guessed. *'Maaf saya,'* he apologized in *Bahasa Indonesia* hoping this would resolve his predicament. Not many expatriates spoke the language with any fluency, and Campbell was prepared for the challenge.

'I am not Indonesian,' she responded, obviously offended by the suggestion.

'Ouch! Sorry.' Campbell was now floundering, desperate to recover lost ground. 'It's just that I don't often meet many beautiful women outside of my own domain.' Then a thought struck home. 'You know my name?'

Sharon Ducay flashed a well-practised smile. 'Yes,' she answered, 'and before you ask, I am from Manila.'

Campbell remained confused. 'I know we haven't met before – I would definitely have remembered.' His confidence returning, Campbell indicated her soiled dress. 'It's hardly obvious now,' he suggested. Without looking down Sharon placed one hand on her abdomen.

'It's still wet,' she replied, matter-of-factly.

'Do you still wish to change?'

'Yes,' she said, looking towards the exit, preparing to leave. 'Will you accompany me?' Before Campbell could respond, she raised her hand and took his forearm, then turned towards the exit and steered the way.

★ ★ ★ ★

'Help yourself to the bar,' Sharon glided through the Regency Club suite, disrobing as she disappeared from view, her guest catching a brief glimpse of her curvaceous lines. Campbell's room was in the other wing overlooking the swimming pool, the disparity between the accommodations significant. The Hyatt's 'hotel within a hotel' concept for its more prominent guests providing lavish furnishings and butler service was a luxury he had yet to afford.

'Can I pour you something?' he called, his offer drawing a silent response. Campbell checked the chilled wines and selected a *pinot noir* Chardonnay, opening the bottle and pouring two glasses just as Sharon reappeared, dressed in slacks. She accepted the Hungarian cased, crystal flute, sipped lightly, nodded her approval, then moved towards the heavily draped windows and opened the curtains to peer outside.

It was early October, yet Christmas fervor had arrived in earnest, with Singaporean traders already dressing Orchard Road's towering hotels with an elaborate display of Christmas lights, and New Year greetings. Campbell remained standing at a respectable distance admiring Sharon's figure as she stood framed by the window, the suite's soft lighting, enhancing her features. She turned, the hand holding her wine resting in the palm of the other, and smiled.

'I observed you at the opening ceremony,' she said, her voice carrying a huskiness not evident before. Campbell was surprised that he could have missed her, even amongst the other four hundred delegates.

'Obviously, I was preoccupied with the program otherwise I would have noticed you, also.' The flattery not lost on Sharon, she placed her empty flute down and lit a cigarette while Campbell refilled their glasses. 'Have you had dinner?' he asked, disappointed that she smoked, surprised that the habit was still tolerated in the Hyatt's rooms.

'No,' Sharon replied, 'I always avoid function food. And you?'

'I could eat,' he hoped she would want to dine in. And then, 'But first, aren't you going to reveal how you knew my name?'

This was met with a playful laugh, Sharon anticipating the question. 'When I saw you at the opening ceremony, I asked,' she parried. In fact, Sharon Ducay was well informed when it came to Stewart Campbell.

'I wasn't aware that I was that popular,' he sensed there was more to it, but decided to let it go. His exploits within the mining sector during the past decade had raised his profile not just within Indonesian resource circles, but also regionally. Stewart had represented a number of major, American international conglomerates and, although he doubted that they had met before, nevertheless, he found something vaguely familiar about this beautiful woman. 'Perhaps you have confused me with someone else?'

Sharon dropped the cigarette in the ashtray, then raised her glass to offer a toast. 'One thing I have never been accused of, Stewart, is being confused. We'll talk later. Right now, I'm famished. Let's get out of here and find something decent to eat. Cheers!'

Campbell accepted the polite rebuff, the resonance of two crystal glasses ringing as they touched.

★ ★ ★ ★

On their way down in the lift they had discussed their choices and preferences, Campbell suggesting a Chinese seafood restaurant he occasionally frequented when in Singapore – Sharon had agreed, the taxi dropping them at the Excelsior Hotel on Coleman Street. There, they caught a lift to the fourth level of the Shanghai Palace and were seated within minutes. Campbell ordered, checking with his companion on each selection.

'You certainly know your way around Chinese food,' she complimented, impressed with Campbell's choices.

They had started the meal with shark's fin soup mixed with fish maw and crab meat, then attacked the fried, shredded-duck laced lightly with dried chili. Sharon raised her bowl and skillfully scooped steamed rice into her mouth. 'Ah,' she sighed, 'this is delicious!'

'Leave room for the braised garoupa,' he warned, as the waiter placed a dish of mushrooms and broccoli on their table.

'You can eat raw chili?' she asked, surprised as Campbell raised part of a green pepper with his chopsticks and placed the sliced chili in his mouth.

'Sure,' he laughed, following quickly with rice and fish, the garoupa's strong taste coming through the black bean sauce. Then, from behind a napkin, 'You can't live in Indonesia for ten years without acquiring the taste.'

'Have you ever visited the Philippines?' Sharon asked, accepting the remaining piece of shredded duck into her bowl.

'Just once,' he replied, 'but only for a few days. I didn't have the time to go sightseeing.'

'Were you there for the mining conference?'

'Yes,' Campbell recalled the brief visit. 'Stayed in Makati the whole time,' he added, referring to Manila's congested central business district. He had not enjoyed the conference although the city's wealth of bars and nightclubs had offered some compensation, remembering playing truant on the second day and missing most of the workshops held by the Filipino Mines and Energy Ministry.

'You should have taken some time off and visited the resorts,' she admonished, 'they are very beautiful.' Then, with a mirthless smile, 'And so are the women.'

Campbell avoided the obvious response. He knew little about her country and wished to turn the conversation. 'Have you been to Indonesia?'

'Yes, I've been to Jakarta several times, on business.'

Campbell was genuinely interested. 'On business?' he asked.

'Yes, on business,' she smiled mischievously.

Campbell pressed on. 'Are you going to elaborate?'

Sharon laughed, softly, and placed a placatory hand on his knee. 'We have something in common, Mister Campbell,' she teased, then sipped the lukewarm Chinese herbal tea, her eyes never leaving Stewart's.

'And that would be…?' he left the question dangling.

'We are both geologists,' she revealed, enjoying the look of disbelief spreading across his handsome face. She dabbed her lips with a napkin before continuing. 'I went to Jakarta on a number of occasions to see if we could entice some of the foreign mining companies to visit the Philippines. It would seem that Indonesia has more than its fair share of foreign investment in the resources' sector, and you know how damn difficult it is to drag American companies away from their own shores.'

Campbell, momentarily overwhelmed, merely nodded.

'A number of Filipino concession holders teamed up to go to Jakarta but, unfortunately, we were unsuccessful in convincing any of the larger miners to slip across and examine our country's potential, while they were exploring in the general area.'

'It's a wonder we did not cross paths,' he told her.

'You were out of town at the time,' she suggested. Campbell leaned back from the table and raised an eyebrow.

'You checked?' he was puzzled.

'We had our embassy try to set up a meeting with you, Stewart, but you were out in the field for the duration of our stay.'

'I was out of town during *both* visits?' he asked, disbelievingly.

'Yes,' she nodded.

Campbell shook his head slowly. 'When was this?'

Sharon answered, without hesitation. 'May and October, 1991.'

Campbell recalled both months; he had, indeed, been out on survey during Sharon's visits. 'Well, that explains your knowing my name,' he said, thoughtfully. 'Do you plan to return in the near future?'

'It's unlikely, Stewart. My country is not one of the most desired destinations amongst the mining fraternity. As long as Indonesian discoveries monopolize resource investment dollars I'm afraid the Philippines will continue to be neglected.'

Stewart knew what Sharon had suggested was entirely true. The Philippines was a low priority in terms of Asian mineral, oil and gas exploration. On the other hand, Indonesia's mining boom continued to attract substantial investment, leaving other South East Asian nations in the shadows. There had been some initial interest in Vietnam but communist dogma continued to prevail throughout most of Indochina, making the area less than attractive as petty bureaucrats continued to dictate policy at provincial levels.

'Where did you study?' he wanted to know.

'California State,' she revealed, somewhat indifferently. 'I traveled for a while, worked in South Africa for three years before accepting a position with a Filipino group. I completed post-grad work for my Masters after that. And you?'

Campbell was not surprised to learn that she was so well educated. The woman was obviously intelligent and determined. He found himself staring at her again, thinking that she had it all; beauty, intelligence and was well connected. 'Washington State.'

'And then?'

Campbell considered the question. After graduating, he had gone on to work with the Canadian-based INCO (International Nickel Company) because of its dominance as a nickel producer in the international market. He had spent his post-graduate years in Canada and, for some time, remained content with his lot. He was then sent to South America for six months where he was assigned to assist Professor Herman von Hugel. The revered scientist's recommendations led to Campbell being offered an opportunity to work in Indonesia where INCO had secured a major deposit in Sulawesi during the early 1970s, and was considering copper and gold deposits elsewhere throughout the archipelago. Stewart had hoped that INCO's fascination with Indonesia would provide him with a springboard for other opportunities, however, local rationalization caused him to re-evaluate his career prospects, precipitating his leap into private consulting. The rest was history. He had become a respected Indonesian mining consultant, his services now in regular demand. 'I've kept myself busy,' he said, modestly. It was now obvious that Sharon Ducay had prior knowledge of his credentials. 'Would you like to expand upon why your group wanted to make contact with me?'

Sharon's response was not what he had expected. 'We were exploring the possibility of engaging your services as a consultant, in the Philippines,' she explained.

'Why?' he said, taken aback. 'I know virtually nothing about your country's geology, let alone its mining policies.'

'The approach was not biased in that direction,' Sharon suggested. 'We needed to attract consultants with the capacity to interest the major players in our country's potential. Your name came up, that's all.'

Campbell thought this through. 'Did you find anyone?' he asked.

'Well, we met a number of expatriates who appeared keen, but none that were convincing.'

'I would have thought that there would be strong, American interest in the Philippines, considering the historical ties?'

'Not so,' she explained, 'at least not in the mining sector. Yes, American companies have established substantial trading ties with our country, but most of this is product based, not resource investment.' She paused to eat, sipping tea before continuing. 'Frankly, I found it so frustrating, I finally withdrew from the promotional tours.'

'And now?' he asked.

Sharon pulled a face. 'Needed to do some shopping. Manila's department stores aren't exactly up there with Saks. The mining conference provided the opportunity, that's all.' Campbell was reminded of the magnificent cocktail dress he had soiled.

'I meant, what keeps you occupied when you're at home?' he pried.

Sharon smiled demurely. 'Do you mean am I married?'

Campbell laughed. 'Yes, something like that. As it would seem that you know considerably more about me, I think it only fair you reveal all your dark secrets.'

'Why would these necessarily be dark?' she countered.

'Perhaps I should have said, 'mysterious'?' He was enjoying the banter.

It was Sharon's turn to laugh. 'Don't you think that a little mystique keeps the men guessing?' At that moment their waiter appeared, saving her from having to elaborate. He divided the remaining fish carefully, and then withdrew.

'When do you return to Manila?' Campbell wanted to know.

'Tomorrow,' was her brief reply.

'Back to work?'

'No,' Sharon responded, affecting a touch of weariness in her voice. 'Let's not talk shop anymore. Agreed?'

'Fine by me,' he promised. 'Would you like anything else?'

Sharon shook her head. 'No. I'd like to return to the hotel now if you don't mind.' She paused, observing Campbell's disappointment then added, 'We could have a nightcap back in the room, if you wish.' The invitation clearly raised his spirits.

'Then what are we still doing here?' Campbell settled the bill as quickly as protocol would permit, and escorted his beautiful companion back down to the lobby where they caught a taxi to the Grand Hyatt.

★ ★ ★ ★

Stewart Campbell placed his arm around Sharon's shoulders and pulled her gently towards him. She did not resist, turning to face him with willing lips and they kissed, the warmth of the exchange and her intoxicating perfume sending exotic signals through to his loins. His hand moved to her firm breasts, their fullness exciting him even more.

'Not here,' she pulled away, taking his hands in hers, the blood beating loudly in Campbell's ears. Neither spoke during the remaining ride, their silence maintained even after they had entered Sharon's suite where they immediately embraced, undressing each other with impatient passion before collapsing to the thickly carpeted floor.

Stewart was in no way disappointed when his eyes fell upon Sharon's naked figure, the soft curves and light brown skin accentuating her beauty. His hands groped her breasts, squeezing her erect nipples roughly and Sharon cried out, biting his lip with the pain. With the taste of blood in their mouths they remained locked, their sexual frenzy driving them together and they coupled, naturally, Campbell's length penetrating her so deeply she cried out, again, lifting her knees high and wide as he moved within her. She felt one hand slide down through the soft mound between her legs, the touch of his fingers causing Sharon to writhe uncontrollably as he continued to thrust with growing urgency. The tempo grew, their bodies rocking together wildly until Campbell's hot, rhythmic moans triggered warm ripples which rose from deep inside her womb and she gasped, her own spasms in concert with his, their climax sending sensuous waves flooding through their bodies. In those few, brief, but delirious moments, they floated together, the warmth of his ejaculation causing Sharon to shudder. Then he sighed, heavily, totally spent.

They remained embraced, each slowly slipping back from the sexual summit they had just climbed, their heartbeats gradually slowing as they lay there, lost in the afterglow. Sharon shivered involuntarily as the air conditioner spilled tons of cold air into the room and Stewart rolled to one side, this time gently caressing her still erect nipples with his tongue, bringing a murmur of delight to her lips.

'Enough,' she pleaded, kissing him tenderly on the shoulder. 'I'm freezing!' With that, Sharon rose slowly and made her way to the bathroom, reappearing shortly after wearing a pink, toweling dressing gown. 'Are you staying?' she asked, lighting her second cigarette for the evening, drawing heavily as she did so. In the dim light Stewart could see the end glow, wondering how offended she might be if he elected to sleep in his own bed.

'I'll stay if you want me to,' he said, gathering his clothing. He felt foolish standing there naked, but did not wish to dress until the matter of where he would spend the night had been resolved.

'I'm okay,' Sharon told him. 'We could have breakfast together by the pool?'

Relieved, Stewart dressed and went to her side. 'We could have breakfast here instead,' he suggested, bending down to kiss her softly on the forehead.

'I'd prefer it at the pool. Besides, I always take an early swim.'

'Then the pool it is,' he agreed, 'give me a ring when you are ready. Okay?'

'I'll meet you there after eight,' she promised, reaching up and dragging his mouth to hers. Reluctantly, he responded, the lingering smell of cigarette smoke on her breath spoiling the moment.

★ ★ ★ ★

Sharon lay back on the sofa thinking about her brief interlude with the American. She had not misled her temporary lover with respect to her having initiated inquiries regarding his availability to work in the Philippines. In fact, Sharon Ducay had spent considerable time and effort investigating Stewart, before arriving at the conclusion that he would not be acceptable for the project that she and her uncle had in mind. General consensus supported her assessment of the well-known expatriate geologist. Stewart Campbell was far too much of an idealist to willingly become involved in anything like what she and the General had planned. Their meeting had been coincidental. Sharon's purpose in attending the conference was to hold discussions with Alexander Kremenchug but, as a last minute change in his plans prevented their introduction, she had decided to stay the day and shop. Meeting the handsome Campbell had merely been a bonus. As she lay stretched out on the well-cushioned sofa, Sharon's hand dropped to the soft, dark mound between her thighs and she closed her eyes, conjuring up Stewart's firm body in her mind, as she stroked herself gently.

★ ★ ★ ★

Stewart Campbell came alive to the eight o'clock wake-up call, showered, dressed for the swimming pool and then rode the lift down twelve floors to the scenic setting. Coconut trees hung over the pool area providing questionable shade, and Stewart settled down with a fruit juice waiting for Sharon to appear.

At eight forty-five he knew she had overslept; by nine o'clock he had returned to his room, disappointed, when the hotel reception's informed him that Miss Sharon Ducay had checked out at seven and returned to the Philippines without so much as leaving him a note.

★ ★ ★ ★

Borneo Gold Corporation

Vancouver – Jakarta

'I have Chris here with me now, Eric, and he is rightfully pissed. The drilling results bear no fucking resemblance to the first survey report you sent him!'

Alex Kremenchug's vitriolic outburst was expected, the party listening at the other end nonchalantly lighting a *kretek* cigarette as he played out the scene, permitting Kremenchug's tirade to appear genuine.

'Mine wasn't a full survey,' Eric Baird's defensive voice could be heard on the speaker-phone. 'Had I been given the necessary funds, I could have provided an extensive drilling survey report.'

'It's just not good enough, Eric,' Kremenchug complained, deep furrows creasing his brow. 'Shit, Eric!' he added for additional emphasis, 'how could you have been so fucking far off with this?'

This comment, as it had not been rehearsed, was met with dumb response. Baird, sitting in the Jakarta apartment that he shared with an advertising executive, suddenly lost his place in the conversation. He checked his notes, taken off an earlier and recorded exchange between him and Alex Kremenchug.

'Are you still there?' Kremenchug's voice bellowed down through the line. An echo repeated his aggressive demand, the final words 'there, there, there' reverberating annoyingly through the speakers in the mining company's Vancouver office.

'Shit,' Kremenchug shouted, this too echoing from ground to satellite, then back to an earth station near the Indonesian capital sending Eric Baird the message, 'shit, shit, shit' as the geologist responsible for the fabricated report started to panic.

'Now, wait a minute,' Baird started to argue, the time lapse between the parties creating the misunderstanding. He was interrupted by the unfamiliar voice of the Canadian company's chief geologist, and Chairman, on the speakerphone.

'Eric,' the hollow sound bounced around the apartment as Baird gathered his thoughts. Speaking directly to Christopher Fielding had not been part of their plan. 'Eric, this is Chris Fielding,' the distorted voice claimed.

'Hello, hello?' Baird continued to panic, wondering if he should hang up and claim later that they had been cut off.

'Eric,' Fielding tried again, 'it's Chris Fielding. Can you hear me?'

Of course, Baird could hear him. He just did not wish to be dragged into a conversation without knowing what he was supposed to say. 'Hello, hello?' he feigned again, 'is that still you, Alex?'

Kremenchug realized what had happened, silently admonishing himself for his own stupidity in deviating from the rehearsed dialogue. He moved quickly to circumvent any possible misinterpretation by Fielding.

'Eric,' he spoke intermittently, enunciating carefully as if atmospherics were, indeed, the problem, the show entirely for Fielding's benefit. 'I think the problem is here, with the speaker system.' He turned to Fielding, his face covered with the most serious of expressions.

'I...am...going....to…turn....it...off..okay?'

Baird understood immediately, the conversation then taking a dramatic turn.

'Eric?' Kremenchug asked. 'Eric. Is this clearer?'

'Can Fielding hear me?

'No? Then wait a moment and I will check the receiver here.'

'What's this shit about being off with the survey?'

'That's good. Yes, I can hear you clearly now.'

'What do you want me to say for Chrissakes?' This, from the Jakarta end where Baird was now sitting with his legs sprawled across a divan, his *kretek* cigarette hanging carelessly from his fingers and in danger of burning the plastic head-cover, which had never been removed since delivery.

'Eric, can you give Vancouver any additional information which would support the earlier survey?' Kremenchug manipulated the conversation as was necessary.

'Are you *sure* that Fielding can't hear me?' Baird asked, worried, ignoring the question.

'No!' Kremenchug responded flatly.

'Then go and fuck yourself, Alex!' Baird yelled into the phone, his Bacardi- influenced bravado tipping him over the edge. At the other end of the line Kremenchug stood speechless. With a click of his tongue, he turned to the Canadian mining executive, shrugged his shoulders then hung up.

'We lost the connection,' Kremenchug lied.

★ ★ ★ ★

Since their first meeting in Jakarta, two and a half years before, the company had been floated, successfully raising several millions from the Canadian public. In fact, the offer had been oversubscribed, such was the interest for mining companies with Indonesian gold prospects and, as the Borneo Gold Corporation boasted several of these within the Kalimantan provinces, stockholder funds filled the subscription offer within an hour of the company being listed on the Canadian Exchange.

Initially, Christopher Fielding had commissioned a more detailed survey of the Palangkaraya alluvial leases, but the findings were not significant. The following year, the BGC President had then decided to embark on a comprehensive drilling program of their East Kalimantan areas, the results causing the stock to fall to less than half their par value once overall results had been revealed to the market. The disappointing results left the fledgling mining corporation with few funds and questionable capacity to raise further capital. Christopher Fielding again found himself fighting off creditors, his occasional consultancy contracts subsidizing his half-salary-income paid by the near-insolvent company.

At the end of the escrow period, Kremenchug and the Baird-Subroto partnership found that their stock was practically worthless, and moved on to other ventures to keep themselves afloat. Kremenchug and Baird kept in touch, both maintaining interests primarily in Kalimantan's burgeoning mining sector. However, as Indonesia's gold fever had revitalized interest in prospects *Down Under*, Kremenchug decided to visit Western Australia where many of his ilk were amassing fortunes, by floating near worthless mining companies. Unable to resist the hordes of speculative investors lining up to be fleeced, Kremenchug headed into the West Australian outback, where he became embroiled with a group of would-be-mining magnates in the small, gold mining town of Meekathara.

★ ★ ★ ★

Chapter Five

March 1993
The Philippines

Sharon Ducay peered through the window, the landscape blurred by sheets of rain. She looked back over her shoulder at the elderly man slumped in an oversized, carved teak and leather chair, and smiled, sadly, then moved to his side.

'Thank you, General,' she placed her hand on his, the threat of tears real as her eyes dropped to the black armband he wore on the anniversary of his younger brother's untimely death. 'It means such a great deal to me.'

'When will you leave?' he asked, Sharon concerned at how he had aged since his recent illness.

'Tomorrow,' she replied, stroking his arm.

'You will return in time for Easter?'

'Of course, General, I wouldn't dream of missing the holidays with you.'

'Are you certain you can't stay a few more days?' he pleaded, not at all looking forward to her absence again.

'I should go, General. The timing is right. Besides, Alfredo will take care of you while I'm away,' she consoled, referring to her uncle's muscular manservant who had served under the Filipino officer and then followed him into retirement, at the President's personal request.

'You should find a young man, get married and settle down,' he suggested.

Sharon gave him her customary response. 'When I find someone like you, General,' knowing how dearly he enjoyed having her say so.

'I will miss having you here,' he complained, but they both knew that it went deeper than that.

'I will ring you every day,' she promised, 'and Alfredo, to see if you are taking your medicine.' The General's wry smile greeted this announcement with a wave of one hand in dismissive gesture.

'Alfredo would be happy to see me gone,' he lied, enjoying this game they so often played whenever Sharon was to leave.

'General,' she warned, participating in the charade, 'if he did so, who would he have to beat so easily at chess?' General Narciso Dominguex's once powerful lungs rasped laughter at the thought of Alfredo ever beating him at his favorite pastime. He looked Sharon directly in the eyes, the exchange filled with love.

'Be careful,' was all he said, and she nodded, squeezing his forearm gently.

'I always am,' she reassured, confidently. She observed Alfredo waiting at a discreet distance. 'Now, it's time for your afternoon nap.'

The General sighed heavily, tapping Sharon's wrist softly with his free hand, signaling that he was ready to be led away. Sharon rose, permitting Alfredo with his powerful arms to lift the General to his feet, placing a cane in his left hand, then leading him down the passageway to his sleeping quarters. The aged officer stopped, mid-shuffle, turned with half-bowed head and spoke.

'We will dine together tonight?' he asked, having forgotten that Sharon had already said so earlier.

'Yes, General,' she tilted her head, 'I'll still be here.' The old man nodded then permitted Alfredo to lead him the remaining short distance to his room.

★ ★ ★ ★

During the turbulent past decade, Sharon had been witness to considerable change in her country that had, in turn, required that she develop her own networking skills as the destabilized situation threatened established relationships. When Cory Aquino took up the torch of opposition leading demonstrations against Marcos, until finally driving the former dictator from office in 1986, Sharon accepted the inevitable, believing that the General and his associates would be completely cut off by those elected through the phenomenon of People Power. When the seventh President took charge, her office was continuously threatened with insurrection, separatist movements in the south, and a spate of various natural calamities such as typhoons, earthquakes, volcanic eruptions and even floods. Because of this ongoing instability, the General's former associates managed to maintain some semblance of influence over the new government. The Philippines military, not unlike their Indonesian counterparts, still called the shots regardless of who was in power, and former generals such as Narciso Dominguez continued to enjoy their privileged positions. After six years of experimenting with democracy, General Fidel Ramos replaced Cory Aquino when he won the presidential election in May of that year. Even her uncle had been surprised as, not only was Ramos a protestant in a predominantly Catholic country, but he managed only twenty-three percent of the popular vote.

It seemed that business circles were satisfied with their new president, the stock market rising significantly as did property prices and inflation. Sharon realized that there were considerable opportunities for promoting mining ventures in the Philippines, and her interest in the stock market grew by the day. The country's mining fraternity boasted that there were viable deposits of nickel, zinc, copper, cobalt, gold, silver, iron, and even chromite but, as these had not been seriously investigated, Sharon found herself traveling extensively searching for foreign investors who might be interested in exploiting these resources. Unfortunately, her endeavors where unsuccessful as the mineral exploration in neighboring Indonesia continued to produce frequent, new discoveries of extremely high traces of gold, resulting in a lackluster response to her entreaties. She had gathered groups of local miners and flown to Jakarta in her attempts to drag visiting mining investors back to her own shores. A number of smaller companies did arrive, but not nearly in large enough numbers to create anything like the minerals boom which continued to grow in Indonesia.

Frustrated by falling interest in her country's deposits, Sharon started looking elsewhere for her own El Dorado, finally convinced that her fortunes lay not in the ground, but by what was perceived to be there. She threw herself into studying the stock market and trading, concentrating on mining companies that were basically in the general exploration game, amazed at how easily many of these had raised capital. Sharon compared the different markets, examining mining prospectuses, monitoring results with growing astonishment, as speculative, public floats were frequently oversubscribed, the millions pouring into operations that were, in her opinion, highly questionable. She visited Canada and Australia to discover for herself why these countries were so active in Indonesia, keen to identify parties she could work with – convinced that the right people for her own operation could be found there. Then, after almost two years in the planning, Sharon Ducay was ready. She laid her plan out for her uncle's consideration, and he had unhesitatingly agreed.

Tomorrow, she would fly to Australia and execute the first step in her strategy, by making Alexander Kremenchug an offer he would not refuse, Sharon believing that if her assessment of the man's character were correct, neither she nor the General would ever have to be concerned with a shortage of money, ever again.

★ ★ ★ ★

General Narciso Dominguez lay stretched out on top of the quilted cover, his eyelids closed and still, sleep would not come, his head filled with concern about Sharon's execution of their plan.

His mind roamed – recalling the beginning of the end to the Marcos era. The incident, which would later become known as the *First Quarter Storm* began on January 26, 1970 when a crowd of some twenty thousand threw rocks and bottles at President Marcos and his wife, Imelda. Although the police successfully scattered the angry demonstrators, four days later, thousands chanting revolutionary slogans smashed their way through the Malacanang Palace gates using a commandeered fire truck. The police killed six of the demonstrators, resulting in an even larger mob attacking the American Embassy with Molotov cocktails. Throughout the next decade, Marcos' position deteriorated, and with changing loyalties, so too did many amongst the officer corps. The President's family ignored growing resentment – their frequent and bitter marital disputes clearly marked for public display, when Marcos built bridges and other infrastructure to support his wife's family-related projects, as a token of his retribution for his many extra-marital affairs.

In the 1970s and 80s there had been a gradual build-up for the Philippine Army in terms of manpower, organization and equipment. The Army's strength grew from twenty thousand to nigh on sixty thousand over those years, primarily to combat anti-dissident campaigns, and maintain Marcos' rule as president. There had been communist rebellions in both Luzon and the Visayas and, in Mindanao, highly trained and well-armed Bangsa Moro Army soldiers fought for their secessionist movement, successfully challenging Marcos' troops. Faced with these challenges the President increased defence spending which, in turn, further filled his coffers with gold and US dollars, much of which was used to secure the loyalty of his Army officers; amongst these, General Narciso Dominguez, whose own wealth had multiplied due to his position as Defence Contracts Coordinator, the collections he made, split equally with his erstwhile President.

Competition was growing among Marcos' officers and envy-driven politicians for a greater share of the spoils. As he was prominent amongst those who had greatest opportunity to siphon off millions during Marcos' time, the General decided to move the fourteen tons of gold he held in trust, to a less conspicuous location. At that time, the USAF worked closely with the Philippines Air Force, and the General was aware that a number of their transports were permanently assigned to the PAF. He summoned his younger brother, a senior PAF officer and arranged for a Hercules C130 to transport the hoard to Hong Kong, his brother taking all the family for a timely shopping spree. When they died tragically in the aircraft disaster, two hundred million dollars' worth of gold bars were lost somewhere over the South China Sea, forever. General Dominguez was left with less than five million dollars to see him through to the end of his days and, although a frugal person, this sum had diminished by half, with time.

Years of corruption and fraud in the 1986 elections provoked a popular uprising that sent Ferdinand and Imelda hastily fleeing into exile in Hawaii. But not before their billions in gold, silver and crates of hard currency had already been shipped to Switzerland and the United States. When it appeared that the military would continue to maintain power even under Cory Aquino, the General became concerned for his own welfare.

Dominguez had been loyal to Ferdinand Marcos, even up to his last days and, although saddened by Marcos' death in 1989, when the former dictator's body was returned to the Philippines, he elected not to attend the funeral, not wishing to attract undue attention to himself.

During Marcos' reign, the General had never wanted for anything, the end to Ferdinand's rule having a most disastrous effect on the Dominguez household finances, and the General's health. A mild heart attack had convinced him to disclose to Sharon how he had survived over the years under Marcos, deciding also to place the remaining gold under his niece's guardianship. He recalled taking her down into the damp cellars, watching as Alfredo opened the steel-covered trap. Sharon had inhaled sharply as the overhead light struck the loosely strewn, half-kilo yellow bars in the ground vault, and squealed with delight. A loving smile crossed his lips as he also remembered Sharon reaching down to retrieve one of the metal bricks, surprise on her face at how heavy such a small amount of gold could be. He'd watched, as Sharon counted the hoard, the tally reaching six hundred and thirty seven bars. The secret cache was worth four million dollars, the war chest his niece would require to rebuild their fortunes.

★ ★ ★ ★

Bandung – West Java

'Boleh juga!' Angela agreed that the guest speaker was, indeed, handsome; one of their fellow students sitting behind playfully hushed the pair. Jonathan Dau's daughter then pinched the soft flesh of her girlfriend's upper arm in friendly gesture, turning her attention back to the American's closing statement.

'…and, it is therefore obvious that mining ventures do, in fact, benefit local communities providing sound environmental considerations are strictly adhered to. The grave consequences of irresponsible mining procedures will have lasting effects on not only current generations, but also those still to come. Today, you are students. In the future, many decisions relating to good-mining practices will fall on your shoulders and I ask you to remember the talk I have given today when you make those decisions, and consider how your future determinations will impact on society. Thank you.'

The hall exploded into applause as Stewart Campbell completed his presentation titled *'Mining and The Environment'*, the students rising to their feet in respect, as their professor moved across the dais to thank the visiting geologist for his address. *'Cakap amat!'* Siti Rahajo thought that the American was up there with her favorite film stars, leaning forward and whispering loudly for all to hear. Angela pretended not to hear, nudging her girlfriend, Nani, and pulling a face. Siti was unpopular with the other girls because of her promiscuousness – and popularity with the boys. This class was now more than halfway through the four-year course and Siti had already slept with most of the male students during their first semester.

All of the female students were in their early to mid-twenties, an age at which most Indonesian girls would expect to be already married, with families.

'Why don't you ask him for a date?' Nani challenged, sending a titter through the group.

'Why not?' the well-endowed Siti responded, standing straight for the boys to see her firm breasts – another reason she was unpopular with the others. Even if Siti had not been loose the young

men would still have chased after her, her classical Javanese features and voluptuous figure enough to guarantee envy amongst her classmates.

'Students,' their professor called for their attention, the assembly falling silent as the Dean cleared his throat. *'We have been privileged to have Tuan Campbell talk to us today. He has kindly agreed to return and speak to those of you who are still here for the final semester.'* This was greeted with nervous giggles and coughs from the students. *'However, our guest has kindly consented to remain a little longer today, to answer any questions you might have. So, please remain seated, and Tuan Campbell will invite you to direct your questions to him.'* The professor stepped back, gesturing with one hand that the floor still belonged to the visiting geologist.

'Terima kasih,' Campbell thanked the Dean. Then, addressing the audience, *'Please raise your hand if you wish to ask a question.'* The seconds ticked away as embarrassed university students searched inwardly for courage to do so, most concerned that they may appear foolish, the remainder unable to think of anything that was relative to the earlier address.

'Tuan Campbell!' a solitary voice rang clearly through the hall. And, without recognition called out, *'You said in your presentation that mining companies and local communities could both benefit through the exploitation of natural resources?'* Those around Angela Dau were stunned, turning to gawk at the Dayak student.

'Yes,' Campbell agreed, *'I did make that statement.'* He moderated his voice, then asked, not unkindly, *'You don't agree?'* Again, all heads turned towards Angela.

'No, Mister Campbell,' she replied, her refusal to use the more respectful address not lost on all present. Up on the dais the professor frowned. Angela Dau was one of his finest students. However, her outspoken views around campus had attracted *Bakin's* attention, and the Dean was aware that Angela was under occasional surveillance by the intelligence agency. Angela continued, *'If what you say is true, then why haven't we seen any examples of such benefits flowing to the indigenous peoples in Kalimantan?'* The room was stunned into silence;

and, with the exception of the faint and nervous shuffling sounds, there was absolute quiet.

Stewart Campbell looked down at the pretty student, the fire in her heart reflected in her face and he nodded, slowly, while gathering his thoughts. He was on dangerous ground here, and anything he might say which could be construed as being anti-government could cost him dearly. Nevertheless, Stewart still felt a deep commitment towards the people whose traditional property had been taken, often without adequate compensation – left to become displaced people in their own land. *'Miss?'* he asked, wondering if being pressed to give her name might make her reconsider her question, *'may I have your name?'*

'My name is Angela Dau,' she responded, confidently, *'and I come from East Kalimantan. My people are Penehing Dayak.'* The pride in her voice instantly moving Campbell, understanding immediately why this student would consider some of the content of his address as provocative. With the surge of foreign investment in the mining sector, it was the indigenous peoples of Indonesian Borneo that had suffered the most.

He smiled kindly. *'I can understand how emotive an issue this would be, for you, Miss Angela,'* he paused, searching for the appropriate words in *Bahasa Indonesia. 'But I'm certain you will appreciate that it is not my position to enter into political debate as a guest in your country. Your question should best be directed to the government representatives.'* Campbell was saddened that he was unable to engage this young woman in open discussion; to do so would be irresponsible, the consequences severe for both.

Angela Dau felt the heat rise around her neck, ignoring her friend Nani's warning tugs at her sleeve.

'You can be confident, Mister Campbell,' she said, her voice clear to all, *'that I most surely will.'*

The professor stepped forward quickly and addressed his students. *'I ask that the students refrain from raising issues which are of a political nature.'* The message was clear, the Dean's interruption saving both Campbell and Angela from further embarrassment. *'Now, are there any other questions?'*

Students turned to look at each other, none now really inclined to speak up. Then, from a girl standing in the third row, *'I have a question,'* she said, raising her hand confidently. All eyes turned to the student in surprise.

'Yes, then,' the Dean wanted this session ended, *'what is it?'*

'I'd like to know if Tuan Campbell is married?' she asked.

To everyone's relief, the student body broke into laughter, Siti Rahajo frowning at the catcalls, brazenly standing her ground. The professor was pleased with this distraction, bending over as if doubled in laughter, then reaching up to slap his guest on the shoulder. Campbell, too, could not resist a smile, addressing the seductive Siti directly.

'Sudah kawin, tapi belum nikah,' he answered, causing the students to roar in response, the play on words suggesting that he was sexually experienced, but remained unmarried, a delight to their ears. Sensing that this had gone far enough the Dean moved quickly to bring an end to the session, thanking Campbell profusely for his attendance, before escorting him away from the lecture theatre.

★ ★ ★ ★

Outside, as they strolled across to the car park, Campbell inquired regarding the Dayak student.

'She's one of my best,' the professor claimed, proudly, *'and will most likely top her class.'* The bespectacled *guru* hesitated, took Campbell's arm and turned to face the younger man. *'You handled that well, Stewart,'* he said, in a fatherly tone. *'Angela Dau can be overly aggressive, but I have a special interest in seeing that she comes to no harm while away from home.'*

Campbell waited for the professor to continue, accustomed to the man's frequent pauses for effect.

'Her father placed her in my care while she completes her studies.' The Dean then looked up into the American's eyes. *'Jonathan Dau and I flew MiGs together during Soekarno's time.'* He observed the moment of puzzlement sweep Campbell's suntanned features. *'Jonathan is her father. He is also a highly respected Dayak chief.'*

Campbell was taken aback, impressed. *'And you flew, together?'* he asked, a new respect creeping into his voice for the balding academic.

'Yes,' the Dean confirmed, *'and there's more.'*

The men stood in the shade, a few hundred meters from where Campbell's driver remained faithfully alongside the Mercedes, the professor revealing that Jonathan Dau was also a revered *dukun.* Campbell expressed surprise, the professor agreeing that it was unusual, but then he went on to explain that, within some indigenous Dayak communities, it was not uncommon to find a hereditary chief who also carried the mantel of village shaman. *'Angela is an only child, Stewart, and, as such, will carry considerable influence within the Dayak communities when she returns.'*

Again, Campbell was surprised. *'She intends returning to the isolation and primitive conditions. Why?'*

It was the professor's turn to show surprise. *'To help her people, of course!'* Then he grinned, mischievously. *'That's what anyone would expect of a Dayak chief.'*

Campbell peered into the other man's wrinkled features, unsure of the professor's statement. *'A woman – as chief?'*

'Yes, certainly, with her people's support,' the professor explained. *'There are matriarchal, indigenous groups throughout Indonesia. The Bataks in Sumatra are an example. And then there are the matriarchal tribes of Borneo where the women practise polygamy.'*

'What was the name of Angela's ethnic group she mentioned back there?' Campbell asked. The professor then briefly explained the origins of the *Penehing Dayaks*, Campbell arriving at the conclusion that if Angela Dau's high-spiritedness was common amongst the Upper-Mahakam women, he should make a point of visiting when the opportunity arose. Although he had frequented *Kalimantan* on numerous occasions, Campbell had yet to venture further upstream along the Mahakam River than the rapids.

On the drive back to Jakarta, he could not get Angela out of his mind, the story of her family so intriguing Stewart Campbell fell asleep that night, with her name still fresh on his lips.

★ ★ ★ ★

'Come on, Nani!' Angela scolded, *'We'll be late again!'*

'Aduh!' Nani wailed, *'They'll wait, 'Gela. Slow down, you're making me giddy.'*

The pair hurried across the square and, as they approached the group of boys Nani pulled Angela back. *'Don't run,'* she whispered, hoarsely, *'they'll think we're too anxious.'*

Angela came to an abrupt halt, the sharp look sufficient exchange for Nani to realize she had already said too much. *'What exactly did you tell the boys?'* she was keen to know.

Her friend cupped one hand and whispered conspiratorially, as if the waiting group of students could hear. *'I didn't tell them anything,'* she embellished, *'just that you agreed to go on the picnic.'*

Angela looked directly into Nani's eyes, the distinct feeling that she was lying causing her to hesitate. *'If you think I am going to go with Didi,'* she insisted, referring to the tall, Menadonese lad who had often made it clear regarding how he felt, *'then you are going to be disappointed!'* With this, Angela stood her ground refusing to advance further. *'So, what have you said to them, really?'* she pressed, arms crossed over her breasts.

'Look, 'Gela,' Nani persisted, *'they aren't expecting anything. Promise! It's just that they are going up to Tangkaban Perahu on their bikes and I thought it would be fun to go for a ride.'* The prospect of revisiting those surrounds did not particularly appeal. Angela had been there a dozen times already, the active site shouldering the surrounding hills of Bandung, a constant reminder that this island of Java hosted most of the world's active volcanoes. Her last visit had resulted in near disaster when the volcano's crater had burst into increased activity, the sulphur-laden air catching her group by surprise as the deadly cloud rose heavily into the air. Angela was not in a hurry to repeat that experience.

Nani then took a stab at Angela's pride – and her Achilles Heel.

'Are you scared of the road?' she tried, referring to the dangerous curved track that led up to the summit overlooking the volcano's crater. Angela unfolded her arms and placed these defiantly on hips.

'Let's go,' she snapped, now in a hurry to prove that she was not,

sauntering ahead of Nani to join the group of youngsters waiting in the large shadow cast by the *beringin* tree.

This one hundred-year-old banyan was a recognized gathering point for the Year Three students – and young lovers. It was said that the founding president, when still a student studying engineering, first fell in love with Inggit Garnasih under this very tree. The male students used this fable to ingratiate themselves with their prey, the number of young women who had lost their virginity within sight of this seemingly perpetual marker over the years, uncountable. Angela waved nonchalantly as she approached the underpowered group of Yamaha, Kawasaki and Suzuki motorbikes, observing that the majority of these already boasted pillion passengers. A moment of concern passed when she spotted an unpopular boy sitting astride his bike, and made a beeline directly to his side.

'Hi, Joko,' she pretended, climbing behind the surprised youth, *'thanks for waiting for us.'* She glanced across at Didi, struggling to contain his anger and disappointment, so stung by what she had done he gunned the inadequate Suzuki which spluttered, then died, adding to his embarrassment.

'Hi, Didi,' Nani took advantage of the situation and climbed on, wrapping her arms around his waist as the T-125 Stinger coughed back into life. Didi attempted to throw dust at those in close proximity as he drove away but failed at this as well.

Angela patted her companion of choice firmly on the back. *'Don't get any ideas. Okay?'* she demanded, Joko eagerly nodding agreement as he too kicked the bike into gear and followed the others. He had seen her throw opponents around, twice her weight as if they were dolls, and had no misconceptions as to why Angela had selected him for her ride.

★ ★ ★ ★

Didi had made it quite clear to others that Angela was his; the major difficulty with this was that he had failed to convince the independent Dayak student that this should be so. They had never dated, Angela constantly sending reminders that she was not interested. Angrily, he tore down through Bandung's streets, narrowly missing pedestrians, mobile-roadside stalls and the occasional beggar being led across the narrow streets.

'Slow down, Didi!' Nani screamed; her pleas ignored by Didi as his mind remained clouded with Angela's humiliating putdown. Within minutes, they had left the others well behind, Nani hanging on for dear life as they tore through the City of Universities' outer suburbia, climbing quickly through the winding road which twisted its way up to the Tangkaban Perahu lookout. Nani clung tighter and tighter, wishing now that she had not misled Didi about the date. Nani knew that Angela would not go with Didi and had banked on this, hoping to manipulate the event so that she could take Angela's place. Now, Nani regretted her decision, terrified that Didi's anger would be the end of them both.

★ ★ ★ ★

'Can't you go any faster?' Angela urged, the wind dragging her fine, black hair in a long, twirling tail behind.

'It's dangerous,' Joko warned, but ready to impress if she said it was okay.

'Just catch up with them,' she shouted, the wind now bringing tears to her eyes.

'Hang on!' Joko warned, pulling back behind a slow moving minibus, just in time.

'What are you waiting for?' Angela complained, gripping and squeezing his waist painfully. Joko did not hesitate. He pulled out wildly and overtook the vehicles ahead, narrowly bringing disaster upon them when oncoming vehicles ground to a halt to avoid smashing into the two.

'Aduh, 'Gela,' Joko cried out, *'let them go!'* Angela could feel Joko trembling and reluctantly decided to let it go.

'Just drive us to the crater,' was all she said, releasing her grip from around his waist.

They continued on for a few minutes, slowing to a halt when they came upon the scene where Didi's bike had hit a patch of gravel, spinning both rider and passenger through the air into the broken asphalt surface. Incredibly, both had landed safely without any injury other than pride. Angela climbed off Joko's machine hurriedly, ran across to where her friend was sitting up against the side of the road, and grabbed her by the shoulders.

'Are you all right?' she shook her gently, more angry with herself than Nani for what had happened.

'Enggak apa-apa,' Nani answered, reassuring Angela that she was not injured. Others had begun to arrive at the scene, most dismounting to see what had happened.

On the far side of the road Didi was still dusting himself down, bragging to his friends, apparently not in the least concerned about Nani's possible injuries.

'Didi!' Angela called, rising slowly and walking towards him, measuring her steps as she did so. Several of the youth's friends turned, Angela's determined, and to some, familiar pose, warning them to stand back. Didi looked up, saw Angela before him, and smiled stupidly just as the palm of her hand hit him squarely on the side of the jaw – deliberately avoiding the lethal point of contact. Without so much as a whimper, Didi collapsed to the ground, unconscious. Angela then turned on her heel, and went back to Nani's side.

'Joko,' she addressed the flabbergasted student, *'can you take us both back home?'* He looked over at the still form lying alongside the road, back to Angela, then threw one leg over his machine and nodded.

'Come on, 'Ni,' she called, affectionately, helping her friend straddle the bike.

* * * *

In her two years attending the Bandung Institute Angela had avoided forming intimate relationships, remaining dedicatedly focused on her studies. In consequence, she was branded cold and distant, the many, rejected young men on campus confused by her apparent lack of interest in their sex. Angela had been tempted – the campus was studded with handsome, young men, but she remained on track and, apart from occasional, group casual outings, was rarely seen in the company of boys. Apart from occasional visits to Jakarta during semester breaks, when she would travel to the capital together with Nani by train, Angela remained in Bandung.

She had returned to the Longdamai, Mahakam village only once since commencing her studies and as the end of the second year came to a close she became impatient to be reunited with her father, and extended *Penehing* family. Contact with the village had been maintained via weekly radio hookup, courtesy of the Dean. Communication was invariably difficult, interrupted when weather conditions deteriorated, their conclusion often leaving Angela angered by the absence of more modern facilities to link the isolated communities in Kalimantan to the outside world. With a growing awareness of the disparity between the wealthy, Javanese elite and their provincial cousins, Angela realized that the *Penehing* people would remain neglected and without adequate representation as long as their voice went unheard. Wise beyond her years, she also understood that there was little that the Dayaks could do to rectify this situation, against the powerful, centralist government in Jakarta.

As she matured, so did Angela's appreciation of the special gift she had inherited, the *'tenaga-dalam'* or inner force phenomenon always evident in her family line. And, under her father's guidance and instruction, she had acquired a sound awareness of the responsibilities she would one day assume. Introverted and calm, coupled with a strict and rigid temper, Angela emulated Jonathan Dau in every way, her devotion and commitment to the *Penehing Dayak* as determined as her father's. Inseparable in mind and spirit, Angela became a perfect copy of the mould; her father's philosophies, spiritual and metaphysical beliefs, all becoming her own.

As a teenager, Angela had already understood that her people and their environment were clearly under threat by the destructive forces of commerce, and centralist government policies. When she first saw the devastation visited upon Dayak traditional lands, she'd cried, the imagery contributing to her decision to follow her father's footsteps in the fight against those who would destroy the pristine forests and fields. She sought her father's advice and decided to study those disciplines associated with the earth sciences, believing that this direction would not only enhance her understanding of the issues, but would provide her with credentials for the future when she took up the fight against those who would destroy the Dayak environment.

Angela had learned that annual, widespread forest fires, blanketing most of Kalimantan and reaching as far as Peninsular Malaysia and Singapore, were primarily the result of the expanding, Indonesian palm oil industry, controlled by the First Family and their business associates, Borneo's corporate arsonists. Prior to her departure from Longdamai, millions of hectares of forest and grasslands had been burned to clear land for the planting of palm. In private, many amongst her fellow students discussed how firmly ensconced all three generations of Suharto's family had become within the industry. The state-owned, palm oil plantations sold their production of crude palm oil to the state logistics agency, *BULOG,* at incredibly low prices. In turn, this organization made substantial profits from sales of its cooking oil, the benefits flowing to Suharto-linked conglomerates owned by Sino-Indonesian businessmen, and generals.

But, of even greater concern to Angela, was the systematic destruction of her environment's tropical peat land. Central government policies promoting the conversion of peat, swamp forests to agriculture had significantly reduced Kalimantan's natural ecosystem. She knew, that at current levels of conversion, millions of hectares of peat land swamps would be devastated at the expense of the Dayak people – and the myriads of wildlife, not least amongst which being the *orangutan*.

During her years studying away from home, Angela's commitment to her people had never swayed, her determination to return to the Mahakam to assist the Dayak communities foremost in her mind. Determined to maximize the benefits of her academic achievements for the betterment of the Dayak people, Angela Dau continued her conscientious role as an honor student and, to the dismay of the community of male undergraduates, remained aloof to their persistent advances.

Chapter Six

November 1993

Perth – Australia

Sharon Ducay's eyes ran over the headlines again, the tingling sensation she experienced one of acute excitement. She stared at Alexander Kremenchug's photograph, convinced that her choice had been appropriate, her investigations suggesting that this man had more skeletons than cupboards to hide them in. Sharon finished dressing and, while waiting for him to call from the hotel lobby, browsed the articles again.

Newspaper headlines reported that trading in Pursuit Minerals had been suspended. The publicly-listed company owned controlling stock in the Meekathara gold leases which had, over past weeks, been the darling of the West Australian stock exchange. Suddenly, it was all over, the suggestion that arrests would be made sufficient to cause the shares to collapse within minutes, photographs of Kremenchug and the two prospectors accused of spiking the original drilling samples, splashed across the front page. Accusations of insider trading, criminal conspiracy and gold fraud were raised in the press and on television and, based on historical evidence, Sharon surmised that Kremenchug had been behind the ambitious scam. That he had been the one to alert the authorities with respect to the fraud had, at first, puzzled her. Then, as the story unfolded in the press, it became clear that Kremenchug had bailed out of the scheme, when falsified documents and tainted soil samples extracted from the Meekathara tenement had come to light. In the days preceding the suspension of Pursuit Minerals shares, millions had changed hands. Now, it would seem, Kremenchug had decided to forgo further participation, the paper losses he would incur, enormous. For Sharon, the timing could not have been better.

Sharon had spent most of November and early December preparing the ground for her approach to Kremenchug. Information she had gathered over the past year had led her to believe that he would be the perfect choice for the project she and the general had in mind. Sharon had finally caught up with Kremenchug in Perth within days of her arrival from Manila. Arranging an introduction had not been difficult once Sharon had alluded to the strong interest her Filipino associates had expressed in Australian and Indonesian gold prospects. They had met at his Dalkeith home in Circe Circle, Sharon's beauty and practised charm captivating Kremenchug from the start. Their initial discussion had led to others over a number of weeks, during which Sharon laid the groundwork for Kremenchug to visit the Philippines and meet the General to discuss their proposition. She was quietly confident that he would take the bait; particularly now he had come unstuck with this latest venture in Western Australia.

The phone rang; it was Kremenchug.

'Shall I come up?' he tried, pleased when she agreed.

'Sure,' she said, 'I'm in 1109. I'd prefer to have this discussion away from the general public, especially as you have your charming face on most of today's tabloids. We can have coffee and sandwiches in the room if you wish.' Sharon checked her makeup one more time, the door chime announcing Kremenchug's arrival as she finished touching up. She showed him in, her guest nodding approval at the junior suite's view.

His eyes fell to the bed. 'Don't believe everything you read in the newspapers,' he moved across the room and slumped into the settee, his worried face awash with the troubles of the day.

'How bad is it?' Sharon asked, sitting cross-legged on the bed, a cigarette dangling from her hand. She wanted to be certain that his involvement would not drag undue attention to her own project.

'Well,' he started to explain, 'I'm not confident that the company will recover all of the money we paid over to the two prospectors. Anyway, it's out of our hands now. The police will most probably lay charges against them.'

Sharon wished there was a way of asking how much of his own capital was involved, her sources suggesting that Kremenchug rarely dipped into his own pocket which, in her mind, would mean that there would be some very unhappy partners, out for blood. 'We had hoped that you could come to Manila before Christmas or even the New Year. How will this affect your visit?' she indicated the newspapers spread across her bed.

'I could definitely be there in January, providing this is acceptable to your party.'

'Good,' Sharon was relieved, 'then I will make all the necessary arrangements as discussed?'

'That will be fine, thanks.' Kremenchug smiled tiredly, the look creased with signs of permanent stress. 'You know,' he began, 'to be totally honest, I'm not one hundred percent relaxed about going in without a brief.' His face serious, Kremenchug reached for a cigarette. 'Are you in a position to reveal more?'

Sharon had anticipated the question. She drew heavily on the cigarette, leaned back on one hand and then softly blew a cloud of smoke away from his direction, gathering her thoughts. 'I can tell you this, Alex,' she slipped off the eiderdown and crossed to the refrigerator, poured a glass of water, sipped this then returned to the king-sized bed. 'This project pales by comparison to what you stand to make with us.' She pointed at the newspapers again, looked up at the ceiling as if to exercise her neck, knowing that Kremenchug's eyes would drop to her knee-line while she was not watching.

'You intimated that funding won't be a problem. Is it all to come out of the Philippines?' he asked, then lighting his own cigarette.

'Not all of it,' she replied, deliberately evasive.

'Will it involve public companies?'

'Look, Alex,' she suggested, 'we agreed to leave the financial discussions until your visit. There are a few issues that need to be addressed from our side before we can reveal the offer. But, you can rest assured, your visit will not be a waste of your time.'

'Your group will cover my expenses?'

'Yes. And, as a sweetener, the General has instructed me to offer you twenty thousand dollars if you don't like what you hear, and wish to walk away.'

Kremenchug was impressed, his curiosity growing by the minute. 'How much information will you need regarding the Indonesian gold prospects?'

'Should we decide to go forward, we will need to have basic survey reports and full concession documentation. We can't afford to become embroiled in local litigation. The prospect area is to be clean, not one that's been worked over by any of the foreign miners. This is a prerequisite. The areas you suggested during our last meeting,' she paused, recalling the specific location, 'are in East Kalimantan?'

'Near the Mahakam River,' Kremenchug confirmed. 'My senior geologist in Indonesia has completed a number of surveys within the area.' He glanced across at the Filipino, then away again as if distracted. 'I was thinking about taking one or two of these concessions up for myself,' he lied.

'If the areas have potential, as you say, then I don't see any reason why our consortium can't come to satisfactory arrangements with you.' Sharon deliberately rubbed one leg over the other, sensuously. 'I see that you have solid connections in Canada,' she mentioned, *en passant*.

Kremenchug's involvement with the Vancouver group had not been mentioned in the press. He stole a look at Sharon, something in the back of his brain warning him not to underestimate this beautiful and intelligent woman.

'I've dabbled a little,' he said, wondering where this was leading.

'It's preferable to Australia,' she suggested.

'For mining?'

'Yes, of course!' she laughed. 'What did you think I meant?'

Kremenchug snorted. 'I'm not so sure about that.'

'But, you would have to agree that it can be a more rewarding place to raise capital for mining ventures?' And then, before he could argue, she added, 'like Borneo Gold Corporation?'

His face broke into a grin. *She really had done her homework!* 'Sharon, I think I'm going to enjoy working with you.'

Sharon deliberately displayed more leg as she stretched, the trouser suit accentuating her lines when she moved. 'What would it take to gain control of BGC?' the question asked, almost innocently.

He blinked with mild surprise. *If the Filipinos were merely after control of a second rate mining entity, why come to him? There were literally scores of listed companies that would bend over backwards to accommodate new capital, even if it did mean surrendering control.* 'Why BGC?' he found himself asking.

Sharon knew when to stop. 'Just curious,' she smiled, enjoying the intrigue. She could see that Kremenchug's mind was working overtime. A dossier in her briefcase revealed the results of the company's share registry search. Sharon knew that Kremenchug's holdings were relatively insignificant based on recent market value. She was also aware, however, that the prospect of having a major player take a controlling position in BGC would revitalize interest, raising the value of his portfolio considerably. Sharon did not think too highly of Kremenchug, finding him vulnerable to close inspection. Although attractive in a middle-European sort of way, she found his rehearsed manners and other affectations in no way endearing. From the information she had gleaned, the man was simply a poser who had few scruples, motivated purely by avarice and greed. Ironically, she thought, these were just the attributes she had expected to find. Kremenchug was, in short, perfect for the job she had in mind.

'I am familiar with other mining companies if that's of interest?' he suggested.

Sharon did not want him running off contacting all and sundry. 'We could discuss this more in Manila?'

'Sure,' he agreed, 'I could make some recommendations once I know more about what will be on the table.'

Sharon smiled insincerely. 'Then, would you like to pick a date so that we can make the necessary arrangements?'

Kremenchug nodded in affirmation. 'Let's see,' he hesitated, dragging a pocket calendar from an inside pocket. 'I'll fly out the day after my wife's birthday.'

She stifled a smile. 'And what date would that be?' she asked, coyly.

Kremenchug wrote it down and passed the note to Sharon. 'Let's just say that I'll be there on Tuesday the Eighteenth of January.'

They concluded their meeting, and, true to his word, Kremenchug arrived in Manila one month later on the Eighteenth of January, the date recorded as one of the more momentous in modern, geological history as an earthquake with a magnitude of six point seven struck the densely populated San Fernando Valley, in northern Los Angeles, killing fifty-seven and leaving more than fifteen hundred seriously injured. It was an ominous sign.

★ ★ ★ ★

Indonesian Borneo (East Kalimantan)

Longdamai – Mahakam River

Once test drilling along the Mahakam River's reaches showed substantial traces of gold, excitement swept through the villages and, in less than a year, a flood of prospectors from neighboring provinces inundated the stretches along the once-deserted riverbanks. The effects had been catastrophic for the Mahakam Dayaks – not least amongst these, Jonathan Dau's *Penehing* whose lands would soon come under threat. He had ventured downriver to the provincial capital, Samarinda, to seek the Governor's support in stemming the flow of illegal miners, his pleas falling on deaf ears. Gold fever had reached new levels within the corrupt, local Administration, with officials accumulating mining lease titles via their cronies in Jakarta's Ministry of Mines. As the State maintained ownership of all natural resources, gold concessions were naturally allocated to vested interest groups associated with the Central Government. Increased foreign investment activity along the Mahakam reaches brought an even greater influx of Madurese and Javanese, the Dayak communities becoming increasingly incensed with these migrant groups' complete disregard over local claims. Although the Longdamai mining rights originally belonged to Dayaks, somewhere along the line officialdom managed to secure these on behalf of a number of Samarinda Chinese businessmen who, subsequent to a number of catastrophic forays into the area, abandoned the site. Within weeks, itinerants had appeared, equipped with the most simple of tools, and started digging, their numbers so great the Dayak chief believed that it would only be a matter of time before all *Penehing* communities were overrun. Not surprisingly, sprawling shantytowns began to appear along the Mahakam, Dayak communities in Longbangun and Batukelau already under threat.

The wave of illegal miners not only occupied traditional land, but brought with them one of the most dangerous of substances known to man – the highly toxic, liquid metal, mercury. Jonathan visited the Longbangun camp, observing the archaic methods used by the miners in the extraction process. Shafts, barely large enough for one man let alone several, had been dug, thirty and forty meters underground, the men unable to swing their hand-picks more than a few centimeters in the cramped and poorly-lit tunnels. Of course, many had already been killed, most buried under tons of rock and soil, the result of poorly shored shafts. But it was the long-term effects of their presence that worried Jonathan most. The ancient process utilized in the crude extraction of gold was poisoning Dayak lands and, undoubtedly, rivers and streams.

He observed as the potential, gold-bearing rocks were crushed by hand and large amounts of mercury were added to small, manually rotated barrels to separate the gold. Jonathan watched as the mercury was strained, and then burned, the deadly gas given off going straight into the atmosphere. None, of course, wore any form of protective clothing such as gloves or masks. Once the precious yellow metal had been extracted, the workers would then discard the deadly residual along the riverbanks where they took their drinking water, washed their bodies and clothes, and fished. It was far too soon for the inevitable symptoms to appear; and, when these did, he knew that the cause of their skin and gum diseases would all be disguised by ignorance.

Depressed by what he witnessed, Jonathan Dau became impatient for Angela to complete her studies and return home, where they could work together to prevent the further spread of devastation to their precious forests and land.

⋆ ⋆ ⋆ ⋆

Canada -Vancouver

Christopher Fielding stared out through the double-glazed windows in the direction of a wind-chilled Stanley Park, the impulse to jump curbed by the knowledge that the windows were firmly fixed into the skyscraper's walls. Borneo Gold Corporation (BGC) shares had plummeted to a new low, the embarrassment eclipsed only by the enormous financial losses he and other investors had incurred.

Minutes before, Scott Walters had phoned, the conversation vitriolic, at best. Walters had provided mezzanine capital initially, to kick-start the operations, his financial backing sufficient to float the company based on a number of Indonesian mining tenements. He made it quite clear that it had never been his intentions to remain involved for the long haul.

'What in the hell are you doing with BGC?' an angry Walters had shouted, Fielding wincing with every word. 'Stock in every other Canadian miner with Indonesian rights has gone through the roof. What are your guys doing over there, for Chrissakes?'

'It's only temporary,' Fielding had tried, 'we have acquired other properties and these should make BGC stock rise once the reports have been filed.'

'And where will you find the capital to fund further operations?' he demanded.

'BGC stock will rise when we release our annual report next month. We have some very attractive prospects in Kalimantan.'

'Don't' give me that crap!' the vehement financier yelled. 'Look what happened after results of the last survey were released. God-damn it, Chris, I could have doubled or even tripled my investment elsewhere by now!'

Walters' claim would have been difficult to refute. Over the previous ten years a rush of new gold mining entities had listed on the Calgary and Vancouver stock exchanges, most of which had remained reasonably solvent, their Indonesian prospects enabling the companies to raise additional capital without too much difficulty.

'You could always vote for a change in the Board's composition next month,' Fielding challenged, then became concerned as the line went quiet, worried that the financier may be contemplating going down that path.

'Don't tempt me!' The menacing voice alarmed the BGC president. Walters was connected, a point he had often raised when recalcitrant associates reneged on their commitments.

'There's not much else I can do, Scott,' Fielding tried another tack. 'Kremenchug appears to have lost interest and hasn't been that communicative since he moved back to Australia. I know he has been negotiating with others over here.' Fielding did not mind throwing Kremenchug to the wolves. He could hear Walters breathing heavily and guessed his mind was digesting this information, and what steps he could take to clip their associate's wings.

'Leave Kremenchug to me,' he insisted, 'besides, from what I hear he is in a heap of shit in Australia.'

Everyone in the industry was aware of the mess Alex was embroiled in Down Under. Fielding's consolation was not having had any capital at the time to participate in the Meekathara prospect when it first went on offer. 'You don't want me to contact him?'

'No,' the banker warned, 'I'll have a few words with him when he shows his face. In the meantime, I'll spread the word that he's *persona non grata.*'

Fielding became further alarmed. Kremenchug's name was still linked to BGC in a substantial way. 'Don't, Scott,' he pleaded, 'we're still trying to tidy up a few arrangements in Jakarta, and, if he gets wind of what's happening, we may as well close up shop there, altogether.' Fielding felt a surge of panic; should Walters have their associate black-listed, he knew that this would stigmatize all involved and, with Kremenchug's very close ties with the Indonesian government, he could retaliate.

Walters' shrill laugh echoed down the line. 'You think he walks tall and carries a big stick? Let me tell you something, Chris. It's whoever carries the moneybags over there that counts. Don't fret about Kremenchug; the Indonesians would dump him faster than you can say, 'how much?' if they thought there was a dollar in it for them.'

Fielding conceded that this may be true, but was still reluctant to burn bridges unnecessarily. 'I still don't think it would do our stock any good to sandbag one of its major players,' he argued.

'BGC stock can't fall any further,' Walters quipped, cynically.

'Who says?' Fielding responded, wishing immediately he had bitten his tongue.

'If it does, Chris,' the other man warned, 'you would do well to consider other pastures.' With that, Walters had slammed his receiver down leaving Fielding wallowing in a sea of desperation.

★ ★ ★ ★

Christopher Fielding's recent marital skirmishes had left him all but impoverished. Since settling with his first wife five years before, the once highly respected geologist's image had been tarnished on a number of fronts. A brief, second marriage had also ended in acrimony, his shareholding in BGC reduced by half, the stock dumped on the market within days of settlement causing most of the company's value-woes of today. Then there was the challenge with respect to the integrity of Kremenchug's senior geologist, Eric Baird, when further investigations had been carried out under a 'farm-out' arrangement which saw the stock all but collapse. Fielding accepted that he must shoulder the greater portion of blame, refusing to permit twenty years of experience and his gut instinct from questioning the veracity of Baird's glowing report. As a result of two divorces his finances were at an all time low. He knew that Scott Walters' ominous threats should be taken seriously and, for one fleeting moment, as he gazed out over Vancouver's, bleak winter skyline, he contemplated finishing it all and saving Walters' goons the trouble.

★ ★ ★ ★

Chapter Seven

JANUARY 1994
MANILA – PHILIPPINES

A warm, moist wall of air greeted the passengers as they entered the Manila International Airport, Kremenchug registering immediately that the air-conditioning was not working. Even dressed in a lightweight safari suit, the sticky, tropical enclosure soon took its toll, blotches of perspiration appearing around his armpits and lower back as he waited, impatiently, for his luggage to appear on the carousel.

With more than thirty minutes passing and his baggage nowhere to be seen, Kremenchug started to curse the inefficiencies of airport systems. When the carousel finally ceased its endless travel and it was obvious that his suitcase had been misplaced, he stormed across to the information desk in heated fashion.

'You've lost my baggage!' he accused, standing with one hand on hip, disappointed also that he had not been met inside the customs and immigration area by someone from the General's office.

'May I see your ticket, please sir,' the tiny Filipino with a heavily accentuated American accent asked.

'You mean luggage receipts?' he responded, annoyed.

'No, sir,' the airport officer replied with a pleasant air, 'please show me your ticket.'

Irritated, Kremenchug produced his ticket.

'And boarding pass, too, please sir,' she requested, still smiling as she slipped off her stool and stepped out from behind her cluttered desk. 'Thank you, sir.' She strolled off slowly to a group of porters standing further down the hall. He noticed her jabbering with these men for several minutes, then turn, and walk back in leisurely fashion.

'Well?' he asked, with growing annoyance.

'Thank you, sir,' she smiled sweetly, returning his documents, 'you are a first class passenger.' Kremenchug looked puzzled. 'All first class baggage is collected and stored over there,' she pointed towards the group of porters. 'Please, sir, take your baggage claim tickets to the airport porters,' she instructed, returning to her stool. Kremenchug walked over to the men and was relieved to discover his suitcase standing up against the wall.

The delay had placed Kremenchug at the end of the immigration queue, the congestion a result of passengers from other flights that had arrived earlier. An hour later he found himself standing outside the building, anxiously looking for some sign of either Sharon Ducay or an escort from General Dominguez's office. Idling engines filled the muggy air with suffocating fumes, and Kremenchug started to suffer the effects. He was tempted to grab a taxi and go to a hotel, shower and change, then phone Sharon to see what had happened when a black Mercedes with heavily tinted windows sped towards him, braking within touch of his shoes. The rear door was flung open and, clad in high heel, leather pumps, the lower half of a woman's leg appeared beneath the open door, and a gloved hand partially extended through the electronically opened window, beckoned him.

'Alex, Alex,' she called, her voice faint against the background of blaring horns and the thousands of Filipinos who had ventured out to the airport to welcome friends or relatives. A driver dressed in a spotless, white uniform, hurried around the vehicle and greeted Kremenchug.

'Mabuhay,' he welcomed, taking Kremenchug's suitcase and storing this in the luggage compartment.

'I'm sorry I'm late,' Sharon apologized. 'I hope you haven't been waiting too long?'

Kremenchug scrambled into the Mercedes to escape the foul,

outside air, passing her tardiness off with a smile. He brushed his lips lightly over her wrist, the lingering scent of a Nina Ricci perfume tantalizing his senses as he gazed up at the Filipino beauty.

'You're not too late,' he said, eyes roaming around the vehicle's interior. He counted no fewer than four separate communication units, ranging from mobile phones to radio links and a miniature television that had been built into the console between the bucket seats. A Saint Christopher medallion hung loosely around the rear vision mirror, under which a quote from the scriptures reminded the driver not to sin. On the dashboard, a number of religious figurines swayed around their spiral anchors in response to the car's movement as the driver moved them away from the congested airport – Kremenchug's eyes returning to the woman alongside, as her hand rested on his.

'The traffic is always unpredictable at this time of the year.' Sharon tapped his wrist to make her point.

Kremenchug placed his hand over hers. 'It could never be as bad as Jakarta,' he offered.

'The beginning of the year is always impossible in Manila. No sooner have we finished with the Christmas and New Year celebrations, the entire population becomes obsessed with Easter.'

Kremenchug was surprised. 'But, isn't Easter still at least two months away?'

'Yes, Alex, it is. However, you must remember that this country is more catholic in its ways than most. Lent will commence within weeks, during which time we will also prepare for the Easter celebrations.'

Kremenchug thought about this. 'Little wonder it's so difficult to make arrangements around this time. Indonesians are preparing for Ramadan, their month of fasting, the Philippines is preparing for Easter, and the rest of Asia is getting geared up for Chinese New Year!'

'Poor Alex,' Sharon teased, 'perhaps you should find yourself a girlfriend to take your mind off such problems?'

Kremenchug laughed. 'My wife is not that understanding. As it is,

I am away more often than not. Besides,' he said, gritting his teeth, expecting to hear the impact as a child narrowly missed being run over by their car, 'I hear that the ladies here can be extremely jealous.'

Sharon's face broke into a huge smile. 'And dangerous,' she added. 'So, if you take a Filipino as your lover, Alex, be faithful – or you might not be of much use to your wife!'

Their light banter continued as they drove through the city's outskirts, Kremenchug now relaxed after the tiring flight from Australia. As they approached the city, the traffic slowed then ground to a halt as he was introduced to gridlock, Manila style.

'Is it always as bad as this?' he asked, drawing parallels between Manila and Jakarta at every turn.

'Sadly, yes,' Sharon confirmed. 'Downtown is impossible, particularly around Makati. We try to avoid driving through the city.'

'Then how do businessmen get around?

'Most executive cars are equipped with a mobile office. Many companies employ drivers who double as messengers, secretaries and spend the majority of their working hours sitting in traffic with senior employees functioning as best as they can.'

'Must drive the government into a frenzy,' Kremenchug suggested, wondering what would happen in the event of a fire emergency.

'The generals, senior officials and the influential businessmen and women commute via helicopters. It's not unusual for a cabinet minister to fly to meetings around the city.'

The driver turned to Sharon and asked for her permission to take an alternate route. She agreed, the less than scenic detour taking Kremenchug through a slum, the roadside shanties home to but a few of the millions of itinerants who had abandoned their fields and villages, for a life in these squalid surrounds.

'It's not pretty,' Sharon said.

'Don't apologize,' Kremenchug peered through the darkened glass, 'every country has its slum areas.'

The driver had chosen well. To their relief, they were clear of the poverty-stricken area within minutes.

'We should arrive shortly,' Sharon announced, Kremenchug aware that they had entered an elite area, evidenced by the presence of armed security standing guard over the villas lining this street. The Mercedes gained speed, braking occasionally to negotiate speed bumps, the palm-lined avenues an idyllic setting for the rich and famous who lived in this suburb.

⋆ ⋆ ⋆ ⋆

General Narciso Dominguez stood, hands clasped behind his back observing the gardener trimming the two-meter high hedge which hid the concrete, perimeter fence. Even with fading eyesight, the retired general could still clearly identify the rolled, razor wire, which had been strung along the top of walls to discourage thieves, and others, from attempting to break into his home.

A cruel smile crossed his lips as he leaned further into the bay window, peering down to his right where both Doberman pincers rested in the afternoon shade. The general regretted not having the strength to play with the pair, envying Alfredo this opportunity when he groomed the animals each day. He had seen the dogs turn on Maria, one of the servants, an attack that was totally unexpected as the domestic staff was as close to the dogs as he. The incident had occurred near the servants' quarters some six months before, when Alfredo had boisterously picked up the maid in one hand and spun her around playfully, before setting her down. The moment her feet had touched the ground, both Dobermans had sprung, tearing at her legs and hands, the injuries significant before Alfredo could bring them to heel.

The General tapped one of the small, oblong-shaped window-panes with the back of his hand, the sound immediately attracting the hounds' attention. They sprang into life, looking up at the blurred image on the second story, then alongside the villa where Alfredo had come into view. The aide snapped a command, sending the guard dogs to their kennels, where they would be chained until nightfall. Under his General's watchful eyes, Alfredo strolled over to the gardener, and reminded him to open the gates when Sharon returned.

General Dominguez continued to view his garden, reminded of a time when he and his late wife would entertain their guests in the magnificent setting. The carefully laid out lawn featured a profusion of flowering shrubs and trees, which she had planted and lovingly cared for, the colorful flowerbeds of red, pink and yellow hibiscus separating the lawn from the driveway grown from cuttings she had taken while on holiday in Hawaii. He turned away from the scene below, the memory of those happier times often painful recollections, now that she was gone.

Alfredo's polite cough as he knocked on the open, study door gained the General's attention, the aide then standing aside to permit Maria, the maid, carrying a silver tray loaded with freshly brewed tea, and biscuits, to enter.

'The driver has radioed that they are almost here, General.'

'When they arrive, bring them directly up here to the study,' he ordered. And, when the maid had exited and was out of earshot, he added, 'and find where my niece has hidden those cigars!' A horn sounded in the distance, followed immediately by a bell ringing somewhere below. 'That will be them,' the General said, returning to observe their arrival, from the window. 'Best you go.'

⋆ ⋆ ⋆ ⋆

Kremenchug was startled when the huge man stepped towards the Mercedes and opened the door for them.

'The General's aide,' Sharon whispered. 'Big, isn't he?' She stepped out of the car, her extended hand gently held by the smiling giant as he guided her to the steps, then turned and bowed at the visitor.

'What a magnificent building!' Kremenchug was struck by the mansion and its setting.

'It's early Marcos and post General MacArthur,' Sharon joked. 'Many of these homes are not as old as they appear. Please, Alex, come in,' she coaxed, leading the way through the formal entry, then up a winding staircase to the study, where they were met by General Narciso Dominguez. Sharon moved to her uncle's side, reached up and kissed him lightly on the cheek, then introduced the two men.

'General, I am so delighted to be here,' Kremenchug beamed.

'*Mabuhay*, Mister Kremenchug, *Mabuhay*!' And then, 'Alfredo, please see to our guest's luggage.'

'General, thank you for the invitation to visit,' Kremenchug continued, surprised at the much older man's firm grip. 'Sharon has told me a great deal about you.'

'Not too much, I trust?' the old man quipped. 'Please,' the general indicated with a sweeping hand for Kremenchug to sit, Sharon taking her cue to pour tea while Kremenchug's eyes roamed the magnificent décor.

Inbuilt teak cabinets lined one wall accommodating rows of shelves, filled with encyclopedias and other reference books, with photographs, trophies and memorabilia placed prominently at eye level, for all to see.

'Is this not your first visit the Philippines, Mister Kremenchug?' the General inquired.

'No, sir, I have been here before.' Momentarily, he fell into thought. 'I was here briefly, around twenty years ago.' He wondered if their government still maintained records of such visits. 'I was only here for a couple of days,' he added, lifting the highly aromatic tea to his mouth. He sipped, nodding in approval. 'Filipino?' he asked.

Sharon raised the delicate cup. 'As good as anything you will find in Indonesia?' she asked, light-heartedly.

'Of that I am sure,' he offered, graciously. 'And you grow coffee?'

Sharon's pretense at disdain delighted the men. 'You don't think the Filipino people can grow coffee?'

'Obviously, I have a great deal to learn about the Philippines,' he offered, in defence.

'Leave the man be,' the General chuckled. 'I'm sure Mister Kremenchug has more important things on his mind than learning about our agricultural products.'

The three sat, talking amicably, discussing topical events as the afternoon wore on, the General finally steering the conversation back to the purpose of their invitation.

'Sharon informs me that you are well known in the mining industry?' Kremenchug was delighted with the comment but, before he could respond, the General pricked his ego. 'I hope you have resolved your problems in Australia?'

The conversation's change in direction caught Kremenchug off guard. His eyes dropped to the Persian carpet square as he considered his response. 'Apart from the financial loss, yes,' he answered, not entirely surprised by the question.

'You will not be further involved with the matter?' the General's thick, gray eyebrows accentuated the severity of his brow.

'No,' he assured, his face stiffening with annoyance.

'Your name was closely associated with the events. At least, in the newspapers.'

'I have a high profile,' he acted injured, 'the tabloids will do anything for headlines.'

'And the perpetrators?'

'Those responsible have been arrested, and charged,' he revealed. 'My company has satisfactorily distanced itself from the prospectors involved.' At this point, he glanced over at Sharon and, recognizing that there would be no help from this quarter, continued alone. 'I can assure you, General, that what transpired in Australia was, in no way, of my doing.' Again, he looked to Sharon, puzzled by her cynical expression.

'And you really did not have any knowledge of what they were doing, Alex?' Sharon interposed.

'Certainly not!' he snapped, paling significantly, 'and any suggestion that I was involved would be considered defamatory.'

Silence consumed the room, broken some awkward moments later by an air-conditioning compressor clicking into life. Sharon looked over at her uncle, disappointment evident in her face. 'Then we have made an error in judgment,' she addressed Kremenchug, confident that they had not. 'It would seem to us that the prospectors could never have manipulated the market without *someone's* help.'

'Well, that person wasn't me,' his denial was delivered with regained composure – color now restored to his suntanned features.

Sharon sighed, resignedly. 'That's too bad,' she said, her statement confusing him even further.

'I don't understand,' Kremenchug sat upright, his forehead creased with a heavy frown. He looked at the General, then back at the man's niece, an uneasy feeling rising from his gut.

'Alex,' Sharon leaned forward, hands clasped over knees, 'don't feel too offended, but you were invited here today specifically because we believed that you were the one behind the...' she deliberately paused, as if searching for an appropriate word, '...the scheme.' She smiled innocently; her words left clinging like pollen to Spring air.

Kremenchug's neck reddened, the suggestion that he had masterminded the Meekathara fraud, even though it was true, was an outrage. He felt the pulse in his temple beating heavily, the muscles in his arms and legs suddenly taught. He stared across at Sharon, his anger apparent.

'Mister Kremenchug,' the General intervened. 'Or, perhaps it is time to put formalities aside. May I call you Alexander?'

Kremenchug turned to his host. 'General Dominguez,' he commenced, looking challengingly into the old man's eyes, 'I'm sorry, but I think it's probably better that I leave.' He moved forward in the chair, preparing to stand.

'Now, now, Alexander,' his host tried to soothe, 'best we clear the air before we start, don't you agree?'

Kremenchug was flabbergasted by their presumption of his involvement in the West Australian gold fraud. 'General, I'm sorry, but...'

Sharon had risen and moved across the room to the General's cocktail cabinet, her graceful movements lost in the heat of the discussion.

'Alex,' she called, Kremenchug glancing over as she poured Chivas Regal into a pair of crystal tumblers, 'it was not our intention to insult you. Please be patient and you will understand.' She carried the amber colored drinks over and placed these in front of the two men, returning to the bar for a wine.

'I apologize if you are offended,' the General offered, Kremenchug remaining on the edge of his seat, undecided.

'Well, the suggestion that...'

'I'm sure that Sharon never intended to upset you. Perhaps we should have left this conversation until later?'

Kremenchug was at a loss as what to do. He had come a long way, the promise of a major mining deal being aborted, foremost in his mind.

'Just so we get it clear for the record, Sharon,' he insisted, 'the only reason my name was mentioned in relation to the Meekathara fraud is because I directed the group which had negotiated a controlling interest in the prospect.' Then, as if appealing his case, he addressed the General directly. 'My group lost millions in the end...' his voice trailed off, the memory of his paper loss refreshed in his mind. He reached for the Chivas, accepting that, having come this far, he may as well remain to hear what else they had to say. 'Sharon,' he continued, his mouth still curled down at the corners, 'if you had suggested that I was involved in the Meekathara mess during our meetings back in Perth, I would never have undertaken to come here.'

'Alex, please listen to what we have to offer. Just be patient a little longer.'

'What is this really all about?' he asked, bewildered.

The General beckoned for Sharon to sit by his side and, with glass in hand, she obeyed.

'Alexander, we have a proposal which requires the most serious of discussions. It is only because my niece, Sharon, convinced me of your trustworthiness, that we invited you here. So,' the old man smiled sincerely, 'let's start afresh.' The General raised his glass in salute. 'Alexander, I offer you a toast,' he smiled widely, the conciliatory gesture obliging Kremenchug, albeit reluctantly, to reciprocate. 'To a mutually rewarding relationship, trust, and friendship.'

Without waiting, General Dominguez drained his glass, Kremenchug following suit, the whiskey's mellowing effect evident as the men placed their glasses down, inhaled deeply, and suddenly grinned at each other.

'Perhaps I was a little hasty in reacting the way I did,' Kremenchug apologized, easing his body back into the comfortable cushions. 'It's just that the past months have been very distressing.' He smiled weakly at Sharon. 'I'm sure you'll understand?'

Sharon did not hesitate. 'Of course, Alex, of course! Now, why don't you freshen up first and then I will show you around the grounds?'

Suddenly, he felt very tired. 'Actually, that would be a great idea.' He rose, and extended his hand to his host. 'General, sorry we got off to a bad start. It's been a long day.'

General Dominguez's eyes twinkled. 'But a fruitful one, I hope. Sharon, please show our guest his room. Now, Alex, you will have to forgive me but these old bones usually take a rest around this time.' He patted Sharon on the knee. 'Take good care of Alex, my dear. We will regroup before dinner to continue our discussions.'

★ ★ ★ ★

'I decided it best to walk you through the main house, first,' Sharon explained, leading Kremenchug around the downstairs formal areas. They wandered through the lounge, filled with ornately carved furniture and paintings, statues and awards, the General's portrait in full uniform highlighted as a centerpiece against one wall. On each side there were two similar sized paintings, and Sharon pointed to these. 'Our family has a proud, military history. The painting on the left is my great-grandfather. He was killed in 1898 when we declared independence from colonial rule,' Sharon stated proudly, indicating an oil painting of the revolutionary hero. She glanced at Kremenchug. 'Did you know that the Philippines was the first constitutional democracy in Asia?'

Kremenchug was intrigued. 'I thought that was Burma.'

'No,' Sharon shook her head, 'it was the Philippines, even though the first republic was short-lived.'

'What happened?' Kremenchug was genuinely interested.

'Well, Spain had lost its war with the United States and my country was illegally ceded to the U.S., along with Cuba and Puerto Rico.' She went on, 'We ended up fighting the Americans for more than ten years. They killed more than half a million of my people.'

'I'm sorry, Sharon, but I find this really incredible to understand.' Kremenchug wasn't sure what he was hearing had not been embellished. He had never read anything regarding the country's history, but if what Sharon said was true, the United States had its first 'Vietnam' almost seventy years before troops were sent into Saigon. 'I was under the impression that the Philippines and the United States were very close. I had no idea that such history existed.'

'You'll find it well documented in libraries and historical archives,' Sharon said, matter-of-factly, before moving on.

'And the other painting?' Kremenchug asked.

'My grandfather,' she answered, tilting her head for Kremenchug to see. 'The General says that I'm just like him.'

Kremenchug laughed. 'No, you're much more attractive,' he complimented her, observing Sharon lift her chin, a fraction, with these words.

'The General had only one brother,' she said, a touch of sadness in her voice.

'And your uncle has no children?' Kremenchug noticed the absence of anything that might suggest to the contrary.

'No,' Sharon confirmed. 'I guess that you could say that we are the only two left.' She took Kremenchug by the arm. 'Let's go out into the garden and I'll show you my favorite place.'

Kremenchug noticed a sudden change in her demeanor and fell silent, conscious that the subject of her immediate family was sensitive. They strolled out to the rear garden and down a pathway to a corner filled with trees.

'The property covers one hectare,' Sharon revealed. 'As a child, I used to spend hours down here playing on the swings whenever we visited. See,' she pointed, 'there's the swing where I fell off and broke my arm.'

Kremenchug raised hands in mock surprise. 'You broke your arm? What a coincidence,' he exclaimed, 'so did I!' An ingenerate liar, Kremenchug had never broken a limb in his life and his tongue slipped.

Sharon was curious. 'Which arm?'

Kremenchug hesitated, then lifted his left arm. 'I fell over playing soccer.'

Sharon glanced at the well-tanned limb as if looking for a scar. 'It's not the same when a girl breaks hers.'

She steered Kremenchug away from the childhood playground her uncle had provided for his brother's children, to a secluded spot surrounded by palms. Here, timeless cycads set around a waterfall, stood alone, their rich-green branches raised, embracing sunlight. Shimmering, golden carp swam carelessly through the shallow pond filled with water lilies, their mouths pumping the surface, expecting to be fed. Amongst the rocks, cannas stood erect, their brilliant reds and yellows in defiance of the *kastubas,* providing a colorful mix against a background filled with *torch ginger*.

'That's from Borneo,' Sharon pointed to the carnivorous pitcher plants. Kremenchug inspected the growth. 'Don't suppose it has any bearing on why I'm here?' he suggested, light-heartedly.

'No more questions until later, please, Alex,' Sharon insisted.

'Okay,' Kremenchug shrugged, earlier tension washed away by the garden setting. With hands clasped behind her back Sharon raised her face to the afternoon sun, and Kremenchug was again struck by the woman's beauty. Something tugged at his insides and, without a second's hesitation he moved in closer and tried to kiss her.

Having encouraged the move, Sharon then stepped out of reach. 'Please, not here, Alex, my uncle might see.'

Kremenchug reached out. 'You are the most beautiful woman I have ever seen.'

'Words every woman wishes to hear. Even your wife?'

He pulled a face. 'We don't have much of a relationship anymore.'

'I'm sorry to hear that, Alex.'

He shrugged, building the lie. 'We don't even share the same room.'

Sharon fought to prevent the smile from blooming. 'I'm sorry to hear that, also. It must be very difficult for you?'

'Yes, it complicates my life.' Then, with even greater embellishment, 'I've almost forgotten what it's like to be this close to an attractive woman.'

Now, Sharon was forced to chew on the inside of her lip to prevent laughter escaping. 'Then we'll have to do something about that.'

Kremenchug's face lit up with hope. 'Then there's no one else in your life at this moment?'

'No one, Alex.'

'I find that hard to understand. You're young, stunning, intelligent…'

'Stop, enough!' Sharon held her hands in surrender and laughed. 'Tell you what, Mister, I'll let you buy me a nightcap after the General retires tonight.'

Satisfied, he beamed. 'That'll be a good start.'

'Speaking of the General, we have to meet with my uncle in an hour.'

'Then I'll just have time to shower and change.'

'The General likes to dress for dinner,' she reminded him.

'That's fine. I came prepared. Shall we go back inside?'

Sharon walked alongside Kremenchug, returning to the main residence.

'I'll knock on your door at six,' she warned, leaving him to wander down the long hallway to the guest quarters, alone.

★ ★ ★ ★

True to her word, Sharon went to Kremenchug's room in the guest wing to show him the way down for pre-dinner cocktails.

'Will I do?' he asked, arms open wide.

'Very handsome, *Mister* Kremenchug,' Sharon was pleased that Alex had heeded her advice when his invitation to visit was first extended.

'And you look stunning, as usual.' Kremenchug's flattery was appropriate. Sharon was dressed in a full length, backless evening gown, in shimmering silk.

When they entered the lounge they found the General standing alone, admiring a portrait. He turned and allowed them both an appreciative smile.

'Ah, there you are!' The General was wearing a traditional, hand-embroidered *Barong Tagalog*, Kremenchug immediately wishing he had done the same.

'Good evening, General,' Kremenchug accepted a glass of wine from the maid, and moved closer to the painting.

'Family?' he asked.

General Dominguez slowly shook his head. 'No. This is General Gregorio del Pilar, one of our national heroes. He died in the Battle of Tirad Pass almost a hundred years ago.' Dominguez selected from the tray of *pulutan,* the *hors d'ouvres* a favorite of his. 'Did Sharon show you our gardens?

Kremenchug followed his host's example, sampling the finger food. 'Yes, General, your grounds are very impressive.'

Sharon disappeared, leaving the two men together, their conversation light and jovial, the General appearing to warm to his guest. They discussed the Philippines under its current president, Fidel Valdez Ramos, General Dominguez outlining how the man had supported Cory Aquino's presidency who, in turn, backed Ramos' successful run, in 1992.

'Don't fill up on those, Alex,' Sharon warned, sweeping back into the room. Kremenchug had eaten half a tray of *pulutan* by this time, whilst engaged in conversation with Dominguez. 'The cook has prepared a number of local dishes for tonight, and you should leave room to try them all.' She looked up at the grandfather clock as it chimed. 'Dinner will be served, shortly.'

Kremenchug looked surprised. 'There are no other guests?'

Sharon touched his arm with long, slender hand. 'Tonight, we are to discuss our proposal, Alex. There will only be the three of us.'

Then, she flashed a smile. 'Why, are you disappointed?'

'No, for some reason I had it in my mind that there were others involved.'

'Later, you will understand why this can't be so.' At that moment, Alfredo appeared in the doorway and nodded to Sharon.

'Dinner is served,' she announced, 'hope you are still hungry, Alex?' Before Kremenchug could reply, she slipped her arms between the two men, and led them into the dining room.

★ ★ ★ ★

'My God, I couldn't eat another morsel!' Kremenchug leaned back and inhaled deeply. 'The meal was delightful. Thank you.' They had started with a soup Filipinos call *tinolang tahong,* an exotic dish made with plump mussels steamed in ginger root, spinach and onion. Then, the long mahogany table was decorated with a most lavish spread, Kremenchug delightfully surprised with the blend of tastes in the food that was served. They ate *lumpia sariwa, pork adobo, pancit* and *rellenong manok,* whole, deboned chicken that had been stuffed with a mix of fowl, pork, ham, sausages and hard-boiled eggs, and sliced and presented in the most mouth-watering way.

'But you still have desert to come,' Sharon had eaten sparingly, her appetite blunted by nerves. Although outwardly she appeared cool and reserved, Sharon's condition was obvious to her uncle whose occasional, reassuring smiles carried her through the meal.

'Don't think I could face another mouthful.'

'Are you sure? Marie has prepared sweets.'

'No, I'm sorry, Sharon. I've eaten like a king, but thank you all the same.'

'Perhaps, when you return, we will organize a *lechon* to celebrate?' the General suggested.

Kremenchug gave a quizzical look as Sharon jumped in. 'The General refers to another of our tasty traditional dishes, Alex. *Lechon* is roast, suckling pig.'

But Kremenchug knew what he had heard. 'The General mentioned, 'celebrate'?'

Dominguez's eyes crossed slowly to his niece, then back to his guest. In the ensuing void he wiped his mouth with a lace napkin, then leaned forward with clasped hands on the table, and addressed them both.

'It's time to take Alex into our confidence, Sharon,' the words came out slowly, 'and explain why we have invited him here.'

They exchanged glances. Sharon rose and left the room briefly, giving instructions to Alfredo to ensure their privacy, then returned to her seat opposite Kremenchug.

'General, would you like to start?' she suggested; they had rehearsed this scenario more than a dozen times together, her uncle's introduction necessary to lay the foundation for their proposal to Kremenchug.

General Dominguez cleared his throat. 'What I am about to reveal to you, Alex, could place us in a most compromising position.' His voice became stern. 'I need for you to promise, here and now, that whatever you learn as a result of our discussions, will never be disclosed to others. Before we take you into our confidence, Alex, we must have your assurance that, regardless of the outcome of our meetings, whether you commit to proceed or not, our secrets must remain with us.' He looked at Kremenchug. 'Will you give us your word, Alex?'

Kremenchug was quite surprised by the melodramatic request, gauging his response as his eyes moved from the General to Sharon, then back again.

'It's a big ask, General,' he replied, 'I don't have any problems with what you request, providing I'm not expected to make any commitments until I hear it all.'

Satisfied with their guest's response, the General continued. 'Have you ever heard of the *"Yamashita Treasure"*, Alex?

At the mention of treasure, Kremenchug's hopes of a mining proposal opportunity were instantly dashed. Disappointed, he shook his head. 'No, General, can't say that I have.'

'Well, Alex, settle back and relax as this will take awhile. It's imperative that you know this background as it has a direct bearing on what we wish to propose.' General Dominguez signaled his niece, who rose and recharged their glasses.

'During the Japanese occupation of the Philippines from 1942 through to '45, for one reason or another, the Japanese High Command had decided to use my country as a staging point for shipping the spoils of war their armies had gathered, during their Asian campaigns. It may have been that they were concerned about growing Allied control over the shipping lanes to Japan, or it might simply have been that General Tomoyuki Yamashita, once he assumed command of Japanese forces here, simply wished to build a future empire of his own. Whatever the reasons, treasures confiscated from temples, precious metals and stones taken from private holdings and tons of gold stolen from vaults throughout the region, were all buried in secret locations throughout these islands.' He looked over at Kremenchug to ensure that he had the man's attention.

'We believe that the bulk of the treasure was buried by prisoners-of-war who were then entombed along with this incredible wealth. Some estimates place the number of secret sites at just under two hundred. To protect the integrity of the holdings, all were booby-trapped, to discourage digging in those locations.'

'What happened to Yamashita?' Kremenchug inquired, his interest growing.

'He was hung as a war criminal in 1946.' General Dominguez waved one hand as if dismissing the Japanese's role as having any import.

'Did he reveal this information?'

'No,' Sharon rejoined the conversation. 'he took his secret to the grave.'

'But...?' Kremenchug started to ask, only to be interrupted by his host waving his hands.

'All in time, Alex, all in time.' The old man then continued. 'After the War, groups of soldiers and treasure hunters spent years excavating sites all over the country. It was not until Marcos' presidency, that any real recoveries occurred.'

'They found it?' Kremenchug was surprised. He had never heard of any such discoveries; knowing that something of this magnitude would certainly have attracted world attention, he could not resist being at least a little skeptical.

'Well, they found some of it. At least, Marcos' troops did. Tons and tons of gold packed in crates. We have to remember that, at that time, gold was pegged at not much more than thirty dollars an ounce, effectively less than one tenth of today's value.'

'What happened to the treasure?' Kremenchug was now back on the edge of his seat, credibility in the story building.

'Marcos ordered that the find be divided; then taken to a number of locations, and reburied. He entrusted the gold to a small number of loyal officers who had supported his presidency.'

'What happened when Marcos died?'

'By then, as he had been living in exile, most of the billions acquired while he was in power had been moved to Switzerland and the United States.'

'Including the gold?'

Sharon glanced at her uncle, who nodded, then leaned forward, permitting his niece to assist as he rose from the chair.

'Please follow us, Alex,' he said, shuffling out of the lounge and along the corridor, where Alfredo waited. 'We are going down to the cellar,' the General then raised his arm so that his aide could hold him steady, permitting Alfredo to guide him along.

Captivated by the Marcos gold story, Kremenchug followed, excitement building as he was led through a maze of corridors connecting to a rear pavilion, where Alfredo, and the servants' quarters were located. They entered, and once the outer door had been secured, the General's trusted guardian opened a false closet, stepped inside and switched on an overhead light, then turned to the retired commander for final confirmation before un-padlocking a heavy, steel door. They were all ushered into a small chamber, Alfredo locking the steel door behind, Kremenchug immediately feeling the rising panic as claustrophobia took hold.

'Some of the lights are not working,' Alfredo explained, turning around to negotiate the steps backwards, so that he could catch the General in the event that the old man missed his footing, and fell down the stairwell.

'There's not much air in here,' Kremenchug whispered. 'Shouldn't we've brought candles or something?'

'It's not far,' the General's voice carried back up the steps.

'God, it's dark!' Kremenchug complained, moving aside to permit Sharon to precede him down the narrow, dark passage.

'Be careful, Alex,' Sharon warned, 'these steps are very slippery.'

Images of creatures scurrying around in the dark filled his mind and he hesitated, before gingerly placing another foot forward.

'Hold on, Alex,' she warned again, 'if you fall, we'll all go tumbling down.'

'Are there any rats down here?' he asked, anxiously.

'Possibly. But don't concern yourself; at least there are no snakes.'

Kremenchug thought he heard Alfredo chuckle, and clenched his jaw, stepping cautiously forward, amazed that Sharon could negotiate her way down wearing stiletto heels.

Slowly, the line made its way down into the dank cellars, built at a time when China had exploded its first atomic bomb, signaling its entrée into the Nuclear Club in 1964. Alfredo guided the General down cautiously, those behind pausing as required, to permit the General to catch his wind.

'I'm sorry to hold you all up, Alex,' the General said, between rests, 'but I don't come down here very often, as you can see.'

'It's all right, General.' Bravado building, Kremenchug now found the experience strangely exhilarating, comforted by the thought that if an elderly man and his niece were prepared to venture down into the cellars, then he should not be overly concerned.

Less than a minute passed when the General's voice warned them to wait, Sharon and Kremenchug obliged to remain standing on the steel staircase until given the signal to proceed. Then, Alfredo flicked a switch somewhere, illuminating the cellar in softened glow, minute beams of light bringing the deep cellar alive.

Kremenchug was stunned. The walls were lined with a collection of wartime mementos reaching back to the Spanish-American

War. On one wall, officers' swords hung in line still sparkling in spite of the march of time. Photographs of the General with Marcos and other members of the Filipino Military establishment hung along one wall reflecting part of the General's military record.

'Good grief!' Immediately, Kremenchug was drawn, moving towards the museum pieces with outstretched hands. Alfredo immediately stepped into his path.

'Don't touch anything!' the General warned, stepping in between Kremenchug and the antiques. Then, with a sweep of his hand, 'The collection pieces are all connected to an alarm above. If activated, the entrance would be sealed.' His voice touched with sadness when he said, 'These have no real value to anyone; not any more.' Then, turning to Alfredo, he ordered him to open the underground vault.

Alfredo moved to the center of the cavern and knelt, his hands easily locating the familiar, iron ring. He lifted the heavy cover effortlessly, exposing the General's gold depository. Sharon took Kremenchug's elbow, moving him towards the center of the generous, man-made cave. With orchestrated movement she stepped to one side, permitting the overhead light to strike the strewn collection of half-kilo gold bars below. Kremenchug leaned forward cautiously and peered into the hole, the glittering effect hypnotic, and he reached down to touch the treasure, to see if it was real. Overwhelmed with the realization that millions lay within his grasp, he lifted his head, and stared up at the others, their smiling faces confirmation that the General had been a trustee, for Marcos' *Yamashita Gold*.

★ ★ ★ ★

'Alex, I need to remind you of our earlier request regarding the need for secrecy.' Sharon's confidence had returned, Kremenchug's acceptance of the *Yamashita Gold* story paving the way for her presentation of their proposal. They had returned to the main house and were now seated upstairs in the General's teak-paneled study. The maid, Maria, had brought coffee, then departed, leaving Sharon to serve.

'Well, I can certainly understand why you wouldn't want this to leak out.' He addressed the General. 'How much is there?'

Sharon's well-prepared answer caught him by surprise. 'In total, around two hundred million, Alex,' she lied; this had been the value of the shipment lost when her parents' aircraft had crashed into the sea.

'That was two hundred million's worth of gold bars I just saw?' Kremenchug's brain had been filled with calculations from the moment he sighted the hoard. In his mind, two hundred million sounded like a great deal more than he would have guessed.

'No, Alex,' Sharon explained, 'you have only examined one of the vaults.'

'There are others, like that?' he asked, amazed.

'Dozens,' again she lied, her well prepared story certain to convince the man. 'There are more, here, on these grounds. The remainder is spread around a number of locations known only to the General – and me, of course.'

Kremenchug could not hide his excitement. 'Well, I've got to say, in answer to your earlier question, General – and Sharon,' he added, 'you have my word that your secret will remain with me. I guess this is where you tell me what my role is in all of this. Do you expect me to help you find a buyer, is this the reason why you have invited me here?' Kremenchug had already calculated the commission on two hundred million, and was ready to accept responsibility for such a deal.

'No, Alex,' Sharon's voice was touched with frustration. 'We can't just sell this gold otherwise the government will go to the courts and have it seized!'

Kremenchug frowned, confusion written across his brow. 'I don't understand, Sharon. What is it that you want of me, then, if it's not to help you sell the gold?'

Sharon Ducay rose from the rattan chair and started pacing the study. She selected a Puerto Rican, machine-made La Corona Whiff from a box on the table, lit this with a table lighter and inhaled slowly, the effect immediate as she commenced outlining their proposition as how to dispose of the gold. 'Effectively, the gold has to be laundered so that its existence never comes to light.'

'That's impossible,' Kremenchug argued. 'Even much smaller amounts are difficult to trade without someone, somewhere, getting suspicious.'

Sharon knew this to be true, as the General had never attempted to sell more than a few ingots at any one time. When the time came to convert the remaining gold held below in the cellars, Sharon accepted that this process would take some months so as to avoid attracting too much attention. Amounts less than five million were often used as collateral amongst the local Chinese community – Sharon had already decided that this would be the preferred way to go. 'Not if we owned a gold producing mine,' Sharon proposed, preparing the ground for Kremenchug.

'I still don't see how,' he said, 'gold produced would be monitored in whichever country hosted the deposit.'

'Yes, but there are countries where such checks and measures can be controlled. We could setup operations in an isolated area where government interference would be minimal.'

'Indonesia?' Kremenchug looked at Sharon with a growing respect. 'How would it work?'

Sharon seized the moment, launching into detail. 'Firstly, we must acquire a viable concession in Indonesia's Borneo provinces. We have selected this area due to the growing interest international gold mining companies have shown in Kalimantan prospects. I'll get back to this point as it relates to phase two of what we have in mind.'

'There are other gold producing countries. What about Africa and South America?' he suggested.

'Too far – and, neither have the investment pull that Indonesia currently has. Because of Kalimantan's proximity to the Philippines it would not be overly difficult to ship small quantities from here to one of the eastern ports without raising suspicion. We would provide sufficient funding to prove the prospect with drilling, establish a full mining operation, and simply recycle the gold bars as if they had originally been mined there, on site.'

'It wouldn't work,' Kremenchug said, 'An operation of that magnitude would require substantial staff, all of whom would know what you were doing.'

'Not if the senior staff were all part of our team,' she pointed out.

'It is imperative that all senior mining staff be sent from the Philippines. I would assume the role of Chief Geologist, and be responsible for the selection of the others. We would bring geologists, mining engineers and control the sampling analysis to establish the prospect's viability and, later, production when we would reproduce gold bars to local standards.'

Kremenchug found the proposition appealing. Although not entirely convinced that the practicalities of recycling the gold bars had been thoroughly thought through, he admitted that the scheme had merit.

'And are you certain it wouldn't be simpler just to offload the gold through intermediaries?'

'Positive. The international banks have frozen billions of dollars in funds and assets belonging to the Marcos family. We can't take that risk.'

'And you won't consider another location – another country, perhaps?'

'No. We want to go with the East Kalimantan concept. We have spent considerable time and energy examining the alternatives. Obviously, this can only work if we have a suitable tenement that could pass inspection. Also, there can be no joint venture arrangements with either the Indonesian government or any local party. We must have absolute control over the operation, from exploration to production. That's where you come in, Alex.'

'Identifying a viable concession wouldn't be difficult. In fact, I have a number which have preliminary survey reports,' he revealed.

'Good. That will save some months in moving the project forward.'

'And phase two?' he reminded her.

Sharon stopped pacing and returned to her seat. 'There is not much point in sending our gold to Indonesia to have it recycled unless we can recover its original value. Obviously, the government there will want its cut. Royalties could rise to twenty percent before we're finished. Tax incentives don't cover income tax, nor do they relieve corporate taxes. Then, there would be operation costs, establishment capital requirements, ongoing expenditures and your own position to consider. You would want, what, fifteen percent for yourself? All in all, we could lose as much as fifty, even sixty percent of the gold's value.'

'It could take years to set it up!'

Kremenchug had taken the bait, and Sharon went in for the kill. 'Another reason why we want control over the concession vested with a listed, public company,' she said, evaluating Kremenchug closely to gauge his reaction.

'Why?'

'To recover that fifty or sixty percent of our losses, of course!'

Kremenchug considered this. It made sense. 'Where would you want the listing?'

Sharon started to pick up the tempo, excited that Kremenchug was hooked. She had watched closely when suggesting that his share of this enormous wealth would be fifteen percent, Kremenchug's eyes dilating with the offer. 'We thought this through. It would make more sense to be listed on an exchange whose members already had substantial gold interest in Indonesia. This narrowed it down to Canada and Australia. After further investigation, we decided that Canada would be the more preferable as it has greater support from North American capital and the number of Canadian mining interests already either exploring, or producing in Indonesia, is considerable.'

Kremenchug's eyes narrowed as he tried to understand why they had specifically targeted him to approach. He asked the question; Sharon responding with rehearsed reply. 'Your name kept on popping up everywhere, Alex,' she justified, 'in Vancouver, Calgary, Perth and Jakarta.'

'Okay, so you've done your homework, but that still does not explain, why me?'

Sharon knew the time had come to be blunt. 'The person we need cannot be hooked on scruples; someone who would appreciate the value of what is on offer – and, of unquestionable loyalty. We approached you, Alex, because of your past dealings, your perceived involvement with Meekathara, and your relationship with Canadian-based mining companies which are already active in Indonesia.'

'You think I'm bent?' he challenged, his expression cold.

'I think you know how to bend the rules,' Sharon answered with disguised contempt.

'Not good enough, Sharon. Do you think that I was involved in the West Australian fraud?'

Sharon took the gamble. 'Yes, I think you helped mastermind the deal.'

Although Kremenchug resented the remark, he knew it to be true. As damaging as it was to his self-esteem, he accepted that Sharon Ducay would never have approached him unless she had been convinced of his credentials, unsuited for others that they may be. His shoulders slumped. The image of a twenty to thirty million dollars success fee being the deciding factor, Alex Kremenchug swallowed his pride, and said, 'Okay. Where do we go from here?'

An hour passed and they were nearing consensus as how best to proceed with their project. 'Do you want to continue with this in the morning?' she asked, conscious that her uncle was struggling to remain awake.

'No, I'd like to get on a plane tomorrow, if possible.' Kremenchug glanced over at the yawning General. 'But, if you want to leave it and get up early, I don't mind.'

General Dominguez was assisted to his feet. 'I will leave you two to finish up here if you don't mind. Until breakfast, then?'

★ ★ ★ ★

Sharon and Kremenchug returned to their discussion as to the best methodology to be used in establishing the relevant corporate structure to suit their needs. They had agreed that the Borneo Gold Corporation would be a suitable vehicle for their scheme. By going 'in through the back door', they could gain control over an existing entity, one that was already trading, and thereby circumvent the necessity of identifying an underwriter for a new venture.

'BGC hasn't been sailing too well. I know most of the players and think that they would be receptive to an offer.'

Sharon did not reveal that she was already conversant with BGC's current status, and the financial predicament the major players faced. Silently relieved that her game plan was working, she asked a number of perfunctory questions, then suggested that they call it a night, anticipating Kremenchug's next move.

'A nightcap to celebrate?' he invited.

'Too soon to celebrate, Alex. Let's save it until you return.'

'But, you promised,' he reminded, taking her by the hand.

'Yes, and I know where you would want that to lead.'

'And you don't?' he moved closer and tried to kiss her.

Sharon was prepared – she pulled away. 'My uncle is very protective, Alex.'

'I need you, Sharon.' He took her by the hand again, and kissed her wrist.

'Alfredo would know,' Sharon had no intention of subjecting herself to this man in any way whatsoever. But, she had a plan.

'I could come to your room later?' he asked, hopefully.

Sharon pretended to be considering this. Then, 'No, it would be better if I came to yours.'

Kremenchug felt his blood surge. 'That's great,' he whispered, conspiratorially.

'You should go first, Alex. If Alfredo thinks we are all asleep, only then will he retire. He can see your bedroom window from his quarters. So, be careful. Leave your lights off and the door unlatched.'

Kremenchug kissed her softly on the cheek. 'I'll be waiting for you.'

★ ★ ★ ★

Sharon returned from her lengthy discussion downstairs with the servant. She looked in on her uncle and, seeing that he was already asleep, went to the study where she poured a Chivas and lit another of her Puerto Rican cigars then stretched out on the deep-maroon, leather, upholstered divan. While savoring the tobacco leaf's aroma, Sharon's mind drifted back over her discussions, unable to resist breaking into a wide smile with the realization that she had successfully manipulated the cunning Alexander Kremenchug to deliver BGC into her hands. Not that Sharon wished to own a near-bankrupt mining company – acquisition was but the first step in her well-conceived scheme. She was counting on historical evidence that Kremenchug would undoubtedly attempt to screw everyone along the way; it was his nature to do so, and the success, or failure of her plan, depended entirely upon Kremenchug remaining within character.

The study clock chimed, breaking its monotonous, metronome sequence and Sharon took a final puff of the Corona before snuffing the cigar out in an ashtray. And, on cue, the maid, Maria appeared and made her way down the dimly lit hallway, and into the guest's room.

⋆ ⋆ ⋆ ⋆

Kremenchug lay erect and naked between the sheets, his thoughts dancing with anticipation when the bedroom door opened, then closed quickly. In the darkened environment he sensed more than actually saw Maria slip out of her nightdress, the woman's brown body but a silhouette in the night. She climbed into bed, her muskiness triggering his senses and he gasped as Maria's warm, soft and moist mouth suddenly encompassed him with delight. He groped for full breasts, their fullness driving him to an even greater urgency and he felt a delicate ripple in his belly beginning to rise. Kremenchug pushed her head away, rolling the maid onto her back – his less than elegant entry penetrating her impatiently, sending a shudder through the length of her body. His erection filled even harder, the blood pumping through his body, threatening to flow and he cried out 'Sharon,' the stench of his breath enough for the maid to turn her head away. He called out Sharon's name again, Maria's body now ready. She arched, welcoming the moment as he suddenly jerked, thrusting his length hard inside her, the warmth of the wave engulfing both their bodies as he surrendered.

Kremenchug rolled away from the now inert body beneath him which then suddenly sprang into life. He lay there listening as Maria dressed silently, and disappeared, leaving him happily spent but curious at his partner's hurried exit.

In the meantime, Maria returned to her quarters, bathed, then lay on her own bed contentedly, visualizing what she might buy when next in the market, with the twenty dollars Mistress Sharon had given her to service the visitor.

★ ★ ★ ★

Chapter Eight

West Papua
(Irian Jaya)

First Lieutenant Subandi acknowledged the signal then advanced cautiously towards the clearing where a group of twenty or more Papuan tribesmen had gathered. There were eight in Subandi's Red Beret team – all highly trained commandos belonging to the one thousand strong, *Kopassus* Strategic Forces spread throughout Indonesia's most easterly province, to counteract the Free West Papua (OPM) separatist movement.

Growing dissent amongst the Indonesian Papuans had resulted in an increase in protests and hostage taking, the *Kopassus* command charged with the task of eliminating those responsible and, in so doing, remove all threats to the massive gold and copper deposits located there. Lieutenant Subandi was not aware that, since the mining operation's inception, his Commander-in-Chief's closest associates had been granted twenty percent of the stock in the billion-dollar, mining investment. And, because of these vested interests, the company had enjoyed a special place under the Suharto dictatorship. With the Indonesia's First Family and their associates firmly ensconced as major beneficiaries of the mine, the company not only enjoyed generous tax concessions and virtually free reign within the province, but protection by the full might of the Indonesian Armed Forces.

The young officer, as were so many of his peers, remained apolitical, interested only in advancing his career, one that had recently suffered a number of serious setbacks – the most significant, the loss of an Iroquois helicopter whilst he was co-pilot. Grounded for a year and reassigned, Subandi now found himself participating in covert operations, in the primitive province.

He had arrived as a major *Kostrad,* Strategic Reserves' operation was under way. Their task, to forcibly relocate several thousand villagers from their traditional land to make way for the mining giant's expanding infrastructure requirements and, of course, a new military base from where the army's special units could operate. A concentration camp had been established to contain the growing unrest, Lieutenant Subandi's current mission to recapture escapees who had managed to cut their way through razor-wire fencing and flee, attacking a transmigrant settlement along the way. The response to the attack on the Javanese settlers had been immediate, with a number of Black Ops being initiated that very day. The young officer knew that select *Kopassus* teams would already be on their way to 'visit' indigenes in their villages, where they would terrorize the local population, killing, torturing, burning in reprisal. Subandi had been trained in such tactics back in Java, but that was before his selection for helicopter pilot training. The intimidation tactics were always successful, he knew, having participated in a number of such raids in East Timor where he had been fortunate to meet the young, *Kopassus* commander, General Praboyo.

The junior officer peered through the bushes as the group congregated in the open, half-expecting to see men with noses pierced with bone. Instead, he was surprised to discover that they carried carbines, and wore their own style of camouflage uniform. Subandi assumed, correctly, that he had stumbled across the OPM. The commandos positioned themselves to advantage then engaged the raggedy band, the ensuing slaughter accounting for most of their number, with only a few managing to escape into the woods. Lieutenant Subandi's successful mission earned the officer accolades and the attention of his superiors in Jakarta. He was reassigned yet again, this time to the anti-terror unit, D81 located in Cijantung, on the outskirts of the national capital.

Subandi would remain engaged in covert operations specifically targeting high-profile political agitators for the next few years, until a chance development would place him back on flying duty, and at the controls of a helicopter again.

★ ★ ★ ★

Over the South China Sea

The Airbus' engines' whine diminished considerably, causing heart palpitations throughout the wide-bodied jet. Then, as the captain banked and corrected the aircraft's course for Hong Kong, to the relief of all on board, the powerful Pratt & Whitney PW4000 engines leaped back into life as the seat-belt signs were turned off, and the cabin crew rose to commence the in-flight service. Kremenchug closed the shades and adjusted his seat, then busied himself with his own business plan during the relatively short flight to Hong Kong's Kai Tak Airport. His concerns over the Philippines' government's propensity to eavesdrop on international calls had discouraged Kremenchug from placing calls to Canada and Indonesia whilst in Manila, as he did not want anyone from General Dominguez's camp even minutely aware of what he intended.

He accepted a glass of champagne from the flight attendant and sipped, quietly revisiting his brief sojourn to the Philippines, and the gratifying, and embarrassing, interlude. A look of disgust collapsed his face when he recalled the revelations, made during that morning's breakfast.

'You should have remained longer,' he had whispered to Sharon across the table so the maid could not hear.

He'd frowned when Sharon held a napkin to her face to hide her laughter. 'You didn't know it wasn't me?'

Kremenchug remembered leaning over the table. 'Excuse me?' He had then followed Sharon's eyes across the room to where Maria stood, hands clasped across the front of her apron, smiling appreciatively, in his direction. He looked back at his hostess, then over at the maid again, the realization of what had really transpired stultifying.

'I'm sorry, Alex, but I just couldn't resist!'

He felt foolish, and with a casual wave of the hand, as if dispensing with the matter, said, 'Well, for what it's worth, the experience wasn't all that bad.'

Sharon had reached across and patted his hand as a parent would some errant child. 'Just remember for the future, then. I don't mix business and pleasure.'

It had taken him the rest of the meal to recover from his embarrassment, Sharon assisting by moving their conversation forward with more important matters, reviewing his brief and their financial arrangements.

She had established a formula with respect to what stockholding the Filipino side required in a revitalized Borneo Gold Corporation, based on the premise that shares in BGC would undoubtedly rise commensurate to the value of the gold deposit's proven reserves. The question of how Sharon Ducay would deliver the necessary drilling results to justify BGC's acquisition of the Kalimantan property remained foremost in his mind. When Kremenchug had raised this most important issue, Sharon had assured him that she was confident that future assay reports would support their valuation, but refused to reveal just how she intended achieving this aim.

Sharon had, however, raised the issue that her name carried no international recognition. There would have to be others clearly associated with the mining operation, those whose reputations would, by name, substantiate her findings out in the field. For this, they would need to bring Christopher Fielding into their fold. Kremenchug was cognizant of the BGC President's financial woes and, in consequence, did not anticipate too much resistance from that quarter. Fielding's own stock position had already been watered down as a result of his marital indiscretions – Kremenchug believed that Christopher Fielding would remain on as the CEO due to his financial predicament, prepared to offer the president an attractive package and options.

Unwittingly, Fielding would become the Ducay-Kremenchug front man.

Borneo Gold Corporation would have to be re structured and shareholder approval sought to accommodate the Filipino's position. Then there was the problem of removing Scott Walters from the Board and, hopefully, completely from the scene. Kremenchug had suggested that Sharon buy Walters' stock and she had agreed to consider this path, once he had raised the question with the financier. In the event that control over BGC became too difficult to achieve, only then would Kremenchug consider other options.

The two hundred million in gold bars would be laundered through the BGC, Kalimantan mine. The restructured company would acquire the proven prospect under an options agreement, in consideration for which, the Filipinos would receive a negotiated value in share scrip, to be issued at the stock's face value, and options. As the stock was expected to at least double, the real value lay in the options. Kremenchug had negotiated a twenty percent position with Sharon, this giving him one fifth of everything the Filipinos received as a result of the deal. He anticipated that Canadian authorities would require their stock to be held in escrow for at least a year, at which time Sharon would gather her own team and commence the 'mining' operations to recycle the existing gold.

Sharon had agreed to fund the operation up to the point when BGC acquired the gold mining property. This would require that she provide capital to cover the costs of establishing a corporate entity to acquire the prospect from the Indonesian government. Sharon would then have to finance the drilling program, and any other expenses incurred in bringing the concession up the point, where they could justify the BGC stock allocation.

From Kremenchug's perspective, he had nothing to lose. The concession would be backed by the Filipino gold, his original shares would rise, and to top it all off, he would enjoy a position on the company's Board. All in all, he thought to himself, accepting a flute the stewardess had filled with Beaumont des Crayeres, he had done very well for himself.

★ ★ ★ ★

Kai Tak International Airport – Hong Kong

'Eric, it's Alex.' Kremenchug had waited to make this call from the first class lounge where some semblance of privacy could be achieved.

'Hi, Alex,' the slurred speech told Kremenchug that he should have gone to Jakarta and spoken to Baird, in person. It had been some time since they had last discussed anything in person. 'Long time, no hear!'

'Eric, I need information on what areas are still available in East Kalimantan.' Kremenchug waited, when there was no response, he tried again. 'Eric, this is very important! I want you to get down to Mines first thing and establish what prospects are still open for direct, foreign investment.'

Baird grumbled unintelligibly, testing his associate's patience.

Kremenchug tried again. 'Eric, can you get me that information tomorrow?'

'I …just told ya,' Baird repeated, 'there's nothing left.'

'Nothing at all?' Kremenchug challenged, disbelievingly.

'That's …right,' the other man's sluggish voice replied.

'Are you sure?'

'Yep,' Baird affirmed, '…all gone.'

'Eric, listen!' Kremenchug was of two minds whether he should delay his visit to Canada, and get down to Indonesia to ensure that everything was in place there, before banging tables in Vancouver. 'What was that place that was passed back in by the locals, Long-something-or-other?'

'Longdamai,' the response came back, 'longtime, Longfellow... Is that what you're referring to, Alex?'

Kremenchug swore. 'Eric, stop screwing around – this is bloody important!'

A moment passed before Baird's impaired brain clicked into gear, the wheels grinding ever so very slowly, as he gathered his thoughts.

'Alex,' he wheezed, the freshly lit cigarette burning his lungs.

'Alex, is that you – shit, man, where the fuck have you been?' This was followed by the sound of a racking series of coughs that belonged to a ward in some hospice. Kremenchug shook his head; there was so much riding on Eric Baird.

'Eric,' he tried again, 'I'm at Kai Tak and need to know if you are up to talking sensibly?'

Baird listened, his face smothered with a drunken frown. He thought Kremenchug said something about being under attack, but knew that probably wasn't right. He looked down the length of his naked body forcing his eyes to focus.

'Where…where…are you?' he moaned, dragging his limbs into a half-sitting position. One hand moved out clumsily brushing an ash-tray aside, knocking the bedside light to the floor. 'Shit' was the next word Kremenchug heard, followed by a string of expletives which would have cost him the connection, had an international operator been monitoring the call.

'Eric, I'm in Hong Kong.' Kremenchug waited, and was about to hang up and go to change his tickets when Baird's voice returned.

'Alex,' the geologist apologized, to the voice from out of the blue, 'sorry. You… woke… me. I'd bombed myself out.' Another pause, interposed with another coughing attack and then, 'What's happening?'

Kremenchug could hear Baird sucking deeply on a cigarette. He spoke slowly, still undecided as to whether he should just drop the receiver and catch the first flight down to meet the man, face to face, or persevere.

'The Longdamai prospect; Eric, I want to know about the Longdamai site.'

'Why?' this was followed by another bout of heavy breathing as the marijuana's effect topped up existing levels in Baird's blood-stream. Mixed with his daily dosage of rum, the cocktail's effect was inevitable.

'If it's available, I'm going to take it up,' Kremenchug announced. 'It's serious, Eric. I've a done deal with a party that's desperate to get into East Kalimantan.' This was greeted with an empty response.

'Eric?' Kremenchug asked, his voice losing its usual confidence.

'Yep, none other,' Baird slowly responded, his slurred speech disguised by the poor connection.

'Eric?' Kremenchug tried again, 'it's Alex.'

A few seconds passed before the Jakarta party responded. 'Hi, Alex,' Baird said, and started giggling.

'Shit, Eric!' Kremenchug wishing he could reach down through the line across the South China Sea and strangle the little, ginger-haired bastard. 'Listen to me!'

'I liselling,' Baird replied, his exceptionally poor imitation of how a Chinese migrant might speak, appalling at the best of times. Kremenchug knew that his chief geologist was not only drunk to his boots, but most probably high on grass as well.

'Eric,' he pleaded, 'get a hold of yourself. We have to talk!'

'Okay, Mastah, you talkie, I glisten,' Baird started coughing as the clove cigarette bit deeply into his lungs. 'Oh, shit!' was all Kremenchug heard at the Hong Kong end. He knew Baird drank far too much and virtually lived with a cigarette hanging from his mouth. That the man had survived this long, with his limited diet and habits, continued to amaze all who were familiar with the geologist.

'Eric, are you okay?' Kremenchug started to chew on the inside of his cheek. Another minute dragged by before Baird answered, his brain partially recovering from its confused trough as the *ganja's* tricky effects produced momentary clarity.

'I'm okay. Damn near coughed up my heart. Fucking cigarettes!'

'Eric, listen,' Kremenchug coaxed, 'I'm going to phone you back again, first thing in the morning. Okay?' This was followed by a frustrating silence. Kremenchug waited for what felt like an eternity, and tried again. 'Eric? Are you still there?'

Another coughing fit proved this to be true. The phone crackled, a more subdued Baird back on the phone. 'Sorry, had to throw up,' he apologized. Kremenchug pulled the receiver away from his mouth in disgust.

'Eric, are you able to talk now or not?' he tried again. He had experienced such fractured communications with Baird before when, for some minutes, the man could be completely coherent and then suddenly flip back into his alcoholic or drug-related state. This time, against a background of distortion, he could hear Baird's receiver being dropped. 'Eric?' Then the line went dead.

It was half an hour before the anorexic geologist answered the phone again, with Kremenchug anxiously counting the clock.

'How do you feel?' Kremenchug inquired, concerned.

'Alex?' Baird asked, waves of nausea threatening to drive him back to the bathroom. 'Sorry. Think I had a bad prawn.' Kremenchug knew that this was unlikely to be true. Baird rarely ate anything that did not come in a can, his many phobias preventing the rather brilliant geologist from behaving in any normal fashion.

'Do you want me to phone you back tomorrow when I get into Vancouver?' Kremenchug offered.

A slight pause, and then, 'No, let's talk now.'

'Are you sure?' Kremenchug needed to have his associate comprehend what was to be said. 'This is really important, Eric.'

'It's okay. I'm okay.' A brief pause filled the airwaves before Baird's voice could be heard again. Staring down at smoldering ash on his lap he brushed at the danger with one hand, only to fan the spark. He then leaned forward and spat, the saliva killing the glow. 'What do you want, Alex?' he asked, his brain-impeded state diminishing his capacity to concentrate. He had started drinking himself impotent much earlier than usual, his binge the result of disastrous news relating to his stock portfolio. Financially, he had never been worse off than now, and had been counting heavily on the Canadian shares to retire some of his debt.

'Are you *sure* you're okay to talk?'

'What's happening to our stock?' Baird asked, hopeful that the woeful tidings Reuters had carried the day before on the stock market's closing prices were, in fact, the result of some dreadful, typographical error.

'Not good,' Kremenchug hedged, 'our holdings are worth about forty thousand based on today's close.'

'Forty thousand?' Baird was mortified. When the shares had been first posted to escrow, their stock in the company was valued at half a million dollars. 'Bloody hell,' his voice became harsh, and nasal. 'What are we going to do?'

'Eric, listen,' Kremenchug pleaded. 'Forget Fielding and those shares for a moment, I've got something else I need to discuss with...'

'Jesus, Alex!' he cut the other man off, 'You want me… to forget that I've lost a quarter of a million fucking dollars… just like that?'

'Eric, that's not what I meant,' Kremenchug knew this was not going to be easy. 'Of course I'm just as pissed as you about the share price but there's nothing we can do right now.' Kremenchug paused, waiting for some indication from Baird that he was still listening. And then, impatiently, 'Eric?'

'Yeah,' his voice was filled with disappointment. 'Is it worth holding onto the scrip?' he asked, referring to their stock in the Canadian gold miner.

'I'd hang in there, Eric,' Kremenchug advised, 'they can't fall much lower. Anyway, I want to talk to you about another group that is keen for some property around the Mahakam. They've seen some of the geophysical data and are very impressed.'

'And so…?' Baird's mind was still locked into calculating his losses.

'They have plenty of capital to commit to surveys and drilling.'

Baird had been listening. He frowned. 'There's nothing left over there. It's all been allocated.'

'What about that Longdamai operation that folded?'

'Longdamai?' Baird wondered how Kremenchug was so knowledgeable about the area.

'I heard that the locals have passed it back in to avoid paying the taxes.'

'Wouldn't surprise me,' Baird had a sinking feeling in his stomach. 'From what I hear, they didn't find anything worthwhile.'

'Sure, Eric, but they wouldn't have had access to someone with your skills,' Kremenchug decided to change tack, appealing to the geologist's latent ego.

'It would be a waste of time,' Baird persisted.

'Well, check it out anyway. I'll phone you again from Vancouver, okay?'

'You don't want me to go back out into that shit-hole again?' Baird contemplated the prospect of returning to the site, a cold chill touching his spine as his mind was filled with vivid recollections of his disastrous visit.

'Longdamai?' it was Kremenchug's turn to be confused.

'Anywhere along the Mahakam,' Baird declared. 'Listen, Alex, get your clients to have a look at Northern Sulawesi around the Gorontalo area, or even in Sumatra. There's still plenty of action left in those areas.'

'No good,' Kremenchug insisted, 'the client will only consider East Kalimantan.'

'Why?'

Kremenchug hesitated. Baird may have been boozed to the gills most of the time, but it would be a mistake to underestimate the man's intelligence. He was not ready to reveal that this prospect would, ultimately, become part of the BGC operations.

'I already explained that, Eric. East Kalimantan has a strong appeal to the investors. They are reasonably plugged in when it comes to mining, especially in Indonesia. They've considered the other areas. Besides, any action close to BGC's leases might drive some life back into our stock. Listen,' a thought came to Kremenchug as he talked, 'if you don't want to go with Longdamai, then why don't you get down to Mines and establish what properties are coming up for relinquishment in that general area?'

Baird succumbed to another coughing fit, the racking noise followed by his delayed response. 'Okay… leave it with me… I'll get back to you. Where… will you be?'

'I'll contact you from Vancouver. I just wanted to make sure that you will be on deck when I ring.'

Baird detected contempt in the other man's tone. He filled his nicotine-lacquered lungs with a deep breath and said, 'I'll be all right… by then.'

'Okay, that's it, for now,' Kremenchug hung up and glanced up at the bank of wall clocks indicating international time zones. There would be no final boarding announcement for lounge passengers and he knew he was cutting it fine.

★ ★ ★ ★

Baird dropped the receiver into its cradle, thinking about the call from out of the blue, and how Kremenchug had abandoned their relationship when things had gone sour with the Canadian company. At the time, Baird had been bewildered by Kremenchug's decision to vendor in the prospect in question, knowing that any drilling commissioned to substantiate his earlier findings would only demonstrate that the deposit was not viable. Baird had received nothing for his efforts other than the few thousands he'd managed to build into the drilling survey. Kremenchug had justified his actions, explaining that he had hoped to offload their stock in BGC as the drilling proceeded.

Kremenchug's plan had backfired, leaving Baird with his reputation even further tarnished, and an extremely belligerent Canadian financier by the name of Scott Walters. Baird had picked some work over the next months, but the income generated from these was nowhere near enough to cover an expatriate's overheads, living in Jakarta. Kremenchug *had* invited him to join in the ill-fated Meekathara project in Western Australia. Baird shuddered; faced with the prospect of leaving Mardidi behind he forwent the so-called opportunity, relieved now that he had not become embroiled in yet another of Kremenchug's ambitious projects. He drifted back into a shallow sleep undertaking never to get too dependent on his former associate, ever again.

★ ★ ★ ★

Jakarta

Campbell had not expected the Papuan separatist leader to drop the documents on him in such a manner.

'It is not really appropriate, Tommy.' At first, Stewart had resisted,

finally accepting the thick folder once his visitor had made it clear what it contained.

'Why not go public with it yourself?' he had asked.

'If I give it to those people,' he nodded his head in the direction of staff waiting anxiously in the outer office, *'nothing would happen.'*

Campbell felt saddened by the look of desperation on the Papuan's face. He knew, that by becoming involved, he would once again jeopardize his position in this country.

'Is this about Freeport?' he suspected it was; Freeport was an easy target, not because of its size, but because of its cavalier attitude towards environmental issues. It was public knowledge that Suharto's closest associates already controlled a major shareholding in what had become the world's richest copper and gold mine. Campbell looked up at Tommy Eluay, his heart going out to the man who had strived to find a forum, any forum to be heard. His country, West Papua had been delivered to the Javanese, by the United States, through the UN, because of political expedience, fulfilling a 1962 agreement initiated by the United States to avert war between the Netherlands and Indonesia. The 1969 process of self-determination, executed under United Nation's auspices, provided that only a thousand West Papuans, all selected by Jakarta, were to vote on behalf of the entire, one-million population. Now, more than two decades later, the Papuans remained disenfranchised, and impoverished but, worse still, their lands were now under threat from the deadly tailings and spills associated with negligent mining practices.

'Yes. This report reveals the extent of the damage already evident and extracts of an environmental impact study conducted by the Indonesian Ministry. When you compare their initial projections with what is now reality, it becomes obvious that whoever submitted that report was either incompetent, or biased.'

'Who compiled the report?'

'Mainly church leaders,' Eluay's eyes dropped. *'We don't have so many educated Papuans, Mister Stewart. We have friends amongst the church who understand these things, including the Bishop of Jayapura.'*

'Okay, Tommy,' Campbell rose and took Eluay's hand in clasped

gesture, *'I'll accept it on the condition that you don't reveal that you have given this to me.'*

'Then you'll read it?' Tommy Eluay appealed, *'If foreigners sympathetic to our problems can help us take a stand, Mister Stewart, then we will have a fighting chance.'*

Campbell was not entirely happy with the Papuan's choice of words. Since the so-called 1969 Act of Free choice which gave Indonesia control over the vast, four hundred thousand square kilometer, former Dutch colony, the *Free Papua Movement* (OPM) had grown in strength and, although most of the freedom fighters were mainly armed with primitive weapons, their resistance was fierce and bloody. As international attention was drawn to their plight, Jakarta initiated even more stringent censorship over the distant province, preventing the foreign press from presenting an accurate view of what really was happening there.

'Yes, Tommy,' he promised, *'I'll read it. But, I won't undertake to circulate it. Okay?'*

Tommy Eluay beamed. *'That's we want, Mister Stewart, thank you.'*

Stewart Campbell escorted his Papuan guest out through reception, and bade his farewell. As Eluay's back disappeared into the lift, the thought crossed his mind that the authorities would be aware of Tommy's presence in Jakarta, and that his activities would certainly be closely monitored by the military intelligence agencies. Stewart looked up and down the crowded corridor suddenly concerned, realizing that any such surveillance would undoubtedly report the Papuan's visit to his offices.

★ ★ ★ ★

Stewart Campbell read the report, again, then locked the document in his desk drawer, speculating that Tommy Eluay would have circulated other copies, with the intention that these be leaked to the press. Campbell was certain that the damaging submission would attract international outrage, if the information could be substantiated.

He examined the black and white photographs and their captions claiming that the dead landscape was of an area more than fifty kilometers downstream from where mine tailings were dumped, into the Ajikwa River. The devastation was complete; Stewart having great difficulty believing that this barren, ghost-like landscape was once pristine rainforest. The report went on to describe the build-up of tailings and how, daily, a hundred thousand tonnes were dumped into Papuan rivers. Stewart was shocked to read that the mine's operators projected destruction of more than one hundred square kilometers of rainforest before the end of this millennium.

Stewart knew that the Papuans were not alone in their call for an end to mining companies' indiscriminate dumping of poisons. Yes, it was true that the Ajikwa River habitat was the most recent of ecological disasters to be caused by the Mines Department's failure to enforce established guidelines, but he also knew that this would not be the last. Stewart's thoughts shifted from West New Guinea to Borneo, and the island's pristine rainforests he had visited along the southern, Kalimantan rivers. In his mind, he applied the projections used by Freeport in their Papuan operations against the number of mining operators moving into Kalimantan, and was devastated to discover the extent of ecological damage that might occur, as a result of gold mining activities there. This thought triggered another, and he was bemused by the fact that he suddenly found himself thinking of the fiery Dayak student he had met in Bandung, wondering what she would say, given the opportunity to read this report.

His eyes scrolled down to where he had underscored a paragraph claiming that the prominent OPM leader, Kelly Kwalik, and three of his followers had disappeared off the face of the earth following their arrest by the Indonesian military. Reference was made to the Australian Council for Overseas Aid which reported that the four men had been tortured, and imprisoned, in a window-less Freeport container for more than a month. Disturbed by the documents' contents and the knowledge that the Indonesian government would consider such to be subversive behavior, he double-locked Tommy Eluay's submission in the desk drawer, then advised his staff that he was finished for the day. Threatened by a cloud of depression, the consulting geologist had the driver drop him off at the Grand Hyatt

Hotel, where he headed to his favorite bar on the fourth floor.

Unbeknown to Stewart Campbell, as he settled down in O'Reiley's Pub to his second vodka tonic, Tommy Eluay's interrogation was already well under way at one of the *Kopassus,* secret detention centers. Campbell's office had been the first visited by the Papuan separatist, subsequent to his arrival that day. Eluay had been arrested in the car park and whisked away by the surveillance team before he could disseminate the remaining nineteen copies discovered in the case he had been carrying. The officer in charge of the covert operation was none other than Lieutenant Subandi, this most recent success guaranteeing his return to flying duties.

The following morning, when Campbell read of Tommy's accidental death in *The Observer,* he immediately went to his office and removed the file from his desk then sent it, anonymously, to the Jakarta representative for Amnesty International. Later that day, he received a visit from immigration officials who asked to inspect copies of his passport and residency permit, and a concerned call from his sponsors at the Bandung Institute for Mines, enquiring as to why Military Intelligence was suddenly so interested in his activities.

★ ★ ★ ★

Chapter Nine

VANCOUVER
JANUARY – FEBRUARY 1994

Alexander Kremenchug arrived in Vancouver only to discover that Christopher Fielding was in Calgary, trying to talk up the Borneo Gold Corporation shares with stockbrokers there. He checked into the Four Seasons on the corner of West Georgia and Howe, and decided to fill in the afternoon researching the Marcos gold cache story, running through dailies stored on microfilm at the Vancouver Sun. Kremenchug commenced his search around the time Marco passed away, and worked backwards from there.

After reading numerous accounts relating to the former Filipino president's final years, he finally stumbled onto a number of court record reports which, in his mind, gave considerable credence to General Dominguez's own account of how Ferdinand Marcos had, in fact, recovered a substantial part of the Yamashita Gold, and that the bulk of the cache remained intact. He read the foreign correspondent's coverage of testimony given by Renato Marcos Vizcarra, a relative of the former dictator who revealed the names of those who had been charged with the responsibility of selling other Marcos gold deposits.

The story was bizarre. Vizcarra, now the Mayor of Ramon, Isabela in the Philippines, claimed that some time after lunch on the Sunday prior to the court proceedings, he had received a cell phone call warning him against testifying before the Senate Blue Ribbon committee. Kremenchug was enthralled by the story.

"Hindi ka ba naaawa sa pamilya mo kung mag-te ka. Huwag mo nang ituloy" the voice had threatened in Filipino. (Don't you pity your family for what will happen if you testify? Don't follow through with it, the mysterious caller had warned.) As a result, it appeared that Vizcarra fell short of revealing much more and now lived in constant fear for his life, accompanied by Marines whenever he ventured out of his office or home.

Kremenchug also learned that Senator Juan Ponce Enrile had claimed that he had sighted photocopies of Marcos' gold certificates estimated by the ailing industrialist, Enrique Zobel, to be worth thirty five billion dollars prior to the late strongman's death in 1989. In Zobel's deposition before the same Senate committee, he estimated the Marco fortune to be worth one hundred billion dollars, producing a photocopy of what he said was a one hundred and sixty million dollar US Treasury Note in Marcos' name. The story then became even more intriguing when Kremenchug discovered another article relating to a lawyer, Dr. David Chaikin who, because of his relationship with an investigator concerned with the missing Marcos billions, noticed an entry on an amount of some eight hundred thousand ounces of gold in a Credit Suisse statement. This had been submitted during the hearings which, due to the European practice of using decimal points where the British use commas to separate the value of thousands, the original report had been misinterpreted as there being only eight hundred ounces of gold, the overall value shy by three hundred million dollars!

Kremenchug smiled in admiration when he followed the other stories, learning that witness after witness alleged that these funds had originally belonged to Imelda Marcos' Trinidad Foundation, and how she had moved it around from Trinidad to her accounts in Fides Trust and, after the Trinidad Foundation's collapse, assets were then moved to yet a third foundation named Palmy. Kremenchug could find no evidence that the First Lady's gold deposits were ever declared, or frozen, and, according to a related article, the Swiss authorities advised that the Palmy Foundation's assets were only seventeen million dollars, of which gold represented less than half a million.

But, it was the reported statement made by Imelda that gave Kremenchug heart – that Madame Marcos had revealed that the bulk of her late husband's fortune was made through clandestine gold trading. By five o'clock, Kremenchug had read enough, and decided to catch a cab down to the Gaslight area for a stroll before catching an early night in preparation for his meeting with Fielding, the next day.

⋆ ⋆ ⋆ ⋆

Borneo Gold Corporation Offices – Vancouver

'Well, if it isn't the King of Kalimantan!' Walters mouthed facetiously as Kremenchug entered BGC's now less than lavish executive offices.

Surprised that Walters had been invited to participate in the meeting, Kremenchug immediately abandoned the speech he had prepared for Fielding.

'I'm pleased you're here, Scott,' Kremenchug improvised, 'saves me having to go all through what I have to say, again.' The men all exchanged greetings, the company President motioning his visitor to a chair.

'When did you get in?' Walters accepted coffee from the secretary, admiring her figure as she moved between the three men.

'Early Wednesday,' Kremenchug replied, 'that's one hell of a long haul from Hong Kong.'

'Worse, going the other way,' Fielding finally spoke.

'I know. Adds two, sometimes three hours,' Kremenchug continued the banal conversation, wondering what had transpired between these two prior to his arrival. He was *au fait* with respect to the financier's role – in fact, he had prepared a separate proposition for Walters and had intended presenting this in private. Now, he was obliged to change his strategy and deal with both men simultaneously.

'How's it all going over in Western Australia?' Walters asked, the barb deliberate.

'The bastards will do some serious time,' Kremenchug answered, not wishing to dwell on the matter, 'let's not go there. I don't need to be reminded of what might have been.'

'Are you all clear?' Kremenchug knew that Walters was trying to bait him.

'And why wouldn't I be?'

'There were enough rumors flying around over here to suggest that some would believe that you had a hand in the spiking.'

Kremenchug held his anger – electing to ignore the remark.

'How long are you staying?' Fielding interceded.

'Just long enough to settle this offer I have, then I'm back to Indonesia.'

'Kalimantan's still drawing a great deal of interest,' Walters suggested.

'Sure, and it's going to get even better, for some,' Kremenchug decided to get straight to the matter at hand. 'That's why I'm here. I've secured a great property, and…'

Walters laughed sarcastically, slapping one leg with his free hand. 'Jesus, you've got balls!' he snapped, 'You've single-handedly broken the back of this company with your bogus prospects, and have the audacity to stroll in here as if nothing had happened!'

'Scott,' Fielding stepped in again, 'let's hear what he has to say. With the company the way it is right now, I'm willing to listen to just about anything that'll get us out of the shit.'

'Drag us in even deeper, would be more like it!'

'Let's hear him out.'

'If you're going to try to stick us with another of your worthless properties, then I can tell you right now, you'd be wasting everyone's time.'

'I'm not here to sell anyone anything,' Kremenchug's voice raised a pitch, 'I'm here to buy!'

'Yeah, right,' Walters' lip curled at the corner.

Kremenchug raised one eyebrow and challenged the financier. 'If you don't like what I have to offer, I can take it elsewhere.'

'You can take it and shove…'

'For Chrissakes, you two!' Fielding shot to his feet. 'I don't need any more of this shit!' He turned his back to the others and stepped towards the window. 'I've had enough!' He turned, and shook his head slowly in disappointment. 'For what it's worth I've been thinking seriously about giving it all away, and going back to working in the field. BGC is all but finished. I had hoped to secure some interest in Calgary but the deal fell through. As far as I'm concerned, that was the last chance we had to raise additional funding to continue. I think it's time to de-list and place this operation in mothballs. Besides, we won't be able to make salaries inside of three months – and I need an income.' He then dropped back into a chair, threw one leg over the other and crossed his arms in a display of disgust.

Fielding's outburst caught both Walters and Kremenchug by surprise.

'You can't be serious?' Walters asked, his voice filled with scorn.

'Never been more serious in my life,' Fielding remained firm.

'The hell you do!' Walters exploded. 'I think we should discuss this in private.' He glanced over at their visitor.

'Can't we just cool it for a few minutes until you hear what I've got to say?' Kremenchug pleaded.

'Stay out of this Alex – you're not exactly flavor of the month around here at the moment.' Then, glaring at the BGC President, 'Have you suggested this to anyone else?' Walters voice was hoarse – he had a major stake in BGC.

'No, not yet.' Fielding looked tired. 'But I think I should make an announcement before the market closes at the end of this week.'

Walters face became ashen. 'That has to be a Board decision,' he rasped, near-spilling his coffee as he fumbled to get the mug down on the table.

'Well, the way I see it, Scott, if I resign then you and the other directors can do whatever you want.'

Shock turned to anger as blood filled the financier's cheeks. 'I've got the best part of half a million invested in this company, ...' he paused, suddenly short of breath, '...invested, I remind you, because of the misrepresentations you and Kremenchug here made for start-up funding.' He glared at both men. 'Now you're telling me that you're abandoning ship?' Walters leaned forward, his face grim. 'My backers will be very, very pissed!'

Kremenchug seized the opportunity. 'Then, why not just sell your position?'

'Offload my stock?'

'Sure, my investors will take it off your hands.'

'What's the offer?'

'A hundred and fifty grand.'

Walters sneered. 'And who'd be stupid enough to pay that, when it's currently trading for less than seventy thou?'

Kremenchug knew that this was his chance. 'I can get you a hundred and fifty grand for your stock, and enough options to double what you initially invested.' He then stretched, clasping both hands behind his neck, and waited, knowing that Walters was digesting what he'd said.

'What are you up to, Alex?' Walters eyes narrowed, anger displaced with suspicion.

'I'm not up to anything, Scott,' Kremenchug knew he had to be careful here; the financier was nobody's fool. 'I came to BGC first as I have a vested interest.' He turned to Fielding. 'You're not the only one hurting because of the company's predicament, Chris. Baird and I have half a million shares we can't sell, don't forget.'

At the mention of Eric Baird's name the BGC President shook his head. 'Wherever did you find that man?'

'He has his uses,' Kremenchug wished to avoid discussing the mistakes of the past. 'What do you say, Scott, are you interested in selling your BGC holdings to me?'

'Why would you want to pay more than double the market?' then, to Fielding, 'Are you in on this?'

'No, he's not,' Kremenchug came to the man's aid. 'I was going to make an offer to you both and I thought I'd discuss it with Chris first as you would need to stay on.'

Fielding stared at Kremenchug as if he were crazy. 'You're offering to buy Scott out?' he asked disbelievingly, 'Why?'

Kremenchug knew that he had to be convincing. 'Because the structure is already in place, the company has a Contract of Work with the Indonesian government and, most importantly, I have backers who are convinced that the BGC leases in Kalimantan have value. I already own five percent. Scott's stock would take this up to just over seventeen.' Christopher Fielding moaned inwardly – if only he had not remarried! Now, his own BGC stock totaled less than that of even Baird's.

'What's the deal?' the financier sounded less belligerent now.

'The incoming investors would want to have control, and...'

'Screw it!' Walters exploded again. 'What you're talking about is effectively a restart. It would have to go to the shareholders *and* the Securities Commission would want to have their say.'

'Sure, but all in good time – we'd take it in two steps. Firstly, my group would acquire your position, I would take a seat on the Board, then we would work towards having BGC acquire their prospects which, by the time all else is ready, results of the full drilling program will be in hand to substantiate initial findings and evaluations.'

'Who's going to fund all of that?'

Kremenchug was ready. 'The investors,' he replied, confidently. 'As I said; your twelve and a half percent for a hundred and fifty grand, cash, and you walk away with enough options to choke a horse.' Kremenchug hesitated, giving Walters time to absorb the offer. 'As for you, Chris, you get to remain in the chair with a five-year contract, also with a fistful of options.'

'For whatever that might be worth,' the BGC President intoned, negatively.

'No, you're wrong, Chris. If you remain in the chair, you'll receive a healthy salary and two million options. Once production commences, the company's stock will leap and the options would follow.'

'Production? Christ, Alex, they don't even have a property yet! How can you sit there and talk about an operational mine, already?'

'They will have a mine,' he assured them.

'Sounds like the same crap you walked in with five years back,' Walters complained.

'If this is bullshit, why would they want to pay you out in cash?' he reminded the banker. 'I'm not at liberty to reveal too much. Who knows, you might reject the offer and that would only cause complications when they took the deal elsewhere? But, I can tell you this. I have never seen a property with such great showings - and it will be assigned to BGC.'

'Then why not give it to one of the majors, and sit back and enjoy life?' Fielding pressed, still suspicious of dealing with Kremenchug.

'They considered this,' he lied again, 'but decided that they would do better with their own publicly-listed company.'

'Where are these prospects?' Fielding appeared confused.

'Indonesia, of course.'

'Shit! Here we go again,' Walters shook his head, as if he knew Kremenchug's offer to buy him out had been too good to be true.

'These prospects will drive the value of BGC shares up to at least a dollar,' he promised.

'Sure, Alex, sure.' Walters' spirits had plummeted with this forecast. 'Sounds like déjà vu.'

'Well, it's your choice, Scott,' Kremenchug now went in for the kill. 'You can either sell your shares to me when nobody else in their right mind would give you even a fraction of what I'm offering, sit on the options we'll give you and make a shit-load of money, or let the company collapse into its shell.'

'Why don't you just go into the market and buy stock – Christ, it's low enough?'

'You *know* why! The stock would climb back once someone stood in the market with such a huge buy order. Besides, the same restrictions still apply with respect to controlling interests.'

'You still won't have control by acquiring my block of stock.'

'I know that. But, at least we'll have the largest individual block and still remain within the legal threshold.'

'What then?' Fielding asked.

'As I've already stated, Chris, once we've taken a Board position and Scott has surrendered his stock, we'll work towards having BGC restructured so that effective control will pass to the incoming investors by acquisition of their Indonesian prospects.'

'And what if I want to negotiate the offer?' Walters' earlier aggression had dissipated somewhat, sensing that his shareholding could be crucial to any deal in the making.

'I'd be obliged to go elsewhere with their money – and leases.'

'Your stocks would also be worthless.'

'Then, I would be looking to the incoming investors for some sort of compensation with respect to the losses I would incur, by taking the deal elsewhere.'

'You'd walk away from your stock in BGC?'

'Sure,' Kremenchug now spoke with authority. 'I've already raised this possibility with the investors. BGC's attraction is nothing more than its existing structure and foothold in Indonesia. They could spend considerably less and buy their way into a Kalimantan concession and, no doubt, I would be adequately compensated should they elect to go elsewhere.'

'Then why don't you?'

'Because, they don't want to go public with their holdings, nor do they wish to hold any positions on the revamped Board.'

Suddenly, the pieces began to fall into place for both Fielding and Walters.

'You'll be voted onto the Board?'

'Yes,' Kremenchug, now over the hump, began to enjoy the charged atmosphere. 'I would hold their proxy. As I stated earlier, Chris will be offered the Presidency and options.'

'When would I receive the options?' Fielding re-joined the discussion.

'You could take them up by paying the twenty-five cents anytime you wish within five years – the duration of your contract.' Kremenchug suddenly felt smug – 'These will be worth a minimum of two million dollars once results of the properties acquired by the revamped BGC are announced.'

'Shit!' Walters threw himself back into his chair. 'You're a nice piece of work, Kremenchug!' He stole a look in Fielding's direction, convinced that this man had advance knowledge of Kremenchug's offer. 'Why not just make a written offer to the Board to inject capital, assign the leases and leave existing stockholdings intact?'

'Because, as you reminded us, that would require scheduling a stockholder's meeting, submissions to the Securities Commission and God knows what else.'

'Then why not go that route?'

'Because that's the deal, Scott.' Kremenchug sat upright, as if preparing to leave, his expression somber. 'Take it or leave it.' He knew that Walters would have to be realistic – it was not as if investors were queuing up outside to save the ailing company.

Walters chewed on this for some moments before looking over at Fielding, who raised his hands and shrugged, in a suggestion of *fait accompli*, then nodded in affirmation.

'Okay. I'll need a few days to think it over. But, just so we're clear,' Walters becoming defensive, 'I'll need to see something concrete as to how we're going to get paid – you know I'm not in this alone.'

'That's fine, by me,' Kremenchug agreed graciously, his insides twisting with excitement at the unexacting win. 'Let's place a deadline on written confirmation by… say, midday Monday?' Kremenchug also needed time to facilitate his own, back-to-back arrangements with Sharon Ducay.

'Agreed.' Walters cocked his head at Fielding. 'Chris?'

Fielding shrugged his shoulders. 'Sure. We'll meet back here on Monday,' he agreed – yet to be convinced that Kremenchug was the benefactor he made himself out to be. Over the past, desperate eighteen months, there had been a number of deals which had collapsed at the eleventh hour and now, due to his extended run of bad *karma*, Christopher Fielding still could not shake his pessimistic mood.

★ ★ ★ ★

Manila – Vancouver

Kremenchug called Sharon Ducay to advise that he had secured an in-principle agreement from the BGC President, and Walters, to facilitate the 'back door' takeover. Sharon confirmed that she would make funds available to complete the acquisition, and finance the costs of restructuring the company when the timing was appropriate.

'What time frame are we looking at here?' she asked.

'Providing Monday's meetings go as planned, we should be able to secure shareholder approval within six to nine months,' Kremenchug advised.

'And the final cost?'

'I had to go to three hundred thousand, for Walters' stock,' he lied. 'Then, there's still drilling costs and whatever it takes to secure the property in Kalimantan. BGC will need some funds to restructure and call the extraordinary stockholders' meeting towards the end of the year to sanction the acquisition, and effectively pass control to us.' At the Manila end of this conversation, Sharon shook her head at Kremenchug's predictability. She had suggested a cap of a quarter of a million for the financier's block of shares.

'Okay, that's fine,' Sharon agreed, Kremenchug's request was still well within her budget. 'Ring me again on Monday, after the meeting. Remember, Alex, the General and I have placed our trust in you to finalize all of this as expediently as possible. The General's not all that well, and I would like to see the arrangements settled while he is still with us.'

'I understand, Sharon,' Kremenchug assured her, 'and I'll definitely phone you as soon as I have their acceptances on Monday.'

'We really don't want to start afresh, Alex,' she reiterated, 'floating an entirely new entity would disadvantage us in every way. We would have to start from scratch with the Indonesians, find an underwriter and secure a property under the revised foreign investment laws – the timing could jeopardize our project. I'm hearing that current, due diligence procedures in Canada have also become more stringent – a new float would require independent drilling reports and you know what that would mean.'

'I'm confident that Fielding and Walters will go through with the offer, Sharon. Don't worry!'

Their conversation ended and, as it was still early the following morning, Filipino time, Sharon then went to the General to inform him that it was time to contact his Chinese friends in Manila, to commence changing some of the gold into dollars. By Tuesday morning, Sharon placed five hundred thousand dollars into her carry-on case, and locked this in the cellar.

★ ★ ★ ★

Borneo Gold Corporation Offices

Kremenchug scowled at the financier. 'I think the offer that's already on the table is more than generous.' They had been locked in negotiations for more than an hour. The remaining Board member had phoned in, advising Fielding that Walters had his vote. The BGC company secretary had thrown his hands in the air and left the meeting, returning to his accountancy practice across the hall, requesting he be called if there was any resolution.

'Listen, Alex,' Scott Walters' counter offer had all but derailed their negotiations. 'I carried this company for the best part of five years, sunk half a million into its start-up and now deserve to remain in the deal. It's crap to want me out now that the company has another backer.'

Kremenchug replied coldly. 'You're in danger of killing this deal altogether.' He looked over at the BGC President. 'Tell Scott again, what happens if I walk?'

'We don't have to go there,' Fielding all but moaned, 'for Chrissakes, Alex, there must be some room for negotiations here!'

'Look, Alex,' Walters stepped in, 'my group simply want recognition for our participation, to date. We bought in for half a million at the start and don't believe it's unreasonable to at least expect to take that much out.'

'You still have the options,' Kremenchug reminded.

'As does everyone else,' he retorted.

'We're not going to give you more than two hundred and fifty thousand,' Kremenchug had already upped the original offer by fifty thousand, but Walters remained stubbornly fixed to his counter demands, cutting into the additional hundred thousand he had earmarked for himself.

'Here's out final offer,' Walters insisted. 'We'll take the deal off-market so that you won't have to disclose the price paid for the stock. That way you will be able to keep the other shareholders biting at the bit to support the restructuring and share allocation to your investors. We'll sell you half of our holdings for what we paid for them originally, the balance of a quarter of a million to be paid by your associates within twelve months. On top of that, we want to keep the options.'

'Impossible!' Kremenchug exploded; Walters counter offer had not really changed in any significant way. 'Looks like we're stalemated here, gentlemen,' he said, hesitating, before rising to his feet. 'I'm sorry, Chris,' he smiled weakly at the BGC President, 'but I gave it my best shot.' He started gathering his notes and slowly placed these inside a black, soft crocodile skin briefcase.

Walters waited, hoping to call Kremenchug's bluff. But when it became obvious that the man was serious and intended abandoning the negotiations, Walters' position changed immediately.

'Come on, Alex,' he cajoled, 'you're supposed to be a great negotiator. Give me something I can take back to the others.'

Kremenchug placed his briefcase on the table. 'We don't want protracted negotiations, Scott. If you're not empowered to settle this now, then I'm afraid we won't have a deal. My instructions are to move on if we can't resolve this today.'

Walters' right foot started tapping the carpet; he knew that Kremenchug's offer was a good deal but wanted to see how far the incoming investors would go.

'Okay,' Walters tried again, 'how about we keep our options, your investors pay us two hundred grand now, the deal still to remain off-market, and three hundred in twelve months?'

'No,' Kremenchug flatly refused. He placed his hand on the briefcase. 'Is that it, then?'

Fielding waited anxiously, hoping that Walters would capitulate.

'Look, Alex, you'll have to do better than a quarter of a mill. My guys won't swallow that.'

Kremenchug could smell success. 'All right, Scott, we'll give you two hundred thou once shareholder approval is in hand and the restructure in place, and another one fifty, a year from now. You can keep your options. You resign from the Board in favor of me.'

'What! Nothing up front?'

'Okay then, Scott, I'll give you a hundred grand now, a quarter of a million when the restructure is in place.'

Fielding's expression pained as soft flesh came away from the inside of his mouth. 'Sounds like a fair offer, to me, Scott. Come on, let's wrap it up and get on with it.'

Walters' eyes locked with Kremenchug's, before drifting across to the agitated President. 'I'm not resigning,' Walters dug his heels in. 'But, you can have Phillips' seat,' he offered, referring to the absent director. Kremenchug had expected this. Once the company had been restructured, he would have the financier replaced.

'Okay, I can live with that,' he said, 'when can you have the paperwork ready?'

'Friday noon,' Fielding was pleased with the outcome. He had discussed settlement with Walters prior to Kremenchug's arrival for the Monday meeting.

'Fine, then there's nothing more for us to do except wait for the lawyers to do their bit,' Kremenchug felt smug with the outcome. 'You know where I'm staying, if anything comes up.' There would be two hundred thousand of Sharon's money to play with after he had paid Walters his deposit. He was in no way concerned that he would be required to settle the balance, once BGC had acquired the Kalimantan lease.

The three men shook hands, Kremenchug then scurrying back to his hotel to phone Sharon, to deliver the good news.

⋆ ⋆ ⋆ ⋆

Manila – Vancouver – Jakarta

When the call came through, Sharon was at breakfast with the General.

'Congratulations, Alex, you've done well!' and in that moment, her excitement began to build. 'When will they be ready to sign?'

'Friday,' he answered. 'We need to give them the names of your nominee company for the documentation. Are you ready?

'Yes, Alex, I will fax the details to your hotel, today.'

'Great.' He paused. 'Are you ready with the funding?'

'Of course,' Sharon replied, 'they accepted the offer as we discussed?'

'Not exactly,' Kremenchug started to explain, Sharon immediately feeling her stomach tighten, 'but it's close enough. Walters insisted on remaining on the Board, at least until BGC has been reorganized.'

'It's manageable,' Sharon was relieved. 'How long before it's all settled?'

'About nine months – getting the shareholders to respond takes time, and nothing can be done until we have completed the drilling program to substantiate the deposit's value.'

'Are you going to Jakarta after finishing up there?'

'No. There's no need, at least, not until the Mines Department signs off on the lease for your company. We'll need a letter of appointment for Eric Baird to submit the documentation on your behalf. Why not send this today, along with details of your offshore entity?'

'Fine, I'll prepare something and have the directors in Road Town execute the documents. You might not receive anything until tomorrow.'

Kremenchug had never been to the British Virgin Islands, but knew that Sharon referred to the BVI capital on Tortola, where most of that country's financial institutions were located.

'What is the company called, again?' unsure that she had already mentioned this.

'Dominion Mining Incorporated.'

'You might want to have a loan agreement put into place as well, to keep BGI afloat. Without it, they could very well go under.'

'How much, Alex?' Sharon waited anxiously – concerned that Kremenchug's original estimates would spill out of control.

'Their holding costs are minimal – they have no field activity. Apart from Fielding's salary, the company secretary and office expenses, I'd say that another two hundred thousand would carry them through until the restructure is in place.'

'But there won't be any difficulties with the Securities people?'

'No, none,' he assured Sharon, 'currently the stock is trading at around five cents. There is likely to be some slight movement either way, particularly if the Indonesian Mines Department makes too much of assuming some of the BGC acreage. Besides, any funds we advance will be considered a loan until the stockholders vote. It's most unlikely that they'd refuse the restructure as it's in their best interests.'

'But the final shareholding will still give us effective control?'

'Absolutely – but to avoid Security Commission interference, we have to keep our interests at arm's length.'

'I don't see that being a problem. How long will it take to finalize the Contract of Work with the Indonesians?' Sharon referred to the Kalimantan prospect that her company would acquire.

'I have confirmation from my man over there, Eric Baird, that he's had the area frozen for us. But, we should get that application submitted in,' he paused, 'Dominion Mining's name as quickly as possible. I'll forward your nominee company's details to Baird, so he can get the ball rolling with foreign investment applications, etcetera.'

'That's great, Alex. We are very pleased with the way you've handled everything so far.' She peered back to where the General was sitting, and raised one thumb in the air. 'The General sends his regards.'

'Thank you, Sharon, please send him mine as well. Okay, then,' Kremenchug was now anxious to celebrate, 'I'll wait for your fax.'

'It will be there before lunch,' she promised, then hung up, glided across to the General's side, and kissed him on the forehead. 'He's done it!' she laughed. 'We're going to own a goldmine in Indonesia!' with which, she dragged General Dominguez to his feet and hugged him with childish excitement.

As promised, before the day was out, Sharon sent Kremenchug details of her shelf company, Dominion Mining Incorporated, and the authority for Baird to make representations to the Indonesian Ministry for Energy and Mineral Resources. Although her name did not appear on any of the corporate records, Sharon's power of attorney and bearer's shares were sufficient to provide for her absolute control over the entity's dealings. The following day, Kremenchug phoned Eric Baird in Jakarta, and warned him that a fax had been sent to his office, containing all the details of the BVI company, which were to be used to file a foreign investment application over the designated area. The Indonesian entity would be known as P.T. Kalimantan Gold (Indonesia).

★ ★ ★ ★

By Thursday that week, Baird had reconfirmed that most of the Mahakam areas had been secured by multinational mining entities following the gold rush into Kalimantan.

'What about Longdamai?' Kremenchug asked.

'It's about the only area left along the entire reach. It's been overlooked as it still appears on the Mines Department books as being under contract. Most of the allocation runs along the course of the river system there.'

'Then we'll have to secure it,' Kremenchug insisted.

Baird choked as the smoke went down the wrong way. 'Why bother?' another debilitating coughing spell ended with Baird out of breath. 'That piece of dirt... has nothing!' Then, as an afterthought he added, 'There are more viable properties around in other provinces. Why not offer your clients something in Sumatra?'

Kremenchug was losing patience with the geologist, 'Longdamai's my first choice, Eric.'

Baird tried again to discourage Kremenchug. 'I had a long conversation with one of the guys down at Mines and he tells me that even the locals won't go near it again.'

'Look, Eric, just go and stitch Longdamai up for us. I'm coming over next week to settle this with you. Okay?'

'Settle... what?' Baird, losing the conversation flow, flicked ash off the sheets.

'For Chrissakes, Eric!' Kremenchug hissed down the line, 'I'm talking about giving you a fifty grand in cash to keep Longdamai clear for me until we can secure the area. Now, are you listening?'

Stunned, Baird fought a drug-induced cloud. 'Fifty grand?' Suddenly, he was alert and groped for the Evian water Mardidi always left on his side of the bed. 'What do you need from... my side?' he burped into the mouthpiece, Kremenchug pulling the receiver away from his own face, in disgust.

'Get down to the Mines Department first thing tomorrow. Send me confirmation that the area is still open; that no one has taken a CoW over the title,' he demanded, referring to the official Contract of Work agreements which effectively allocated control over Indonesian mining prospects.

'Where... do you want me... to send it?'

'To...' he hesitated, about to instruct Baird to send the information to Vancouver, but decided against this. 'I'll phone you back and let you know.'

'Okay. You know... where to reach me.' And then, 'When do I get my fifty grand?'

Kremenchug ground his teeth. 'You'll be paid when the deal is finalized. Do your bit, Eric, and you'll make an easy fifty thou. There might even be a bonus if this works out. Okay?'

The conversation was then marked by a series of chest-racking coughs. Finally, Baird confirmed. 'Sure, I've got it Alex,' he managed to get out, his breathing as heavy as any asthmatic, 'but are you sure you really want... to run with Longdamai?'

Kremenchug suppressed his immediate response; instead, he sat limply, prepared to let Baird ramble. 'Why?' his voice filtered down the line. 'Is there something you know, that I should?'

Baird thought about this, but even in his alcohol cum marijuana haze, he knew better than to mention it. 'Nah,' he said, 'but I don't... particularly want to go back to...Kalimantan right now. If you need to have any work done there, you'll have to find someone else.'

Kremenchug was not disappointed. This would remove the possibility of bad blood when the time came to announce Sharon Ducay's appointment as Chief Geologist – assuming the Longdamai site *could* be secured on behalf of Dominion Mining.

'You're not holding out on me, Eric?'

Baird did not hesitate, having now recovered use of most of his faculties. 'Nothing that's important,' was all he said; then hung up.

* * * *

Baird remained in bed, determined to make the best of the interrupted mid-afternoon siesta opportunity. Kremenchug's conversation prevented him from returning to sleep and, as he lay there, he recalled what had happened at the original Longdamai site and was again, revisited by the uneasiness that accompanied these thoughts.

He was intrigued by Kremenchug's insistence that they apply for the Longdamai site. There were other opportunities in other Indonesian provinces and, understanding how Kremenchug operated, he found the man's choice of Longdamai for his current venture mystifying. Baird was aware that his associate gleaned information from a well-informed circle of mining contacts, this thought raising the possibility that Kremenchug had accessed data relating to Longdamai, that had yet to be made available to others. Baird considered this possibility, finally drawing the conclusion that the entrepreneur was sitting on vital information that had galvanized him into committing his own funds.

Of one thing Baird was certain – that Kremenchug had offered to pay him fifty thousand dollars without being asked sent a clear signal that he knew a great deal more about Longdamai than he was prepared to reveal. Baird was now convinced that Kremenchug was, indeed, on to something. He would go to the Mines Department early the following morning and initiate steps to secure the rights to the prospect. Then, he would wait for Kremenchug's next move. One, he now felt confident, that would replenish his rapidly dwindling, financial reserves.

The following morning, before proceeding to the Indonesian Ministry, he checked his account at the Standard Chartered branch, to confirm that Kremenchug had transferred the funds as agreed. During the course of the next days, he submitted an application on behalf of Dominion Mining to acquire the concession area known as Longdamai, including the site that lay in the very heart of Jonathan Dau's treasured, ancestral spiritual surrounds. The request was approved within a fortnight, subject to the formation of a legal Indonesian corporate entity.

Three months later, P.T. Kalimantan Gold (Indonesia) became a reality.

* * * *

Chapter Ten

Jakarta – March 1994

The hand-delivered letter started,

'Dear Stewart,

As a fellow expatriate involved in the mining industry, I feel that I must communicate my concerns with respect to many of the mining operations along the Mahakam tributary system. I have attached copies of river sampling and soil testing which will evidence…"

The extensive report cited companies by name, their blatant disregard for the environment, and the obvious political umbrella under which they operated. The author had underlined eight of the ten exploration mining companies, highlighting the fact that these were all associated with the Palace, or those closely associated with the government.

Stewart Campbell read the letter with a deepening sense of foreboding, speculating that the Suharto clique was well on the way towards monopolizing the country's natural resources. He had already witnessed the shift in ownership of downstream investments in the oil and gas industry. The President's children had manipulated control over pipelines, refineries, by-product production and distribution and Campbell questioned how much time remained before further pressure was applied throughout the mining industry, enabling the six children to improve the family's holdings over the nation's vast mineral resources.

Stewart turned his attention back to the expatriate geologist's letter reporting the growing incidence of mercury poisoning evident now amongst ethnic, river-communities. The similarities between what he had evidenced in West Papua, and what Mahakam villagers were reporting, was alarming.

He read on.

"...and, the majority of Dayak communities will be faced with continuing human rights violations, and significant environmental destruction, including air, water and land pollution, all of which adds to the overall devastation of their traditional ways of life. Last month, the Galian gold mine was forced to shut down after negotiations with local community representatives reached stalemate. Dayak villagers blockaded access to the Galian mine, preventing supplies of lime (which, as you know, Stewart, is used for treating acid waste) and diesel fuel oil from getting through to the site. The Dayaks are incensed with the methodology used in disposing of waste, their calls for more stringent controls resulting in a number of village heads being arrested, and interrogated. The Dayaks also have a legitimate case with respect to their land claims. Compensation has either been too little, or not forthcoming at all. Their claims cover land taken for mining operations, access roads and damage to crops. Sadly, allegations of human rights abuse against two of the foreign mining companies include sexual abuse and rape committed by senior company staff against Dayak women."

Stewart put the letter down and rubbed tired eyes, contemplating the enormity of the problems associated with the exploding mining industry in Indonesia. With computer-aided mapping and advanced techniques in geochemistry and geophysics, much of the guesswork had been removed from the geologist's trade. Ore bodies which had previously been passed over as being uneconomically viable in terms of gold content, were now being mined due to new, innovative extraction processes such as cyanide heap leaching, the modern version of mercury separation. Stewart knew that this process offered extremely high pollution risks and long-term toxic contamination, as the process required the spraying of a solution of cyanide over crushed ore which had been heaped into open piles, permitting the miners to extract gold from ore bearing as little as half a gram, per ton of rock. As a result of this technique, a plethora of small, illegal mining operations had followed foreign mining companies into the field, their activities resulting in extreme ecological damage.

With the growing demand for gold, the future for ethnic groups such as the *Dayaks* in Kalimantan and the *Amungme* people of West Papua was grim. He was deeply concerned that, with more than fifty percent of all worldwide mining exploration being dedicated to gold, more than one out of five of the prospects were located on indigenous lands, supporting the claim that this activity sets the stage for community dislocation, cultural erosion and environmental degradation. And, he believed, as long as powerful mining conglomerates remained aloof supported by corrupt government officials, public debate regarding environmental issues would remain gagged in countries such as Indonesia, preventing any significant change.

His thoughts returned to the letter. He was reminded of an earlier incident involving a number of environmentalists who had taken their own soil and water samples at a mining site, where extreme ecological damage was evident. All three of the men had been arrested, and deported. Stewart suddenly frowned – it did not pay to be outspoken in this country, particularly if comments were directed in any way, at those in power. With this in mind, he rose to his feet, gathered the pages together, then went into the adjacent office and ran the documents through the shredder.

'Love letters?' his secretary, Laila teased, following him into the room. She had never seen her boss dispose of correspondence in this manner, before.

'How did you guess?' he managed to smile.

'Who is it this time?' she asked, *'another of those young students from Jogya?'*

Stewart turned to Laila, his face covered with surprise wondering if nothing ever escaped this woman. He had dated a post-grad student in Jogyakarta a number of times, but they had never communicated and she had not visited Jakarta.

'Not this time.' He finished shredding the lengthy letter before picking up the banter again. *'An irate father from Madura.'*

'Madura?' his secretary pouted. *'When are you going to start dating some Batak girls?'*

'Soon, Laila, soon!' he laughed, *'but I'm still working my way through the other islands.'*

'By the time you reach Sumatra, you'll be worn out,' the middle-aged Batak woman scolded. *'Or, too old.'*

Stewart took Laila by the arm and led her back to her desk. *'If that starts to happen, you'll be the first to know.'* The secretary was still giggling when the phone rang, the caller asking for Stewart Campbell.

'It's from Houston,' she said, and Campbell pointed to his office, moving quickly to accept the call.

'Stewart?' Phil Samuels' deep, familiar voice boomed down the line. 'How the hell are you?'

'Hi there, Phil.' Samuels continued to be one of Campbell's staunchest allies, and friends. 'Are you coming over?'

'Nah, not for a couple of months.' Phil Samuels heavy, southern accent fell comfortably on Campbell's ear. 'Say, Stew,' he continued, 'what do you know about BGC?'

'BGC?' Campbell's mind clicked into gear. 'Oh yeah, Borneo Gold Corporation.' He thought for a few moments. 'They got stuck with some heavy acreage over in East Kalimantan. Why?'

'Just chasing up some rumors, Stew, that's all.'

'Have they made an announcement?'

'No, nothing like that – there's been talk that they've acquired a hot property over there. There's probably not much to it, just thought you might have heard.'

'They're Canadian based,' Campbell searched his memory, unable to recall anything which was of real interest, 'and from what I remember, not all that financial.'

'Precisely,' was all Samuels said.

And then it dawned. 'Jesus, Phil, that's one of the deals Kremenchug helped put together!'

'Yep,' Samuels drawled, 'I remember the name. You introduced us a couple of years back.'

'You're not seriously thinking of getting involved with them?' Campbell had not seen or heard of Kremenchug for some time.

'Well, something's going on. A friend of a friend claims that he has reliable information suggesting that BGC's going to accommodate some party over your way that definitely has the goods.'

'Indonesian?'

'Can't say but, by the sounds of it, yes. Do you think it's someone from the President's family?'

Campbell thought about this. 'Could be, Phil. Do you want me to check it out?'

'Sure, thanks, Stew – if nothing comes of it, what the hell. But, if the boys over there are going to play then I wouldn't mind a piece of the action. BGC shares aren't worth shit right now – if you can confirm who the players are and the stock starts to move, do you want me to pick up a parcel for you?'

'Wait 'till I check it out, Phil. I'll get back to you.'

'Don't be too long, my friend,' Samuels warned, 'in my experience, when these things go off, they do so with a major bang.'

'Okay. I'll get onto it right away and get back to you as soon as I have something concrete.'

'Great.'

'Can you give me anything else?'

'Nothing much,' Campbell could almost hear Samuels thinking, 'except that whoever's privately underwriting the deal is going to considerable pain to keep their identity secret.'

'And this leads you to speculate that the First Family is involved?'

'That's what I'd like you to establish, Stew.'

'It will take a few days.'

'Guess we'll just have to live with that.'

'All right,' Campbell agreed, 'I'll get onto it right away.'

'Thanks, Stew, I'll be waiting for your call.'

Stewart Campbell slowly replaced the receiver, considering his friend's inquiry. He knew that BGC had been unsuccessful with its general exploration program and had heard from Mines Department colleagues, that BGC was one of the foreign mining companies currently under review with respect to their failure to meet work commitments on their block. He instructed Laila to request an appointment with the Ministry, then started phoning around to see if the local market had already picked up anything relative to Samuel's request.

The next day, during his meeting with the Director General of Mines' personal assistant, Campbell was given a list of all recent applications for general exploration in Kalimantan. Amongst these was a British Virgin Islands' registered company, called Dominion Mining, and he was surprised to discover the speed at which approvals had been issued, giving the offshore company rights over the area designated Longdamai. When he ran his eye down the detailed information sheet and discovered Eric Baird's name listed as the consulting geologist, Campbell immediately concluded that Dominion Mining was, in some way, associated with Kremenchug – and therefore linked in some way to BGC.

★ ★ ★ ★

P.T. Subroto & Associates

When the summons came, Eric Baird had hurried to the office where he found Subroto in one of his moods. *'What is our involvement with this company, Dominion Mining?'* Subroto shuffled papers officiously, in a loose file. *'I was asked by the Mines people today, and couldn't tell them anything.'*

'I was asked to submit an application on their behalf for acreage along the Mahakam,' Baird explained.

'You, personally?' the tone was accusatory.

'Yes, Pak,' Baird answered, realizing that he should have kept Subroto better informed. *'At this time there's nothing much in it – I'm hoping that we will get some of the consultancy work, that's all.'*

'Who's behind Dominion Mining?'

Baird wished to avoid naming Kremenchug because there was history between the parties. *'It's a British Virgin Islands company,'* he said, hoping that would suffice.

'British what?'

'A Caribbean company, Pak,' Baird squirmed, expecting Subroto to push for more.

'Dominion Mining is a British company?'

'Not exactly, Pak,' Baird cursed himself for not having laid the groundwork for his sponsor cum partner. *'Obviously, the company has been set up by the principals, to avoid paying taxes.'*

'Do you know the owners?'

'No, Pak, I don't' Baird replied, lamely. *'That's another reason why some companies establish subsidiary interests in these tax havens, so that no one can determine just who they are.'*

'Are they involved with drugs?'

'No, Pak, No!' Baird responded, vehemently. *'This is a legitimate mining operator wanting to build an interest in Indonesia.'*

'How do you know this to be true, if you can't tell me who the owners are?' Subroto challenged, suspicious of anything he did not understand.

'Because the company's documentation was stamped by the Indonesian Consulate over there.' Baird had asked that the letter of appointment and other relative correspondence be affirmed as originals by the Honorary Indonesian Consul, in Port of Spain, Trinidad as the Republic had no representation in the BVI.

'There must be someone you communicate with?'

'It's another Canadian group,' he revealed, steeling himself for what most certainly would follow.

'Kremenchug?' Subroto's roar bounced off the walls. *'Does Kremenchug have anything to do with Dominion Mining?'*

Eric Baird crossed, then immediately unfolded his legs realizing that Subroto might find this offensive. He had hoped that Kremenchug's involvement could be disguised somehow but, in the absence of any other name, he had no choice.

'All I know, Pak, is that Kremenchug introduced the Dominion party, that's all.'

'Sialan, Eric,' Subroto cursed, slamming the desk with a heavy hand, rising from his seat in anger. *'I forbid you to have anything more to do with this group!'*

'But, Pak!' Baird implored, panic rising, *'I have already received an advance payment for the work they want done!'*

Subroto's anger caused his cheeks to quiver. *'Why didn't you seek my permission first, before accepting anything from that bangsat?'*

Baird avoided Subroto's eyes. *'I needed the money, Pak,'* he justified, fidgeting his hands and adjusting his seat on the chair.

For a few moments nothing was said between the two men, the air heavy with unspoken recriminations. Baird had hoped that by now, his association with the retired and influential air force General would have created far more opportunities than what had materialized over the past years. As for Subroto, his roller-coaster ride as an entrepreneur had not been what he had imagined – his disappointment with Baird, further exacerbated by this most recent revelation that Kremenchug had somehow managed to manipulate his way back into promoting mining ventures within Indonesia.

'How much has he paid you?' Subroto asked.

'The money didn't come from Kremenchug,' Baird pointed out.

'Then, how much has Dominion Mining paid you?'

Baird did not hesitate. *'Fifty Thousand dollars to secure their concession.'*

'Fifty Thousand?' Subroto's eyes widened.

'Yes, Pak,' Baird's relief was instant, observing his senior partner's reaction to the figure. *'And, we will be involved in the drilling program,'* he added.

'What happened to the Fifty Thousand?'

'I had to pay half to the bastards down at the Mines Department,' he lied. *'I've got the rest in my account. I was going to use that for…'*

Suddenly, Subroto's face broke from ear to ear. *'To get married?'*

Baird paled immediately. *'Pipi is a wonderful lady,'* he stammered, *'and I think very highly of her.'* He was about to explain that he hoped to use the money to find more suitable accommodations when Subroto sprang.

'Wonderful, Eric!' he rose, his pear shaped body rippling as body

fat gravitated and rebalanced, *'Have you decided on a date?'*

Baird was instantly gripped with anxiety as Subroto leaned across his desk, one bulbous hand supporting his huge weight, the other extended in congratulations. Baird stood speechless, his mouth as dry as a wind-swept desert unable to offer the words that could rectify this dreadful misunderstanding. His eyes fell to Subroto's chubby fingers; dismayed when his own hand, as if of its own volition, rose to the occasion.

'N...no, Pak, we haven't... not yet!' he stammered, casting a furtive look towards the door, but knew there was no escape.

'Wait here!' Subroto ordered, forcing his bulk between desk and chair as he exited the office with surprising speed. Moments later the room filled with staff following Pipi's uncle's announcement. Baird, not yet recovered from the shock of his predicament, grinned sickly as, one by one, they offered their felicitations.

'Where's the lucky girl?' someone shouted happily, sending both secretaries scrambling for the phone.

'I am so very proud of you, Eric,' Subroto placed a heavy arm around Baird's frail shoulders. *'Pipi and all of the family will be so pleased!'*

Baird, engulfed with the enormity of what was happening, lost his balance as the room began to swim before his eyes. Before he knew what had transpired, Baird found himself stretched out on the air force General's sofa, with one of the staff administering a cold washer to his face.

'You fainted!' the girl giggled, turning to the concerned group standing quietly, blocking the doorway.

Baird blinked a number of times, frowned, rose to a sitting position and gazed at the familiar faces, then bent forward and threw up over the General's carpet.

★ ★ ★ ★

Summoned by Subroto, when Pipi Suhartono arrived within the hour awash with tears of joy, she formally kissed her fiancée on the cheek then promptly disappeared to inform friends and relatives, across the country. Baird, shocked to a state of anesthesia, was driven to his apartment where Mardidi took charge, unaware of what had transpired until a late afternoon call from Pipi revealed all, Mardidi's threats to suicide if Baird went through with it casting a gloom of morbid finality across their world.

★ ★ ★ ★

The Philippines

Alexander Kremenchug patted his forehead with a saturated handkerchief, cursing the stiflingly hot, humid reception, and the fact that the airconditioning had remained in a state of disrepair since his visit in January. He strolled slowly across to where he now knew from experience he would find his luggage, and tipped one of the porters to carry his suitcase through immigration and customs. When he approached the officious-looking officer, the man's face suddenly broke into a wide, beaming smile.

'Mabuhay, Mister Kremenchug,' the man welcomed, stamping his passport without examining the accompanying, complicated forms. Within minutes, he had completed the formalities, and was whisked through the VIP section where Sharon Ducay waited.

'Welcome back, Alexander,' she offered her cheek, and Kremenchug obliged. 'How was the flight?' Kremenchug's eyes traveled the length of her body, marveling at her beauty as she stepped away and issued instructions to the porter. Then, he recalled the trick she had pulled, and her justification for doing so.

'From Vancouver to Hong Kong, like it would never end; the last leg, a little rough coming in but, apart from that, nothing to complain about.'

'I see you've not lost your tan,' Sharon observed.

'Canadian skiing – and the slopes were virtually empty.'

'How long can you stay?'

'If it's okay, I'd like to leave by the weekend.' He flashed recently capped teeth and placed one hand nonchalantly in a trousers' pocket. 'How is the General?'

Sharon had already moved towards the exit. 'He is very keen to catch up, Alex. His health is reasonable, for a man of his age, but I would not overtire him with lengthy discussions.'

Kremenchug understood, shifting the conversation as they entered the waiting Mercedes. 'The place seems to be more festive than when I was here last?'

Sharon nodded. 'It's practically Easter. With more than eighty-percent of our population Catholic, the celebrations will be intense. Over the next week we'll have everything from re-enactments of the Crucifixion to mass flagellation – another of Spain's lasting legacies.' She looked over at her guest. 'I know that it's considered impolite to ask, but are you, by chance, also Catholic?'

Kremenchug laughed softly. 'Yes, and no.' His family had been communists; he had never stepped inside a church other than out of curiosity and, out of habit, had responded in a manner that might give him some edge. 'I was born into a Catholic family.' He hesitated, groping for an acceptable explanation. 'When I migrated to Australia, I just didn't continue with church. That's all.'

'Once a Catholic...' Sharon removed her long, pastel green gloves and touched his arm gently. 'Perhaps you would accompany us to mass while you are here?'

Kremenchug became uneasy with this thought. 'Sure, I'd be delighted,' he found himself saying. Then, looking to deflect further conversation along these lines, inappropriately broached the subject of their project. 'I trust that the General is pleased with the BGC developments?'

Sharon shot him a warning look, shaking her head, admonishing Kremenchug for his slip in the presence of the driver. They then continued with their journey to General Dominguez's home, in silence.

★ ★ ★ ★

'Ah, Alexander, we have been waiting for you to return,' the General greeted Kremenchug warmly. 'Sharon informs me that you have been most successful in your endeavors.'

Sharon lifted a glass from the polished, silver tray as Alfredo moved forward offering drinks.

'Yes, General,' Kremenchug felt uncomfortable dressed in the white, *Barong Tagalog* Sharon had left in his rooms with a note that he might wish to try the traditional Filipino shirt. 'The project is moving ahead smoothly.' He glanced over at Sharon. 'Thanks to your niece's planning.'

Dominguez choked on his wine. When he recovered, he moved to Kremenchug's side and gripped his upper arm then shook it playfully. 'She is very clever,' he said, eyes twinkling brightly.

'Now, General,' Sharon's voice carried a noticeable warmth. 'We must give Alex most of the credit.'

'Nonsense,' Kremenchug responded, obviously pleased. 'It wasn't all that difficult.' Sharon led her uncle to his favorite chair then took a seat alongside, waiting for Alfredo to disappear.

'Might be an appropriate time to brief the General on where we're at, Alex.'

Kremenchug noted the change in her tone and nodded, leaning forward with clasped hands as he cleared his throat.

'Well, you know most of it already, Sharon. At this point in time everything has been agreed, subject to a number of requirements being met. BGC shareholders will still have to be given the opportunity to vote on acquiring Dominion Mining's Indonesian leases, and support the company's proposed restructure. But, as far as we are concerned, that will only be a formality once you have proven up the value of the leases.'

'Where does that leave us now?' she asked, mainly for the General's benefit so that he could hear it all, first hand, from Kremenchug.

'As I suggested, we can safely assume that the shareholders will agree. The original stockholders will retain around forty-five percent of BGC, the remaining stock will be issued to your nominees and, of course, twenty percent of that value, or eleven percent, will be mine.'

'What about the options?'

'That will be set as part of the overall proposal.'

'So, effectively, full control?'

'Yes.'

Sharon lit a cigarette then blew a cloud of smoke into the air, before continuing. 'Your man over there did well to have the initial survey license issued so quickly.'

'He had the funds to get it done,' Kremenchug offered, matter-of-factly. 'Will you go to Jakarta to oversee the mobilization?'

Her face became serious. 'No. I'll go into Samarinda once the drilling team and the equipment is loaded and ready to move up the Mahakam. I intend keeping a very tight rein on this operation, Alex. Everything depends on what happens next, in the field. I will wait until the rigs, equipment, personnel and all supplies are in Samarinda before I arrive.'

'Why aren't you using a Filipino drilling crew?'

Sharon viewed Kremenchug with hidden disdain. 'It's a matter of credibility, Alex. Best to have other drillers there, seen to be carrying out the work. It would be risky to have too many people aware of what's going on. We'll have two expatriate drilling assistants on site during the initial phase. That's enough.'

'Do you still want Eric Baird on the team?'

'I'd like to keep him around as he could be helpful. Besides, we'll need someone to take responsibility if it all goes sour.'

'He's not too keen to go.'

'Offer him more money,' Sharon suggested.

Kremenchug nodded in agreement. 'Okay, I'll fix it so that he goes.'

* * * *

Chapter Eleven

May 1994

Bandung – Java

'Aduh, dong, gue pasti basah!' Nani complained, threatened with being drenched. Angela waited patiently as water trickled down through the torn umbrella, and onto Nani's shoes.

'It will blow over,' Angela's words were of no comfort to Nani, her new jeans now damp from the knee down, the flimsy, but colorful parasol inadequate protection against the rain. Angela hugged her friend as they ran down the broken footpath into Pasar Kota Kembang, a narrow lane lined with shops and stalls. There, with some protection, they slowed their pace, venturing out into the intersection where the lane connected with the streets of Jalan Asia-Afrika, and Jalan Dalem Kaum. At that moment, the dark sky flashed with a brilliance only a tropical thunderstorm could deliver, the air shattering with a terrifying, piercing crack as deep, rolling thunder collapsed upon the city's populace, momentarily stunning them all. While winds fought to escape the surrounding Parahayangan Mountains, another lashing downpour followed. Raindrops beating helter-skelter across the provincial capital brought traffic to a standstill, leaving Angela and Nani pressed up against a partially covered doorway, shielding their eyes with dreaded anticipation of the next lightning strike. Wind tugged at their clothes, the deafening roar of

thunder interspersed with the brilliance of lightning kept Nani huddled closely to her friend. Then, without warning, the wind fell across the plateau as the gods cast their attention elsewhere and, within minutes, the storm was gone, the young women faced with crossing ankle deep water, flooding the street.

'Let's cross here, and go down to Bandung Indah,' Nani suggested, the capital's luxurious shopping plaza off City Hall, where those who could afford to do so, hang out. During Colonial times, Bandung was often referred to as 'the Paris of Java' because of its ambiance and sophistication but, now, the provincial capital was nothing more than just another overly crowded, Indonesian city. Lost amidst the rush to build glass and aluminum towers, Bandung's once magnificent legacy of tropical deco architecture and charm, dating from early Dutch times, was now disguised by the city's town-planners' enthusiasm to approve structures mimicking avant-garde trends, the Bandung Indah Plaza no exception to these conflicts in design.

Angela took Nani's hand firmly as they waded, shoes in hand, across the wide street, barely reaching the other side when a jeep ploughed past, throwing spray in every direction.

'Sialan lu!' Nani turned with ferocious look, cursing the driver. Angela laughed happily, dragging her friend up the stairs and into the plaza. No sooner had they entered when the skies collapsed into darkness once again, and what had commenced as a distant, low rumbling roll, tumbled into the capital, rupturing the inner city air, with spears of terrifying lightning dancing behind the tumultuous groans.

'Kopi, yo!' Angela urged, leading the way to one of their favorite haunts, her call for coffee welcomed by Nani. The pair found a table, ordered coffee and cream cake, then settled back to observe the constant flow of pedestrian traffic passing through the mall. Most, Angela knew, were window shoppers as Bandung's community was not wealthy. Although centered amongst rich plantations and supported by the government-owned aircraft industry facilities, the city was, nevertheless, basically an educational center. Students flocked to Bandung from all corners of the Republic, most with limited

financial resources. Angela recognized a younger student from her campus, observing the girl's flirtatious movements as she guided past a number of foreign men. Angela felt saddened by the number of undergraduates who depended on part time prostitution to see them through college, grateful that her Dayak community continued to support her studies so vigorously. Soon, Angela would be in a position to repay her people for their trust, and generosity, a commitment she had given to her father, and one she intended to keep.

As Angela's eyes continued to roam the café, she was attracted to a young child of around six sitting alone, expressionless, her lips quivering as if she were cold, her presence engulfed in an epileptic aura of anxiety. Concerned, Angela looked for the girl's parents and, seeing none, rose and moved quickly to the youngster's side, catching the child in her arms as the seizure took hold.

'Nani!' Angela called to her friend, *'try and find her mother!'* with which, Nani scoured the area quickly, and then hurried through the café to check the toilets – returning empty-handed when she found no one there.

'We'll just have to wait here,' Angela held the girl to her chest, the child's convulsions easing with the student's comforting words.

'I saw her mother leave and go into that shop over there,' a patron leaned across to say, *'in fact, there she is now!'*

Nani sprang to her feet and made her way outside, alerting the woman to her daughter's condition. They returned, together, Angela suddenly angry at the mother's indifference.

'Enny, have you been a naughty girl again?' the woman scolded.

'Is this your daughter?' Angela continued to hold the child, rocking her softly from side to side.

'Enny, what have you been up to? I can't leave you alone for one minute!'

'She fainted,' Angela glared at the mother.

'Enny, come along now, I'll have to take you home.' The woman reached down and gripped the girl's arm. Frightened, the child, pulled away.

'Are you sure you're her mother?' Angela challenged.

'Of course! Now, Enny, get up, I'll have no more of your tantrums. We're going straight home!'

She stepped forward, furious, but Angela turned, protectively, continuing to stroke the child's short, black hair. She looked into Enny's eyes, reassuringly and, placing a hand gently against the side of the young girl's head, started to hum. By now, the other patrons had fallen silent, observing the conflict, expecting the child's mother to explode. Then, a most curious thing occurred as the young, Dayak woman started to chant, softly, the prayer she had learned in her native, *Penehing* dialect. Angela swayed softly, the hypnotic effect of her movements and voice mesmerizing the spectators as they, too fell under her spell, their minds suddenly oblivious to the cacophonous crowds outside. The soothing, melodious effect relaxed the child and, as Angela completed her chant, she turned back to face the mother. *'You should take her to a doctor,'* she reprimanded. *'Enny fainted, and had convulsions.'*

'She's done this before,' the woman remonstrated, making a more determined effort to drag her daughter out of Angela's arms. *'It's purely attention seeking.'*

Angela rose, her face a mask of wrath. *'Your daughter is a very sick child.'*

'She is not! She is faking!' the woman's voice rose, the café's customers now following the unusual confrontation.

'You should never have left her alone!' Angela's tone now matching that of the child's mother, several of the café's clientele whispered to each other and staff ceased serving, observing the exchange.

'She strayed away by herself,' the woman became openly hostile, waving a threatening finger at the trembling six year old.

'You are a bad mother to blame your child.' Angela again stepped back slightly, keeping Enny out of her mother's reach. Someone called out for her to leave the child alone and, aware that she was the center of unwanted attention, Enny's mother snapped.

'Give me my daughter!' she shouted.

'Not until you promise to take her to a doctor!' Angela refused, her friend, Nani, anxious with the escalation in hostility.

'*This is none of your business -give me my daughter!*'

'*No!*' Angela pulled back as the woman lunged, Enny burying her head into Angela's shoulder, terrified of her mother.

Enraged, the woman screamed abuse, smashing cups and plates to the floor, then reached over to an adjacent table, in search for something else to throw. When she turned, wielding a knife, Angela stepped back cautiously, the throng of café guests unwilling spectators to what happened next. Enny's mother's hand flashed, her face contorted in manic expression, the outstretched palm of Angela's free hand blocking the attempt, without any apparent sign of physical contact. In that brief, emotionally charged moment frozen in time, lightning struck the mall missing its ineffective conductor, throwing the building into semi-darkness – and sending the Plaza's stand-by diesel generators coughing into gear, the power-outage throwing the mall into pandemonium. In the ensuing darkness, someone screamed, '*She's got a knife!*' Compounding the chaotic scene, panic-driven customers yelled and shoved in their stampede to escape, sending tables and chairs crashing around, spilling crockery, smashing plates and delicately designed coffee sets onto the floor.

In the days that followed, and only in the company of close friends, many of those present would recall hearing a woman's near-death, chilling scream pierce the scene, their nostrils assailed by a suffocating, wild stench that permeated their surrounds. A terrifying, hoarse cawing cry added to their confusion as the surrounding air was ruptured with the sound of a bird's powerful wings beating overhead and, above all this, a commanding voice shouting, '*No!*'

In that instant, power was restored, the lights blinking their momentary message, before fading once again. Someone called out that there was smoke, the mere mention of fire plunging guests recklessly towards the exit. Meanwhile, deep in the Plaza basement, the switching gear which sent generators automatically across to the internal power distribution system in times of such crisis, failed, minutes passing before the system could be manually reset, the flow of electricity finally restoring the plaza with light. An audible sigh of relief swept through those unable to escape via the congested exit, many standing around straightening disheveled hair and clothing, as some sense of normality slowly returned to their surrounds.

★ ★ ★ ★

Enny's mother was clearly in shock, her face smothered with bewilderment as she stood, lost in unfamiliar surroundings, appearing genuinely surprised, when it became apparent that her daughter was there. She stepped forward with outstretched arms, her eyes suddenly filling with tears, Angela, in what appeared to be an about face, willingly surrendered Enny to her mother, who then clutched the child, smothering her with kisses. *'Where have you been, Enny?'* she asked, *'I have been looking everywhere for you!'* And then, *'Are you all right, my darling?'*

Nani rubbed her puzzled eyes, trying to make sense of what had transpired. She looked at Angela, questioningly, and then back at the woman to see if she was still armed.

'You should take your daughter to a doctor,' Angela moved forward and stroked Enny's soft face. *'She is not well.'*

Nani stared at Angela, struck by her friend's peaceful glow.

'I have been meaning to,' the woman found herself saying, a tear falling from her cheek.

'Then you should do it, and soon,' Angela advised, her voice now soft and reassuring.

'I will, thank you,' the older woman agreed, edging closer, and when her fingers touched Angela's arm, she looked searchingly into her eyes – that moment of recognition becoming clouded with doubt. *'This may sound strange, to you,'* she said, *'but I'm sure we've met before, somewhere.'*

Angela shook her head, and placed her hand comfortingly on the mother's. *'I don't think so.'* Then, she squeezed Enny's tiny hands, and glanced at Nani. *'We're late. We should go. Goodbye Enny,'* she pretended to pinch the girl's tummy, playfully, nodded knowingly at the woman, then led a confused and apprehensive Nani outside.

★ ★ ★ ★

The weather had cleared, the two undergraduates now standing near the corner of Jalan Martadinata and Merdeka, where tempting, mouth-watering aromas wafted towards them from the roadside, *sate* stalls. Rows of red-hot, charcoal-fired braziers lined the footpath, offering Madurese, Javanese and an array of Sumatra's famous Padang food. Further down the street, vendors offered *comro* to passers-by, the mashed cassava filled with fermented soybean cake, a favorite amongst the students. The street offered a virtual smorgasbord of national dishes, from deep-fried *Tokek,* the colorful, tropical lizards sought after for their curative properties for those who suffered skin diseases, to fruit bats, believed to improve sexual prowess.

Nani held a polystyrene cup filled with palm sugar-sweetened, coconut milk in one hand, and a roasted cob of corn in the other. Although still struggling to understand what had happened in the Plaza earlier, Nani avoided mentioning the incident, content to wait for Angela to offer an explanation, when she was ready. During the four years she had come to know Angela, she had learned that her friend was indeed very special, and experience had taught her not to press.

★ ★ ★ ★

That evening, as Angela sat alone on her veranda, captured in contemplative mood, she gazed up into the early evening, equatorial sky, recalling the events of that day. She was reminded of those first lessons her father had given, when he'd explained the power of the shaman, and the extraordinary gift generations of Daus had enjoyed. Angela recalled his warning, that although she, too, had been blessed with this *'tenaga-dalam'*, the inner force phenomenon would become more apparent and demanding as she matured, and could be lost, forever, if not nurtured in the traditional way.

The morning's confrontation with the belligerent woman could have been avoided, she knew – but Angela was also aware that she had inherited her father's stubbornness, reminding herself to be more circumspect in the future, even with him looking over her shoulder.

Angela peered up at the stars as a puff of wind caressed her face, and she inhaled, the suggestion of jasmine in the air filling her with pleasure. Her body relaxed, then became lethargically still as another form of energy commenced flowing through her body. Angela willed her mind to clear, slowly drifting into an altered but blissful state of consciousness, where she remained, until morning.

★ ★ ★ ★

Jakarta – Manila

'It's very professionally presented,' Baird admitted, grudgingly, when asked for his opinion with respect to Sharon's initial drilling program. Kremenchug had phoned from Manila, to discuss mobilization plans.

'Any problems sourcing the rigs and other equipment?' Kremenchug asked.

'There's some second hand gear coming in from Western Australia. I've already had a sniff around and there doesn't appear to be a problem, providing we put our stamp on the equipment quickly. The rest is coming directly from the Philippines?'

'Yes,' Kremenchug confirmed, 'Sharon has organized a couple of small containers carrying laboratory sampling equipment.'

'Tell her to make sure it's packed tight,' Baird warned, 'the handling gets rough as hell once gear is moved along the Mahakam.'

'I'll remind her.'

'And she's going to ship the rest of the inventory from Manila?'

'Yes, Eric, she's highlighted what you have to source locally.'

'Yeah, I've been through the list. Don't see any problem with most of it, but I'll still have to dig around for some of the items. I'll let you know if I have problems there.'

'What about the riggers?'

'I thought Ducay was bringing her own team?' Baird had discussed this earlier with Kremenchug.

'No she decided that it would be best to recruit some locally experienced hands.'

'I can get a couple of guys I've used before,' Baird offered.

'Then you'll go?'

'I didn't say that.'

'But you will?'

'No.'

'I need to have you on site, Eric.'

'I really don't want to go back into the field just yet,' Baird resisted.

'You need to get out there and do this drilling for the Filipino,' Kremenchug sounded convincing. 'Besides, it's time we all made some real money. Come on, Eric!' he cajoled, 'for you, this should be a walk in the park.'

Baird had anticipated Kremenchug's request to participate in the drilling operation. Had it not been for Subroto's insistence that he respond to the invitation to marry Pipi Suhartono, the suggestion that he might return to Longdamai would never have been considered. Now, given the opportunity to avoid confrontation with his sponsor, Baird was seriously considering accepting Kremenchug's offer to participate in the new project. Numbed by the hand-rolled, *ganjah-kretek* combination cigarette and far too much rum the evening before, Baird's eyes began to swim casually, the familiar marijuana affect, soothing.

Baird was unaware of Sharon Ducay's indirect control over P.T. Kalimantan Gold (Indonesia), the approved operator for the Contract of Work. A Filipino-based, foreign accountancy firm operating in Jakarta had provided nominee directors conditional, of course, that they be appointed to oversee the mining venture's financials. Baird had pressed Kremenchug as to why Sharon had been appointed Operations Manager, but his associate had been less than forthcoming. Having never met Sharon Ducay, Baird drew the conclusion that Kremenchug had become involved with this woman and was now paying the price for his indiscretions. Baird also concluded that this was the primary reason that his services were required on site, as the Filipino obviously was incapable of overseeing the project without the benefit of an in-country expatriate, experienced in dealing with the Indonesians. He expected that a few days in the Kalimantan jungles would see the end of her. 'I'll think about it, but only if Ducay isn't placed in charge of the operation,' he said, one hand searching for the joint inadvertently dropped somewhere amongst the cushions.

'What does it matter who's in charge?' Kremenchug's voice rose in pitch. 'If you don't go, Eric, then I'll just have to find someone else.'

'Yeah, sure, Alex – we both know there's no one else you could trust to get the job done,' came the response. Then, after second thoughts Baird added, 'You could hire some of the local geos from the Mines Department.'

'Come on, Eric,' he appealed again, 'do this and I'll take care of you. Okay?'

Having successfully retrieved what was left of the joint, Baird could now smell smoke. He stuck his hand down the narrow gap, cursing loudly when the tip of his fingers came into contact with the burning seat. He dropped the phone, yelled for Mardidi then retrieved the handset. 'You still there, Alex?'

Kremenchug shook his head in dismay. 'Yes, Eric, I'm still here. Will you go back out to Longdamai and help Sharon oversee the drilling? If it all works out, we'll be able to recover what we've lost on the BGC shares,' and without hesitation added, 'plus some.'

Baird looked over at his companion, Mardidi, the suggestion that Pipi Suhartono might be lying in his place, and he reluctantly agreed.

'Okay,' Baird's voice echoed down the line. 'I'll get the drillers and do the work. But,' he added, 'we'll need to throw them some dollars.'

Kremenchug did not hesitate. 'What do you need?'

Baird thought for several minutes – Kremenchug could hear the man wheezing.

'It's a six months project. Let's see; three expats, plus local support crews, around two hundred grand should see them right.' Sharon Ducay's budget had allowed for more, but Baird knew that her costs were still to come out of that.

'Two hundred thousand?' Kremenchug was stung. 'Isn't that a little over the top?'

Baird was prepared. 'Not unless you want to bring in a team from offshore – and you know what that will cost. You'll have to pick up airfares, hotel accommodations, get the drillers work permits and make allowance for a much longer lead time to mobilize. As it is, I'll really have to scratch around to find drillers with all the work that's going on. With the number of survey teams stomping around over in Kalimantan, we're lucky that there are rigs and men available right now. Even two hundred thousand might be a bit light on,' he suggested.

'Okay,' Kremenchug capitulated, although not entirely convinced that Baird was not sticking it to him, 'get started and I'll transfer the funds.'

Baird was having none of that. 'I'll need it all up front, Alex, or there'll be no start.' He waited, a marijuana-induced smile crossing his face as he imagined Kremenchug worrying whether the amount was enough to tempt him to take it all and disappear.

'What about mobilization costs?'

Baird again referred to Sharon's budget. 'We'll need to set up something with the rig owners so that we hire their equipment and make monthly payments into their account. I'll nut something out over the next days and let you know what we're up for. Ducay's budget seems about right, so best you make arrangements to send a another hundred grand to cover mobilization costs as well.'

'I'll have the company transfer fifty thou for you and the drilling teams, and another fifty to cover mobilization.'

'No, I'll want at least half of both budgets, now.'

'Okay, Eric,' the voice in Manila responded, 'you'll have a hundred grand in your account by the end of the week, another hundred when you've mobilized. The balance will be paid at the end of six months. Fax me a copy of the rig rental agreement and I'll set up regular transfers to cover that and other budgetary items. Sharon will bring additional funds for contingencies.'

'Fine,' Baird was smiling, 'I'll get back to you in a couple of days.'

★ ★ ★ ★

Eric Baird sighed and accepted that although the commitment he had just made which would take him out of Pipi Suhartono's way for at least six months, it would also place him in a most indelicate position with General Subroto. He decided not to visit the office unless it was absolutely necessary, terrified of the arrangements Pipi's uncle was so determined to put into place.

Encouraged by an imminent change in fortunes, Baird finished the remaining joint, rolled over onto his side and nudged Mardidi, bringing him awake.

'Ada apa, sih?' the slim-framed Javanese appeared groggy, rising on one elbow, asking what was happening. Baird assumed that he would have been eavesdropping on their end of the conversation.

'We're going back to Kalimantan,' Baird said, slowly, losing focus as his attention slipped.

'Why?' Mardidi asked, with growing concern. He had no difficulty in recalling the recurring malaria bouts suffered during the first and fateful excursion. Eric Baird moved closer to his companion, his foul, stale breath an offence to clean air. Mardidi's eyes looked for an escape, opting to raise a pillow to the lower half of his face to cover his squeamishness.

'We have a drilling contract on the Upper Mahakam,' Baird revealed, playfully grabbing the kapok pillow and tossing this into the air.

Mardidi was trapped. *'Why should you be happy with this?'* He leaned to one side and raised his head to see how much of the Bacardi had been consumed that afternoon.

'I'm not.' Half-heartedly, he threw the pillow at Mardidi, hitting him in the face. *'But, at least we're going on the payroll again.'*

'When?'

'Immediately. I'll be able to give you that money for your family by the weekend.'

'How much?' His partner's foul breath no longer of consequence, Mardidi moved closer with this news and started tickling him furiously.

'Whatever you want!' Baird cackled, grabbing his lover and wrestling him to the floor.

* * * *

Chapter Twelve

AUGUST 1994
LONGHOUSE VILLAGE
UPPER MAHAKAM RIVER

'How is Nuri?' Jonathan Dau wanted to know, anger and deep resentment running through his veins as he looked down on the badly beaten, Dayak village girl.

'She will live, if she has the spirit,' the old woman attending the teenager answered philosophically, whilst gently sponging wounds. The girl's body bore evidence of a most savage attack. Blows to her chest caused a shattered rib to pierce a lung, and cigarette burns to her lower abdomen determined that her attackers could not have been of Dayak origins.

'Call me the moment she regains consciousness,' the chief ordered, leaving the gray-haired woman to care for her grandchild. Jonathan then returned to his quarters and summoned the youth who had discovered Nuri, questioning him, before gathering with the other elders to discuss the attack. Then, he waited, praying that the young woman would survive and reveal who was responsible for the brutal rape and beating. An hour passed, then another, a child sent to fetch Jonathan tripping over in her excitement as she ran down the main Longhouse corridor and into the meeting hall, where he had been waiting for word. The chief's long, powerful strides took him to the little messenger's side and, with one arm, scooped her up, placing the child on

his hip then made his way back to where the injured teenager lay.

For Jonathan, it was now obvious that Nuri had but a short time left; with each lung-racking cough she dribbled blood. Under the anxious eyes of her family, the *dukun* sprinkled potions over her body whilst calling upon her ancestral spirits to come to her side, the air so filled with grief it was clear that those gathered accepted she would surely die.

★ ★ ★ ★

Nuri had been one of a number of young villagers to leave the Longhouse environment, attracted to the mining camps downriver where they sought employment as laborers, cooks and other domestic roles. Although saddened by this exodus, Jonathan did not blame them for leaving in search of greater opportunity, understanding why the village girls ventured down to the mining camps, enticed by things foreign, and the money they were offered. He knew that once they had fallen into the trap, only an occasional few would return to their communities – those with child, abandoned by their transient lovers and others, who had been dismissed because of injury, sent home without compensation.

Nuri had gone to seek work at the newly established drilling camp downstream.

When her broken body had been discovered, the camp manager ordered the youth to take her away, indifferent to her condition. The young Dayak man had requested assistance and, when none was forthcoming he had stolen a powered, rubber dinghy then transported Nuri home to their Longhouse. It was not until the family had removed what was left of her clothing did the extent of her injuries become apparent. When word spread through the village that she had been raped, the mood amongst the men was one of retribution, the call for all Dayaks to abandon working at the mining site, all but closing the foreign operation down.

Jonathan observed her eyes flicker, and he leaned forward to speak.

'Can you tell us who did this, Nuri?' he whispered, holding her

hands reassuringly, brushing strands of matted hair that had fallen over her brow. She struggled to respond, her throat offering only a hoarse, gurgling rattle and she choked, her eyes struck wide open in panic as she drowned in her own blood. Jonathan felt her hands go limp and he knew that nothing could save her now. *'Rest now, Nuri,'* he spoke, softly, placing a cloth across her eyes.

Amongst the babbling, background cries of anguish, Nuri recognized the *dukun's* voice and heard the soft, beating wings of a bird, and her weightless spirit was swept away by an intense calm, the crushing pain in her chest extinguished as she surrendered her physical presence, and drifted peacefully away. Jonathan, sensing the moment of transition, closed his eyes and commenced the chant for the dead, to lay Nuri's spirit to rest.

The Longhouse community tendered to her remains as custom dictated, after which Jonathan slipped quietly away and climbed to his own, special place set high amongst Bukit Batubrok's cloud-draped slopes, where he remained in meditation throughout the night. He prayed for Nuri, pleading that her ancestral spirits view the young woman with kindness and accept her into their world, asking also for guidance to reveal those responsible for her death. Enveloped in darkness, Jonathan lapsed into an induced trance in which he transcended his earthly surrounds, his spirit wandering the forests and rivers and floating through moonless skies across seemingly endless seas. In his *latihan* state the shaman was transported to a place where men gathered around, shouting and screaming with strange tickets held high in their hands, the scene convoluted by an image of others, their pockets filled with gold, sobbing as they lay incarcerated in cells. And he saw Nuri standing in the distance, waving, calling out to him and, as Jonathan approached he cried out in dismay, the face of the dead girl transposed with that of his daughter, Angela.

Even after Jonathan returned from his spiritualist wanderings he remained anxious for his daughter's life. The shaman hurried back to his village and made radio contact with Samarinda, and sought their assistance in contacting Angela to see if anything had befallen her. Later in the morning a hook-up was successfully arranged and

Jonathan spoke to his only child, the relief in his voice immeasurable once his fears had been allayed. Confused by his dream, he concluded that Nuri's spirit was hostile and would remain so until her death had been avenged. Jonathan decided to visit the mining campsite to determine for himself what had transpired there. Two days passed when word was sent from the drilling site that one of the expatriate drillers had died, ostensibly of alcoholic poisoning.

That evening Jonathan returned to the mountain and again induced the *latihan* state, the dreams that passed through his mind confirming that the dead driller had indeed been the one responsible for Nuri's demise. With his concerns for Angela assuaged, Jonathan Dau, chief and shaman to his Dayak community, smiled for the first time in months as he strolled back through his beloved forests to his Longhouse enclave.

★ ★ ★ ★

P.T. Kalimantan Gold (Ind.)
Drilling Site – Mahakam River

'Screw this! I'm not working this fucking rig without laborers!' Calvin Alderson picked up a rock and angrily tossed this at a stand of dieseline fuel drums, missing widely.

'What's the bitch doing about it?' Carl Patrick's dark mood matched that of his fellow expatriate driller, the pair deeply annoyed with not only having to do most of the manual work themselves, but also the Filipino's refusal to replace their late colleague.

'She sent one of the locals back downriver to recruit more men from his village, before she pissed off to Samarinda.' Patrick looked on sullenly as the other driller selected another rock, tested this for weight then discarded it.

'I knew this would fucking well happen!' Alderson kicked at the ground with his heel, his eyes filled with loathing as he looked over at the camp. 'What a fucking mess!' He removed a grease-stained cap, running a filthy hand through his wiry mat of hair. 'Why don't we just shoot through and leave them to it?'

Carl Patrick wiped sweat from his brow with a forearm, dragged heavily from somewhere deep inside his chest then spat, aiming the phlegm at a discarded packet of cigarettes. 'Don't tempt me.'

'When Ducay gets back, let's go and read her the riot act. Tell her we want time off to go down to Samarinda for a few days.'

'Think she'd let us hitch a ride out on the chopper?'

'Nah,' the other roughneck snarled, returning to reality, 'she's not about to let us go.'

Patrick's wandering hand found a used toothpick in a trousers' pocket, absentmindedly playing with this as he considered their position. 'You don't get the feeling that's just what the bitch wants?'

'Whaddya mean?'

'Shit, Cal, she's done nothing but fucking complain about us since she set foot on site!'

'You reckon she wants us out?' Alderson squinted, cocking his head at his workmate.

'Dunno. But what she really wants is a bloody good screwing, ' Patrick had, by now, retrieved the dirty toothpick and was worrying something loose from between his teeth.

'Do you think Baird's been slipping her one on the side?' Alderson's comment brought a half-hearted laugh in response.

'That bastard may have tickets on himself, but it's not bloody likely. I could hear the dirty little turd-burglar going twenty to the dozen with that poofter mate of his the other night.'

'Mardidi?'

'Yeah.'

'No wonder Baird's been wandering around half the bloody time like a stunned mullet!'

'Had a drink with a guy in the *Tanamur Bar* who used to know of Baird when he was married,' this from Carl Patrick, referring to one of his regular haunts in Jakarta. 'Said that his missus back in Melbourne tossed him out, cause he couldn't get it up.'

Alderson thought about this for a moment, then twisted his face in disgust.

'Doesn't seem to have that problem with little boys.' He returned to breaking the heavily crusted soil with the heel of his boot. 'Why do you reckon she won't let anyone into the shed?'

Carl Patrick glanced over in the direction of the locked shed built from a half-container. A galvanized roofed lean-to had been erected alongside, providing shade as a comfort station for Sharon Ducay. She had caused a rift by declaring her premises off limits to all.

'Hasn't Baird been in there yet?'

'Nope.'

'Wanna go and take a peek while she's away?'

Alderson shook his head. 'Nah, that'll only give her an excuse to shunt us out.' He stretched, then put both hands on his hips. 'Got any of that rum left?'

Patrick raised an eyebrow, then glanced at his watch. 'Yeah, why not – I've had enough of this shit for one day.' With that, the two men strolled slowly away from the silent rig, the intense tropical heat beating down on their backs as they made their way up the slope to where their tents had been erected.

★ ★ ★ ★

East Kalimantan Provincial Capital – Samarinda

Within hours of the expatriate driller's death, Sharon Ducay had radioed Samarinda and called for a chopper to airlift the man's body to the local morgue. She had not even considered the alternative, as a voyage downriver would require at least two days. The only available helicopters fitted with sufficient fuel reserves to cover the distance were based in Balikpapan. Sharon had already made one such return flight, the month after establishing the mining site when she felt the necessity to speak privately with Kremenchug, by phone. Once mobilization had been completed and the heli-rig and ancillary equipment finally transported to the site, supplies of the Jet A1 refined kerosene fuel had been placed on standby at the Longdamai camp, for such an emergency. The helicopter had arrived within hours, Sharon certain that the surrounding jungle had filled with inquisitive eyes, as Avtur was hand-pumped into the aircraft.

Uneasy with leaving the field operations, but also accepting that it was in her interests to convince the provincial authorities that the driller's death had been by misadventure, Sharon boarded the Bell JetRanger for the two-and-a-half hour flight.

She had accompanied the deceased to the provincial capital, but even wrapped with heavily scented sheets prior to departure, the driller's remains still reeked of death. Sharon had filed the necessary reports at both the hospital and police headquarters, and made arrangements to have the body flown to Balikpapan, then on to Jakarta. The authorities had treated the incident with indifference and, as they concluded that there was no question of foul play, accepting the cause of death as alcoholic poisoning, Sharon was able to complete the formalities within the day. Tired, and desperate for a bath to cleanse the lingering memory of the driller's corpse, she booked into the Mesra Hotel, had her clothes taken to the laundry, bathed and ordered room service. Then she spent the evening in air-conditioned comfort preparing for the return charter flight arranged to depart at 0600 the following morning.

★ ★ ★ ★

As the helicopter beat its way back across the dense jungle Sharon could see the devastation inflicted upon the rainforests, the bleak tracts of scarred landscape carved across the earth below, stretching as far as the eye could see. Unconcerned, she turned to her notes, re-checking geological data obtained from core samples extracted at the Longdamai site, determined now to accelerate her plan to initiate the 'discovery' process in view of the expatriate driller's death. Although tempted, Sharon resisted spiking the core samples until then, conscious that she had to build credibility by demonstrating that a serious drilling program had been undertaken, before any discovery occurred.

Within two weeks of first establishing camp, drilling samples were already being taken and recorded. Sharon had opted for the rotary air blast-drilling program (RAB), a percussion method that grinds the rock by vibrating vertically, then uses air under compression to blow the residual to the surface, where the sample is collected. It was her intention to build a credible report based on a series of shallow holes drilled to around forty meters, doctoring the samples in such a way as to demonstrate a consistency in the findings.

Sharon's program required for a progressive increase in the amount of gold to be 'discovered' in the primary drilling operation. She understood the import of credibility associated with such findings, determined to demonstrate that the integrity of the recovery process had been monitored within industry parameters at all times. Sharon had decided to send samples to a well recognized Australian laboratory where further analyses would be conducted, the results surely to support her own findings at the Longdamai site. She knew that there would be skeptics but, with such objective, supportive evidence and the locality of the site, Sharon was convinced that her scheme would succeed.

The helicopter yawed momentarily, thumping along through the morning's thermals, sending Sharon scrambling for the contents of her aluminum briefcase as these were scattered across the metal floor. Ignoring the pilot's admonishing shake of his head for not wearing the safety harness, Sharon gathered her papers, relieved that the hypodermics and half-kilo gold bars secreted inside her case had not been dislodged, her fingers tapping the securely sealed, glass jars which contained solutions of potassium cyanide, essential to the successful execution of the salting process.

Sharon Ducay's plan was not dissimilar to that used by Kremenchug's associates in the West Australian scam more than a year before. She would simply ensure that there would be a gradual 'spiking' of the samples, her methodology creative in its original conception. Prior to the project's commencement, Sharon had considered a number of means to introduce the gold traces, but before taking a final decision, she had to know precisely what the geology could offer, and what drilling methods would be employed. Once the RAB system had been decided upon, she had then set about developing a methodology for introducing the gold into the samples.

Industry practices required that samples be split, with one being sent to a recognized analyses laboratory for testing, the other, retained under lock and key at the mining site in the event future scrutiny be deemed necessary. Sharon intended introducing minute gold samples into the potassium cyanide solution which would dissolve the dust, permitting her to inject the metal through the canvas bag and its plastic liner, directly into the sealed samples. When the cyanide solution evaporated, the gold particles would appear throughout the sample as if in a natural state.

Sharon reflected on the foreign drillers engaged on site, accepting that she had to be very, very careful to avoid raising their suspicions. The remaining Australians, Eric Baird, Calvin Alderson and Carl Patrick would remain only for the primary drilling operation, their presence an integral part of her scheme. Sharon expected that, although cautioned, they would be amongst the first to reveal information relating to the high-yield results, counting on their lack of integrity to create even greater interest through rumor and speculative action. Alderson and Patrick were sure to swear that the find was real, pointing to the fact that they were the onsite drillers, and that there could have been no way for others to tamper with the samples.

Her thoughts then shifted to her fellow, on-site geologist, Eric Baird, and she frowned, undecided as to how long to keep him on contract. Although indifferent to the man's peculiarities, Baird's behavior around the camp *was* causing distractions and Sharon detected growing hostility between him and the drillers – a situation she needed to correct.

★ ★ ★ ★

P.T. Kalimantan Gold – Longdamai Drilling Site

'Tell that miserable son-of-a-bitch to get his skinny, little rear-gunner's arse out here now!' Carl Patrick bellowed, the combination of his foul breath and the Bundaberg Rum too much for the frightened, *Modang* laborer.

A week following Sharon's return from Samarinda, a number of down-river villagers had trickled into the camp, having learned that work was available. As this was *Penehing* territory, the *Modang* workers were too terrified to venture outside the camp's perimeters.

'Baik, Tuan,' the small-framed man kowtowed to the drilling superintendent, terrified of the Australian's reputation for striking his men. The villager turned and fled, running across the slippery surface, falling and cracking his knees against larger rocks that were strewn around the disorderly site. He ran to the geologist's tent, and called from outside. *'Tuan!'* his voice reflecting the urgency of his mission. *'Tuan Eric!'* the laborer called again, this time stepping back to permit the expatriate room to exit the four-man tent.

'What is it?' Mardidi came out of the tent in half-crouched position, bending to avoid the myriad of ropes he inevitably tripped over at least once each day.

'Mas Mardidi,' the field hand was relieved to see the *Tuan's* companion. At least he could make himself understood. *'Tuan Carl is very angry. He sent me to invite Tuan Eric to join him down where we are drilling.'*

Mardidi's eyes searched the scene, his eyes inadvertently coming into direct contact with the intimidating bully, designated drill boss. His sphincter muscles tightened with the eye contact, and he turned to retreat back inside the tent where Eric Baird lay dehydrated from yet another bout of the dreaded stomach infection that had beset the expatriates at this site.

'Eric,' Mardidi sat down beside Baird and touched his forehead again. *'Are you strong enough to get up?'* he asked, knowing that he was not, but hoping that the man would find the energy to do so.

'What is it?' Baird's slurred voice was without strength. He had swallowed more tablets than would have been recommended for two with this affliction, and had added a couple of painkillers to boot.

'It's Mister Carl. He wants you to go down to the drilling pits.'

Baird understood, but knew he was just not up to staggering around the site, even for Carl Patrick. He closed his eyes, questioning his judgment at having given the drilling to this group. *'Tell him I'll be down shortly,'* he ordered, hoping that the problem, whatever it might be, would disappear quickly and leave him in peace.

★ ★ ★ ★

In the months since Eric Baird's interlocution with Alex Kremenchug had led him to commit to undertake the fieldwork with Sharon Ducay, the Australian geologist had begrudgingly acknowledged that the Filipino was capable of conducting the operation even without his support. Although he questioned Kremenchug's insistence that he remain on site, Baird elected to continue, if for no other reason than to avoid both his partner, Subroto, and the General's niece, Pipi Suhartono.

Mobilization had not been without incident. Gathering equipment and supplies in Jakarta for shipment to Balikpapan had presented the usual problems with freight forwarders – space being finally secured on board a smaller, coastal freighter, by paying a premium to the captain. The vessel had then been delayed, throwing Baird's schedule into chaos from the outset. Once in Balikpapan, the shipment had been trucked to Samarinda, where his three expatriate drillers had been waiting for more than a week. Sharon Ducay had arrived soon thereafter on a direct charter flight from the Philippines, assuming operational control over the programme. Baird had hired a houseboat and a number of small barges to take them up as far as the rapids, from where the difficult work commenced, shifting the cumbersome RAB transportable rig, compressors and ancillary gear to the site by helicopter, where the Australian drillers would reassemble the equipment.

As labor had been one of their primary concerns, Baird had suggested that they employ the *Modang* river people to assist with the transportation and, once on site, approach the local villagers for their labor force. Before departing Jakarta, Baird and Sharon Ducay had spent considerable time discussing the operation by telephone and facsimile, reaching agreement where to establish the main camp, prior to his departing the capital. They had sent a small group ahead to prepare for the main body's arrival, and to scout for local workers. For a brief time, there had been a reasonable semblance of harmony between drillers and the local laborers who had followed the expedition upstream, to the site. Mardidi however, had a falling out with one of the expatriate riggers and, from that moment, the atmosphere around the camp had deteriorated dramatically.

As he lay listlessly listening to others moving around the camp Eric Baird wondered if he might have succeeded in another field of endeavor, wishing at that particular moment that he had followed his mother's advice, and studied law.

★ ★ ★ ★

He had never been overly interested in sports at school, his small, frail frame often the object of both bullies and pedophiliac teachers of the middle persuasion. Academically, he was not considered overly bright, although he did manage to achieve sufficient grades to enter university. Severely influenced by a demonstrative mother, he selected what was then perceived as the easiest degree course to undertake, and then proceeded to fail Geology One. He repeated the year, managing to scrape through under the guidance of an overly doting tutor, then went on to complete the course, graduating without any significant degree of achievement.

Baird's foray into the Indonesian mining arena had been by accident. Once he had graduated from university and bowed to family pressure by acquiring a wife, his ensuing, colorless life had left him directionless, and unmotivated. Early into his marriage he had become addicted to alcohol, the resulting divorce not entirely linked to his incapacity to maintain his role in the marital bed, but more his growing adoration for the father figure who had given him his first job, as a geologist. From the outset, Eric Baird strove to emulate the Fine Gold Search NL company chairman, the effort keeping him in near poverty as he shopped for wristwatches, cufflinks and other jewelry, acquiring duplicates of those worn by his mentor. As gold was considered fashionable at the time, Baird discarded his silver Seiko and purchased an Omega, identical to that worn by the chairman. Months later, when the chairman strolled into the office sporting a new, platinum Cartier wristwatch, having forgone his customary gold accoutrements, Baird went out immediately and purchased the same make and model, throwing himself into even greater debt than before.

Although the company secretaries sniggered at the young geologist's ways, his capacity to produce results out in the field gained him considerable respect with management. He became the company's golden boy, selected to go overseas with the Sydney-based mining group – rewarding their decision by returning a most professional and positive survey for their Malaysian concession areas. Baird had moved over to Sarawak to take up the post of senior geologist, taking with him the chairman's undying support.

It had been Baird's glowing submission that had served to punch the company's stock up noticeably, permitting the Board to raise sufficient capital to maintain their high-flying lifestyles as mining entrepreneurs. It was through this corporate relationship that he had first met Alex Kremenchug, whose meteoric rise to Fine Gold Search NL's board had not only raised eyebrows amongst Sydney's mining elite, but also provided corporate rumormongers with sufficient gossip material for them to dine off for weeks. As Kremenchug continued to consolidate his position within the gold mining company's corporate structure, his influence over operational decisions precipitated management changes, and Eric Baird's most-favored position as senior geologist came under threat.

In time, Baird learned how to deal with Kremenchug whose penchant for expensive acquisitions and a good time at shareholder's expense, ultimately resulted in his resignation from the Fine Gold Search NL Board. A company secretary overheard the heated argument when Kremenchug was ordered to step down for inappropriately disposing of shares without advising the relevant authorities at the Sydney Stock Exchange. Weeks later, Kremenchug had appeared in Jakarta, relegated to the lesser position of company representative. Since then, their relationship had grown only as a result of their interdependency, with Kremenchug consistently dragging potential investors into the country, while Baird's role was to provide supporting evidence that the mineral prospects Kremenchug touted around were viable prospects of considerable potential.

Now, after so many years treading the jungles being bitten by ticks, mites and having his blood sucked by leeches, he found himself desperately in debt. He had been counting on the BGC shares to buy a small house in the mountains outside Jakarta, a place he and Mardidi could call their own. Of course, Baird accepted that ownership would have to be in Mardidi's name, as Indonesia Law did not permit foreign ownership outside a very limited number of condominiums. His mind turned to his companion, and Mardidi's incessant requests for more money to be sent home to his *kampung,* back in Java. Apparently, there had been another death in the family. It seemed to Baird that Mardidi's clan had lost so many uncles, aunts, cousins and other family members over recent years, there would be few relatives left. Baird was convinced that he had covered the costs of funerals for the same identities on more than one occasion and, as he lay there with this thought annoyingly amongst his wanderings, he was reminded of the expatriate driller's death just days before.

When the man had joined their group in Jakarta he had reeked of alcohol. The three-man expatriate drilling team had troubled him at first, but once they had arrived at the site and settled down to the task at hand, he dismissed earlier concerns, relieved that the drilling was proceeding without any meaningful incident. He was, however, aware that these men had brought a substantial supply of alcohol to the site. When it became obvious to Baird that the drillers' stocks had been depleted, the men's surly behavior prompted Baird to seek Sharon's approval to send Mardidi back to Samarinda in one of the longboats, under the pretext to source additional medical supplies. Mardidi had returned three days later with the shopping complete, totally humiliated by Carl Patrick when it was discovered that he had not purchased the specific brand of Bourbon the driller had ordered. Fortunately, Baird's intervention prevented his companion from taking a beating, an act that would surely have resulted in the driller's contract being terminated – and a possible walk out by all.

It was around that time that a number of Dayak village girls had appeared seeking work. The drillers had all winked at each other, and given the teenagers laundry and other chores to keep them occupied. The following morning, no one noticed the absence of one of the girls until a young man discovered her badly beaten body, hidden under bushes some distance from the drilling site. The camp atmosphere had immediately turned tense, and the young *Penehing* men, in their thirst for revenge, had attacked the *Modang* laborers. One of the victim's fellow villagers had then stolen the expedition's inflatable dinghy, and taken the girl back to her Longhouse. Baird recalled that the girl had been the one signaled out by the now dead driller, and wondered if the man had somehow been implicated in the villager's demise. Whatever had happened, Baird resigned himself to never learning the truth as the driller had overdosed himself on alcohol, his body hurriedly transported to Samarinda, for examination and burial. The remaining two expatriate drillers, Patrick and Alderson, had become extremely belligerent with the additional workload, Baird suspecting that they were about to quit. When he heard Mardidi calling for him once again, wearily, he dragged his debilitated body out of the tent and shuffled down to the excavation site to face yet another dose of drillers' vituperation.

★ ★ ★ ★

Sharon Ducay remained lethargically still, standing within the shaded area quietly observing the hostile body language exchanged between the drillers and Baird, their voices carrying up the slope to the makeshift verandah. Overhead, the tarpaulin flapped intermittently under occasional, dry mid-afternoon gusts and she glanced out at the weather, discouraged by the absence of cloud. With the most economic of movements she raised a cloth to her brow, removing minute droplets of perspiration before these could gather and flow. Gently dabbing the nape of her neck, Sharon suppressed a sigh, reminding herself why she was there – and the golden harvest that awaited her.

Her attention drawn back to the feuding expatriates, Sharon revisited her decision not to remove Baird, agreeing that she had made the correct choice – even if this had meant sacrificing harmony within the camp. To further reduce the possibility of suspicion, Sharon had decided that it would be best to have him around the site when she spiked the samples, and when the results were returned. She looked over at the shed which housed the bagged material, impatient to begin, her thoughts interrupted as Baird's advancing figure crossed into her peripheral vision.

'What's up?' Sharon asked, nodding in the direction of the drillers. Eric Baird came to rest under the shelter, wiped an arm across his forehead and shook his head disconsolately.

'They want more money,' he replied, with disgust in his voice.

Sharon remained standing, arms crossed as she responded to the geologist's response. 'How much?'

Baird licked dry, cracked lips, as if considering the question. 'They're demanding another grand a week.'

'Each?' Sharon was taken aback by the drillers' audaciousness.

'No. A grand would cover them both.'

'And that's it? They'll stay on until we finish up here?' she asked.

Baird frowned. 'You're not seriously considering giving it to them, are you?'

Sharon unfolded her arms and, with fingers hooked inside the top of her trousers, shrugged resignedly. 'Tell them we'll give them what they ask. But,' she continued, 'make sure they understand that this will be treated as a bonus, to be paid only if they remain to the end of the drilling program.' She could see that Baird was not at all happy with her decision and, without hesitation, added, 'There will be bonuses for all who see it through, Eric.'

Baird's frown slipped down his face, slowly turning into a narrow grin. 'You're all right, Sharon,' he offered, 'they'll go for that.' He looked back down the slope at the men, wondering how long it would be before they made other demands. 'I'll go and tell them now.'

Sharon permitted Baird no more than a few steps before calling after him.

'Make sure they get the rest of those sample bags up into the shed before they finish up today,' she insisted. Satisfied that Baird would see to this when he nodded, Sharon returned to her quarters where she reexamined the most recent analysis reports carried out by the Western Australian laboratory, then settled down to wait for the drillers' shift to finish for the day.

★ ★ ★ ★

'Here, top this up,' Calvin Alderson held a metal mug out, and Carl Patrick obliged, reaching over and pouring the rum carefully from cross-legged position. Alderson took another swig, grimaced, placed the mug down and lit a cigarette, then leaned back on one elbow as the alcohol and nicotine took effect. The temperature had not dropped noticeably with the advance of evening, both men now resting outside their tent.

'We should have held out for more,' Patrick complained.

The other man considered this, scratched his unkempt hair, and nodded in agreement. 'Shouldn't have let that little prick take it to her. Should've gone to her ourselves.'

Patrick squinted as his eyes roamed the camp, the late afternoon rays piercing lofty treetops across the river. He spotted the object of their conversation moving determinedly through the camp towards the storage shed dressed, as always, in jodhpurs and a matching, armless, khaki jacket. He continued to observe as Sharon Ducay hesitated before the compact building, unlocking the door and disappearing inside without so much as a glance back. Annoyed, the driller shook his head as the door closed behind her, then dragged heavily from deep inside his throat and spat, throwing a lump of phlegm over one shoulder.

'She's over there checking up on us again,' he griped.

The other driller cast a casual glance in the direction of the shed, and his lip curled. 'The bitch doesn't mind showing that she doesn't trust anyone.'

Carl Patrick sneered. 'We ought'a rip up there, and slip 'er one.'

Calvin Alderson's mind had already gone there. The local laborers would not guard her back and Baird would be unlikely to intercede.

★ ★ ★ ★

Unaware that the two drillers' fantasy moved dangerously towards becoming reality, Sharon busied herself, syringe in hand, bending down to examine each of the sample bags she would inject with the potassium cyanide gold solution. Sharon was conversant with the three basic sampling rules involving integrity, transparency and posterity. The industry demanded that, in order to preserve sample integrity after extracting and logging samples, these should be placed in sealed, numbered plastic bags and dispatched as quickly as possible to an independent assay laboratory.

Sharon knew that she was in danger of exceeding acceptable time parameters, but believed she could justify the delays in sending samples away due to the difficulties arising from the isolated location – another reason why she selected this site. As for transparency, Sharon was prepared to demonstrate to future inspection teams that the practices carried out were in accordance with industry standards, assured that the drillers and her assistant geologist, Baird would support the results. With respect to the question of posterity, Sharon would provide access to all records and duplicate samples retained on site believing that this would satisfy future inspections and potential detractors.

Confirming that the samples matched her log, she inserted the industrial size needle through the canvas covers, puncturing the plastic liner and releasing the clever cocktail directly into the powdery samples through the hypodermic needle. Sharon was particularly careful to match bag lots which would be shipped to the laboratory for testing, with those which would be retained on site for future examination and comparison. An hour passed and, with her task completed, Sharon placed the hypodermic and other evidence inside her leather case, unlocked the door to leave and stepped outside, startled when confronted by the expatriate drillers blocking her exit.

Sharon had been in similar situations before whilst working in African and Canadian mining camps, her eyes quickly assessing the situation. She looked beyond the two men for help, realizing immediately that none would be forthcoming. 'What can I do for you gentlemen?' she challenged, mustering whatever bravado she could.

'Calvin 'ere wants ya to join us for a drink.' With Carl Patrick's slurred delivery Sharon's heart sunk; handling drunken drillers could be a difficult task.

'Yeah,' Alderson joined in, 'Whaddya say?'

Sharon knew where this was leading. Her grip firmed on the

briefcase, instinct suggesting that she use this to defend herself against attack, abandoning this thought when reminded of the contents. Her eyes dropped to the bottle in Alderson's hand.

'Sure,' she said, extending her free hand, 'why not?'

Patrick's face cracked from ear to ear and he reached over, pulling the bottle free from Alderson's grasp, and offering the rum to Sharon. She accepted the alcohol with her free hand, rolling her wrist over the neck and in one continuous motion, slammed the bottle against the shed, then stepped forward and swung the jagged remains across the closer man's body, to within inches of his face.

'Now get out of my way!' she hissed, adrenalin pumping as she waved the broken bottle threateningly. 'I mean it!' she shouted, relieved when both men shied away.

Sharon advanced slowly, her confidence building as the drillers retreated. With arm extended, she made her way cautiously around the men, walking away with an eye over her shoulder in the event they might charge. Willing her knees not to fail her, Sharon strode across to her quarters and locked herself inside, where she remained, considering how to resolve what might be an ongoing threat with the drillers. The men needed women – but she could not afford another incident with the local tribes. Also, this was not the time to alienate the drillers as they would unwittingly add further credence to the find.

The following morning Sharon called Baird, a sulking Alderson and an apprehensive Carl Patrick, advising the surprised trio that they could all take a few days off, sending the expatriates down river to Samarinda where they would airfreight the first batch of compromised samples for analyses. And, hopefully, return to complete the remaining two-months drilling program required to substantiate the results, which Sharon was confident would flow from the independent laboratory.

Days later, when Baird returned with the drillers, harmony was restored to the camp, Sharon then deciding to send the men downriver on a regular basis to reduce the possibility of future conflict.

* * * *

Chapter Thirteen

BANDUNG
WEST JAVA

The auditorium burst into applause as Stewart Campbell finished addressing those present, the intensity of their appreciation growing in crescendo as Professor Hadi Utomo, Dean of the Faculty for Mining and Natural Resources Studies, made his way across the dais. The audience rose, their mark of respect more directed to the ageing professor than his esteemed guest.

'Gentlemen and ladies,' he commenced. *'Over the past days we have been privileged to have witnessed…'*

Angela Dau and Nani were amongst those who had attended the closing speech, delivered by the American, Stewart Campbell.

'Aduh, Gela!' Nani placed her hand on Angela Dau's and shook it with excitement. *'He is even more handsome than before!'*

'Sshh!' Angela grabbed her friend's hand, squeezing it hard. *'Listen to what the Bapak is saying!'*

'He's looking our way!' Nani grabbed Angela's knee with her free hand, and squeezed.

'Stop it!' Angela whispered, pretending to dig her nails into Nani's wrist, while her eyes remained transfixed on the speaker.

'Oh my God!' Nani slipped into one of her usual routines, grossly exaggerating the situation. *'He smiled at you!'*

'Nani!' Angela shushed, her voice sufficiently loud to cause a number of other attendees to turn their way. *'Now see what you've done!'* Angela applied pressure to Nani's wrist, Nani's eyes opening wide in astonishment.

'You're hurting me, Gela!' she pulled away, miffed, rubbing her wrist.

'Then behave yourself.' Angela slipped down into her seat to conceal her embarrassment.

'...and, in conclusion, on behalf of the Bandung Institute of Technology, I wish to thank my dear friend and colleague, Mister Stewart Campbell, for his closing statements tonight.' Again, the hall erupted, a number of male graduates towards the back whistling their appreciation. The delegates and guests were then invited to an adjoining hall where soft drinks and *makanan kecil* were served, the exodus immediate as the throng headed for food.

Overhead fans turned lazily, gently moving rising warm air around the building as white-jacketed waiters drifted amongst the guests, offering chicken, beef and goat *sates* to the eager crowd.

'Come on, Gela,' Nani urged, *'Let's get some food!'* and dragged Angela directly to where Stewart Campbell was engaged in discussion with the Dean, Stewart immediately breaking off their conversation, struck by the approaching graduates dressed in traditional costume. His eyes fell upon Angela, her breathtaking beauty a picture that would remain with him forever.

Angela's classical features were accentuated by her rich, black hair, combed back and rolled into a bun, then held in place with gold, filigree pins. She wore *kain kebaya;* the colorful, hand-woven Dayak sarong wound tightly around her waist covering all but her high heels – the matching, fine lace, long-sleeved blouse tailored to follow the lines of her graceful figure as she stood, *selendang* over one shoulder, facing the Dean.

It was Nani who spoke first. *'Maaf, Professor,'* she apologized, *'but Angela and I were wondering if Tuan Campbell is returning to Jakarta tonight?'*

Angela broke loose from her friend's grasp, embarrassed by Nani's shameless behavior. She stole a glance at Campbell, the defiance in her eyes triggering a memory.

'Angela Dau, isn't it?' he asked, recovering his composure. *'We had a brief encounter during my last visit.'*

'Yes, Mister Campbell,' Angela stepped to one side permitting a waiter to advance.

'The Dean tells me that you graduated with distinction. Congratulations.'

Angela, surprised that her name had been raised in conversation, asked, *'And how is that of interest to you?'*

Stewart wiped peanut sauce from the side of his mouth. *'Your name came up.'* He caught the Professor's eye then continued. *'The Dean was most complimentary in his remarks.'*

Before Angela could continue, her friend jumped in. *'My name is Nani, Mister Campbell,'* she smiled sweetly, *'I graduated with Angela.'*

'Then I should congratulate you as well. Did you also take environmental studies?'

'Yes, but I did not do as well as Angela,' Nani revealed.

'Don't believe what she says, Stewart,' the Dean warned light-heartedly, *'these two topped their class, and are like inseparable twins.'*

Stewart raised the glass of sickly, oversweet soft drink he had been juggling in his hands. *'I wish you both success with your careers. And, no, I am not returning to Jakarta until Monday.'*

Nani was quick to take advantage of the opportunity. *'We are having a party later,'* and before Angela could prevent her best friend from making a complete fool of herself, Nani asked, *'and we would like to invite you to come.'*

Aware that he had been staring at Angela, Stewart turned to the Dean for support. *'And is the Dean also going to attend?'*

'Of course, Bapak Utomo is invited,' Angela intervened. *'Will you come, Pak 'Tomo?'*

Professor Hadi Utomo laughed generously. *'I don't think so, ladies, but thank you.'*

'*And Mister Stewart?*' Nani persisted.

Stewart caught a wisp of a smile cross Angela Dau's lips, now totally captivated by her beauty. '*I'd be delighted*,' he agreed, as other members of the Faculty joined their group.

'*Ah, I see that our handsome guest has captured the two prettiest girls on campus!*' the senior lecturer placed his hand on Stewart's shoulder.

Angela peered across the gathering and waved.

'*Mister Stewart is coming to our party,*' Nani bragged, Angela taking her arm to lead her away. '*Wait, Gela,*' she propped, frowning at her friend. '*Where are we going to meet?*'

'*Where is the party being held?*' the Dean asked, '*I could drop you off if you wish, Stewart?*'

'*No, no, that won't be necessary, Pak 'Tomo,*' Nani insisted, then addressed Stewart Campbell. '*We can meet you and show you the way if you like?*'

'*Well, if it's not too far out of your way. What time should I be ready?*'

'*How about eight o'clock – that will give you time to finish up here. Where are you staying?*'

'*Savoy Hoyman,*' Stewart replied. '*Is that okay if we meet there?*'

'*Wonderful!*' Nani responded enthusiastically, resisting Angela's impatient tug. '*We'll pick you up at eight.*'

By now Stewart was acutely embarrassed by the attention he was receiving. '*Sure, that's fine. I'll wait for you in the lobby.*' And, as the two started to move away, he added, 'but no '*jam karet', okay?*' the reference to 'rubber time', a national characteristic, causing the others present, to laugh. Stewart continued to view the pair as they moved through the hall, catching one final glimpse of Angela as she glanced back before disappearing altogether, swallowed by the crowd.

* * * *

Stewart expected that Nani and Angela would be late. He left a message with reception and wandered into the Garden Bar where he waited, listening to the light entertainment, while nursing a vodka tonic. The atmosphere was light, Stewart's thoughts transported back to how this scene might have been during colonial days, imagining Dutch plantation owners sitting in these same cane chairs, pampered by white-clad servants, the air filled with classical music and familiar tropical scents.

Halfway through his drink he looked up, and noticed Angela's friend, Nani, standing alone, looking lost in the hotel surrounds. He rose, waved, signaled the waiter for the check, and moved across to greet the young woman.

'I'm sorry I'm late,' Nani offered, *'have you been waiting long?'*

'No,' Stewart answered, looking beyond the pretty girl, for Angela. *'Are you alone?'*

'Yes,' Nani explained, *'Angela will meet us there.'* She waited while Stewart signed the bill, then turned to lead the way out into the front courtyard where she had left her motorbike. Stewart took one look at the machine and shook his head.

'We'll go by taxi,' he said, waving at the horde of eager drivers, negotiating an hourly rate before shepherding Nani into the car.

They drove through Bandung's congested boulevards and into the poorly lit suburban streets, the driver following Nani's directions as she guided the taxi into a maze of narrow lanes, finally coming to rest outside a whitewashed, two-story dwelling. Even before alighting from the vehicle, Stewart could hear the distinctive sound of party revelry emanating from the building. He instructed the driver to wait, then followed Nani inside, shaking hands and smiling as he eased his way through the overcrowded room to where Angela Dau stood, engrossed in conversation with a handsome, Javanese youth.

'Quite a gathering, you have here,' Stewart introduced himself to Angela's companion.

'Well, for most of those present, it's a celebration,' the host explained, *'graduation party...'* His voice trailed off as Nani took the young man by the arm and dragged him away, leaving Stewart alone with Angela.

Dressed in jeans and high heels, with her jet-black hair pinned to one side accentuating her aquiline features, Angela's natural beauty was breathtakingly striking.

'Nani wasn't certain that you would come, Mister...'

Stewart Campbell cut her off, mid sentence. *'It's Stewart, Angela,'* he said, *'you make me feel like an old man.'*

Angela laughed, her hand gently touching his arm. *'Stewart it is, then. Would you like something to drink?'*

'No, not just yet,' he glanced around to confirm that the party was dry, experience telling him that it would be most unlikely to find alcohol on the premises. At best, he knew there might be a few bottles of rice wine sitting forgotten, somewhere in the larder, but he was not anxious to drink anything that sweet.

'Will you be returning home, now that you've graduated?' he asked, maintaining the conversation.

'Not immediately,' Angela replied, *'I will be spending a year in Jakarta, with the Office of State Ministry of Environment.'*

Stewart recalled that, as the problems of population and the environment became more complex with Indonesia's rapid development and increasing prosperity, this office had been created two years before, with Sarwono Kusumaatmadja as its first Minister.

'Practical training?'

'Yes.' Her expression suddenly became serious. *'The Ministry has established a number of organizations to handle environmental management, and the Dean has arranged a position for me there.'*

'Then, no doubt we'll see more of each other in Jakarta?'

'Are you a member of any of the organizations involved with the Ministry?' she asked, surprised.

'Sure,' Stewart advised, *'all foreign mining interests have to clear their projects through the appropriate departments, before they can proceed on their Contracts of Work. From time to time, I've been engaged to evaluate some of the submissions on behalf of the Ministry.'*

Angela appeared impressed. *'Have you done any work in the Mahakam area?'*

'Yes,' Stewart found it necessary to bend down to speak as the noise level rose. *'Why don't you come around to my office when you move to Jakarta, and I'll show you what we've done, to date?'*

'Said the spider?' she teased.

Campbell laughed. *'No, the invitation was sincere.'*

'Your Indonesian is really quite fluent,' Angela commented, changing the subject, *'did you learn to speak Bahasa from a girlfriend?'*

Stewart crumbled into laughter, unprepared for such directness.

'No, Angela, believe it or not I actually took lessons.' But he could not resist adding, *'Although, I have to admit, there have been a number of friends who helped smooth the rough edges for me.'*

'Well, they certainly did that,' she acknowledged, a hint of seriousness in her voice, *'I don't imagine there would be too many foreigners who have made the effort that you have.'*

Stewart enjoyed the compliment as he prided himself at the level of fluency he had achieved. *'Can you speak other languages?'* he asked.

Angela did not hesitate. *'Well, apart from Bahasa Indonesia I'm still fluent in my own dialect, Penehing Dayak. I have studied English here at the Bandung Institute but it's difficult to find anyone to practise with.'*

'We can use English now, if you wish?' he offered.

'No, not now,' she replied shaking her head, *'besides, it makes me think too much and I'd end up with a headache.'*

'Well, we can't have that. Perhaps we'll have the opportunity some other time, then?'

'When are you returning to Jakarta?'

Stewart shrugged. *'I had planned on going back sometime tomorrow but, as it's the weekend, I thought I might stay, and drive back on Sunday.'* He smiled warmly at Angela. *'Are you busy over the weekend?'*

Angela looked up, feigning surprise. *'Are you inviting me out?'*

Stewart did not hesitate. *'Yes, why not? We could have lunch at the Homan, if you like.'*

'Are you sure you wouldn't prefer to ask Nani?' she baited.

He shook his head. *'I'm sure.'*

With her name still on their lips, Nani stepped up and took Stewart's hand.

'Ayo, handsome, dance with me!' Nani cajoled.

'Don't know if I am up to it,' Stewart pleaded, but Nani dragged him away in spite of his protests.

★ ★ ★ ★

Angela was impressed; Stewart Campbell swayed rhythmically, his tall, thin form standing head and shoulders above the others in the cramped quarters and she smiled back to him, acknowledging the wink he threw in her direction. When the tempo slowed, Angela was surprised at her sudden pang of envy as Nani pressed closer into Campbell's body, relieved that he held her at bay. The tempo slowed further, Angela pleased when the American abandoned the floor and a dismayed Nani, returning to her side.

'This is one of my favorites,' Campbell explained, taking Angela's hands in his. She did not resist, suppressing a giggle when she sighted Nani's playful face and poked tongue from the corner of her eye, moving into his arms as the lights dimmed, and the golden voice of Bob Tutupoly singing *Wuduri,* filled the room. Their bodies pressed together as the number dancing increased, and Angela found herself humming the familiar song, content to be where she was at that very moment. She felt her partner's hand move down to her waist and did not resist, but moments later, conscious of how close their bodies had become, she pulled away – suddenly uncomfortable with what she was feeling.

The cloying fragrance of clove cigarettes hung heavily in the air as the lounge continued to fill, guests spilling out into the garden, when someone inside turned the tape off and broke into song, drawing instant applause from all present. Campbell knew that it was considered mandatory to participate in the traditional, *jail-jali* verse, opting immediately to join those who had made their way to the jasmine-filled air outside. He steered Angela away from the room, unaware of the envious glances and comments which followed, relieved to be able to converse, finally, without shouting. There, in the courtyard, with the moon casting its spell from above, they stood facing each other, Campbell increasingly drawn by Angela's intoxicating presence. Separated from the other guests by a bougainvillea-covered trellis, he moved close to her side, raised her hand and kissed her softly on the cheek, unaware that he was entering into a courtship ritual with the psychic and mystical world.

'Please...please don't,' Angela turned her head, anxious that others had seen.

Stewart continued holding her hand. *'I'm sorry, Angela. That was stupid of me.'*

Slowly, she withdrew her hand from his. *'Do you always try to kiss girls you have just met?'*

'Only when they are as beautiful as you,' he tried.

'You should ask, first,' the reprimand was aloof.

'You might have said no,' he argued in defense.

'I would most definitely have said no,' Angela crossed her arms in defiance.

Suspecting that this was not true, Campbell decided on another tack. *'Shall we start again?'*

'I don't think so,' she leaned back and peered into another corner of the garden.

'Well?' he asked, *'will you come to lunch with me?'* But he could see that she was now distracted by the couple sitting together on white, wrought iron garden chairs under moon-cast shadow not ten meters away and, out of curiosity, followed her gaze.

'They are taking putauw,' Angela whispered, her hand gripping Campbell's forearm tightly.

'Putauw?' he asked, unfamiliar with the expression.

'It's heroin,' she explained, turning away from the scene. *'Let's go back inside, please.'*

'They're taking drugs, here?' Campbell's voice was filled with concern. He had read that Indonesia's drug users now exceeded three million, most of who were still in their teens.

'Yes,' she sighed heavily, *'it's all over the campus. That,'* she paused, *'and shabu-shabu.'*

'Which is?' Stewart was confused, recalling that the term referred to the thinly sliced Japanese beef dish.

'Crystal methamphetamine,' Angela shook her head, glancing once more over at the university students. *'They call it shabu-shabu – I don't know why.'*

'Do you want to leave?' he asked, placing both hands comfortingly on her upper arms. Her flesh was cold and he turned her gently, away from the distressing scene.

'Yes, but you can remain if you wish.'

'I'll take you home,' he offered, urging Angela with one hand cupped under an elbow, leading her back inside.

Campbell led the way, squeezing through the congested mass. Someone dug his ribs playfully, and he turned.

'Hey, 'Gela,' Nani called, *'you're not leaving already, are you?'*

Angela stretched, leaning close to her friend's face and whispered something. Nani glanced outside, and nodded unhappily.

'Will you be alright for a lift if we leave you here?' Stewart all but shouted.

'You can come with us now, if you want,' Angela suggested, accepting that it would be most unlikely that Nani would want to leave, even if drugs were being taken on the premises.

'No, 'Gela. I'll be all right. We can catch up later if you like.'

'Okay, 'Ni,' Angela patted her friend's hand, *'but be careful of what you are drinking – promise?'* There had been a spate of incidents with female students being drugged, then raped.

'Sure, 'Gela,' Nani agreed, *'I'll be careful,'* immediately falling back into the rhythmic swaying motions demanded by the intoxicating music.

Stewart escorted Angela out through the entrance and front gate where his taxi driver congregated with a number of others, leaning against their vehicles enjoying the sounds emanating from inside. Caught off guard, the man leapt to open the taxi's door for his fare.

'Would you like to go straight home or come back to the Savoy Hoyman for coffee?' Stewart Campbell asked. Angela seemed to consider her options before responding.

'You don't think it's too late for me to be visiting a hotel?'

'We can sit in the lounge and talk for a while, if you wish. I can have the driver take you home when you're ready.'

'I've never been inside the Hoyman,' she said, *'and I'm not really comfortable being seen entering a hotel, particularly at night, and especially…'* her voice trailed off, Stewart detecting her embarrassment.

'Especially with a foreigner?' he quipped, his face then cracking wide in the semi-darkness.

This was greeted with an uncomfortable pause, and then, *'You're not offended?'*

With this, Campbell reached over and squeezed her hand gently.

'No. Not at all. If you prefer, I could drop you off first, on my way?' Angela agreed, and gave the driver her address.

The taxi headed back towards Bandung central, Angela in pensive mood. Then, as the driver slowed and pulled into the student accommodations' gravel driveway, she turned to Campbell and said, in the clearest English, 'I hope you understand, Stewart, but I don't want you to have the wrong impression about me.'

'It's okay, Angela,' he assured her. 'How about I meet you here tomorrow, and we go out somewhere for that lunch?'

Angela then fell back into Indonesian, whispering so the driver could not hear. *'Thank you Stewart, I would like that. You could keep this taxi so you won't get lost.'*

'I'll be here around midday, then.' Campbell moved to exit the car as Angela opened her door, the vehicle's interior immediately lit with a soft yellow glow.

'Don't get out,' she asked earnestly, *'it's getting late.'*

Stewart reached into his wallet, Angela's face instantly clouding, misconstruing the imminent gesture.

'Please, don't!' she all but shouted.

Puzzled, he hesitated, then slowly extracted a card and offered this to her. *'It has my cell number – in case you can't make it tomorrow.'*

Embarrassed, Angela accepted the card, thanked him again, and hurried indoors. Campbell's eyes followed until she disappeared, annoyed with himself for his earlier mistake back in the garden setting, but now reasonably confident that he could win her trust, given the opportunity.

★ ★ ★ ★

Alone with the abandoned foreigner, the driver wasted little time in offering to take the *Tuan* to a number of bars where, he assured, Stewart would not be disappointed with the young ladies.

'The girls are very beautiful, Tuan,' the driver urged, *'and you won't have any trouble with security at the Hoyman.'* Stewart Campbell glanced at the time.

It was still early, and he refused to spend the remainder of this evening sitting in a hotel room viewing censored television – the alternative would at least help him kill some time.

'Okay, Mas,' he tapped the driver on the shoulder, *'forget the beautiful women, just take me down to one of the local bars.'*

* * * *

Angela had watched the taxi leave from the darkness of her room, saddened that the evening had ended so. She undressed, climbed between well-worn cotton sheets and lay on her side wondering what might have been, permitting her thoughts to wander as she lay there curled alone. Recalling Campbell's soft touch, his hand now hers, as fingers traveled slowly circling her breasts then traveled down to where no man had ever been, she touched herself gently, and moaned.

Overhead, the moon's brilliance was snuffed under gathering, rain-filled clouds, and Angela fell into rehearsed trance, the day's events soon twisting into distorted imagery, before blending into impossible dreams.

* * * *

Campbell came awake with a start, his dry and scratchy throat demanding water. Vaguely, he recalled that his companion had complained about the airconditioning being too cold, the compromise resulting in their opening the suite's windows. Groping for the *Evian* water, his hand brushed the bedside thermos in the darkness – the heavy metallic thud accompanied by shattered glass causing him to pause, his compulsion to laugh a clear signal that he was drunk. Bewildered by his condition, he attempted to rise only to be coaxed back by the caress of a soft, moist, experienced tongue gliding slowly down his firm stomach, the tantalizing effect causing instant arousal. He shuddered, once, the consuming warmth of the girl's mouth teasing, moments before she mounted him, thrusting down heavily as they grunted, loins locked in heated race. Impatient, the girl placed an arm under Campbell's back and, with rehearsed motion, rolled to one side, placing him firmly on top and between her thighs, then began stroking the length of his back with long, sharp fingernails as he fought against the deep, demanding tide, rising from within.

★ ★ ★ ★

The familiar sensation of soaring high above fields and forests carried Angela Dau into the night, her mind totally devoid of earthly inhibitions. With arms spread wide she floated up into the darkness carried by unseen thermals, her excitement immeasurable as she looked down at the sleepy city's blinking lights, confused and startled by dream-fed images of Campbell lying naked, locked in love tryst with another. She paused, midair, her arms flapping violently as she fought to maintain flight, the overwhelming sense of betrayal so great she surrendered to more powerful forces, the shape now assumed that of the great hornbill as she folded her great wings and dropped towards earth as would a stone, fisted talons anticipating the kill.

★ ★ ★ ★

Campbell tensed, the first climax-driven shudder thrusting him even deeper into the girl's sensuous pool, the shrill, terrifying call which seemingly emanated from nowhere filled the room driving his partner's nails even deeper into his back as he arched and screamed in pain, then convulsed again, before collapsing, totally spent.

★ ★ ★ ★

Morning came, and Bandung's city traffic woke him with a start. Head pounding from whatever had been slipped into his drinks, Campbell rose, slowly favoring one side, squinting painfully at white lace curtains wafting lazily with the morning breeze. He was alone. Hazy recollections battled an excruciating headache and he staggered over to his briefcase in search of medication, the sudden stabbing pain running the length of his back as he moved away from the bed, sobering in severity. He turned, startled to see that he had left a trail of spotted blood on the bed, the freshly opened wounds bleeding eagerly once the sheet had pulled away, a fine black feather which had floated to the carpeted floor, going unnoticed. Standing naked, he glanced groggily over his shoulder into the full-length mirror, confused at the deep scratches evident along the length of his back. He cursed, staggered back to sit on the bed and phoned reception, requesting the house doctor. Campbell then remembered to check his valuables, relieved to discover that only the cash he was carrying was missing.

★ ★ ★ ★

'You should report this to the police,' the concerned doctor advised. *'Why didn't you call me when this happened? You should have phoned security immediately. Was it a prostitute?'*

Stewart Campbell grunted as the doctor attended to the lacerations. *'I don't remember, Doc,'* he winced, painfully, *'but I am sure that I was drugged.'*

'What did she cut you with?' the doctor wanted to know, closing the last tear.

'That's just it,' he answered, deeply distressed that this could happen to him. *'I thought she had just scratched me with her fingernails!'*

The doctor covered the deeper wounds then went into the bathroom to wash up. When he returned, his face was serious. *'When you get back to Jakarta, I recommend you do some blood tests, to be safe.'*

'Blood tests?' Stewart became alarmed. *'Why?'*

'Well, amongst other things, you should check that you have not been infected as a result of your sexual contact. And, as for those wounds, you can come down to my surgery now if you wish, and I'll give you a tetanus shot as a precaution.'

★ ★ ★ ★

The day wore on. Campbell stepped into the Fokker and gingerly lowered himself into the aircraft seat. Angered by his stupidity, he vowed to be more careful with his choice of drinking venues in the future. The aircraft banked as it climbed, low cloud preventing any view of Bandung and its surrounds, adding to his depression.

He was deeply disappointed that he had missed his appointment with Angela Dau, accepting that she was most likely offended that he had not kept the commitment – concerned that she had not called on his cell-phone. The previous evening's driver had all but vanished and, although he did eventually locate Angela's lodgings on the way to the airport, it was Nani who had greeted Stewart at the door, informing him that Angela had waited, but when he had not turned up as promised, she had gone out alone. He suspected that Angela was inside at the time, but did not press, soliciting an undertaking from Nani that she would encourage Angela to phone.

Over the following days Campbell made a number of concerted attempts to contact Angela, his interest in all matters relating to the fairer sex tempered by a severe and painful urinal infection, the result of his Bandung misadventure. After another month passed, aware that Angela had commenced work with the Environmental Agency in Jakarta, he decided not to pursue her any further, relieved when he was finally cleared in subsequent months of not having contracted the now rampant AIDS.

★ ★ ★ ★

P.T. Kalimantan Gold – Longdamai Mining Camp

Sharon resisted the temptation to burst out laughing, faced with the expression of disbelief spreading across Eric Baird's face as they sat across the desk opposite each other.

'This can't be right!' he exclaimed in astonishment, eyes darting from one sheet to another as he absorbed the laboratory's findings.

'It says so, there,' Sharon stabbed a finger in the report's direction.

Baird checked the data again, shaking his head at the results verifying the grades and the thickness of the strike zones. He rose and leaned closer to the wall graph recording drilling undertaken, adjusting his glasses as he read off the numbers, correlating these with the laboratory's findings. Baird had no reason to suspect the results, having monitored Sharon's procedures with respect to maintaining corresponding samples on site. He knew that if the samples had been tampered with during shipment, future checks would reveal that the split sample maintained at the camp would not produce identical results. It was just that he had all but given up discovering anything of real value, the years of trekking through swamps and jungle failing to produce anything even remotely resembling the Longdamai grades before him.

'It's a major strike, Sharon,' he announced, his throat dry with excitement. 'Have you released this information to anyone yet?'

The results had been couriered to Samarinda as in the past, then delivered by helicopter to the camp. Under the terms of her Contract of Work with the Indonesian Government, she was obliged to file duplicate copies of all reports with the Department of Mines.

'No. Apart from the laboratory, you and I are the only ones privy to these results. But,' she added, 'you know I can't sit on them too long, what with the mandatory reporting to the government agencies.'

Eric Baird seemed pleased. He cleared his throat, in preparation for his pitch.

'Sharon, my understanding is that the holding company, Dominion Mining is privately owned. It won't make any difference to the company how this information is released as the shares are not traded in the market.'

'Go on,' Sharon insisted.

'Well, I know it's probably a big ask but, after years of slogging around these areas without any real success, it would severely improve my own lot if you would agree that I take the information down to Jakarta...sort of bask in some of the glory, so to speak?'

Sharon suppressed a smile; Baird, like Kremenchug, was predictable. She had expected his request, pleased that her assistant continued to remain in character, his eagerness to release the data further confirmation that he in no way questioned the integrity of the results. Sharon had no doubt that Baird would also be on the phone, first opportunity, to inform Kremenchug. That she maintained absolute secrecy as to how the samples were spiked further consolidated her control over her devious associate. 'As you said, Dominion Mining is not a publicly listed company. The directors will also have to be informed as to these results, Eric, so why don't we both fly down to Jakarta and take a well-deserved break? I'll contact Dominion's director's and you can submit the results to the government.'

Baird grinned gratefully. 'Thanks, Sharon, you don't know how much this means to me.'

* * * *

In the week following their visit to the Indonesian capital, the city was abuzz with the find. Speculation as to the ownership of Dominion Mining and its Indonesian subsidiary, P.T. Kalimantan Gold (Ind.) increased, Sharon and Baird returning to Longdamai to complete the drilling program, further results suggesting that the Longdamai find had potential reserves of at least two million ounces.

Having secured the results necessary for the next phase in her audacious plan, Sharon Ducay then placed the operations on standby, paying off the expatriate drillers along with their promised bonuses, and retaining Baird on half salary. The drilling rigs were kept on standby rates, Baird agreeing to arrange onsite security not only to prevent indigenous prospectors from establishing claim over the area, but also to protect equipment, machinery and the integrity of the samples retained on location.

Then Sharon left for Canada.

* * * *

MAKAHAM RIVER SYSTEM

Part Two

THE MIDAS TOUCH

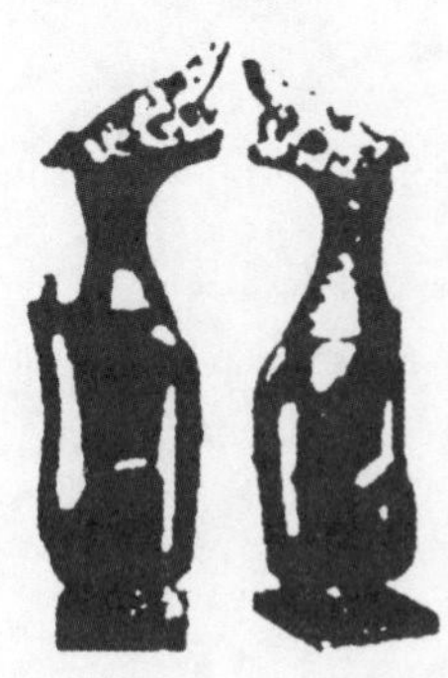

Chapter Fourteen

1995
VANCOUVER

The Vancouver Tribune September 16, 1995 – Borneo Gold Corporation Vancouver, British Columbia: Borneo Gold Corporation has announced the restructure of its resource company involved in the acquisition and exploration of mineral properties on the island of Kalimantan in Indonesia. BGC, through a share placement with offshore Dominion Mining, now effectively owns 80% of the issued and outstanding shares of P.T. Kalimantan Gold (Indonesia). PTKG holds a 1994 general exploration contract with the Indonesian government encompassing 531.2 square kilometers of primary gold exploration at the Longdamai Prospect in East Kalimantan. BGC currently maintains a contract of work (CoW) with the Indonesian Government for adjacent properties in the general area through its subsidiary, P.T. Tambang Mas Kalimantan but these have failed to produce any significant results since operations first commenced in 1990. Initial reports from PTKG drilling carried out last year estimated gold reserves at 2,000,000 ounces. BGC has also announced that it intends conducting a comprehensive drilling program over the next twelve months within the Longdamai general prospect area.

* * * *

Champagne corks popped, signaling the moment Sharon Ducay and Alexander Kremenchug had worked towards throughout the past eighteen months had finally arrived. The gathering was small – deliberately exclusive to Board members, senior management, a number of selected shareholders and an overly inquisitive journalist. Against his better judgment, Christopher Fielding had agreed for Scott Walters to attend, the consequence, a flood of irritating calls from the Press, a result of the financier's blatant attempts to talk up the value of the stock. Over the past months, the market had lifted BGC's value only marginally, but not enough for Walters or other option holders, to want to exercise their rights.

'Have to admit, never thought it would go through,' Christopher Fielding raised his glass in salute.

'There were times when I would have agreed,' Kremenchug winked at Sharon.

'Seems you've made history today, as well,' Fielding acknowledged Sharon's appointment as the company's new Operations Manager and Chief Geologist for Indonesian exploration. As President, Fielding had also cast his vote in favor of the Filipino geologist, influenced not only by her startling beauty, but also by her impressive curriculum vitae – and Kremenchug's inference that BGC's new, majority shareholder, Dominion Mining would have it no other way.

'When could we expect to see a mine?' the journalist wished to know.

'We are going to mobilize again, early in the New Year,' Fielding answered. 'The next phase will be to conduct a much wider survey and drilling program, before we can start digging huge holes in the ground.'

'You were appointed to carry out the initial drilling program?' the journalist directed this towards Sharon. 'Didn't you find it rather primitive out there?'

'Yes,' bemused by his attitude, 'to both questions.' She smiled widely, captivating her male audience.

'I'm sorry, Miss Ducay,' the journalist persisted, 'but I tried to do a historical check for the article I am writing on Canadian miners in

Indonesia. I couldn't find anything about you. How was it that you were first engaged by Dominion Mining?'

Her smile underwent a slow and total eclipse, disappearing as she pointedly raised her head and looked directly in the man's eyes, 'If you check Anglovest Reef Mines in Johannesburg and the Philippines Ministry, you will discover that not only did I work in the field for a number of years, but was also actively engaged in advising the Filipino government with respect to natural resources in my country.'

'Sorry, Miss Ducay,' the journalist wasn't taking notes, 'may I call you Sharon?'

She smiled again. 'Of course.'

'Thanks. Well, Sharon, Scott Walters tells me that this area BGC has acquired looks very promising. Are you in a position to tell me why?'

Sharon was well prepared. 'Why don't we set up something before I leave?' This was accompanied by the demurest of smiles. 'Obviously, the drilling results demonstrate that the Longdamai site is potentially one of the major gold finds in Indonesia. But I can fill you in on some of the history, later.'

'That's a great idea,' Kremenchug stepped in. 'Besides, now's not really the time to discuss the serious side of business.' He gestured to the secretary relegated to pouring drinks.

'That's fine by me,' the journalist held his glass as it was replenished, 'I'll give you a call tomorrow.'

⋆ ⋆ ⋆ ⋆

With the function over, Kremenchug heaved a sigh of relief.

'You handled that media guy well,' he complimented.

'Had plenty of practice,' Sharon said.

'With the Press?'

'No, with men,' she laughed, tossing the hair off her shoulders.

Kremenchug, suddenly wistful, was embarrassed that she caught him staring.

'Something wrong?' she asked, with a deliberate tilt of the head.

'No,' Kremenchug replied, with a touch of genuine sadness, 'it's just something that crossed my mind, that's all.'

Sharon recognized the look, inwardly pleased that she had this effect on men.

'How is your wife?' she asked, bringing Kremenchug back into line.

He shrugged. 'No change on that front.' And then, 'Will you have time for dinner before flying out on Sunday?'

'I'm leaving tomorrow, instead,' she disclosed.

'Why so soon?'

'I want to visit the General again before returning to the field and I think it wise to avoid the inquisitive Press.'

'You can still do that.'

'No point in remaining here, Alex; there's plenty still to do before drilling recommences.' She looked up into his face, knowingly. 'Once we've achieved what we set out to do, who knows what the future might bring?' the deliberate suggestion enough to carry Kremenchug forward.

'When will you arrive back in Samarinda?'

'On schedule,' she promised, her mind already elsewhere.

'Would you want me to come over and visit the site sometime?'

Sharon, caught off guard, showed her surprise. 'Why?' There was nothing that he could contribute and a great deal that he might disrupt.

'Thought it might be an idea, that's all,' he moved forward to light Sharon's cigarette. 'It'll be tougher, this time around.'

Sharon raised her chin, sending a thin stream of smoke upwards, towards the airconditioning vent. 'I know,' she said, accepting that the operations would come under close scrutiny. 'That's why it's best that *you* don't visit the site.'

★ ★ ★ ★

Road Town - Tortola British Virgin Islands

True to her word, Sharon did depart Vancouver the following morning – but her destination was not the Philippines. Instead, she flew to Los Angeles and purchased a ticket for Puerto Rico to complete the next phase in her grand scheme. Once in Puerto Rico, Sharon purchased another round ticket, this time for a thirty-minute flight over the Caribbean Sea, to Beef Island Airport, which adjoins the British Virgin Island of Tortola. A short taxi journey took her to the capital, Road Town and the Village Cay Marina Hotel, where her booking had been arranged through the offices of the locally based law firm, Rankin, Daworth & Double. She went directly to her suite and phoned Charles Daworth confirming her appointment, showered, changed into a cotton trouser suit, then visited the lawyer's offices.

★ ★ ★ ★

'Welcome to Road Town, Miss Ducay – we meet at last!' Sharon had established Dominion Mining Inc through these offices, the arrangements put into place via written instructions. For a fee, Charles Daworth acted as the single nominee director for her company; Sharon therefore permitted to disguise her beneficial interest and control over the entity. He squeezed her hand perfunctorily, and waited for her to settle on the sofa before offering tea. 'I trust you had a pleasant flight?'

Sharon flashed a smile at the balding, middle-aged lawyer. 'Thank you, yes.' She glanced, deliberately, at her wrist, opened her briefcase and surrendered her passport for verification. 'Will you be able to complete the documentation we discussed, today?'

Daworth opened the passport, checked the photograph, and then buzzed his secretary. 'The formalities are really quite simple, Miss Ducay. In fact, we could have completed these by fax and phone.' He handed Sharon's passport to the woman who had knocked and entered. 'My secretary will photocopy your passport, and I will need to ask you to sign these forms and declarations.' Daworth indicated the file on his desk. 'I just need to go over a few points to ensure that establishing the Trust is, in fact, what best suits your needs, Miss Ducay.'

Now that Dominion Mining Inc had secured a substantial interest in the Canadian listed company, Borneo Gold Corporation, Sharon required to establish yet another firewall which would enable her to receive and transfer funds in her own right, under the protection of British Virgin Island law. To accomplish this, Daworth had advised she establish a Trust and Sharon had decided to visit and meet with her legal representatives, as a measure of comfort to herself. After all, she planned on placing her financial future in their hands, and needed reassurance that this firm had the credentials required for her purpose.

'I will run over the basics with you again, if you don't mind?' Daworth opened the file and commenced explaining what was involved. Sharon nodded. 'Our firm has already prepared the Trust deed following your instructions. Rankin, Daworth & Double will act as the Trustee which, as I pointed out when you called last week, creates a separation of legal and beneficial ownership. Is this quite clear, my dear?'

'Yes, this is clear. And the Trust would be recognized in other jurisdictions?'

'Most certainly; all common law jurisdictions such as the United Kingdom, Canada and the United States recognize the legal concept of a Trust.'

'Will I have absolute privacy protection, a guarantee that third parties will not be able to determine that I am the beneficiary?'

'Of course!' Daworth paused when his secretary returned with Sharon's passport. He nodded at the woman, then continued once she had left the room. 'The Trust is a private agreement and is not publicly filed unless you personally request that this be done. Otherwise, details of beneficial ownership would never be publicly disclosed or made available. In the eyes of the public, we, as Trustees, would be the legal owners of the assets in the Trust and your interest would not be disclosed.'

'Well, Mister Daworth, what would happen if, for example...' she hesitated, not wishing to alarm the man, '...if my government decided to investigate my holdings and discovered, somehow, that I was the beneficiary?'

Daworth shook his head emphatically. 'The Trust will shield your assets from future political risk including government sequestration, confiscation orders from foreign governments and protection from future creditors. Believe me, Miss Ducay, your interests will be totally secure – safeguarded by BVI law.'

'What about tax implications?' she wanted to know.

'You would be exempted from all local taxes.'

'Then,' Sharon rose, 'you have addressed my concerns, Mister Daworth, thank you.'

'Wonderful, my dear,' the lawyer beamed. 'Shall we finalize the documents now?'

Within a few minutes, Sharon had added her signature to the deeds and was on her way back to her hotel, filled with exhilaration at having completed the second phase of her complicated plan. She spent the rest of the day and night in quiet seclusion, not tempted by the sounds of calypso and *reggae* drifting up to her balcony. She departed early the following morning, retracing her steps back to Los Angeles, where she caught Malaysian Airlines to Taipei, then Eva Air to Manila. Reunited with her beloved uncle, General Narciso Dominguez, Sharon Ducay prepared for her return to Longdamai, and her appointment with destiny in the Kalimantan goldfields.

★ ★ ★ ★

Jakarta – Indonesia's Ministry of Mines

'The Indonesian Government has absolute ownership of all gold recovered. Of that there is no doubt. What is required, however, is to enact some legislation which leaves the door open for further negotiation, in the event any of these deposits prove to be as lucrative as the reports suggest.' The speaker reached over, insolently, and tapped the document on the Minster's glass-topped, polished-teak desk. *'Bapak is not happy,'* he added, leaving the threat of his father's intervention hanging in the air. This was how Suharto's offspring spread their father's goodwill throughout the emerging, economic powerhouse.

The Minister for Energy and Mineral Resources had heard this all before. The President's son had been positioning the Palace so that they could simply manipulate for control over the foreign investors' concessions, which had been guaranteed by Ministerial Decree.

'There will be a mass exodus if we change the profit sharing arrangements,' he warned.

'They'll come back,' this, with the arrogance of not only youth, but the knowledge that none present would hold their jobs five minutes longer than it would take him to lodge a complaint with his father.

'It will flow to other sectors,' the bureaucrat warned, recalling when the state-owned oil and gas company, Pertamina, under General Ibu Sutowo had arbitrarily changed the profit sharing arrangements with all foreign contracts back in the early 1970s. With the exception of Total Indonesia, all major operators had collectively withdrawn, leaving the Indonesian oil industry in turmoil. Indonesia suffered a credibility crisis as a result of the government's reneging on existing contracts, the oil sector observing nervously as tens of millions of dollars committed to general exploration throughout the archipelago, suddenly floated into limbo.

'No it won't,' the President's son rebutted, obstinately.

'Then the changes should be effected by Presidential Decree, and not directives from my office,' the Minister suggested.

'No, that is not acceptable,' was the response.

'We could effectively position Indonesian interests so that they could benefit from a greater share of profits by increasing royalty payments,' Doctor Sugit, the Director General interceded. He could see that the Minister was in difficulty. It had not been his intention to challenge the Palace's perpetual drive for increased wealth, it was just that he recognized who would be signaled out by the international business community as having effected the inappropriate changes to existing mining, contracts of work – and blamed accordingly.

'That is not transferring ownership.' The statement was made with a yawn. *'Indigenous Indonesians who have the capacity to acquire shareholding should be given the opportunity to do so. After all, it is our gold!'*

None there really wished to engage the young man in debate; to do so would be to invite the collective anger of not only the Palace, but all associated with the billion-dollar powerhouse. The Minister coughed nervously and turned to Brigadier General Sukirno, a senior member of President Suharto's rubber-stamp parliament who chaired the ruling political party, Golkar's, mining committee.

'Can we have this issue raised in Parliament first?' He was looking for support, his old friend's eyes darting immediately to the President's son before answering.

'That might be the best way to go,' Sukirno answered, hesitatingly.

'Okay, it's settled then,' the brash youngster announced, rising to his feet. *'I'll tell Bapak that you have all been most supportive.'* He did not extend his hand, waiting for the others to clasp theirs in supplication and bow in respect. Satisfied, he swept out of the timber-clad office, leaving behind an air of concern as how this latest request from the *Jalan Cendana* heirs could most appropriately be finessed.

'It's going to raise many concerns,' General Sukirno suggested, his voice a whisper. Even with his rank and position, one had to be circumspect about what one said.

'I agree,' Doctor Sugit shook his head, loading a hand-carved pipe, the Savinelli a gift from his brother who had served as Ambassador to Italy. *'Is there any way we can head him off?'* He played with the pipe, placing it in his mouth where it would remain, unlit.

'Your suggestion to run it through a Parliamentary committee would cause an appropriate delay,' the Minister said; Sukirno not surprised that he had somehow been credited with the idea. Later, he would clarify everything with the Party Chairman, to ensure that his own motives did not come under question.

'Yes, I believe this would be the best way to resolve the situation,' General Sukirno concurred, wondering how long the Minister and his faithful Doctor Sugit would retain their positions once the Palace became aware of their unwillingness to accommodate recent requests. He felt saddened with the weight of this responsibility, particularly because of the timing. It was the month of *Ramadan*, when tempers frayed by the demands of fasting tested relationships to their full, those resident within the Palace no exception.

★ ★ ★ ★

Longhouse Dayak Village – Longdamai Upper Mahakam

Jonathan folded Angela's letter carefully and placed this with the others, the collection started when she first left for Java, more than four years before. He sat, quietly, contemplating his daughter's achievements, proud as any father could be, the framed photograph sitting on his desk a constant reminder that Angela had graduated with honors, topping her class. The village chief reached with outstretched fingers, touching her portrait gently, uttering a familiar chant to see her safely through her time in Jakarta. Then, as was his habit, he went into the community hall where the longhouse children waited eagerly, knowing that it was their chief's custom to select one of their number, to accompany him into the forest for the day. When he entered, children sprang to his side, Jonathan taking the time to speak to each individually, addressing them by name. Occasionally, he would stop and reward a child with a touch, the aura of love he carried through the village longhouse, lighting their day.

With his tiny companion in hand, Jonathan ventured into the forest in search of rare fungi, essential to the production of a number of compounds used in traditional cures – and one which he knew would regenerate at this time. Within the hour, having located the poisonous *polypores,* Jonathan carefully removed the caps and placed these in a specially prepared pouch, explaining to the child that these mushroom-shaped growths were extremely poisonous. The chief's eyes then scanned the forest canopy in search of wild fowl, the young boy quietly observing in awe as Jonathan withdrew a finely carved shaft from one of his two quivers, then, from the other, a poisonous dart head. The boy watched, fascinated, as his chief attached the two sections, placing the deadly dart in a long, hollow, hardwood tube. The child knew to be quiet – and still, his eyes now following the direction in which the dart would fly. There, high up in the branches where light trickled through the dense leaf cover, a wild fowl perched, its natural colors blending against the backdrop, providing near perfect camouflage. Jonathan inhaled deeply, the child at his side flinching at the familiar sound of escaping air, propelling the miniature dart to its target.

The bird fell dead at their feet; the child old enough to know not to touch the kill until the hunter had extracted the poisonous dart head, the shaft having sheered away upon impact. Jonathan's knife flashed, and the dart fell to the ground – later, the flesh around the killing wound would be cut away, the rest eaten. The chief smiled down at the seven-year old, the boy's eyes opening wide when Jonathan surrendered the prize for him to carry.

Their return journey took the pair along a course that touched fallow fields, Jonathan explaining to the child why the ground had been left to recover, that within ten to twenty years the *ladang* which once bore harvest, would revert to forest. The chief always took his charges along this, or similar paths, instilling into the children the Dayak custom of shifting cultivation, a practice that observed the need for forest regeneration.

Not far from their longhouse, Jonathan suddenly stopped, looked towards the heavens, and gripped the child's shoulder, pointing towards the sky.

'Can you see that bird?' he asked, the young boy shielding his eyes against the afternoon sun could barely make out the disappearing shape. *'Look closely,'* the chief encouraged.

'What is it doing, Bapak?' the child asked, respectfully.

'It is sending us a sign – an omen,' Jonathan whispered, his eyes locked on the striped kingfisher.

'What is it saying?' the boy could now see the bird with its elongated, brilliant orange bill, and teal-blue crested coat, and sea-green tipped wings.

'Shh!' Jonathan's powerful hand continued to hold the child's shoulder with gentle grip, the two an odd couple as their heads moved in tandem, observing the kingfisher's erratic flight.

'Bapak,' the boy now engrossed in the bird's aerial display, *'can you catch the bird for me?'*

Jonathan bent down effortlessly, his face alongside the child's. *'To do so would be like stealing the sun's rays, the moonlight, or evening stars.*

What you see is a message; to capture the bird would be to interfere with the sign – the omen.'

'Is it talking to you, Bapak?' the boy moved inside the safety of Jonathan's crouched body, unsure if he should be afraid.

'Yes,' the chieftain answered, placing a comforting arm around the youngster's shoulders, *'but it is also sending a message to you.'*

The boy's eyes opened in wonder. *'To me?'*

'Yes, to you,' Jonathan assured, *'and to everyone in the longhouse.'*

The child was impressed, pumped now with import and already visualizing the tale he would impart to his parents and friends. *'What has the bird said, Bapak?'*

Jonathan rose slowly, conscious of the unkindly noise his knee joints made as he did so. *'The kingfisher has told us that one cycle has been completed, and that another is about to start.'* Jonathan knew that this would be too much for the boy to understand, and went on to provide an explanation more suited to the youngster's age. *'The kingfisher is a messenger and brings hope, to make us ready to plant seed. He understands when it is time for the rain to fall and, by observing the direction in which he flies or how he twists and turns, we can predict when it is best to prepare the soil for the new season. When you are older, you will be able to tell what he is trying to say to you by observing whether he flies from left to right, or right to left, or if he flies away or towards you, and even if he dives suddenly while you have him in sight. We are part of all life, the kingfisher but one of many in our family.'* Jonathan noticed that the child was tiring, the wild fowl now resting on the ground, held by weary hands. *'Give me the kill; I will carry it for you until we reach the village. Then you can carry it into the longhouse and give it to your mother.'*

The boy willingly returned the prize, tired from the outing. Jonathan bent down and scooped the child up with one hand, and carried him piggyback.

★ ★ ★ ★

Transmigration Village

One hundred kilometers further down the Mahakam River, in the newly created village of Pamekasan Baru, machete-wielding

Modang Dayaks beheaded forty-three Madurese villagers, and threw their bloodied corpses into the migrants' temporary mosque.

Earlier, tempers had flared when a Dayak farmer had inadvertently permitted a piglet to escape its bamboo cage, the terrified animal running helter-skelter through the predominantly Moslem community, before being slain by one of the migrants. A fierce argument had ensued and, in the absence of any real police or military presence the Dayaks unsheathed their deadly goloks, and proceeded to decapitate those embroiled in the dispute. Within the hour, many of the Madurese dwellings had been razed to the ground, the air filled with blood-curdling screams as Modang youths wearing red head and arm bands and waving traditional mandau swords sought revenge against the outsiders, who had forcibly occupied their traditional Dayak lands.

The terrified Madurese knew that once a Dayak placed a red headband around his forehead, tradition demanded that he kill, and drink his enemy's blood. Migrant families, many of which having lived in the area for more than twenty years, fled in terror as their worldly possessions were torched, the weak, infirmed and those too young to flee in time, butchered in their tracks. Armed with bottles of magical oil to protect them, the Dayaks ran amok. By sundown, Pamekasan Baru's entire migrant population of six hundred had fled into the forest, the black pall of smoke evidencing the day's horror, visible from other villages along the Mahakam River. That evening, the air filled with the porky stench of burning human flesh, the Dayak youths sat around fires boasting of the day's events eating their victims' livers, believing that these, the head and heart, contained magical properties. When the festivities were over, the heads would be secretly 'warehoused', brought out in years to come when arak-filled stomachs afforded the inebriated the opportunity to display their gruesome treasures.

News of the slaughter spread faster than fire, the ethnic confrontation in Pamekasan Baru becoming the catalyst for provincial-wide action. Within days, smoke billowed into the air along the Mahakam reaches as migrant villages were torched in rapid succession, the death toll exceeding one thousand. In the provincial capital, Samarinda, the military commander received instructions to move swiftly against the Dayaks after Jakarta-based timber tycoons spoke with the President, voicing their concerns that production schedules would be disrupted with the loss of migrant labor. One of the TNI's Army Strategic Reserve *(Kostrad)* three, airborne infantry battalions stationed in Ujung Pandang, Sulawesi, was placed on standby – the troops arriving in the area within days to bolster territorial defence commands responsible for the areas north, and south of the Mahakam River. By then, more than five thousand migrant dwellings had been destroyed, a number of timber companies taking advantage of the confusion to commence wide scale burn-offs, later accusing the fleeing Madurese of starting the fires. The bloodshed was reported by State controlled media, Indonesia's *Antara* news service mentioning only that tourist permits to travel along the Mahakam had been temporarily withdrawn, due to government concerns that foreign tourists' lives may be endangered by the raging brush fires in that area.

For Jonathan Dau, the proximity of the fires was of great concern, and he watched with dismay as the surrounding forests became thick with haze, smoke carrying more than fifteen hundred kilometers across Borneo, into Malaysia and Singapore, where Changi Airport shut down for an entire day due to the pall. And, even with the deluge of rain that followed, the jungle continued to burn, Longdamai spared when winds finally died, and the great wall of fire fell away, the longhouse only thirty kilometers upstream from its path.

★ ★ ★ ★

Chapter Fifteen

November 1995

The Betawi Ball – Jakarta

Towering chandeliers gracing the Hotel Borobudur ballroom dazzled as a thousand guests stood resplendent in glittering gowns and the finest cloth suits. Stewart Campbell remained transfixed, glass in hand, staring across the room at Angela Dau, radiant, even more beautiful than he remembered. When she looked over in his direction and their eyes touched, Campbell raised a hand to wave but, she suddenly turned away, the American unaware that her smiling face masked surprise, and uncertainty at his presence. Annoyed, he drained the remnants of his vodka, effortlessly, determined not to allow Angela's snub to ruin the evening. After all, the *Betawi Ball* was one of the major events on the Indonesian social calendar, attended by the country's political and military elite, and the capital's indigenous power brokers – Campbell, but one of a small number of foreigners to be invited.

Moving amongst the other guests Stewart remained distracted, surprised at his vulnerability – that he permitted her offhandedness to offend. He stole another glance, curious as to whom the young men engaged in conversation with Angela might be, unprepared when the taller of the two stepped into full view, his boyish features unmistakably those of the President's son. Stewart was impressed

– and somewhat curious as to what interest the Palace might have in attending this function. Then the realization that Angela could be the powerful youngster's date struck home, Campbell instantly touched by a twinge of jealousy. Without realizing he had crossed the floor, he was already at her side, the President's cocky son raising an eyebrow at this effrontery.

'Selamat malam,' Stewart bowed his head in token gesture towards Angela, nodded at the younger men and, without waiting for their response, exclaimed, *'what a pleasant surprise!'*

'I'm sorry…?' Angela feigned bewilderment, the President's son uncertain as how to handle the awkward moment.

'It's me, Stewart,' he said, embarrassment at her obvious refusal to acknowledge him creeping into his voice.

'Mister…?' Angela frowned, her pretence convincing.

'Stewart Campbell,' he offered, lamely, Angela refusing recognition.

'Stewart…?'

Blood drained from his face and he clenched his jaw, humiliated. He regained his composure and, with the coldest of stares directed at Angela, he apologized. *'I'm very sorry, I was mistaken.'* Then, with a curt nod to the others Campbell walked away, his ears burning from the snide remark and accompanying laughter that followed.

★ ★ ★ ★

Campbell found a quiet corner where he sat, gathering his thoughts, his ego urging him to consider the possibility that Angela really had not recognized him, recalling that their last encounter was well over a year before. Deep in thought, he missed the *gong's* deep, hollow reverberations when the metal drum was struck several times, calling those in attendance to dinner.

'Not staying for the rest of the show?' someone asked, Campbell looking up at a familiar face, rising to his feet to greet the Director General for Mines.

'Usually best to let everyone else scramble for their seats, first,' he offered, lamely.

'Where are you sitting?' the other guest asked.

He remembered that the seating arrangements had been annotated on guests' invitations, but was now of two minds as to whether he should remain, or simply disappear. He extracted the envelope from an inside coat pocket, checked where he would be sitting, then peered across the maze of candle-lit tables set for ten.

'*Enjoy the evening,*' the Director General patted him on the arm, leaving him standing alone. Campbell looked again at the intimidating expanse and decided to leave, his exit blocked by a concerned usher.

'May I assist, Tuan?' He smiled weakly and passed his invitation to the man.

'Please follow me, Tuan, your table is towards the front.'

The hotel staff had already commenced serving the first course as he threaded his way through the ballroom, bumping into a number of chairs and near tripping over numerous handbags that had been placed on the floor. Thunderous applause for the onstage comedians drowned Campbell's voice as he thanked the usher and took his seat, smiling at his fellow guests – convinced his eyes were playing tricks when he found Angela Dau sitting across the table – and without the company of the President's son.

She smiled; then, adding further to Stewart's confusion, she mouthed the words in English, 'I'm sorry,' then spent the remainder of the evening ignoring him again.

★ ★ ★ ★

The following day, Campbell's staff whispered amongst themselves at the American's unusual behavior. He had arrived mid-morning in foul mood, snapping at staff unnecessarily, sending the junior office girl into tears when he was overly critical of her coffee-making skills. Even the senior secretary, Laila, treaded carefully, having never seen this side of their boss before. Campbell locked his door leaving explicit instructions that he was not to be disturbed, glaring at Laila when she knocked on his door around midday, poked her head inside, and smiled sheepishly.

'I think you wish to take this call,' she said.

'Damn it, Laila, can't anyone around here do as I ask?' His secretary hesitated, suddenly unsure.

'She says it's very important.'

'She? Who, Laila, who?' he snapped, face muscles taught.

'It's a lady from the Ministry of Environment. She insists on talking to you personally.'

'Environment?' his brow creased.

'Yes, from the Office of the State Ministry of Environment – her name is Miss Dau.'

'Angela?' his face came alive.

'Angela?' Laila mimicked.

'Angela Dau, Laila.' Then, with forced smile, *'Okay, put her through; let's see what she wants.'* His secretary raised one eyebrow knowingly and, within minutes, relayed her thoughts to the other staff. The mood in the office immediately becoming upbeat with this revelation, anxious faces now smiling smugly when Campbell appeared in his doorway, his face apologetic.

'I'm going out for lunch, Laila. Cancel my appointments for the afternoon.' And, with the speed their employer departed the office, the staff giggled knowingly, gossip having him deeply involved in an affair, with someone by the name of Angela.

★ ★ ★ ★

'I miss looking out over the water,' Angela said, with a touch of sadness. *'As children, we were never more than a stone's throw from the river. Our home, the longhouse, was built right to the water's edge.'*

'How long is it since you returned home?' Campbell asked, confident that their conversation could not be overheard. Angela had insisted that they go somewhere quiet, out of the way, and he had agreed to meet her at the Horison Hotel's *Pondok Samudra.* At first, their conversation had been awkward, Campbell's mind drifting as the talk bordered on the banal, his eyes roaming down to the shoreline where the Java Sea's muddy green waters lapped a man-made beach, against a backdrop of occasional *Bugis perahus* sailing by.

'This time, almost six months,' her voice sounded weary. *'But, I*

plan to visit again, soon.'

'Your family must miss you,' Campbell constantly reminded himself not to stare, Angela's magnificent features such, the task nigh impossible.

'That would be the entire village, Stewart,' she pretended to pout, the effect beguiling.

'Now that's what I call a large family,' he teased, enjoying the change in mood. *'Tell me about your parents.'*

Angela appeared to be gathering her thoughts, her eyes distant, Campbell observing the shift in her demeanor, as if she had suddenly been transported, elsewhere.

'My father and I are the family,' she said, quietly, and he detected an underlying sense of pride in the statement. *'I grew up in his shadow.'* She looked up and smiled. *'He is a wonderful man and greatly respected by the Dayak people.'*

'And you, obviously, amongst his most dedicated admirers.' Campbell searched his memory to when he first met Angela, vaguely recalling some conversation with a professor in Bandung. He could not believe that three years had passed, the strong-willed challenge Angela made in the auditorium, coming to mind.

'Yes, of course,' Angela replied assertively, *'I try to be like my father in every way. For me, there could be no greater role model.'*

'And you intend filling his shoes, one day?'

Angela's face became serious. *'No one will ever be able to do that, Stewart.'*

He waited for her to elaborate but, when nothing further was forthcoming, he pressed. *'Your father is the village head?'*

'Yes, Stewart.' She seemed amused. *'I thought you already knew that?'*

'I don't remember you mentioning your father. Come to think of it, you never told me much,...at all...' his voice trailed off, the memory of that fateful Bandung visit revisiting. Then, *'Why didn't you return my calls?'*

Angela peered deep into his eyes, Stewart suddenly uncomfortable that she could read his thoughts. *'Because you let me down.'*

'I came by to apologize,' he reminded her.

'There are some things that can't be changed,' she said, obliquely.

'Then why are we here, now?' he challenged.

Angela attempted a smile. *'Because of what happened last night – you deserve an explanation.'*

He leaned back in his chair, placing both hands on the table. *'Well, I have to admit, I felt extremely foolish.'*

'And angry?'

'Sure, but that's understandable. My ego was hurt.'

'I didn't have much choice, Stewart.'

'How so?' he asked, unconvinced.

'I'm here to explain. But, first, I want you to understand how difficult this is for me.' She reached over and placed her hand over his, uncertainty written across her face. *'If only I could be sure that I can trust you.'*

He studied the young, charismatic Dayak closely, the alluring blend of beauty and intelligence, seductive – a woman who could have her choice of partner, and one he could easily fall in love with, if this were not already so. Drawn as he was, Campbell accepted that there was a great deal more he would have to learn about Angela before he would consider moving down that path – troubled, but not intimidated, by her strong will and determination.

'Angela, I do understand that trust is something one earns. I can't undo what happened in Bandung and, to tell you the truth, I don't understand what the fuss was all about. Sure, I missed taking you to lunch – but, I did try to retrieve the situation. Why is it that I get the feeling that I'm missing something here?'

'What do you mean?'

'Well, firstly, why would you bother to explain about last night? Why is how I feel, suddenly so important to you? You've already made it quite clear that you were not interested. What's happened to change that?'

'You're not making this any easier for me,' Angela withdrew her hand.

'Trust is a two-way street, Angela,' he said, still prickled by the past evening's events.

Angela leaned back closer to the table. *'I couldn't sleep last night, with worry. And, Stewart, none of this is really about you.'*

He encouraged her to continue. *'Now you really do have me intrigued.'* He reached over and offered an upturned palm, Angela hesitating before accepting the gesture.

'You will be tempted to tell others,' she insisted.

'Okay, you have my word,' he promised. *'Whatever you say will remain with me.'*

'Promise?'

'Yes,' he replied, patiently.

Satisfied, Angela took a sip of water, then asked, *'Have you heard anything about the government's plan to renegotiate all existing mining contracts?'*

Stewart heard the words, the gravity of her statement catching him totally off guard.

'That's absurd!' he scoffed. He searched Angela's face for some sign that she was toying with him.

'And that Jalan Cendana will pick up the majority of whatever additional holdings the Mines Department manages to extract as a result of those negotiations?' Although her reference to the Palace added substance to the suggestion, Stewart still refused to accept that the First Family would be so naïve as to believe that they could plunder foreign mining ventures in Indonesia.

'And you heard this from...?' He left the words hanging, believing he already new the answer.

'Let's say I overheard the President's son confirming that he had full Palace support to arrange legislation, obliging mining companies to surrender a greater share of the country's natural resources, and that the real purpose of the new law will be to shift ownership of all successful, gold mining ventures.'

Stewart totally rejected the idea. *'They'd never get away with it. The suggestion's preposterous!'*

'Then we can finish here, now, and forget that we ever had this conversation.' Angela's disappointment was evident; she looked out in the direction of *Pulau Edam,* the lighthouse nothing more than a vague, miniature silhouette in the distance.

Stewart's jaw hardened. If what Angela said *were* true, there would be massive upheaval in the industry, with all of the concessions under negotiation sure to be aborted – amongst these, two of his own clients.

'Why me, Angela – why are you telling me?' He searched her face for a sign, the message her eyes sent, fiercely convincing.

'Because there's more...' Campbell's cell-phone disrupted their conversation. He raised his hand to interrupt, switching the mobile off.

'Angela, before you go any further, I have to ask you something.' The question had been nagging him since the night before.

'Then ask,' she suggested, Stewart unable to detect the annoyance in her voice.

He drew a deep breath. *'I am really curious as to what you were doing there, last night?'*

'I just told you,' her impatience now evident.

'No you didn't,' he argued.

Angela's eyes came alive. *'I don't understand. Are you asking me what I was doing there, or what was I doing there with the President's son?'*

'Both,' he answered, lamely.

Angela shook her head in dismay. *'You think I am sleeping with him?'*

As that was precisely what he had thought, he felt his face color, turning in search of a waiter to cover his embarrassment.

'Stewart!'

Reluctantly he turned to face her. *'That's not what I said.'*

Angela was determined not to let him off the hook. *'But, that's what you meant, wasn't it?'*

'No, it wasn't,' he lied. *'Guess I felt that you were a little too anxious to have me disappear, that's all.'*

'I told you, I would explain.' Campbell noted the exasperation in her tone.

'Okay, then let's get that out of the way first.'

'All right, then, let's do that!' she all but snapped. *'I had been with a group of friends from the Environmental Agency, fresh from the Mines' Minister's home. Enny Sutanto was there...'* Angela paused when she realized that Campbell might not know the name. *'The current Miss Indonesia,'* she explained for his benefit. *'That's where I overheard the*

conversation. There was quite a gathering, the President's son indifferent to the fact that I was present – guess he assumed that I was part of the usual trappings. When we felt it appropriate to leave, the Minister's wife asked Enny and me to stay. I won't say I didn't understand why we were asked to remain after the others had gone, it was just that I hadn't thought that far, my mind preoccupied with what they plan to do with the foreign mining contracts.'

By now, he was totally absorbed in her explanation.

'Enny was also supposed to be at the Ball last night – thankfully, she insisted on being given a few minutes to apologize to the Governor in person. After all, he is her uncle. It had something to do with her responsibilities as Miss Indonesia. I think she was going to sing, or whatever.' Campbell did not respond to this, indifferent to her role in the events of the previous evening. *'Stewart?'* Angela wanted to know that she had his full attention. He nodded to signal that he had understood, and she continued. *'It was Enny who became his date, not me. I realized later that, had it not been for her insistence that she speak to the Governor in person, today, my father might have had every right to be ashamed for me. They drove us to the Ball after their meeting, staying long enough for Enny to apologize to her uncle, then return with them.'*

She paused long enough to take another sip of water, before continuing.

'I had no idea that you would be there, at the Ball. When I saw you, I knew you would come over and start talking about what you do, or mention gold mining. My God, Stewart, if they thought you and I were connected, that would have been disastrous for me! Don't you know what they are capable of? That's why I couldn't sleep.' Her face fell. *'I should phone Enny. We're not friends, but I'd feel partly responsible if she met the same fate as that young actress.'*

Stewart was familiar with the story. When one of the Palace siblings discovered her husband having an affair with an emerging screen star, the girl was murdered, her body placed on the back seat of a Mercedes, the message sufficient to keep the President's daughters' stallions well behaved in their stables, for at least some months.

'You said there was more,' he prompted.

Angela nodded sadly. *'Yes, and for the Dayaks, an even greater impact than all the precious gold yet to be found in Kalimantan.'*

'Go on,' he urged, his face grim.

'One of the guests, I think it was General Sukirno, told the Minister that the President had agreed to send Special Forces troops into Kalimantan to protect a massive migration of Madurese settlers into the area. The President's son confirmed that the timber tycoons have secured approvals to expand their concessions by more than a million hectares. Stewart, do you realize what this will mean? They plan to strip even more of our land, take the timber and in so doing destroy the environment, give the Madurese our property, and then chase the Dayaks into the mountains!'

'What was the connection with gold mining?'

'That's how the conversation commenced. The Minister made the comment to the President's son that one of the major difficulties foreign mining companies faced was inadequate labor in the field. Stewart, I can still hear Sukirno's laughter when he explained how the Palace had decided to rectify the so called labor problems.'

Campbell considered what Angela had said; accepting the depressing scenario she painted as highly probable, recalling that Indonesia's history had been marked with many, parallel scenarios, when the country's generals fought over the nation's wealth. He looked up, aware that Angela was monitoring his reactions. *'Why are you really telling me all this, Angela?'* he asked, dropping his voice, and moving his head to force direct eye contact.

She replied without hesitation. *'I had not planned to but, after seeing you there last night, I thought...'* she paused, stared out the window as if searching for something or someone out there, then turned back and sighed. *'I thought you would understand.'* Angela hesitated again, before continuing, Stewart's gut telling him he was about to learn what this meeting was really all about. Then, she asked, *'What would happen if the foreign mining companies got wind of what was planned?'*

He sat stony-faced, staring across at Angela, her expression washed with child-like innocence as she sat, elegantly poised, her long, black flowing hair set in a waist-length pony tail, all too perfect a picture. In that moment, the realization that he was being used became all too apparent. Disappointment written across his face, Campbell signaled for a waiter, and ordered vodka for himself. Minutes passed, the ensuing silence rapidly eroding whatever rapport they had built between them. The waiter returned, and he demolished half the cocktail before returning to the conversation.

'I thought you had sworn me to secrecy?' he said, the sarcasm deliberate in his voice.

Angela looked away, again, as she spoke. *'I was referring to the fact that I was the source of information, Stewart.'*

'Why don't we just be honest here,' he suggested, *'you want me to be the conduit that alerts the foreign miners to the proposed changes in ownership. Isn't that why you're really here?'* With one, long swallow, he emptied the vodka and signaled the waiter for another.

'I wish you wouldn't,' Angela asked, her tone sincere.

'Standard lunch procedure.'

The remark brought a concerned rebuke. *'My father used to drink a great deal.'*

'You're digressing,' he accused.

'Dayaks produce their own alcohol,' she continued, ignoring his remark. *'Both the women and men drink, but mainly on ceremonial occasions.'*

'And you father doesn't drink at all, anymore?'

Angela's face became expressionless. *'He does what he wishes,'* was all she said.

'So, he still drinks?' he persisted.

'When he wants.' The absence of warmth in her response caused Campbell to steer the conversation back to the troublesome issue at hand. *'Was I right in saying that you want me to warn the mining companies?'* he pressed. *'You think that, by revealing what's planned, the foreign mining companies would seek their own government's intervention to prevent acquisition of their assets?'*

'Yes,' she answered, flatly.

'And that's the only reason?'

Angela shook her head. *'No.'*

'Then what else?'

'I wanted to see you again.'

'Really?' He refused to disguise his skepticism.

'It's true.'

'Then, why did you refuse to return my calls last year?'

★ ★ ★ ★

Angela's mind revisited that time of confusion, unable to explain what had prevented her from seeing him on that day. Even if he *had* arrived in time to keep their appointment, Angela would still not have met with him, her interpretation of the vivid dream a clear warning that he was not ready – and of this, she had been absolutely convinced.

Shortly thereafter, Angela had moved to Jakarta and entered government service with the Environment Agency, where her request to be engaged in issues relating to Kalimantan was granted. She had soon proven her worth, attracting the Minister's attention and rewarded with the recognition she deserved. Within the year, Angela Dau's credentials as a dedicated research analyst were highly respected. Although her determined style, and stands on issues that contradicted departmental policy did attract occasional criticism from vested interest groups, she was forgiven, her youth and beauty carrying her through.

Angela had dated, but always avoided serious involvement. As attractive as she was, Angela was not popular with men of her age, her independent nature and strong will, traits the younger men abhorred. When Stewart Campbell ceased leaving messages, Angela regretted not having returned his calls. And, although her attraction to him in no way diminished as the year wore on, she refused to accept the distraction, prioritizing, driven by her commitment to find solutions for the dilemmas facing the Dayaks in her beloved Kalimantan.

Unfortunately, Angela's apparent indifference towards men did, however, produce a negative effect, with whispers suggesting that her preferences lay elsewhere being aggressively promoted, by a steady string of rejected suitors behind her back. Relieved by the rumors, the Minister's wife and her peers were no longer threatened by Angela's natural beauty and their husbands' exposure to her presence, frequently inviting her to their functions to adorn their expensive nests. Such was the atmosphere the evening before, when she had inadvertently become witness to yet another, Palace-sponsored conspiracy, one which would not only damage the country's international image as a safe investment destination, but would also destroy the natural habitat of thousands of species and displace Dayaks from traditional lands.

Angela felt dispirited, desperate at this time for Campbell to be her friend. If there were any possibility that they might progress forward from there, it would be necessary for him to demonstrate now, that he supported her, unequivocally. *'One day, when there are not so many issues clouding our horizons, Stewart, I will explain. I can't right now, it's too complicated. Please don't assume that because I came from an isolated, village community that my people are simple, or that decisions we make are based on clear-cut issues of what might be right or wrong, good or bad, or even black and white. I was raised to consider consensus. I believe in ancestor worship, the spiritual and natural worlds, and reincarnation. I am dedicated to serving my people. On the other hand, you come from a world that scorns cultures such as mine, without any understanding of our beliefs, all too ready to compartmentalize ethnic minorities as primitive tribal groups that require Westernizing. My people have occupied Kalimantan as far back as time itself, and as we speak, their holy sites are being desecrated, their lands confiscated and their forests destroyed. As for your precious goldmines, to be totally honest, I don't really care too much one way or the other who owns the gold mines, or enjoys the benefits. These are material things. What I do see, however, is an opportunity to prevent a major catastrophe for the Dayak people. If by exposing the Palace's move to monopolize the production of gold I can somehow take advantage of the international press and world opinion, to demonstrate what ecological damage is planned for our forests, then I would be satisfied with that. You know as well as I, Stewart, my voice would carry no weight – but yours would get their attention.'* Angela could feel her voice breaking, struggling desperately so as not to lose control. '*Yes, I was wrong not to return your calls; perhaps I could have handled that better.*

Yes, I came here today to seek your help, and yes, I counted on your interest in me to gain your support. If you consider me a poorer person for doing so, then you would not be the only one to leave here, today, disappointed.'

She hesitated, willing tears not to flow, relying now on *tenaga-dalam,* her inner strength to carry her through. Angela bowed her head slightly, forcing images of tranquil forest scenes to mind – instead, the concerned face of her father flashed by. Angela took those seconds to regain her composure, angered now with the realization that her hands were shaking, so she clenched these tightly, out of sight, buried in her lap. With unmoving lips, Angela's silent chant summoned her inner strength, the words uttered in her mind, immediately self-comforting.

Deep in the Kalimantan forests some two thousand kilometers to the north and across the wide Java Sea, as if by some given signal a black hornbill was shaken from its daytime reverie, its familiar caw striking concern in Jonathan Dau's heart as bird took to the air, flying over the isolated, *Penehing* village.

★ ★ ★ ★

Captivated by the determination in Angela's voice, Campbell remained silent from the moment she commenced speaking, and through the void that followed. The gentle movement of delicate, ceiling-to-floor lace curtains which, until then, had hung unobserved in monotonous serenity filtering outside views, caught his attention as these suddenly danced, caressed by an invisible suggestion of wind. The immediate surrounds became suffocatingly still, his throat felt dry and, as blood flowed from his face, he started to faint. Startled, Campbell fought rising panic, the subsequent rush of air and beating wings that accompanied the spell, strangely familiar. He turned from the table and, with head between knees, inhaled deeply.

'Are you alright, Stewart?' With Angela's concern registering, he blinked, breathed deeply again, then rubbed his face vigorously.

'Not enough sleep,' he explained, his hands trembling as he reached for a pitcher of water.

'Perhaps we should go?'

Campbell remained short of breath. Then, as circulation was restored and oxygen filled his lungs, he regained his composure. *'I think perhaps we should,'* he hoisted a weak smile, the sensation of *déjà vu* clouding his mind, his hand unconsciously moving to the minutest of scars, running the length of his back.

★ ★ ★ ★

Chapter Sixteen

JANUARY 1996

JAKARTA

The aroma of freshly brewed *Robusta* coffee greeted Stewart Campbell as he entered Angela's shared accommodations, her flatmate away for the day, visiting friends. Framed photographs adorned a reproduction, Raffles, teak sideboard table against one wall, Campbell's attention drawn to a head-and-shoulders portrait of Angela's father, recalling how she had talked for hours about the Dayak chief during his previous visit. In the months following the *Betawi Ball*, Stewart had met with Angela Dau frequently, although none of these occasions could truly be called a date. They had become friends; Campbell aware that Angela was not ready to move their relationship forward, an expectation he personally harbored.

Nothing had eventuated with respect to Angela's conspiracy theory, Campbell then doubting that what she claimed to have overheard amounted to anything more than posturing by those present. He knew that to suggest so would surely damage their burgeoning relationship, irreparably; but, as time had passed without any indication by the Ministry of Mines that contracts would be renegotiated, he found it increasingly difficult not to question the veracity of what she had said. Now, it would seem, the advancing activities of foreign mining companies had arrived at her own communities doorstep, the intrusion, from what he could glean, threatening to embroil the

Pehing Dayaks and Central Government, in bloody confrontation. Angela had insisted that the mining activities in Longdamai were related to her conspiracy claims, pointing to the deliberate desecration of her people's ancestral, spiritual site. Although he was not of the same mind, concerned that she had lost her objectivity when it came to Dayak affairs he had, nevertheless, agreed to approach the mining company concerned, which he learned shared offices with P.T. Subroto & Associates in CBD Jakarta.

Campbell was aware that the Borneo Gold Corporation had been granted concessions in the Mahakam area through its Indonesian operating arm. Operating anywhere in the archipelago required the formation of a legal, Indonesian corporate entity. He was pleased that most foreign firms managed to retain some of their original identification when choosing local company names, if for nothing else but to avoid confusion in the market place. His interest in the Canadian miner had grown with the recent announcements regarding restructure, and the appearance of a dominant shareholder, Dominion Mining. He had become suspicious when investigations into that company's ownership had ended in the British Virgin Islands, disappointed when Alexander Kremenchug and Eric Baird's names arose, repeatedly, whenever he mentioned the Kalimantan prospects to others in his field.

He was also aware that Dominion had established a strong presence during the past eighteen months with its successful drilling of the Longdamai prospects, through an Indonesian entity, P.T. Kalimantan Gold. That the Filipino, Sharon Ducay had been in charge of field operations for the company when it produced results indicating that its Longdamai prospect could have reserves in excess of two million ounces, in his opinion, only provided credibility to the find. After their brief and exciting interlude in Singapore some years before, Stewart had made inquiries regarding the woman's credentials, and was impressed with what he learned.

'Have you heard from your father?' he asked as Angela served the coffee.

'No, not since earlier in the week; communications are becoming increas-

ingly difficult for us — I can't even get a permit for a transmitter-receiver here, at home.'

He was aware that Angela had accessed a radio link from Bandung during the years she studied there. Until recently, she had been able to utilize the Samarinda link but, due to the ethnic unrest in the province the facility had been closed to all but military personnel. He also knew how difficult it would be for a civilian to obtain a direct radio link permit, with most members of the Indonesian military xenophobic by nature, and the strict censorship rules imposed upon the media.

'*What are you going to do?*'

'I don't know,' she answered, despondently.

'*Can't anyone senior in the Agency help?*'

'Well, I spoke to the Secretary General. He phoned both the Department of Communications and Defence, but they are sitting on the request – and I think we all know why.'

'Why not speak to the Minister's wife?' he suggested.

Angela shook her head and frowned. *'We're friendly, but applying pressure to Communications and Defence wouldn't go down too well at this time.'*

'What are you going to do?'

Angela looked at Campbell calmly and said, *'There's no other choice but to ask for some time off, and return home for a few weeks.'*

He appeared worried. *'Is it safe?'*

'It would be, for me,' she answered, and Campbell wondered if she had meant to be patronizing.

'Would you like me to go with you?' The Moslem month of Ramadan had commenced, Campbell hopeful that he would be out of the capital when the *Hari Raya Idulfitri* celebrations arrived, with the breaking of the month-long fast.

Angela knew he would offer. *'No, Stewart. It would be best to leave it for another time.'*

Campbell glanced at the chief's photograph, unaware that Angela was suppressing a smile when his expression became somber.

★ ★ ★ ★

P.T. Kalimantan Gold (Ind.) – Longdamai Operations

Barely a month had passed since his wedding to Pipi Suhartono, the demanding three-day long Javanese wedding extravaganza was no sooner at an end, when Baird announced to his new bride that he was urgently required back in the field. Although disappointed that their honeymoon was to be postponed, Pipi Baird was not overly concerned, as Eric swore he would take her to Singapore for an extended holiday, upon his return. For the Australian geologist, Sharon Ducay's undertaking to guarantee ongoing employment could not have come at a better time, the earlier BGC restructure now proving to be a godsend as his finances had again fallen to desperate levels, because of the wedding. Baird had discussed his contract with his partner and now uncle by marriage, Subroto, who was obviously pleased not only with the recent union, but his reversal in fortunes with respect to the Canadian mining shares he still held.

Sharon had spoken to Baird by phone from Vancouver, offering him the opportunity to continue working with her as Assistant Chief Geologist under the restructured BGC arrangements. Baird had agreed, and had no difficulty in contracting the same expatriate drillers he had originally engaged for the Longdamai site. After drying out for a couple of days, both Calvin Alderson and Carl Patrick were in reasonable enough shape to fly back to Samarinda, where they completed the journey to Longdamai aboard the longboat supply vessel. Baird had sent them ahead to prepare the rigs and other equipment, following with Mardidi within that week. Baird then reinstated the drilling program, in anticipation of Sharon Ducay's return, without knowing that this initiative almost destroyed any chance of her ever achieving her objective.

Well into their second week Baird lost radio communications when the receiver went down, deciding to take the broken equipment down to Samarinda and meet Sharon, who was scheduled to arrive at that time. Unfortunately, Baird also decided to transport the revitalized operation's first batch of drilling samples for analysis, believing this is what the Chief Geologist would have wanted. Following established procedures, he split samples, retaining half on site for future crosschecking as Sharon had done and, along with Mardidi accompanied the remainder down river to the provincial capital. He dispatched the bags to the laboratory and, while waiting for the radio to be repaired purchased additional supplies, then visited the Mesra Hotel's business center and booked a call to Canada, to check when Sharon Ducay would arrive. He spoke to a secretary in BGC's Vancouver office, learning that they had been trying to contact Baird by radio to advise that Sharon's return had been delayed, and that she would now return to Indonesia from the Philippines, in another two weeks, at which time she would recommence the drilling program. Baird failed to mention that he had already started drilling, and taking samples.

When the Vancouver office radioed Baird the following week and advised Sharon's revised, arrival details, he loaded the latest samples and returned to Samarinda, forwarding these to the laboratory on the morning Sharon stepped off the Garuda flight. As instructed, he had arranged for a chopper to be standing by at the airport to transport them directly to the site and, once airborne, he had briefed Sharon with respect to the operational status of the rigs. Baird was perplexed by the Chief Geologist's tirade when he revealed that two batches of samples had already been dispatched for analysis, bewildered by Sharon's anger that drilling had commenced without her instructions.

★ ★ ★ ★

Following the disappointing test results from these two batches Sharon had taken Baird aside and spoken in confidence. She knew, that to return to the practice of spiking samples after two consecutive samplings had indicated that the reserves may just not be there, would be to attract suspicion. Instead, although this would mean more expense and a considerable delay, Sharon decided on an elaborate deviation from her original plan, opting to move the drilling program to another site. She was aware that Baird held a substantial number of shares in BGC, Kremenchug having explained this when she discovered their names in the company's share registry. Confident that her assistant would not wish to see the value of his holdings depreciate as before, she invited him to her quarters to discuss the recent results.

'The way I see it, Eric, we have two choices here.' Sharon could see that Baird was pleased she had sought his opinion. 'One, we go back and re-drill that last line which failed to support our earlier findings, which could be disastrous if the results are the same or, two, we could decide to move on to other prospective areas and hope that these prove up to expectations, leaving this site on hold. BGC could simply announce that it wishes to prove up a number of other attractive sites as part of the overall drilling program.'

Baird tapped the geological wall chart reflecting work completed on the site. 'Why don't we run a series of holes out in this direction while we're still here?'

Sharon could not reveal that she had spiked samples with incremental increases on a path leading away from where Baird pointed. She knew what he said made economic sense in terms of logistics, but to do so would still be wildcat drilling, and Sharon refused, as she was now impatient to re-establish credible results – and this meant relocating to another site. 'Eric, how many shares do you have in BGC?' she asked, the question taking Baird by surprise.

'I picked up a few when they first moved into Indonesia,' he replied, cautiously, but Sharon already knew the number.

'What do you think they would be worth if the market thought that Longdamai was not up to expectations?'

Sharon suspected that Baird would have agonized over this since she showed him the disappointing results, only days before. At the time, she had isolated access to the radio and given Baird explicit instructions not to reveal the results to anyone else on site. She did not need Baird dumping shares, as word would undoubtedly spread.

'Guess the bottom would fall out of the market,' he mumbled, despondently.

'Yes, and if we did drill over there,' she indicated to the wall diagrams, 'and found nothing, that would be the end to this site. Wouldn't it?'

Baird nodded, wondering where she was going with this.

'Besides,' Sharon continued, confident that Baird's potential losses would encourage his support, 'we would not be misleading anyone. We will return to this site and complete the drilling, once work has been carried out on other locations. As a matter of fact, Eric,' she said, convincingly, 'I almost opted for an alternative site before choosing where we are today. The choice came down to which required the least logistical support.'

'What about the recent results?' Baird had asked.

Sharon's response was that of co-conspirator. 'What do you say if we just sit on those for the time being? You see, Eric,' she rose in weary manner, her shoulders slumped, 'I took a reduced fee for the work that's been done to date, Dominion Mining's arrangement was that I would receive a success fee for last year's results. Now they have become part of a revamped BGC, I agreed to accept a small allocation of shares in the restructured company, and these won't be free of escrow until next year.'

'And if the last test results were known?'

'Well, BGC's shares would fall drastically, I'd dare say and,' she added, heaving a sigh for greater effect, 'by the time my shares came out of escrow, they would most likely be back where BGC's shares were, before the restructuring.' Sharon knew from Baird's sympathetic look, that he was hooked.

'But, if we relocated and continued with the drilling program, you would be able to offload your position before returning to re-drill this site?'

'Precisely,' she confirmed, then prompting Baird with this reminder. 'And then there's your own shares to consider.'

The next morning Sharon Ducay ordered the camp's demobilization, unprepared for the difficulties they would face in relocating to the site she had selected. The rigs were dismantled in preparation for the heli-lift, Sharon utilizing the helicopter's presence to fly upriver to the new destination, reconnoitering the area to determine where best to establish camp. During their first run over the potential site, Sharon asked the JetRanger pilot if he could take them down closer to the ground, where head-high grass not fifty meters from the Mahakam's banks, lay in green and yellow splendor, a mask covering the Dayak sacred ground. In the course of the aerial survey, Dayak *hampatong* statues, unseen from the air, were destroyed by the helicopter's landing skids, the centuries-old pair of human-like sculptures ironically decapitated as the pilot performed a pirouette, providing a 360 degree view of the proposed site.

Within the week, a small flotilla of longboats arrived at the site, the Modang laborers working desperately to complete the unloading and depart, whilst there was still light. And before the sun disappeared over the Kapuas Range, Bukit Batubrok'*s* dominating shadow enveloped the Upper Mahakam River reaches, the drilling rig's metal bodies stood amazingly like gigantic, petrified grasshoppers in the subdued, gray light. Sharon looked around the maze of unpacked equipment and stores, cursing the Modang laborers in *Tagalog* for having abandoned them – the two expatriate drillers, along with Baird and Mardidi, the only other inhabitants of this site.

★ ★ ★ ★

With darkness descending upon the small group and their hurriedly erected tents, a lone figure stood between wild sago-palms, fierce eyes tracking Baird as the unsuspecting geologist stepped closer to the camp fire. In Jonathan Dau's world, all five had desecrated *Penehing-Dayak* sacred soil – and, in consequence, all five could not go unpunished. Like a man possessed, Jonathan Dau raised his head and roared into the night, his blood-curdling cry an oath to ancestral spirits, a promise that he would rectify his error in not having taken the white man's life those years before, when the opportunity first availed.

★ ★ ★ ★

Eric Baird rubbed gritty eyes, yawned with the tranquillizer's continuing effects, looked over at the adjacent sleeping bag and gently shook the sleeping form, awake.

'Get me some coffee,' he told Mardidi, who unquestioningly sprang to his feet, tied a sarong around his narrow waist, and left Baird alone in the tent, fumbling around, half-awake, searching bundled clothing for cigarettes. He placed one between his lips, remembered there was no lighter, his hand searching again until he realized that this was not his tent.

Massaging throbbing temples, Baird scratched his thighs, yawned again, and was about to lie back in wait for the coffee when he suddenly sat bolt upright, reminded of where he was. Trembling, he cocked an ear listening for signs that the others had risen, overwhelmed by the possibility that they may have been taken during the night. Then, when he heard the familiar voices of the drillers, Alderson and Patrick, he scrambled outside, climbing into heavy-duty trousers as he went. Naked from the waist up, Baird averted Calvin Alderson's eyes when he realized how foolish he might have looked, reaching back inside the two-man tent for the rest of his clothing. At that moment, Sharon Ducay appeared, nodding to the three men as she approached.

'I've recalled the chopper,' she announced, addressing Baird. 'I'll stay here with Alderson and Patrick while you to fly to Samarinda and do whatever is necessary to get half a dozen armed soldiers back here, today.'

Baird shook his head. 'I might be able to persuade the military to give us security, but they sure as hell won't get their hands dirty. Who's going to fix all of this?' he waved an arm in the direction of the disorderly array of boxes and unassembled rigs.

'Then what do you suggest?' Sharon asked, agitated that her project was in jeopardy.

Baird observed Mardidi returning from the river's edge, where he had washed the previous evening's used utensils. The young man set about preparing coffee for all, deliberately subservient to everyone present as he filled tin mugs and offered canned biscuits around. 'Well, it's obvious from what happened that the *Modang* people won't work here.' Baird scratched again, opening a partially healed wound on his neck. 'If you were counting on the local villagers for their support, I'd forget that. The fact that they have not shown their faces is not an encouraging sign.'

'Could we send Mardidi out to talk to them?'

Mardidi overheard the conversation, spilling coffee over himself at the suggestion.

'He would be the last one to send,' Baird advised. 'No, Sharon, I'm sorry to say, we have a real problem here. You might recall, I did warn you about this area.'

Sharon's face clouded. At the time, she had not taken Baird's opposition to her choice of sites seriously, her eyes unconsciously lifting to the nearby forest, uncomfortable with the thought that they were being observed. 'Can't we ask anyone for help?' Sharon's confidence was eroding quickly, the possibility that they might have to leave the site and all this equipment, unguarded.

'How long since you spoke to the charter company?' Baird asked.

Sharon checked the time. 'Less than fifteen minutes,' she said.

'Why not get back on the blower and ask if they can bring half a dozen men with them now, then I'll go back and arrange for soldiers to join them later in the day?'

'That's still not going to solve our problem,' Sharon complained. 'What we need here is a large labor force.' She stared at Baird. 'Without some real numbers, this project will fail.' She turned on her heal. 'First priority is to get hold of the pilot before he takes off. I'll do that now.'

Eric Baird clearly understood the inference behind Sharon's statement. Had it not been for the recent ethnic clashes further downstream he would have suggested visiting the Pamekasan Baru villages but, since the clash between Madurese and Dayaks, most of the migrants had fled. Baird knew that without the support of local villagers, the only remaining source for labor was with migrants. *But, the question was, where would he find these?*

Over the next hour Baird came to the conclusion that he would be best seeking the assistance of his Jakarta ally, and now uncle-in-law. He pondered how to approach Subroto, deciding that he would first speak to him from Samarinda when he flew downriver that day, then proceed to Jakarta if the Governor was unable to resolve their dilemma. When Sharon returned and signaled with raised thumb that help was on the way, he discussed proceeding onto Jakarta, and she agreed. Just after midday, Baird boarded the JetRanger, leaving a disconsolate Mardidi behind to cook for the others.

Baird spent three fruitless days in Samarinda, attempting to raise a labor force, those initially interested, declining once the destination was revealed. But, he did manage to organize interim security for the operations. The Governor contacted the local military commander who, for a fee, loaned five of his armed troopers to be stationed at *Longdamai Sial* for a period of two weeks. Baird relayed this message, organized for the JetRanger to transport the soldiers to the site, then flew to Jakarta to seek his erstwhile partner's intervention.

★ ★ ★ ★

Jakarta
Indonesian Defence Headquarters (HANKAM)

Deep, maroon curtains hung listlessly covering an insulated, concrete wall behind an oversized, carved Javanese teak desk to create the illusion that a window lay hidden behind, the backdrop reminiscent of some miniature vaudeville stage. The Indonesian flag, *Sang Merah Putih* held prominent place alongside a hand-embroidered, suede-backed canvas, army *Siliwangi* Division banner – the tiger-face, emblem memento a constant reminder of the tenant's former command. Matching trophy cabinets stood prominently along one wall, the impressive array of highly polished plaques, shields, crystal and silver cups, reflecting the owner's golfing prowess, under a gracious handicap.

Mandatory photographs of the President and his inept V.P. hung solemnly overlooking the room's centerpiece setting, a late Nineteenth Century, beveled-glass-topped, coffee table, saved from the Sultan's *Kraton,* in Jogyakarta during the Indonesian struggle for independence. A hand-woven, Pakistani, Peacock, woolen carpet lay spread underneath, its rich colors in no way humbled by the historic piece, above. Studded library armchairs completed the setting – on this day, all occupied, the meeting called by Major General Umar Sudopo, the Chief of Socio-Political Staff at Defence HQ, at the request of Brigadier General Sukirno. The latter not only now headed the military's powerful parliamentary block of allocated seats, but also chaired the ruling party's energy and mineral resources, and forestry committees.

The billionaire Chinese Indonesian timber tycoon sitting alongside Sukirno was Bobby Djimanto (a.k.a. Tan Khu Sui), the unofficial timber and logging partner to the Palace, a man comfortable in the knowledge that he was untouchable, his own fortune protected by presidential, vested interests. Also present was the *Kopassus*, Special Forces Commander, General Praboyo, who had accompanied the Governor designate, for East Kalimantan, to the meeting.

Umar Sudopo was the first to speak. He addressed the Minister whose portfolio, inter alia, also included Transmigration. *'Mas, perhaps it would be appropriate for you to bring us up to date regarding numbers etc, with respect to the trans-migrants relocation?'*

The Minister nodded, then referred to his notes. *'The bulk of families willing to migrate to Kalimantan are from the island of Madura. Last month, we completed preparations to transport families totaling fifteen hundred and twenty-seven men, women and children, from villages near to Sumenep. Their original destination was Palangkaraya in Southern Kalimantan. The ship conveying these families, their personal possessions and government subsidized rice stocks, having been diverted in the last twenty-four hours, will arrive in Samarinda before the weekend. Once they have been offloaded, they're all yours.'*

General Umar Sudopo thanked the Minister and asked, *'Are you ready for their arrival?'*

All eyes went to the Special Forces officer who replied, *'Yes. We've organized trucks and buses to move them to holding camps.'* Those present were not surprised that Praboyo's *Kopassus* troops had been delegated the task, as this operation had been devised to provide cover for the Special Forces' deployment into the timber and oil rich province.

'And from there?' Umar Sudopo wanted to know.

'We'll move them upriver in one operation, so that none take root in the city. The transfer shouldn't take more than a week.' The *Kopassus* officer's lip curled slightly. *'They haven't been informed of their precise destination, yet.'*

'They will be aware of what happened at Pamekasan Baru,' Bobby Djimanto muttered, his only concern, the millions in revenue lost since the slaughter. *'How are you going to keep them at Longdamai?'* In other provinces where Djimanto maintained logging operations he had provided barracks where the military had tortured prisoners, and heavy equipment for the digging of mass graves.

The Special Forces officer's mouth twisted further, into a cruel smile. *'There will be a small contingent of Kopassus troops on site to assist with their assimilation. I don't think there will be too many problems.'*

'What's happening with land allocation? General Sukirno, who had remained silent until now, directed his question to the man who would take up office as the newly appointed provincial governor, within the week.

'Each family will be allocated two hectares. A team from the Agrarian Department is already on their way to Longdamai, to survey and oversee the process.'

'How many workers are amongst this group?' Bobby Djimanto asked.

'Three hundred and eighty two,' the Minister responded, apparently pleased with the number. *'We intend increasing the size of the settlement by another seven or eight hundred over the next months. Within six months, the population should reach at least three, perhaps four thousand.'*

This announcement appeared to please the timber baron. *'The more, the merrier, as far as I'm concerned, send ten, even twenty thousand if you can. We'll need as many hands as we can muster, what with the recent increase in demand from Japan, for Kalimantan timber.'*

General Sukirno concealed his distaste for the Chinese *cukong*. Since the President had assumed power, Djimanto had benefited greatly from his association with the Palace. In the Chairman's buckled opinion, this man's insatiable greed was responsible for much of the current ethnic conflict, and it seemed that his demands would never end. In 1990, when *Jalan Cendana* had ordered a ban on the export of all rattan products from Kalimantan, Dayak growers were forced to sell their raw material to Djimanto who, armed with the presidential decree had established a massive furniture factory at Semarang, in Central Java. The monopoly resulted in a great famine throughout Central Kalimantan, where more than one and a half million hectares of rattan farms supplied eighty percent of Indonesia's rattan export. Where there were once thriving Dayak communities there was now pestilence and starvation. With increased, Japanese demand for timber, Djimanto's quest for even greater acreage of prime forest had brought the President's transmigration dream into question.

'At least half of the first contingent will be assigned to work for local mining operations,' General Sukirno insisted. Bobby Djimanto remained silent, aware that his powerful Palace associates had shown more than passing interest in the area's gold mining potential.

'As soon as the Madurese are settled, we will take one hundred men, and their women if they wish, upstream to Longdamai Sial.' The Special Forces officer had already been briefed as to the urgency in providing labor for the site, to demonstrate to the foreign investment mining community that Kalimantan remained secure.

'Will any of your men accompany them?' the future governor inquired.

'No more than half a dozen,' was the response. Most around the table accepted that the number would be adequate. *Kopassus* troops had a fearful reputation, the mere mention of their command sufficient to bring most to heel.

'Then you're not expecting further interference from the Dayaks?' Umar Sudopo appeared unconvinced.

'We have another two hundred men camped a hundred kilometers west of Samarinda, should the need arise.' The Special Forces general did not elaborate; he knew that those present would assume, correctly, that these well-trained troops would have heli support and could be transported to any trouble spot in the area, within hours. With the recent explosion of ethnic violence between the Dayaks and trans-

migrants, Jakarta had quietly moved this elite force into the province, to protect Palace timber interests.

General Umar Sudopo turned to his fellow officer. *'Mas Sukirno?'*

Sukirno placed both hands on his knees, and stretched, straightening a weary back. He sat, thoughtfully, confident that the decision to redirect the Madurese would resolve a number of pressing issues. Having an increased military presence in Kalimantan would deter the Dayaks from further insurrection and, with a restored transmigration program underway, within a few years, the former headhunters would be pushed further into the mountainous regions where the difficult terrain precluded economic timber extraction, at this time. The Madurese would clear the way for future generations of migrants, providing a less hostile environment for the Javanese. General Sukirno was familiar with the government's forward planning estimates which forecast that the number of trans-migrants to Kalimantan, from Java's teeming millions, would match the indigenous population within thirty years.

'I think that just about covers it,' Sukirno said, the meeting ending abruptly, General Umar Sudopo quietly relieved that he would still have time for eighteen holes at the *Pondok Indah* course, with a number of close, Chinese business associates.

★ ★ ★ ★

Borneo Gold Corporation – Vancouver

Christopher Fielding threw the brief and enigmatic radio message onto his desk, scratched the back of an ear, then punched the inter-office line connecting to Alexander Kremenchug's office.

'Got a minute?' Fielding then leant back in the leather, upholstered swivel chair, waiting for his associate to enter.

'What's up?' Kremenchug wandered in, Fielding waving the typewritten memo for Alex to read. When he did so, a frown creased his deep, suntanned brow, his healthy coloring a product of a recent visit to the Caribbean. 'Sharon has moved the drilling program further upstream?' Kremenchug rechecked the message, baffled by her decision.

'And that's not all,' Fielding elaborated, in customary, defeatist style, 'she's all but brought the entire project to a halt.'

'What's happened?' Kremenchug's stomach sent a signal that he had forgotten his medication, the minute ulcer reacting to copious amounts of coffee and concerns arising from the moment.

'Reading between the lines, looks like she has a strike on her hands.'

Kremenchug shook his head. 'No – not in Indonesia. Striking is prohibited by law.' He reread the memo, bewildered by Sharon's arbitrary decision to move the operation. *What was she up to now?*

'Either way, they don't have any labor on site,' the worried company president imparted. 'Do you think you should get out there and see what she's up to?'

Kremenchug had been thinking just that. 'When's the next radio link scheduled?'

Fielding checked the papers on his desk. 'Around five this afternoon.'

'Okay – I'll make a point of being here.' He looked over at Fielding. 'Let's not make any announcements, yet.'

★ ★ ★ ★

Fielding's limpid expression reflected the frustration he felt, the radio link distorted due to weather between the Mahakam area and Jakarta, where the transmission was interfaced with a standard telephone connection, back to the offices in Vancouver.

'Would you say again, Sharon?' he pleaded, one hand taking notes as both parties struggled with the airwaves' distorted connection.

'Baird has radioed that we will have men on site within twenty-one days,' she advised.

'I confirm,' Fielding finally understood. 'Will you be back into full swing by then?'

'Yes,' he heard her voice break up, reappear, only to fade away again, the garbled sounds alien to the ear. 'We will have the first drilling results within four to five weeks,' the voice reverberating down the line advised.

'Do you want Alex to come over?' Fielding asked. This was greeted with an extended silence, punctuated only by interference caused by the lightning storm over West Java.

'...not necessary,' was all he could glean from the lengthy reply. Kremenchug indicated to Fielding that he wished to speak to Sharon, taking the other man's place behind the desk.

'Sharon, this is Alex,' he strained to separate the sounds emanating from the phone, shaking his head in annoyance. 'Sharon, it's Alex. Are you sure everything's all right?'

'...fine, Alex,...nothing's...' was all he heard, before the line went dead. He looked up at Fielding and shrugged.

'Well, at least we know she's still operational,' Fielding said, with some relief.

'Are you clear as to why she moved to the new site?' Kremenchug asked, not having been party to both conversations between Sharon and the company president when connection had first been made.

'Sure,' Fielding said, his voice unconvincing, 'although, I would have preferred she'd discussed this with us first.' He made a mental note to see what could be done to improve communications with the field.

'Baird's in Jakarta,' Kremenchug said, 'I'll give him a call, later. He'll be able to fill us in with more detail.'

Fielding stooped his shoulders and looked glum. 'Let me know in the morning. I don't want to make any announcements until we can confirm that drilling has recommenced.'

Kremenchug considered this, clearly aware of the game that was constantly played by publicly listed companies, forever striving to keep market interest alive in their activities, hopeful that frequent media releases would drive stock values higher.

'Fine, Chris,' he said, 'I'm sure that Eric will be able to shed more light on what is going on.'

★ ★ ★ ★

Jakarta
P.T. Subroto & Associates

Baird took the call in Subroto's office, the General present at the time.

'For Chrissakes, Eric, you're going to have to do something about the communications,' Kremenchug complained.

'I know,' was all Baird said.

'Can you talk?' Kremenchug was aware of Subroto's feelings towards him.

'Within parameters,' he warned.

'What's the real reason behind Sharon's move?' Kremenchug was still mystified by her actions, still seriously considering a visit.

'She felt it a wise decision.'

'And you agree?' Kremenchug was pleased that Baird had remained on the project, if for no other reason than to keep an eye on his Filipino partner.

'Under the circumstances, I don't think she had much choice.'

'Eric,' Kremenchug was becoming rattled by the evasive answers and considered setting up another call when Baird could speak more freely, 'we will need something over here to satisfy the market.'

'It's too early to give them anything on the new location.'

'You know I didn't mean that,' Kremenchug's voice rose, 'let's talk again later.'

'I'm off in two hours,' Baird advised, 'The main problem has been fixed, and I need to get back to the site.'

'What was behind the walkout?' Kremenchug asked.

'Domestic politics, that's all,' Baird explained, 'ethnic rivalry.'

'Why not employ locals from the area?' Kremenchug sensed there was more to it than what Baird had revealed.

'Already tried that,' Baird had nothing to hide, 'their not overly pleased that we're drilling on their land.'

'Will they cause more trouble?'

'It's unlikely,' Baird smiled at Subroto stern face, 'Pak Subroto has become involved. We'll have a labor force there by the end of the month.'

'Where from?' Kremenchug's curiosity was aroused.

'*Pak* Subroto has made arrangements for a trans-migrant group from Madura to be directed to Longdamai.'

On the other side of the globe Kremenchug listened, not at all surprised that an entire community could be encouraged to proceed to a relatively unknown destination, with the stroke of a pen.

'What's it going to cost?'

'We can talk about that at another time,' Baird wanted to grin, the opportunity sure to be to his advantage, as well as Subroto's.

'Okay, Eric,' Kremenchug managed, 'let's set up something when you're back in camp.'

The exchange ended, Baird then turning to Subroto.

'I'd best be going,' he said, anxious to leave Jakarta, but not over-joyed with having to return to the site.

'You should spend more time with your wife,' Subroto criticized.

'*I agree, Pak,*' Baird dropped his tone respectfully after a slight pause, *'I hate to disappoint Pipi like this but, if I don't get back quickly, anything could happen.'*

'When she has children, she won't be so lonely,' Subroto was unaware of his partner's failure to consummate. He was also ignorant of the fact that Mardidi had accompanied Baird on the extended drilling project.

Eric Baird disguised the shudder that ran down his spine. *'I know,'* he replied, lamely. He gathered his gear and hurried to the airport before Pipi could pressure her uncle to have him remain behind.

★ ★ ★ ★

Chapter Seventeen

JAKARTA

Angela had returned to the capital from her brief visit home, depressed and uncommunicative, the mood lifting only when she learned that her name had been added to the list of Indonesian Mines & Energy delegates, to attend the ASEAN sponsored conference in Kuala Lumpur. With the Ministry's support, *Immigrasi's* formidable mountains of red tape were circumvented, and Angela's passport was issued within days.

'I still can't believe that I was selected to be part of the team!' she called Campbell, her voice filled with pride, the green travel document open in her hand. Angela had tied her long hair into a bun at the back, the unsmiling photo now staring back with an officious look. *'The conference will focus on the social, economic and environmental impacts of regional mining. I have been asked to provide a paper on the 'social' aspects. Will you come?'*

'It's great news, Angela.' Campbell congratulated her.

'We could travel over to Malaysia, together,' Angela urged. *'You might even find the discussions interesting.'*

'Sure – and we could also make it sort of a trial honeymoon?' the suggestion heavy with innuendo.

'All the delegates will be staying at the Equatorial,' she continued,

ignoring Campbell's remark. *'You could come and give me moral support.'*

'Moral support?' he laughed, *'me?'*

'You do still believe in these issues, don't you?'

'You've convinced me, I'll go!' he offered, playfully.

Angela became serious. *'I'm not taking this responsibility lightly.'*

Stewart then regretted the tease, sensing the change in her tone. *'You've every right to be excited – and proud. Of course I'll accompany you.'*

This was greeted with an audible sigh. *'Thank you for that, Stewart,'* the compliment lifting her spirits, *'I'm really pleased that you'll be there.'* And then, *'Though I don't think my father would approve of his daughter being asked on a trial honeymoon.'*

'In English, we call it a 'test run'.'

'Run is exactly what you'd be doing if Jonathan Dau got wind of your plan.'

Stewart Campbell laughed comfortably, delighted with the repartee. *'Then, why not make it official?'* the words spilling from his mouth without realizing the impact these would have.

'Are you asking me to marry you, Stewart?'

'Would you say yes, if I did?' Campbell rejoined, attempting to keep the exchange light.

'I'd say, marriage is something I should consider, but not right now.' It was Angela's turn to tease, leaving Campbell unsure whether this implied promise.

'Okay, I'm a patient man,' he responded. *'And you're a practical woman. Who knows what the future holds?'*

'What do you mean by, 'a practical woman'?'

'I meant, 'intelligent',' he replied, his spirits climbing.

'You mean I'm not both?'

'That, and much more,' he said, in surrender.

Angela's next words were preceded by a soft, peal of laughter. *'I might ask you to remember those words, one day.'*

★ ★ ★ ★

Their conversation ended leaving Campbell contemplating their imminent visit to the Malaysian capital, and the possibility that whilst in that environment, Angela might be more receptive to advancing their relationship to a more sensual level. He smiled to himself, recalling his casual offer of marriage. Since they had reconnected, following the *Betawi Ball,* Campbell had ceased dating others altogether, drawn increasingly closer to the beautiful Dayak. Having already forsaken all others he would, indeed, consider taking her as his wife. But, he knew in his heart that Angela was not ready to proceed to that level of commitment. For Campbell, he needed more than the companionship that she offered, his previously, active sex life now a thing of the past – and no suggestion by Angela that this was about to change. Whenever they were alone and a moment of opportunity had appeared, she had consistently resisted his advances, leaving him confused. Restless, and desperate for something more physical, Campbell decided to review their relationship after the Malaysian visit. If the situation had not changed by the time they returned to Jakarta, he would abandon any further attempts to pursue her further. He checked his diary, noting the dates Angela had proposed they travel, reminded as he checked the appointments listed there by his secretary, that he still had an outstanding report to complete for Phil Samuels. Campbell's thoughts turned to more mundane matters, reexamining the information he'd gathered with respect to the Longdamai mining operations.

Having delved even further into P. T. Kalimantan Gold activities and discovered that the recent move to *Longdamai Sial* had been at the expense of further developing a mine at the original site, his curiosity grew, questioning why Sharon had not proceeded at the proven site. Expanding the drilling operation to other prospects made sense but, throwing all her resources into a new drilling program and forgoing an obvious cash flow opportunity, did not. He believed that Sharon Ducay would now most likely be regretting the company's decision to drill the new site, without first having secured a reliable workforce and, as Operations Manager she was responsible for resolving the problem at hand. Through reliable contacts in the Mines Department, Campbell obtained a clearer picture of the labor difficulties Sharon Ducay currently faced, resolvable in his opinion, with money and time. He had experienced similar problems in isolated mining operations before, Indonesia's burgeoning mining industry's growing appetite for Kalimantan prospects certain, he was confident, to test even the most resilient of foreign operators committed to working in this difficult environment.

★ ★ ★ ★

P.T. Kalimantan Gold – Longdamai Sial Site

Perspiration spilled down Sharon Ducay's back as she rose slowly to her feet. With an economy of movement she removed the wide brimmed Akubra, ran a hand through her now shortened hair then replaced the hat squarely on her head. She inspected her clothing to ensure that trouser ends remained tucked securely inside the tops of her knee-length field boots, slapped the sides of her legs with a length of rattan she now carried everywhere to ward off snakes, then strolled across the camp towards the recently constructed jetty. There, she stood, arms crossed and feet apart staring across the fast flowing Mahakam waters in introspective mood, occasionally cocking an ear as she waited patiently for the helicopter to arrive.

Three months had passed since Sharon had ordered the relocation of BGC's drilling operations, a move only she could entirely comprehend, and one which was imminently to bear fruit. Exposed to Calvin Alderson and Carl Patrick's constant bellyaching, Mardidi's cooking, the sleepless nights and constant fear of everything that slithered and crawled, by the end of the first month Sharon had been tempted to abandon the site and return to civilization until the labor problems had been resolved.

She filled the long, empty days by improving her Indonesian under Mardidi's limited guidance – the latter's English benefiting also from the exchange. But, even boredom could not drive Sharon to venture into the nearby, dense forest, deterred by what might lie hidden there. Apart from bathing at the river's edge, she never strayed more than a few hundred meters from the center of camp, across the treeless area between the Mahakam's shore and the towering forest trees, which was once dominated by shoulder-high grass. A twenty-meter clearing had been prepared in the area surrounding their tents, Alderson and Patrick refusing to cut further into the thick growth when confronted face to face by a king cobra. Alderson had wanted to torch the grass – but was prevented from doing so by Sharon, for fear that they would lose control, and set fire to the forest.

Mosquitoes, ticks and even leeches somehow managed their way into the tents, the expatriate drillers becoming belligerent when, well into the third week, they ran out of liquor. Then, to her great relief, Baird had arrived by helicopter, confirming that the longboat flotilla carrying her laborers and other supplies would arrive within the day. He brought fresh provisions, including a case of bourbon for the drillers, and a kerosene-driven ice chest filled with steaks and frozen sausages, which when cooked, restored some semblance of camaraderie within the camp. The next morning, when the collective whine of the flotilla's twenty outboard engines reached their ears, they gathered to oversee the migrant workers' arrival. Once the longboats had been unloaded, the *Modang* riverboat drivers wasted no time in placing as much distance between their vessels and Longdamai Sial as they could before nightfall.

Sharon had moved quickly to make up for lost time – relieved that the government had sent soldiers to accompany the Madurese settlers, although their presence had not reduced the unsettling losses amongst the migrants, incurred from the moment they had stepped ashore. She had counted one hundred and twenty-seven laborers gathered on their first day, amongst these, eighteen women all breaking into nervous laughter when they discovered that a woman was in charge. The Madurese had thrown themselves into the immediate task at hand, slashing through nearby jungle for the materials needed, erecting their temporary village within days; amongst the first structures, a mosque. A communal laundry cum ablution block was built on the river's banks and, within the week, the camp had taken on a shantytown air, and Sharon was able to finally resume drilling operations.

At first, drilling had proceeded slowly, due to near-insurmountable problems associated with clearing prime forest without the support of heavy equipment. There were no bulldozers, front-end loaders or any other motorized vehicles here, the location so isolated, the nearest road was more than one hundred kilometers to the east. Had it not been for the tireless efforts of heli-crews, even the rigs would never have made it to the *Longdamai Sial* site. The treeless, but heavily grassed area, where base camp and operations had been centered, covered an area less than the size of an average football field. Electric power was generated on site; the Cummings-driven units voracious demand for diesel fuel a constant headache, requiring fuel supplies to be ferried upstream, hundreds of kilometers from Samarinda. Only essential equipment and supplies were delivered by helicopter – the JetRanger a welcome sight, never failing to bring the operation to a standstill whenever it appeared.

Sharon instructed the drillers to commence sampling in a direction that required clearing paths into the forest for more than five hundred meters, the work tedious and dangerous, the cost in terms of human life, far more than any had imagined. Five Madurese workers vanished during the first, extended shift, forcing Sharon to goad the remaining men back to work the following day by stepping into the forest, ahead of the teams. At the end of that week, she decided it was an appropriate time to announce an increase in daily labor rates, lifting their basic, daily rate from two American dollars to three, placing her laborers amongst the highest paid in the country. Sharon expected that this would drive the men forward and she was not to be disappointed. By the end of the second month, a pattern of six-meter wide access roads had been cut, crisscrossing fifty hectares of what was once virgin forest, the constant screaming pitch of chainsaws ripping through giant, towering trees forever present, as long as light permitted.

Once a tree had been felled, teams descended upon the ageing giants with chainsaws, tearing at trunk and limb, cutting and sawing, reducing the timber into manageable blocks, leaving behind nothing but sawdust-filled air. These wooden blocks were then carefully placed as foundation material along the newly created tracks, the smaller trees utilized as rollers to facilitate the movement of drilling rigs and ancillary equipment, dragged with rope and chain by human hands, along the once moist, forest floor.

The expatriate drillers punched into the forest, their grueling ten-hour days producing samples along the designated grid, these bagged, split and sealed as practice required, the first shipment sent to Samarinda by helicopter for on-forwarding to the analytical laboratories. And, as she had absolute control over all these procedures, Sharon Ducay carefully spiked the first samples in the same manner as before, knowing that the results would reveal that this geologist had not lost her Midas touch.

Having achieved this milestone, Sharon was desperate to maintain the drilling program's momentum; her deepest concern now, how best to retain her dwindling labor force. She decided to demonstrate how pleased she was with their efforts, ordering that additional rations of rice and canned beef be broken out for a *selamatan,* to celebrate the project's third month in operation – and, more importantly, to ward off evil spirits. The Madurese women prepared the mini feast – Sharon was then treated with a newfound respect for understanding the importance of the traditional ceremony.

The morning following the *selamatan* Sharon awoke, startled by women's screams. Suspecting that yet another of the laborers had succumbed to snake bite, she called for Mardidi to join her. Together, they hurried through the camp to where the laborers gathered around the body of a young man, Mardidi interpreting for Sharon.

'Not die from snake,' she was told.

'Was he killed in an argument?' Sharon asked, unnerved as she stared down at the man's features – twisted grotesquely in death. Swept by a sudden chill, she rubbed her upper arms and turned away, uneasy, anxious to be away from the smell of death.

'They say he was killed by the forest spirits,' Mardidi reverted to Indonesian, his nervous voice adding to her concern.

'Saya tidak mengerti – I don't understand,' she explained, Sharon's frustration evident in her tone.

Mardidi pointed to the forest. 'Ghosts,' was the only word his limited vocabulary could provide.

'That's nonsense!' she snapped, 'get *Tuan* Baird over here, quickly!' Mardidi jumped to obey, the urgency in Sharon's voice clear. She moved away a few meters from the corpse, alarmed by the growing attrition rate amongst her workers. At last count, seven had now been lost to the jungle's venomous creatures, this figure not including the eleven that had simply 'disappeared'.

Sharon had challenged the camp's Madurese spokesman when the numbers had escalated, questioning whether these men had returned to the newly established settlement downriver. The headman had refuted the accusation, suggesting that if Sharon believed this to be so, she might wish to consider sending the soldiers to the settlement to check for themselves. She knew that this was a 'no-win' situation, realizing that to challenge the headman's word would create disharmony, and decided instead to solicit his support to recruit replacement workers. She had waited another two weeks and, when the supply longboats appeared with monotonously regularity without additional labor, Sharon knew that it was not just local mumbo-jumbo that was working against her. Now she was faced with another suspicious death.

Baird had arrived and spoken to the Madurese workers, avoiding their requests to examine the body. 'They believe he was killed by forest spirits,' he confirmed.

'Is there any evidence of a wound – perhaps a bite?'

'They say there isn't.'

'What do you think?' she asked.

'It's possible he died from poison. Did you see his face?'

'Do you think one of them did it?'

'Anything is likely. The Madurese have their own way of dealing with each other. Could've been someone decided to settle a dispute. It's hard to say.'

'Will the soldiers investigate?'

'What do you think?' Baird nodded in their direction. 'They're only interested in not having anyone rock the boat. What they earn from us in a month is more than the army pays them for a year.'

'Why don't you ask them to check it out?'

'Okay,' Baird agreed, the accompanying sigh signaling that he felt it would be a waste of time. He knew that the presence of the *Kopassus* soldiers offered no protection against snakes and wild animals, deducing that they were there only to observe, as some foreword guard. When the first Madurese workers had been reported missing, the soldiers had displayed disinterest, their apathetic attitude unchanged, even when the number grew.

Sharon checked the time. 'Chopper should be in, around noon.'

Baird was reminded of their conversation, from the evening before. 'They'll have the results with them?'

'That's what Jakarta said,' she looked skywards then back at the group huddled around the body. 'I'll leave this mess to you, Eric,' she said, then made her way down to where the drillers were starting their breakfast, determined not to permit the untimely death of another worker spoil what she expected would turn out to be a momentous day.

★ ★ ★ ★

Baird's eyes followed Sharon Ducay as she left him alone to deal with the death, the Filipino's shapely figure in no way stirring dormant desires – only distant recollections of an earlier life. He accepted that Sharon was, indeed, a beautiful woman, his admiration more for her resilience faced with these extreme, adverse conditions, than her obvious, physical charm. He had met a few female geologists and engineers in his time, but never anyone with Sharon Ducay's confidence and determination, nor skill in the field. Not for the first time since she appeared in his life did Baird wonder if there was someone waiting for her, back home. Although their relationship was symbiotic, Sharon had not made any attempt to share such secrets, the substance of their conversations almost always revolving around the Longdamai Sial operations.

His thoughts then turned to Mardidi, and what might lie ahead for them both. Now he was married to Pipi, Baird accepted that he would be expected to conform when in Jakarta, and that his ongoing liaison with Mardidi would need to be even more covert than before. As for appearances on site, he now openly shared his tent with Mardidi, in spite of the expatriate drillers' sniggers. He was concerned that he, too, did not simply disappear during the night.

When Sharon had moved the entire drilling operation upstream, relocating the camp directly where his Modang escorts had been slaughtered some six years before, Baird had been more than apprehensive about the move. Now, whenever darkness fell, memories of his narrow escape from death filled him with dread – the irony of the situation in no way lost, conscious that Sharon's decision to relocate to that specific location had been influenced by the very field notes he had fabricated, back in time.

Since then, exploration activities in Kalimantan had grown demonstrably. There had already been substantial discoveries made to the south, north and east of Longdamai. Baird knew that it would not be long before the Indonesian government would insist that BGC relinquish a substantial part of its area to other investors; this provision had been built into the CoW agreements to prevent large tracts of land being monopolized, without exploration work being carried out within a prescribed period of time. Once BGC slipped down the forfeiture trail, Baird knew that his stock in that company would be worthless, his own motivation for remaining with Sharon Ducay, to see the drilling program through.

With this in mind he, too, was anxious to learn how the assay reports read, the likely possibility that there would be no significant showings in these initial results, all too real.

★ ★ ★ ★

Jonathan Dau remained rock-still, stretched along the thick branch not three meters above the forest floor, his form perfectly blurred against its surrounds, the approaching Madurese worker unaware that he was about to die. The Dayak chief's hawk-eyes narrowed, measuring the distance between them, his grip on the base of the double-tipped spear firming as the laborer's head and shoulders came into reach. Exhaling slowly, he reached down with deadly aim and, with an almost effortless jab, punctured his victim's throat with twin, poisoned-tipped barbs, his second kill in less than twenty-four hours.

Jonathan's hate-filled eyes watched dispassionately as the man's head snapped up, eyes wide in disbelief as poison gripped his heart, the migrant's body locked in seizure as he collapsed, dead before hitting the ground – the only witness to the barbaric act, a solitary, black hornbill perched high in the canopy above. With one arm, the chief lowered his lean, powerful body from its perch and with a controlled fall, landed on his feet alongside the Madurese migrant's lifeless form, then slipped silently away, disappearing into the forest depths before the body was discovered.

Two hours passed before the Dayak chief arrived at the familiar gorge where he paused to admire the cascading waterfall, and the serene setting that embraced his Longhouse community below. Across the deep pond where the river split into two, long, twisted vines dangled from treetops, and he watched, observing the village children frolicking about in the water, their boisterous play triggering memories of his own, uncomplicated childhood. A shout carried across and up the escarpment and he spotted a boy high in a tree, preparing to plunge. Jonathan waited for the splash – silently applauding the dangerous act before continuing on his way.

Following a narrow, timeworn path down to the water's palm-covered banks Jonathan vanished as he entered an elongated cavern, the natural pathway hidden by thunderous spray. He crossed to the other side, exiting onto a rope walkway that led him home, waving and returning children's calls as he went, his return observed from a distance, sending the village mechanic scrambling to start the Perkins diesel. Before Jonathan Dau had entered the Longhouse, the generator's familiar beat could be heard throughout the community, their concerns for his safety immediately put to rest. As he walked through the maze of rooms, he stopped to acknowledge others, bending down to speak briefly to an ageing, toothless woman who peered up through loving eyes, greeting him with a wide, betel-nut red smile.

'Have you been faithful to me in my absence?' he teased the widow.

'Go away with you or I'll take you to my knee!' she cackled, warding him off with one hand, while covering her mouth with the other.

'Here, I have brought you something.' Jonathan reached into the canvas bag attached to his waist and extracted a black dotted orchid, placing the flower in her hair. *'Now you will have to beat the young men off...'* he laughed, rising to full height and continuing to his own quarters. The villagers knew not to disturb their chief at this time, their activities respectfully subdued while Jonathan bathed, then meditated; the cleansing process a matter of routine and discipline, and in a way, an act of expiation on his part.

Refreshed, the Dayak leader attended to his administrative chores, then opened his door to his fellow villagers, encouraging them to come to him with their problems. Together, they would resolve these through discussion, deliberation and, hopefully, consensus. With village matters cleared from his mind, Jonathan would join other elders following the evening meal, a forum that provided the unofficial council the opportunity to discuss matters of relevance and import to the *Penehing Dayak* people. On this occasion, as leader, Jonathan opened the informal meeting by reading a response from the newly appointed, provincial governor in Samarinda who continued to parrot Jakarta's official line. When he finished, Jonathan passed the official letter around, the elders' faces grim as they absorbed the import of what their future might now bring.

'The Governor has again refused to intercede on our behalf, with respect to our sacred locations,' the chief explained, solemnly, *'which we should interpret as meaning that the homes of our ancestral spirits will no longer be sacrosanct.'* Jonathan swept an arm through the air. *'The Javanese are carving up our ancestral land for others and, soon, if they are not stopped, we will be under their feet.'*

'Perhaps you should go to Samarinda?' one proposed, others nodding their support.

'I intend doing so, next week,' Jonathan revealed, *'I think it's time I met the new governor.'*

'Don't forget the radio,' another reminded. The provincial authorities had also refused to fund replacement equipment, the communi-

ty's communications frequently down due to Samarinda's failure to send spare-parts.

'While I am away, it is imperative that the younger men avoid any open conflict with the interlopers. They are not to cross the river for any reason.' The elders again nodded, all in agreement with Jonathan's instructions, aware that hot-blooded village youths could easily embroil the community in direct confrontation with the migrants.

Jonathan knew that the one-man war he had waged against the migrants was certain to inflame Jakarta interests. Sadly, he also realized that his measures merely delayed the inevitable, that the powerful timber and mining factions would eventually push further and further into the territory, bringing armed soldiers to defend their interests. In the absence of any resistance, he firmly believed that the Dayaks would be pushed from their land and become as endangered as other Kalimantan forest dwellers had – possibly, within a relatively short space of time.

For Jonathan, it mattered not whether the migrants were Madurese or Javanese. It was clear that Madura's poor soil and lack of industry had driven waves of poverty-stricken villagers to accept the central government's offer to relocate and, although he understood their plight, in no way could he accept that Dayaks should be displaced in their favor. In his mind, the entire transmigration scheme had been doomed from the outset, the architects of the plan having failed to identify the irreconcilable differences that existed between the ethnic groups. The *Penehing Dayaks* retained their traditional culture of ancestor worship, and animism – these beliefs in fierce contradiction to Islamic code.

★ ★ ★ ★

Jonathan was aware that at least half of the men gathered around him had, at one time or another, taken enemy heads, as this had been an accepted practice during their generation. He recalled his father often breaking into laughter, while recounting how the Dutch colonialists were convinced that they had succeeded in persuading the Dayaks to use buffalo heads in place of human sacrifice. In reality, the practice of using human skulls never really died; his secretly hidden harvest, evidence of this – the ultimate penalty imposed on those who had desecrated the holy site.

Months before, when the distant, but familiar sounds of helicopter activity first alerted Jonathan that outsiders had entered his domain, alarmed, he had hurried through the forest – overwhelmed when he discovered what was happening. He crept as close as the forest's thick underbrush would allow, selected an observation post in the fork of a tree, then settled down to monitor the scene. When a number of sturdily built foreigners climbed out of the JetRanger and made their way along the river's edge, he feared the worst, his suspicions confirmed with the arrival of longboats carrying supplies and equipment, and a task force of men. Jonathan waited, his chest filling with rage as an area was cleared, and what he correctly determined to be a drilling rig, was transported to the site. The helicopter returned; the Dayak chief recognizing Eric Baird as he climbed from the aircraft. An Asian woman had followed – lifting a wide brimmed hat from her head she ran her fingers through short, black hair then stood, hands on hips in arrogant style absorbing the scene. Jonathan's attention focused on her face, attempting to determine her origins. He could see that her features were not dissimilar to those of Menadonese Indonesians but, from her confident strut and authoritative manner, Jonathan decided she was foreign.

As the day wore on and it became apparent that the longboat men and their coolies were to withdraw, Jonathan reconsidered his assessment of the situation, concluding that the incursion was temporary in nature – and that the area was to be used only as a staging point for operations, further upstream. He returned to his village, satisfied that the intruders would soon be gone. The following morning he established radio contact with the governor's office in Samarinda, to determine the exploration group's final destination. As village chief he was entitled to such information and, when he was advised that Longdamai Sial was, in fact, the area to be drilled, Jonathan had called a meeting of the elders to establish what could be done. Incensed with the news, the council had decided unanimously to take whatever measures available, to prevent the operation from proceeding.

Over the next weeks during what became a waiting game, Jonathan maintained vigil at the site, his curiosity aroused by the absence of any real activity. Then, when a flotilla of longboats arrived carrying more than one hundred Madurese, he set about hindering the operation by killing those who ventured into the jungle alone, poisoning many with his deadly-tipped tine; his tally, after three months of stalking the Madurese as they penetrated deeper into his forest, now rapidly approaching twenty.

Even with his moderate success, Jonathan was forced to accept that he was losing the battle. Saddened by the inevitable, Jonathan knew that survival of the *Penehing* and other Dayak communities could only be guaranteed through a united, Dayak front. And with this purpose in mind, Jonathan Dau, respected leader and spokesperson for the Upper Mahakam tribes, initiated dialogue with other community leaders, to determine how they could achieve this aim.

★ ★ ★ ★

Chapter Eighteen

MALAYSIA – KUALA LUMPUR

After almost an hour of suffering the taxi's monotonous, diesel-engine drone as they were driven along Kuala Lumpur's congested freeways from Subang Airport into the city, Stewart could only wonder how long this journey would take once the new Sepang Airport had been completed, in 1998.

Although their view remained hampered by the weather as they passed by landmarks, many, remnants of British colonial times, Campbell wiped breath-fogged windows clear enabling Angela to see, unaware that her mind was elsewhere. Rain fell, incessantly, reducing the inner city, early-evening traffic to a crawl and, as they entered the central business district, the Indian-Malay driver's erratic driving and the constant stop-start jerking motion came dangerously close to taking its toll.

'If he doesn't take his foot of that brake I'm going to throw up,' Campbell announced. Finally, they passed through the Golden Triangle, revitalized central city district and arrived at the Equatorial Hotel, Campbell groaning thankfully when hotel porters appeared and gathered their luggage. They checked into the hotel Angela, surprising Stewart by suggesting an early night.

'Will you have breakfast with me before the opening ceremony?'

'Of course,' he assured, *'but what about right now? It's still early.'*

'I hope you don't mind, Stewart, but I'd like to spend time going over my presentation.'

He tried to hide his disappointment. *'But that's not until the second day. You can't stay in your room on our first night away together. Why don't you freshen up, then I'll take you for a walk around town?'*

Angela waved when she recognized a delegate from her Ministry. *'Only if you promise that we'll be back inside an hour?'*

Campbell acquiesced. *'Okay.'*

They had completed the registration formalities and were now being escorted to their rooms. *'Give me a call when you're ready,'* Campbell suggested, then went off to unpack.

★ ★ ★ ★

Angela took the time to read through her dissertation. Absolutely determined to maximize the opportunity destiny had provided, she remained resolute in her commitment to raise international awareness of the indigenous communities in Kalimantan. More than two hundred delegates from the ASEAN member nations would attend the conference, and Angela remained confident that such an august gathering would attract immense media attention. She would take advantage of this forum to raise regional awareness with respect to the demise of the Dayak people, and destruction of their traditional habitat. When the phone rang, she glanced at the bedside clock, surprised that it was already past nine.

'Thought you might have dozed off,' Campbell's concerned voice reminded her of their appointment.

Angela frowned. *'I'm really sorry, Stewart.'*

'I understand,' he offered, *'but it's not that late. Do you want to slip out and get something to eat?'*

Angela sat twirling a biro between thumb and forefinger, her thoughts preoccupied with the papers spread across her bed. *'Stewart, if you promise not to hate me too much, I'd prefer to remain in the room revising my presentation.'* She waited, the ensuing break in their conversation evidencing his disappointment. *'Stewart?'*

'Have they changed the program?' he came back, *'I thought you weren't on until the second day?'*

Angela knew now that he was annoyed. *'No, the program hasn't been changed. It's just that I really need to have this…'* She looked around the bed in quiet desperation, wishing he would understand. *'…this…finished in time. There's still so much I have to do. You do recall that this presentation is entirely in English?'*

A wordless vacuum filled the line while she waited for his response. Then, *'Okay, Angela,'* she heard Campbell surrender, *'conditional that you give me all of your time once the conference is finished.'*

Relieved, she was already sorting through papers with one hand as she gave him this commitment. *'All yours…I promise!'* and replaced the receiver leaving Campbell waiting for more.

★ ★ ★ ★

Wondering why he had even bothered to accompany Angela on this journey, Campbell decided to go out alone, determined to salvage whatever he could of the evening. Making his way through a lobby crowded with conference delegates returning from dinner, the doors to the lounge on his right opened as he was about to leave the hotel, the music spilling from inside immediately grabbing his attention. He stepped into the Latino, music-charged atmosphere, his spirits instantly lifting as he was escorted to a dimly lit table. Campbell sat, spellbound, fascinated with the scene, the crowded dance floor filled with guests tangoing to the band's rendition of Julio Iglesias' *Viejas Tradiciones*. Staff slipped between tables taking orders, Campbell soon settling down with his first drink, caught off-guard when a young, Eurasian girl slipped alongside and ran her hand, suggestively, along his thigh.

'You dance with me, *lah*?' she asked, voiced raised in competition with the band. Although tempted, he had never learned the steps and had no desire to learn.

'No, not tonight.'

'You stay in this hotel?' she inquired, nestling closer.

Campbell finished the remaining Chivas and, when a waitress

appeared he refused another, motioning for the check.

'You take me to your room, okay?' the girl insisted, misreading the signs, gathering the remaining bar nuts in one hand, and shoveling these into her face with practised speed. Campbell grimaced as her salty palm touched his leg, and he brushed it aside.

'Not tonight.'

'You pay me two hundred *ringgit*. Okay-*lah*?' she insisted, Campbell silently scoffing at the inflated offer which translated into a hundred U.S. dollars.

'I'll give you fifty ringgit,' he said in Malay, hoping the insult would drive her away.

'So, you speak Malay, very fluent, ya?' she seemed pleased. *'Tell you what, make it one hundred and I will spend the whole night.'*

By now, Campbell's eyes had adjusted to the smoke-filled surrounds and he could clearly see the girl's face, hard, devoid of any animation, and lavishly treated with cheap cosmetics. He had seen thousands like it before, lining the roads that meandered through Jakarta's Ancol red-light district, back in Indonesia. He signed the tab, extracted a ten-*ringgit* note from his wallet, and placed this in her hand. *'I have a wife, upstairs,'* he explained then rose, leaving the bargirl behind examining the crisp note while one eye roamed the room for another challenge.

Outside, Campbell considered taking a stroll to kill time, abandoning this idea when confronted by an ankle-twisting array of broken-concrete slabs, lining the footpath. He checked the time and, as it was still too early to retire, caught a taxi the short distance to the Hilton Hotel. In introspective mood, he remained propped at the bar re-examining his feelings for Angela Dau, returning to the Equatorial in the early morning hours, slightly drunk and none the wiser.

★ ★ ★ ★

Royal-blue banners inscribed with gold lettering had been affixed to stage curtains and surrounding walls, celebrating the event, the main hotel conference hall already filled to capacity. Towards the rear where latecomers had been obliged to stand, journalists' cameras rolled as the conference chairman introduced the first speaker, for the second day of the conference. The room broke into applause when Angela Dau walked elegantly across the podium, and curtsied lightly to the Malaysian prince, who had agreed to chair the proceedings.

Dressed in traditional *kain-kebaya*, the colorful sarong and lace blouse combination accentuated Angela's beautiful form, the high heels and meticulously wound hair earning gasps from the younger men sitting in the front rows as she appeared. '*Terima kasih,* your Excellency,' Angela thanked the Prince, and the Malaysian hosts, then turned to her audience, and smiled. Hushed by her beauty, the predominantly-male assembly crushed into attentive silence as her eyes roamed the sea of faces, settling finally on Stewart Campbell – reassured, when he raised clasped hands in support. Then, recognizing a number of media representatives that had been introduced earlier, she deliberately widened her smile in their direction, the hall instantly erupting with dazzling, electronic flash. Angela's beauty alone was enough to gain her the attention of the crowded hall but, when she commenced speaking, those in attendance immediately fell under her spell, captivated by the alluring, husky resonance and conviction in her voice.

'...and, when we talk of implementing policy to guarantee environmental integrity, more often than not, social considerations, which are fundamental to the very survival of many our indigenous groups, are ignored by governments in favor of foreign investment.' Angela paused. 'Today, I wish to present, as a case study, how mining has impacted on the people in my home province of East Kalimantan where, as I speak, women and children are dying, victims of ignorance – victims of multinational mining interests which are so obviously devoid of any social conscience.' As she paused, a murmur of concern swept the room. Unfazed, Angela continued. 'Ladies and gentlemen, in order to gain a clearer picture of what is happening, we must identify the driving forces which continuously deliver such disastrous outcomes. I can state, quite categorically, that amongst the

Penehing Dayaks of Eastern Kalimantan, although the ongoing harvesting of forests contributes most to the destruction of our natural habitat, it is the international mining houses' endless pursuit for gold across our traditional lands, that consistently threatens the survival of our culture, and directly, the Dayak social order.'

At the back of the hall, a New Zealand journalist dropped the lens he was changing, distracting all present. Angela recovered from the interruption then drew a breath before continuing.

'It is now possible to measure many of the long term effects gold mining operations will have on the Mahakam River catchment area and the indigenous groups that live in these surrounds. But, first, I believe it imperative that we understand more about this precious metal which, unfortunately for the Dayak people, has been discovered in abundance throughout our traditional lands – a metal that is, in fact, non-essential to society's survival, yet manages to generate more harm than good, throughout most societies.

'More than eighty percent of all gold mined ends up as jewelry. In short, the metal is almost entirely cosmetic and this, ladies and gentlemen, is the real tragedy.' Angela glanced at her notes. 'In the United States of America, for every one ton of gold produced, there are three million tons of waste rock left to scar the landscape. This is the home of RTZ-CRA and Anglo-American, which, together, control a third of all global production. Last year, more than three thousand, six hundred tons of gold were mined, worldwide, an increase of fifty percent over the past fifteen years, and most at the expense of our environment and indigenous communities in Asia, Africa and South America.

'In the distant village of Longdamai where I was born, for the immediate future, the people can still eat the river fish, without concern. But, if one were to travel only a hundred kilometers downriver where the foreign miner, Newton International operates, the situation would drastically change. There, we would find thousands of children in danger of becoming idiots because they consume mercury-polluted river water or fish caught along the mighty Mahakam or its tributaries – where dangerous chemicals are used in separation processes, the residual recklessly discarded, endangering the health of those who live in this environment. The tailings from the Newton mine leach sulphuric acid, mercury, copper and arsenic into the river system rendering its water unfit for drink or use. And, wherever mercury is dumped, bacteria transform the liquid metal into a far more toxic form of methyl mercury. Almost all of the village children tested in the past year have ten, to twenty times the normal levels of mercury in their systems. Young children suffering muscle weakness, breathing difficulties and blurred vision is not uncommon, because economic expediency over environmental considerations is turning the once pristine Mahakam eco-system into an unsafe habitat for us all.

'But, contamination comes in other forms as well. The influx of transmigrant laborers and their families from Java and Madura has created overwhelming social and health problems amongst the indigenous peoples, many of whom have now been forcibly resettled to accommodate mining operations on their soil. This has led to numerous outbreaks of cholera, and the introduction of sexually transmitted diseases. Now, when we walk through the back alleys of our provincial capital we find children of ten and twelve years working as prostitutes, and once-proud landowners having lost their traditional land, begging at the side of the road. Of course, gold has always been…'

Angela continued, her spellbound audience unaware that she was now using her father's words, as she went on to describe how Dominion Mining had arrived, unannounced, and proceeded to desecrate the *Penehing-Dayaks'* most sacred site.

★ ★ ★ ★

Stewart Campbell remained transfixed, engrossed in her emotive presentation, amazed with Angela's apparent oratory skills as she built her argument, while reaching out and touching the delegates so deeply. Spontaneous applause frequently interrupted the proceedings as indigenous Malays, Filipinos and Thai groups, recognizing issues so close to their own hearts, acknowledged Angela's courage in raising these, at so public a forum.

'…and, it is an unfortunate fact that most of the of the so-called 'new gold' is being produced here, in South East Asian countries, because of our governments' less stringent waste minimization requirements. Ironically, with my fellow Asians responsible for more than seventy percent of all gold jewelry purchases, we are guilty of creating the very demand that drives the multinationals to our shores and we should, therefore, shoulder some of the consequences.'

Campbell checked his wrist for the time, staggered to discover that she had already been speaking for the best part of an hour. Turning his attention back to the dais where Angela's hypnotic effect continued to captivate, he smiled, an intimate thought passing through his mind and he closed his eyes, briefly, allowing Angela's velvet voice to fill his ears.

'I therefore call upon the mining industry, both foreign and domestic to take radical steps to curb the deadly social and environmental impacts unleashed upon our communities. *Terima kasih.'* Angela closed, thanked the audience and bowed respectfully in the direction of the Malaysian Prince, the hall exploding into tumultuous applause as delegates rose to reward her with a standing ovation.

Campbell felt nothing but adoration as she stood before her peers, her adrenaline-filled face ablaze with confidence, savoring this most important milestone in her career. Thronged as she stepped down from the dais to make her way to the back of the hall, Campbell kept his distance permitting Angela to respond to the barrage of eager journalists, impressed as she addressed a number of foreign correspondents in fluent stride. Finally, observing that the Press was done, he approached, clapping politely as he stood before her. *'Well, you certainly made an impression – and won more than a few hearts!'*

Angela beamed. *'To tell the truth, I was terrified when I stepped onto the dais. Then, when I made my first comments about the multinationals, I wasn't all that confident that the delegates would be as supportive as they were. I'm really pleased with their response, Stewart.'* She placed her hand on his arm. *'How do you think it went – did I make many mistakes?'*

Campbell smiled reassuringly. *'I'm sure tomorrow's papers will be filled with nothing but accolades. They all fell in love with you.'*

Angela laughed, and pinched his arm, affectionately. *'Including the Prince?'*

'Including his royal highness or excellency or whatever…' he teased. *'Say, Angela, do you plan on attending the remaining lectures?'*

'There are a few speakers I wouldn't want to miss. Why?'

'No, it's just that I thought we could take some time to have a look around the city, take in some of the sights. Perhaps even celebrate?'

Angela mused before responding then, indicating her costume, *'I'd like to change out of this. There's another presentation I'm keen to attend before lunch, and the other around three this afternoon. Why don't we meet for lunch then I'll go to the other session and, when it's finished, take a look around the city together?'*

'Great,' Campbell was pleased. *'We can grab a sandwich, poolside, if you like?'*

Angela considered this. *'The pool is tempting.'* Then, as an idea came to mind, *'Stewart, I haven't been swimming for months. Why don't we meet at the pool, say, around four when the last session is finished, take a swim and then go sight-seeing later?'*

'What about lunch?'

'I'll join the other delegates for the buffet. That way, I'll be able to clear everything so we can have the rest of the time here to ourselves.'

Campbell knew he could not refuse, recognizing that Angela was still pumped with success, and would enjoy the moment amongst her peers. *'Okay, that's fine. It wouldn't do me any harm to attend some of the other discussion groups. The pool it is, then. We can have a swim then go for an early dinner. I have something I want to show you.'*

★ ★ ★ ★

For Angela, the day continued to reward. Given the opportunity to meet and mingle with respected environmentalists, geologists and politicians, she quickly realized the value of networking, openly soliciting commitments for future communications from many of the delegates. Also, in response to her own presentation, Angela found herself included in general discussion – flattered by the recognition, as she had not expected any real support, in what had traditionally been a male-dominated, mining world. Angela had been deliberately provocative in her address, and was pleased to observe that she had at least sparked some semblance of open debate amongst the few female delegates present.

Although Angela accepted that her participation at the ASEAN convention would not bring immediate relief to the Dayak people, she remained determined that persistent lobbying outside of Indonesia would eventually fuel international outrage, causing Jakarta to revisit its humanitarian issues. But, of one result she could be certain – the other members of the Indonesian delegation were not at all pleased with Angela, several warning that she would be asked to account for her speech, upon return to Jakarta. Angela had accepted their criticism, graciously, confident that her newfound profile amongst the other ASEAN participants would provide her with adequate protection from potential, disciplinary measures.

The rest of the day passed quickly, by which time Angela had attended the remaining lectures of interest and, as the hour approached for her appointment with Campbell, she slipped down to the hotel's shopping arcade for something appropriate to wear at the pool. Angela knew that she had seriously neglected him over the past days, even at the official banquet when, at the insistence of the Malaysian Prince, seating arrangements had been altered to accommodate her presence at his table. She acknowledged that Stewart had been most understanding with the unexpected demands on her time, and was determined to make amends.

Now, back in her room, concerned that she should have searched wider for a single-piece suit she stood, naked, facing the full-length mirror, gently running her hands from breast to thigh, contemplating her figure and the challenging two-piece swimming costume, laid out on the bed, behind. Then, with an air of resignation, she tried the bikini – troubled with the signal this outfit would surely send to Stewart Campbell. She finished dressing and peered out the window down towards the beautifully sculpted tropical garden surrounding the pool, relieved that the sky was relatively clear.

★ ★ ★ ★

Campbell lay reading, poolside, when a low, soft whistle of appreciation from a group of goggle-eyed guests drew his attention and he glanced up, instinctively flashing a smile as the naturally tanned, bikini-clad figure came into full, frontal view – his face collapsing into disbelief when he recognized the stunning form approaching was Angela. Paralyzed with surprise, Campbell could then only gape while the click of high heels on paving registered time as Angela's long, slender legs carried her sensuous shape into immediate focus.

She wore a shoulder-to-knee chiffon wrap that trailed from her side, the lines of her body accentuated by a natural, rhythmic sway. Angela came to a stop, placed her towel on the empty deck chair, the loosely worn wrap sliding from her shoulders as she turned.

'It's hot,' was all she said, removing sunglasses and wide-brimmed hat, then flicked her head to one side.

Campbell continued to admire in speechless wonderment as she bent down and slipped out of her shoes, providing him with a generous view of firm breasts.

'Aren't you coming in?' she invited, stepping towards the pool.

Realizing he had never seen Angela even partially undressed, until now, he could do nothing but stare in awe as Angela launched herself into the water, glided to the other side of the pool, and then beckoned.

'Come on, Stewart, what are you waiting for?'

Campbell could not help overhearing a male voice remark that if Stewart did not go to her, he would, the response from the man's fellow guests filling their surrounds with guffaws and other inaudible comment.

He rose, stretched to full height, walked as casually as he could to the water's edge, and dived into the pool. With two powerful strokes he was by her side. *'I was beginning to think you'd forgotten me, again,'* Campbell placed his hands on her waist, pulling her gently forward, her long, black hair trailing behind.

Playfully, Angela resisted, slipping easily from his grasp. *'I'll race you to the deep end!'*

Campbell smiled mischievously. *'Race? Okay!'* and plunged forward, attempting to catch her off-guard.

Without hesitation, Angela struck out, her graceful strokes taking her to the front, their race over within seconds. His heart racing, Campbell could only stare at his companion in wonderment.

'My God, Angela, where did you learn to swim like that?' he asked, breathless. *'Why didn't you tell me you were this good?'*

She laughed. *'I haven't been swimming in such a long time. All the children in my village learn to swim at an early age.'*

'I always thought that Indonesians were terrified of swimming,' he managed, deciding at that moment to spend more time in the gym when they returned to Jakarta.

'Then you're in for quite a surprise, Mister Campbell!' Angela's hand hit the water playfully, the stinging spray momentarily blinding him before he lunged, locking her inside his arms.

'You're the one in for the surprise, Miss Dau,' he retaliated, dragging their bodies down together, Angela twisting and kicking defiantly as she struggled to escape. His feet touched the bottom, just as the calf muscle in his left leg locked and he doubled with the severity of the pain, swallowing water as he struggled for the surface.

'Are you okay?' Angela held an arm and attempted to steer him to the pool's steps. Campbell spluttered, coughing up chlorinated pool water as waves of excruciating pain gripped his leg muscle, and he heard voices call out, suddenly aware of others in the water, alongside.

'Heart attack?' the guest suggested, supporting Campbell's weight as they moved back to the edge of the pool.

'I don't think so,' Angela replied, with concern, 'more like a cramp.'

Assisted from the pool, Campbell's acute embarrassment grew as others came to his aid, everyone present offering medical advice.

'Massage his leg,' someone suggested.

'No, that won't do any good. She's cracked him in the balls. Look at how he's holding himself!' quipped another from a distance.

'Should we ask the attendant to call the hotel doctor?' the man who had come to Campbell's aid asked, unable to take his eyes off

Angela.

Campbell managed a string of squeaky words, insisting that he would be all right, refusing their offers of assistance.

Gradually, the pain subsided, and he was able to walk. Angela supported Campbell's limping shape as he hobbled back to the other end of the pool.

'Well, that was embarrassing!' he slumped into a chair.

'Could happen to anyone, Stewart.'

'I know that. It's just that the timing couldn't have been worse.'

'Why?' Angela threw the wrap around her shoulders.

Campbell watched as she dried her hair. *'Cause I was about to challenge you to another race; I think I gave you too much start back there.'*

'There'll be other opportunities,' she smiled impishly. *'But the result will be the same.'*

'We'll see,' was all he said, relaxing now under the afternoon sun's fading rays.

They remained resting in the deck chairs until the tropical night descended, the light variation in temperatures enough to drive them back indoors.

★ ★ ★ ★

'Are you certain that you're up to it?' Angela asked, not overly anxious to go out.

'Absolutely, I asked management to send up a masseur from the gymnasium. He says it's not unusual for calf muscles to lock like that. Something to do with a low salt diet – speaking of which, I'm starved. Are you ready?'

'Why don't we have something in the room, Stewart?'

'No, I'm really okay now. Besides, this is our third night in KL and you haven't seen anything yet. I thought we would grab a taxi down to the Petaling Street night-market area and find a restaurant there.'

'You're only going out because of me. I'd be just as happy to stay in and have something here. Besides, it's raining again. There's not much point in going out sightseeing in this weather.'

'We'll borrow an umbrella from the concierge,' he tried, frustration creeping into his voice.

'Stewart, there'll be other opportunities. Let's stay in.'

'No,' he refused, stubbornly. *'We'll go out for dinner, first, then find a quiet lounge somewhere.'*

★ ★ ★ ★

An hour later they faced each other across a table littered with broken, Sri Lankan crab shell. The messy, Singapore-style, stir-fried whole crabs that had been cooked in the traditional, buttery, milk and curry sauce now but a culinary memory. Across from their table where the room lay divided by a series of display tanks filled with live seafood, lobsters, fish and crabs, all on offer for the restaurant's patrons, Angela observed a large group of children standing together, discussing their preferences.

'They seem happy,' she commented, Campbell following her gaze.

'Why wouldn't they be?' he asked.

'You don't see it?' she asked, surprised.

'See what?' he turned, but still did not understand. *'Just a bunch of kids working out what they're going to eat.'*

'It's more than that, Stewart,' she pointed out, *'there's at least three different ethnic groups, all happily spending time together. Something that one would never see outside of a school in Indonesia.'*

'It's probably a community outing,' Stewart surmised, *'and before you become too supportive of Malaysia's ethnic tolerance, I remind you of the bloody race riots of 1969 when Chinese children were barricaded inside cinemas, the buildings then torched. The death tolls resulting from those riots were on a par with what we've seen in Jakarta.'* He filled a glass with soda and quenched a *sambal*-inspired thirst, hoping he would not regret the generous servings of chili sauce and bell peppers that had accompanied the meal.

'Perhaps so,' she argued, *'but look at them now. At least there is evidence here that multi-cultural groups can co-exist, unlike you know where.'*

Campbell shook his head at her naiveté. *'Angela, believe me when I tell you that this country is far more likely to explode into race-related riots than Indonesia. Suharto keeps the lid on everything back home whereas here, that's not so easy with the Chinese and Indians representing something like forty percent of the population. The indigenous Malays are split, ethnically, with diverse cultural differences. Granted, these are not as extreme as one would find in Indonesia, but they do, nevertheless, exist. It's not so easy here for the government to suppress the people as it is in your neck of the woods, although some might argue that the Internal Security Act provides the Prime Minister with far too much power. Malaysia grew to nationhood out of a British colonial past, whereas Indonesia became a republic only after warring with their Dutch masters and Japanese occupation. Malaysia had the advantage of an orderly transition to independence, and follows the Westminster system of government, draconian in many ways that it may be. But, don't be fooled by what you see on the surface. There is a growing Islamic fundamentalist movement here, and that could result in Malaysia being torn apart should extremists start to exert influence over the relatively moderate, local Moslems.'*

Angela peered across at Campbell. *'So. You seem to be very well versed in local affairs. Ever had a Malay girlfriend?'*

Her question caught him by surprise. *'No...why?'*

She smiled, widely. *'Just curious, that's all.'*

'Would it bother you if I had?'

'Not at all,' she answered, observing him closely. *'What you did before is of no interest to me – providing it remains in your past.'*

'Everyone has some baggage in their life.'

'I don't,' she declared, lightheartedly.

'Then you are indeed a very fortunate young lady.'

'And one with principles?' dark, pencil-thin lines above her eyes turned upwards with the questioning face. Campbell knew she was hiding a smile, familiar now with many of her ways.

'If you say so.'

'You don't think I have principles?' Angela feigned surprise.

'Or course you have,' he raised his hands in mock defeat. *'I think it's time to go.'*

Angela hesitated. *'No, Stewart, if you don't mind, let's talk some more. Here, not back in the hotel.'*

Campbell frowned. *'Something I've said has upset you?'*

'No. It's nothing like that.'

'Okay, then what?' he asked, filled with a sense of foreboding.

'Well, it's difficult to know where to start – or continue.'

'Does it have something to do with our relationship?'

'Yes.'

'Then tell me what it is, that's bothering you.'

'I meant to say something at the swimming pool, earlier.'

'What, Angela? God, you're killing me here!'

'It's about the costume I wore. I didn't want you to get the wrong idea.'

'That stunning outfit that barely covered your beautiful figure? – Don't remember a thing,' his frivolous attempt fell flat, into an empty silence.

The Chinese manager ordered staff to clean the table and remove remaining dishes, sending the couple a message that it would be appropriate for them to leave. More than twenty guests remained queued, waiting patiently for a table in the popular restaurant.

'It was the only costume I could find, Stewart. I was in a hurry to get there on time. Having let you down so much over the past two days, I didn't want to disappoint you again.'

'You didn't disappoint me, Angela. You are a very beautiful woman. Why hide it?'

'You don't seem to understand,' she looked around the crowded restaurant, unaware that they were expected to leave. *'I need to discuss where we are, together, as friends.'*

'Friends?' Campbell jerked back in his seat. *'Surely we mean more to each other than 'friends'?'*

'I'm sorry, Stewart. I'm not expressing myself very well.'

'You didn't seem to have that problem, today,' he said, somewhat churlishly.

'Please, Stewart, I don't want us to argue. I only wanted to…'

Campbell leaned over the table. *'Let's get out of here and go somewhere quiet. There's something I need to say to you and this is not the place.'*

'Stewart…'

'Angela,' he interrupted, again, leaning on the table with arms crossed. *'Tell me this. Do you love me?'*

Angela had expected he would ask. *'Yes, I do.'*

'Then, what is this all about?' Campbell demanded, glancing angrily

at a woman on the adjacent table whom he thought may be eavesdropping.

'It's about commitments, Stewart. That's what I'm trying to explain.'

'Commitments?'

'Yes.'

'I don't understand, Angela. I haven't seen anyone else for at least five, maybe six months. That should say something about my feelings for you.'

'I don't mean that type of commitment.'

'Angela, help me out here. I'm lost. What are you trying to say?'

It was Angela who now leaned closer. She lowered her voice. *'I'm trying to explain that I'm not going to have sex with you.'*

Campbell's disappointment edged closer to anger. *'If you had no intention of pursuing a relationship with me, what in the hell am I doing here?'*

Angela could see that his judgment was now impaired. *'Stewart, don't do this, please?'*

She reached out, her open hand lying on the table too difficult for him to resist. His hand slipped into hers, both grasping the other in that moment of uncertainty.

'What brought you to this decision?' he asked, grimfaced.

'It wasn't an easy decision,' she said.

'But, one you made all by yourself.' He fabricated a smile, withdrew his hand, looked around with a touch of desperation, spotted a waitress and waved her over. *'I'll have a double Chivas,'* he said. The manager stepped forward before the girl could take the order. Experience told him that the couple was likely to remain and he intended inviting them to the bar, releasing the table.

'Thank you, sir, would you mind…'

'Stewart, is that necessary?' Angela interjected.

He looked up at the manager then back at Angela. He shook his head. 'No, I guess not. Cancel that. We're going home. Would you mind giving us a few more minutes?'

The man looked down towards reception, mumbled something in Chinese and, spotting another group in the process of leaving, swept across the room to arrange for the table to be reset.

'You must try to understand,' Angela said, sadly, once the manager was out of earshot.

'Seems already clear enough, for me.'

Angela reached back across the table and took his hand, again. *'Stewart, we have known each other for some time now and I do have deep feelings for you.'*

Campbell's mouth cracked wide with a forced smile. *'Well, at least that's…'*

'Please, Stewart, let me finish. There's a great deal more that you have to learn about me, my people, my responsibilities, just as there's so much left for me to achieve before I can consider entering into a commitment to marry. Somehow, I knew you were going to ask, and I believe that you really, do love me. But…'

'Why is it that I suddenly have this feeling, that all of this has something to do with what happened today?'

'The conference?'

'Yes.'

Angela's eyes fell. *'I don't feel it's possible for us to have the relationship you want, right at this time. There's so much more that I can do for my people, Stewart, and it wouldn't be fair on either of us if we were to consider marriage, at this time.'*

Campbell's image of their relationship was rapidly disappearing into shadows. He had not expected any of this. *'There's no reason why you couldn't continue with your career,'* he argued.

'Working for my people's rights is more than a career,' she shot back, not intending to rebuke, *'and must take priority over everything else.'*

'Are you saying that you'll never marry?'

'No. What I'm trying to explain is that I need more time.'

'How long?'

'I'm sorry, Stewart,' she answered, *'I can't answer you that, right now.'*

★ ★ ★ ★

During their flight back to Jakarta the following morning Stewart Campbell remained distant, contemplating a future without Angela Dau. They would remain close friends and, although she had not said it in so many words, when they had parted the evening before

Campbell was left with the impression that she would not overly object if they were to terminate their relationship, completely.

Disappointed, hurt and in disconsolate mood, he had woken with a Chivas hangover, and prepared for the two-hour, return flight to Indonesia. He phoned Angela and suggested they meet for breakfast, then sauntered down to the ground-level coffee shop to wait. By then, most of the conference delegates had already departed, one, recalling having seen Campbell and Angela together, reached over and tapped Stewart on the shoulder.

'Have you seen this yet?'

Campbell turned, his face a blank of recognition and, with a forced smile, accepted the newspaper, his eyes falling immediately to the page-one photograph, of Miss Angela Dau. The caption announced, *"Dayaks Deserve Better Deal"*, and when Campbell had finished reading the feature story, he knew that Angela's career, if not personal safety, would now be in jeopardy. That Angela may have anticipated the possibility of a negative reaction in Jakarta to her speech, and had deliberately placed their relationship on hold, to protect him, came to mind. He had challenged her at breakfast, Angela raising his ire when she refused to discuss the matter further. They had left for the airport together, in awkward mood, exchanging only a few words during the flight, Campbell now resigned to the reality that he may have lost Angela to the greater, Dayak cause, forever.

⋆ ⋆ ⋆ ⋆

Longdamai Sial Mining Camp – Mahakam River

The yellow-toothed grin on Eric Baird's face said it all. He cast his eyes over the data once more, his expression that of a man who had just won the lottery.

'According to this,' he said, one hand tapping the analytical laboratory's report, 'you, Miss Ducay, have done it again!'

'We, Eric, we! After all, it's been a team effort.' Sharon needed that they all bask in any credit associated with the fabricated find.

'We should do a preliminary estimate on tonnages,' Baird

recommended.

Sharon could see that Baird's infectious excitement could as easily work against them. 'I'd prefer to wait for the next batch of assays.'

'Why?' Baird had already run some basic estimates through his head, 'No harm in getting a little enthusiastic, Sharon.'

'No point in getting them excited,' she indicated Alderson and Patrick who had finished for the day, and were quietly observing them from a distance.

Baird wasn't sure. 'Wouldn't hurt to let them know that the first results are promising,' he suggested.

'We need to finish this drilling run without anymore holdups,' Sharon stated. 'If those two realize what's going on before we complete this month's program, they will ask for more money.' In fact, had the situation arisen, she would have agreed – Sharon acting her part as if the results were genuine.

Baird considered this. 'Why not just give them a teaser, then?'

She seemed receptive. 'Tell them that we have some positive showings, but don't get them too excited.'

'Bonuses?' he asked, the timing appropriate.

'I'll put it to Vancouver,' she agreed.

'How much?'

Sharon wanted to smile. 'Let's wait and see how we fare with the next batch of results before we start putting the screws into head office.'

Baird seemed content with this. 'I've got a very strong feeling in my gut, Sharon, that this is the big one.'

'It's early days, don't you think?' she parried, enjoying playing the man.

'Maybe,' he said then fell quiet, Sharon taking her cue to re-enter her quarters where she unlocked an aluminum trunk, returning moments later with two tin mugs and a bottle of Hennessy's XO Cognac. Baird looked up, surprised, his grin immediately returning with the gesture.

'To Longdamai Sial,' she toasted, smiling at her unsuspecting associate, secretly excited with the prospect that when her stock was released, unencumbered from escrow, she would have at least twenty million dollars for her trouble.

Drilling continued uninterrupted and, when subsequent assay results flowed back to the Longdamai Sial site over the next weeks supporting earlier expectations, Sharon arranged for a telephone hook up between Longdamai Sial, the analytical laboratory and BGC in Vancouver – the connection arranged via their Jakarta office. She asked that the laboratory verify the results directly to Christopher Fielding, the company President and, following the euphoric exchange, set about raising the grades of subsequent assay results, by increasing the volume of gold injected into the samples.

★ ★ ★ ★

Jakarta

General Sukirno listened intently as the retired Air Vice Marshal disclosed the salient points in the three-way, international communication exchange.

'Are you absolutely sure?' Sukirno was staggered to the point of disbelief, the numbers Subroto had thrown around beyond comprehension.

'One hundred percent,' Subroto confirmed, his chubby fingers extended in the air, *'I have confirmed the information with my man in the field.'*

'It sounds…' the army officer paused, selecting his words, *'…almost too good to be true?'*

Subroto snorted. *'The first results were similar. They have deliberately kept the information from the government.'*

Sukirno considered the accusation, an opportunity immediately leaping to mind. *'Do you have a full transcript of the conversations?'*

Eric Baird's overweight partner moved uncomfortably in his seat. *'No. We had no idea that they were going to discuss the assay results.'*

The other man showed his disappointment. *'Pity. We could have used it.'* He looked down at scribbled notes, unable to comprehend the number of zeros running across his notepad. *'There has to be some mistake, Mas,'* he said, punching blunt, but well-manicured fingers at a desktop calculator. *'According to your information, there's more gold in the Longdamai deposit than what they're projecting from the Freeport Grassberg mine.'*

'Mas 'Kirno,' Subroto looked pained, *'if it wasn't for the fact that my niece's husband confirmed the information, I wouldn't have believed it either. I have known this man for more than ten years. He's greedy, but not stupid. If you're not sure, why not send someone out there to confirm the find?'*

General Sukirno concurred. *'Perhaps it is time the Mines Department visited some of the Kalimantan operations. Better still, as the government has a vested interest in these ventures what better way to demonstrate our support than by offering some of our own expertise to be positioned on site?'*

Subroto smiled at his fellow officer's cunning. *'The foreign operators couldn't refuse.'*

'And why should they?' Sukirno challenged, *'after all, aren't we the hosts in this game?'*

Subroto nodded his concurrence.

★ ★ ★ ★

Eric Baird's senior associate departed, leaving the powerful General Sukirno alone, deep in thought. Sukirno had been charged with laying the foundations for official seizure of any significant finds, then orchestrating for these assets to be shifted to Palace interests. He called for the file on P. T. Kalimantan Gold's arrangements with the Mines and Energy Ministry and, within the hour, the documents were hand-delivered to his office. The information revealed that P.T. Kalimantan Gold had been granted a preliminary survey permit for the Longdamai area but, as yet, had not finalized an exploitation agreement.

New protocols to facilitate the government increasing its position in all mineral resource ventures were imminent, and as head of the Parliamentary Committees for both Mining and Forestry, the General would also benefit, financially, from such acquisitions. Confident that P. T. Kalimantan Gold foreign partners would realize that they would have little choice but to accept the revised provisions, once these were announced, Sukirno wrote a memo to the Director General of Mines and Energy, outlining what action was required with respect to ownership of the Kalimantan operations.

Satisfied that the question of control would be resolved without difficulty, General Sukirno then turned his attention to organizing for government personnel to be assigned to the Longdamai operations. He composed another memo with copies to all relevant Ministers, noting that the *Golkar* parliamentary faction deplored the current levels of environmental damage caused by foreign contractor's operating in Kalimantan, and proposed that government inspectors be placed on location to monitor their activities. Sukirno then phoned the Minister for Mines and Energy directly, to prepare the way for his next move.

★ ★ ★ ★

When word spread that their Minister wished to assemble a specialist team to monitor mining activities in deepest Kalimantan, within days, the ranks of those qualified for such positions thinned dramatically. As the majority of government officials were Javanese, and all had read the government-censored memorandums revealing the true extent of covert, Dayak ethnic violence, the department was inundated with requests for leave – even reassignment. A highly confidential recommendation was presented to the departmental head, suggesting that this would be an ideal opportunity to remove the high-profile Dayak spokeswoman from further media attention, and the wheels of injustice spun into motion.

On the Ninth of May 1996, Angela Dau was selected to lead the mission, and instructed to proceed immediately to the Longdamai Sial site as the government representative to monitor P. T. Kalimantan Gold activities in the area.

★ ★ ★ ★

Vancouver

Christopher Fielding's hands continued to tremble with excitement as he reached for the whiskey-filled tumbler, emptying the contents with one swallow. He searched for another bottle, breaking into an alcohol-induced smile with the realization that he had demolished a fifth of Scotch, alone, in quiet celebration, and in less than an hour.

Rising to unsteady feet, Fielding struggled to gather his thoughts, his hands searching amongst the reams of reports and notes scattered across the desk for the Longdamai Sial projections. Identifying the papers, he placed these carefully aside, then leaned across and with one arm brushed everything else to the floor, the effort causing him to sway drunkenly, and fall heavily to the carpet.

Fielding lay on his back with the ceiling spinning overhead, aware that he had missed both lunch and dinner, this oversight mainly the cause for his current predicament. He rose slowly to his feet and, unfazed by his condition, picked up the file containing the most recent drilling and laboratory analysis reports, straightened his glasses then reached for the phone and dialed Kremenchug's number.

'It's confirmed,' Fielding's succinct message was deliberate; he knew that his associate had been waiting for this call.

'Are you absolutely sure?' At the other end, Kremenchug twitched nervously.

'Ab…so…lute…ly!' Fielding replied, emphatically.

'What's your final estimate?' Kremenchug was anxious to learn.

'Well, even if we halved the estimates,' Fielding's celebratory mood was evident in his slurred voice, 'we would have one, if not *the* richest find in history!'

'What's the figure?' Kremenchug asked, impatiently.

'Conservatively?' Fielding leaned forward and focused hazy eyes on his notes. 'More than twenty million ounces.'

In his semi-drunken state Fielding waited for Kremenchug's staggered response to the figures as he digested the extent of the claim, which, based on current gold prices, valued the Longdamai Sial deposit at around six billion dollars. What the BGC president did not know, was that Kremenchug had expected the estimates to come in well under a tenth of that. Kremenchug regained his ability to speak, with a flood of unprepared questions. 'When do we make the announcement? Do you want me to come over now? Have you told anyone else? What do you think the stock will go to?'

'Anything could happen, Alex, I just don't know. My feeling is that they could go through the roof but, there again, there's going to be one hell of a lot of skeptics out there!'

'Jesus!' Kremenchug whispered hoarsely to himself.

'I thought we'd inform the market first thing in the morning,' Fielding suggested.

'Sounds okay to me,' Kremenchug sounded tired, 'maybe we'll start to realize on our investment, at last.'

'Don't be too anxious to dump your stock,' Fielding warned, 'and keep the Exchange informed if you're selling. You know the reporting requirements, Alex.'

'Sure, I'll keep everyone posted,' the other man promised.

★ ★ ★ ★

In the first half-hour following Christopher Fielding's announcement to the Canadian stock exchanges, Borneo Gold Corporation's shares exploded in value as news of the extent of the Kalimantan gold find spread. Kremenchug started dumping his original stake when they tripled to seventy-five cents, bailing out finally when the stock went through the one-dollar-fifty mark then, becoming near suicidal, when they continued to rise throughout the day until reaching twelve dollars. He knew Baird would be livid that he had offloaded their parcel of shares for less than three quarters of a million, especially when their worth at closing would have exceeded six million dollars. Although this lost opportunity was cushioned by the knowledge that the value of his entitlement in Sharon's holdings had grown significantly, Kremenchug's own 'bird-in-the-hand' mentality drove him to near nervous collapse.

That his Filipino partner had manipulated the assay results was clear – why she had suddenly become so heavy handed now of paramount concern, Kremenchug apprehensive about the attention and scrutiny which would undoubtedly follow. His agreement with Sharon had been that she would build a credible profile for the Longdamai prospects; one that would indicate reserves, commensurate for the recovery of her uncle's gold. The results arising from the initial drilling program justified Sharon's nominee company acquiring controlling interest in BGC – and was sufficient to lay the foundations for a future mine, one which would provide the mechanism to launder General Dominguez's gold. BGC investors would expect a mine to materialize with such promising drilling returns. Sharon and Kremenchug had agreed from the outset, that the falsified samples should show no more than projections of four to five hundred million in realizable reserves, as such numbers would be acceptable by international standards – and it was therefore essential for assays to reflect results within these parameters. Their scheme to recycle the gold was viable, only as long as Sharon could maintain control over the operations for the few years required to 'mine', and produce the metal. Once Dominguez's hoard had been laundered, the plan was to close the operation, announcing that the mine's life had come to an end, that further extraction was no longer economically viable.

Now, with claims that Longdamai contained more than twenty million ounces in reserves, he dreaded Jakarta's reaction to the announcement, deeply concerned that the entire scheme could somehow collapse. Why she increased the levels of gold to such gigantic proportions confounded Kremenchug. The tantalizing possibility that she had actually uncovered a bona fide deposit, causing the additional traces added to the samples to grossly exaggerate the find, now paramount in his mind.

Although concerned by the outcome, of one thing he was certain – should BGC stock continue to trade at current values over coming months, he would insist that Sharon sell his share of their joint holdings the moment the escrow period had lapsed. Then, Sharon would have the option of continuing on, alone, to execute her gold laundering scheme – although he doubted that she would wish to continue with the original plan, considering the value of her find. He decided to fly out to Indonesia and warn Sharon to cease manipulating the drilling results if, in fact, she was still doing so, as the eyes of the world were now upon them.

★ ★ ★ ★

Part Three: Final

Gibbous Moon

Chapter Nineteen

June 1996

Baron Mining – Toronto – Canada

The multinational, mining conglomerate's chairman paused momentarily as if measuring the man sitting opposite, then opened the leather bound file filled with handwritten notes, jotted down, during his return flight from Texas. 'The U.S. ambassador in Jakarta has been briefed,' the former Canadian Prime Minister referred to the folder. 'He has undertaken to make the necessary calls, personally, to arrange access for you to meet with the Indonesians in private.'

'Will that include the President?' Phil Samuels asked.

The chairman shook his head. 'The old man's English is poor. Besides, he leaves all business discussions for the children to resolve.'

'What if they don't accept our offer?'

The retired statesman smiled. 'They'll agree. What we are suggesting is a far greater share than their customary ten percent would generate. I don't anticipate you'll have too much difficulty in persuading them to go with our deal. Besides, who in their right minds would refuse fifteen percent of a six trillion dollar asset?'

Samuels did not share the chairman's confidence. In his fifteen years consulting to the mining industry he had seen less complex deals fail to materialize. Baron Mining's impressive Board consisted of highly respected entities from amongst the mining fraternity, and also boasted both American and Canadian former heads of state. Although this represented a powerful mix on any continent and it was this assembly of wealth and power he would take to the table in Jakarta, Samuels felt uneasy in negotiating with the Indonesians without some local support, other than that of the American Embassy.

Recently invited to join this august group's Board of Directors, Phillip Samuels had discovered that potential conflict of interests required he reassess many old allegiances, and professional relationships forged during his years as an independent consultant. Amongst these, a friend from college days with whom he had worked for more than a decade, Stewart Campbell, whose knowledge of the Indonesian mining sector had indirectly assisted Samuels climb the corporate ladder. Now charged with the responsibility of sealing what amounted to the largest corporate deal in mining history, he was not only unable to utilize Campbell's unique industry and language skills, but was also obliged to exclude him completely from the information loop.

The decision to attempt to supplant Borneo Gold Corporation as the foreign operator to the Indonesian Government had been based on the premise that BGC's contract to mine had yet to be ratified by Jakarta. When the Vancouver Stock Exchange had queried BGC's position, precipitating this alarming disclosure, Baron Mining's chairman did not hesitate. He called his fellow director at the former United States President's ranch in Texas, to determine what pressure could be applied to secure control over the Longdamai discovery. Samuels was aware of the powerful links that had been forged between past American Administrations and the Suharto dictatorship. Freeport's West Irian operations enjoyed similar support, with both the Indonesian First Family and Henry Kissinger influencing decisions at the highest level; Samuels prepared to offer similar shareholdings in the proposed Longdamai takeover, on behalf of Baron Mining, in order to supplant BGC.

'Well, that's it then, Phil,' the Baron Mining chairman rose, terminating their meeting. 'Don't give them anything more than we absolutely have to.'

Phil Samuels departed for Indonesia, returning before the week was out to confirm that he had acquired an 'in principle' agreement for Baron Mining to assume control over the Longdamai gold concession. He had not met with members of the First Family, as expected. Instead, he was introduced to a powerful Chinese *cukong,* who had been delegated the responsibility of negotiating on behalf of Palace interests.

The deal that was struck guaranteed Baron Mining control over P.T. Kalimantan Gold in consideration for twenty percent of all revenue and stock in the operation, to be assigned to the President's offshore nominees. Phil Samuels then set about planning for an interim team to take over P.T. Kalimantan Gold's Longdamai operations, while Jakarta-vested interests initiated steps to encourage the Borneo Gold Corporation to surrender the Longdamai concessions, to Baron Mining.

★ ★ ★ ★

Indonesia
Longdamai Sial Mining Site

Having returned from early morning exercises and a bucket-fed shower, still dressed in a sarong, Angela re-entered her cramped quarters and prepared for her customary moment of meditation, just as the first cock crowed. She unrolled a small, *tikar* mat over a treated canvas ground cover then lit an incense stick, placing this carefully in a minute, ceramic holder, one she had carried since first departing her village to study in Bandung. Crouching forward on bent knees, she placed the smoldering, aromatic incense on the woven mat then clasped her hands together and, with eyes closed, continued the ritual, with synchronized breathing exercises. As her mind cleared, Angela slipped quietly into trancelike state where she remained, until some rehearsed signal triggered her return and she awoke, refreshed, cleansed, and ready for prayer.

Crouched in solemn silence and supplication, Angela sought the understanding of her ancestral spirits for her presence at this most holy of places, and direction in how to deal with those who had desecrated this site. With her head bent in prayer, she could sense her father's reassuring presence nearby, her lips moving in silent chant as she pleaded for the spirits to watch over them both and, as an afterthought, she included Stewart Campbell's name on her list. With growing camp activity encroaching upon her thoughts Angela completed her ritual, and prepared to dress.

As a precaution against scorpions and smaller snakes, Angela Dau banged her knee-high, laced leather-boots against the steel framed, folding bed, peered inside with the aid of a torch just to make sure, then finished dressing. She buttoned a collarless, long sleeve cotton shirt, tucked her jeans inside the boots and, without the aid of a mirror brushed her long, black hair back into a ponytail. Before leaving her tent to attend the onsite briefing with P.T. Kalimantan Gold management, Angela strapped an army hunting knife around her waist, donned a baseball cap, then checked that her personal belongings were safely locked away. Satisfied with her routine, she then ventured outside in search of Mardidi who, much to Eric Baird's chagrin, had been seconded as her personal aide.

In the week since her arrival, Angela had grown somewhat ambivalent towards the expatriate drillers and their lecherous looks. As for Sharon Ducay, the Filipino Chief of Operations, from the moment Angela had first set foot in the camp their relationship had been less than lukewarm. She took Sharon Ducay's perceived, professional resentment to her presence in stride, unaware of the underlying reason for the Filipino's pique. After observing Ducay at work and learning what had been achieved at the Longdamai field under her supervision, Angela accepted that the other woman was, indeed, deserving of her envious reputation and decided to establish rapport in some way.

Of all the foreigners, only Eric Baird appeared cooperative and, although friendly, Angela remained cool as she set about establishing her team under the suspicious eyes of the Madurese migrant workers.

★ ★ ★ ★

Angela's team of three had been given explicit instructions as to what the Ministry required of them. Her two associates, both experienced geologists who had worked with the government-owned gold mines in Cikotok in West Java, were ethnic *Bataks* from Sumatra. She had positioned each of the experts on mining sites further downstream to report on the spread of illegal mining operators along the Mahakam. They maintained contact via scheduled, daily radio transmissions, linked through the mining camp's network, each charged with the responsibility to maintain their own base of operations, reporting directly to Angela. Now, with one week on site already behind her, she was anxious to visit her village and planned to do so, that day. As she made her way down to the general mess where cooks busied themselves preparing breakfast for the foreigners, she spotted Mardidi hurrying towards her.

'Selamat pagi, non,' he greeted, *'would you like me to prepare some bubur for you?'*

Angela had mentioned that she preferred the traditional porridge dish to what the foreigners were offered at breakfast. *'Terima kasih, 'Di,'* she thanked him, *'but not too much as I'm going out on the river this morning.'*

Mardidi immediately became tense. *'Must I go with you?'* he asked.

Angela suppressed a smile. *'No, 'Di, I will go alone.'*

'Alone?' he asked, shocked. *'I'll go, non, if you wish?'* he offered, but with tongue in cheek.

'It's okay, 'Di,' Angela put him at ease, *'I can handle the speedboat, by myself.'*

'But, what if you break down?' he insisted.

'Don't worry, 'Di,' she patted the knife at her waist, *'I'll have this with me.'*

'Will you be gone long?'

She knew that politeness prevented him from asking where she was going. *'I am going home, 'Di,'* she answered, enjoying the confused look spreading across the other's face.

'Home?' Mardidi's jaw dropped. '*You are a Penehing-Dayak?'*

'Yes, 'Di,' she replied, amused by the disbelief spreading across his face.

They entered the thatched-roofed shelter, Mardidi leaving her alone to prepare the simple meal. Angela positioned herself at a roughly cut, timber bench which, prior to her arrival, had been reserved solely for the expatriates, and propped both forearms on the table. An unsmiling Madurese girl brought coffee and placed the enamel mug down heavily in front of Angela, leaving her alone, without so much as a word. Angela ignored the behavior, pushed the mug to one side suspecting that there might be more than coffee in the brew. She sat, quietly, anticipation building as she contemplated the day ahead when Baird entered the mess, and waved, then stopped to talk to Mardidi – Angela suspecting that she was the subject of their whispered exchange. When Baird came over, he wasted no time in quizzing her about her intentions for that day.

'Surely you're not thinking of going out on the river, alone?' he asked, lowering his thin frame down gently.

'Sure, why not?' Angela responded, wondering how far Baird had explored the area.

'Why don't you take someone along, just to be safe?'

'Do you think I'd be in danger?' she asked, annoyance creeping into her voice.

'We've lost more than twenty men since we started work here,' Baird argued.

'How many women?' she challenged.

'None…,' he shook his head, then added, *'yet.'*

'What happened to the men?'

Baird shrugged. *'Mostly snakes,'* he answered, almost uncaringly. *'Some of them probably took off and returned to the main migrant body downstream. There've been a few accidents with chainsaws and the like but, as I said, snakes are really bad around here.'*

Angela was, of course, unaware that her father had been actively culling the number of Madurese workers, and that the greater majority of deaths attributed to cobras had been his handiwork. *'Seems like a lot to blame on the snakes,'* she commented.

'It'd be smart to take someone with you.'

'Didn't Mardidi tell you that I know the area?'

'You've been here before?' he asked, feigning surprise.

'I was born not too far from here.'

'You're a local?'

'You can't tell?' Angela noticed him squirm.

Baird shook his head. *'No. I guessed you were from Kalimantan, somewhere, by your features.'*

'You mean the flat nose?' she asked, enjoying his discomfort.

Baird's face flushed visibly. *'Good... grief, no!'* he stammered, glancing around for help. *'I just meant...'*

Angela remained expressionless as she asked, *'Have you met any of the local people yet?'*

'No,' he replied, lamely. *'There's no village nearby. That's why we had to import labor.'*

'How did the company come to drill this location?' Angela shifted the direction of the conversation.

'We finished proving up the other site, downstream, and Sharon thought that the geology here warranted further investigation.'

'Then the find was more or less accidental?'

'No, not really,' he revealed, *'I did some preliminary work up along the river around here a few years back. Sharon came across my report and decided the area was worth a closer look.'*

Stunned, Angela stared at the foreigner sitting across from her. *'Then it was you who first recommended the area for drilling?'*

Baird frowned under her gaze. *'You could say that,'* he admitted, *'but, back then, no one acted on the advice.'*

'Dominion Mining did.'

Baird considered the remark, and waited for some moments before asking, *'And why is this significant?'*

Angela's heart hardened, but she remained calm. *'You don't feel any responsibility for what is happening here?'*

'Responsibility?' Baird waited for Mardidi to finish serving the porridge to Angela before continuing. *'Of course I feel responsible – and proud. And who wouldn't be? This has to be one of the most significant resource discoveries in Indonesia's history!'*

'Gold at any cost?' Angela's response was touched with sarcasm. *'I have examined all of the records going back as far as the earliest mining applications covering this area, and there's nothing to suggest that any environmental study had ever been undertaken, or that the Penehing people had been invited to have any say in what was going to take place here. You most probably have no idea as to how the Dayak people have been affected by timber and mining companies. Are you aware that forest cover is being depleted at more than twelve thousand square kilometers every year?'*

'That's not our fault,' he said, defensively.

'Why not?'

'Because that responsibility rests with the central government.'

'No it doesn't,' she refuted, confidently, *'the foreign investment laws require that companies conduct a full impact feasibility study before commencing timber and mining operations.'*

'You're right, of course. But there's no mine here...' he paused, *'...yet. And when there is, then I'm sure that the company will meet all of its responsibilities.'*

'And that will, of course, include compensating the Dayak people?'

Baird looked around, spotted the expatriate drillers dragging their heels in for breakfast, and turned back to Angela. *'To be honest, I don't know.'*

Angela Dau fell silent, staring down at the porridge. When the drillers joined them, she ignored them all and rose, leaving the table and her meal, untouched.

* * * *

Sharon reread the letter, saddened by its contents. Her uncle's health continued to deteriorate, the inference that he might not see out the year casting a pall over her mood. She folded the letter and placed it in her breast pocket, annoyed that she had not thought to include the General's home in the radiophone link via Jakarta.

Attached as she was to her uncle, Sharon was unable to leave the operations as long as drilling continued, worried that the tainted sampling procedures might be discovered – the possibility of this occurring even more so now with the presence of the Indonesian

Mines & Energy representative, conspicuously on site. Sharon knew she had no choice but to remain at Longdamai Sial until she could dispose of her BGC stock, and that moment was still a few weeks away. Kremenchug had sent clippings covering the sensational escalation in Borneo Gold Corporation's value, the most recent highs far beyond her greatest expectations. Her original projections of earning twenty, even thirty million dollars from the sale of her stock, was all that she had wished for. The market's reaction to the high gold grades had driven the value of her position to levels beyond her greatest expectations – and she was unable to realize on this asset, as long as her shares remained in escrow.

As for Kremenchug, Sharon expected that with the meteoric rise in BGC stock values, he would most probably wish to liquidate his stake in her holdings the moment the shares became available. With stocks at their current levels, Sharon believed that the original premise to establish a mine solely to launder Filipino gold would no longer carry any long-term appeal to Kremenchug, another aspect of her complicated endeavors. She had calculated that it would have required at least one hundred times more gold than her uncle was supposed to have hoarded, to drive shares to their current, giddying levels. Sharon knew that Kremenchug would have thought this through, and banked on his wanting to bail out without waiting for his partner to launder her non-existent hoard. She had counted on the man's greed, and he had not disappointed. When BGC did eventually collapse as she expected it must, and the true value of Longdamai Sial had been exposed, it would be the BGC directors who would become embroiled in an aftermath filled with recriminations. Kremenchug was a member of the BGC Board – it would be *his* blood that the investor-shareholders would demand once the extent of the hoax had finally been revealed. Sharon Ducay was confident that when this time arrived she would be comfortably ensconced in a secure jurisdiction, well out of harm's reach.

Sharon's thoughts turned to Angela Dau, suspicious that the timing of her visit coincided with an increase in the complement of Indonesian, Special Forces' soldiers. Previously, there had been a small contingent of four *Kopassus* troops, supported by helicopters on a regular basis from their main camp from somewhere downstream. Now, there were more than twenty of these well-armed, elite soldiers, based at the Longdamai site. Although they went about their business without interfering in her drilling and sampling operations, nevertheless, Sharon could not help feeling that their presence was, somehow, linked to Angela's mission.

When Angela Dau had arrived armed with a Ministerial directive instructing P.T. Kalimantan Gold (Indonesia) to provide any assistance she might request, Sharon's immediate response had been cool, but professional. Sharon had introduced Angela around the camp, shown her the operations, and pressed Baird to second Mardidi to assist, suggesting that it would be in their interests to have someone trustworthy keep an eye on the newcomer, at all times. Baird had reluctantly agreed and, after a week on site, Sharon's earlier misgivings had all but disappeared as Angela's presence had in no way interfered with the operations, and, more importantly, the implementation of her covert sampling procedures.

* * * *

Eric Baird caught a glimpse of Angela's disappearing form as she threaded her way through the maze of semi-permanent, palm-thatched roof structures, past Sharon Ducay's cabin, where she fell out of sight.

He reflected upon their conversation, surprised by Angela's accusatory tone, unable to shake the nagging thought that her presence in camp was directly related to the mining operation's high grade assay results, and not environmental issues as she had claimed. Years of dealing with the Indonesian government had taught Baird never to accept anything at face value, especially when there was money involved. In his mind, the unexpected appearance of Mines & Energy officials on site signaled third party interest in the Longdamai Sial site, Baird's concern that if these were Palace-associated lobbyists, then possession might be at risk. Partial acquisition might ensure future, trouble-free operations, such as had been the experience with the massive Freeport Grasberg gold and copper mine, in Indonesia's West New Guinea, but any such involvement would, as had been demonstrated in the past, be at the expense of other investors.

A speedboat roared into life and he spotted Angela again, briefly, when the craft's nose lifted above the waterline and gained momentum, the trailing rooster-tail spray indicating Angela had gunned the fiberglass boat to full power. His eyes drifted back across the shoreline where Sharon Ducay came into view, Baird reminded not for the first time, of the startling similarities between the two, strong-willed women.

★ ★ ★ ★

Longhouse Village

Angela eased the throttle back to idle, slowing the speedboat's momentum as she guided the craft to within reach of eager, outstretched hands.

'It's 'Gela, it's 'Gela!' children lined the boardwalk chanting, waving, giggling, pushing forward to be the first to touch Angela as she stepped from the vessel. A number of youths secured the fiberglass boat, removing the cargo of packages she had brought from Jakarta, which contained as many gifts as she could afford.

'Where's our 'oleh-oleh'? The children eyed the parcels, their expectations growing when Angela pointed to these, telling them to be patient. The throng grew with the news of her arrival spreading throughout the village and, as she climbed ashore and she grasped her father's extended hands, the Dayak chief drew her into his arms.

'Welcome home, my daughter,' Jonathan's proud moment shared by all as the air was filled with clamorous joy. With one arm around her shoulder, the shaman turned Angela for all to see, his chest swelling in response to the villagers' roar of approval.

Before she could take another step, Yuh-Yuh, Angela's pet *orangutan* broke through the crowd and wrapped herself around the young woman's thighs. *'Hello, Yuh-Yuh, I expected you'd be eaten by now!'* she laughed, reached down and embraced the small ape, now clinging furiously to her side.

Jonathan prized the *orang-utan* loose. *'Enough, Yuh-Yuh!'*

They threaded their way through the gathering, Angela bending down to respond to a child who called her name, kissing another and touching as many of the villagers as she could manage whilst making her way into the Longhouse proper. There, as tradition demanded, she sipped from a bowl of hastily poured *tuak*, the fermented palm-wine bringing with it a warm glow of well being, her father's soft, reassuring chant blessing Angela and thanking the spirits for bringing her home safely, a melody to her ears.

'Tonight, we will hold a 'selamatan' to celebrate your return. The evening will be even more special, as the morning skies will be graced by a full moon, heralding in both the new calendar, and lunar months. This is another obvious sign. No doubt you remember the significance?'

Angela nodded solemnly. *'Yes, father. The new month will be filled with signs to guide us, blessed as it closes with a second full moon. You taught me the importance of this event at the time of my initiation.'*

Jonathan placed his arm around his daughter once again, and squeezed. *'I am very proud of you, Angela, that you have not lost our ways.'* He then released her and turned to the sea of admiring faces, clapping his hands for attention. *'A double celebration it is, then,'* he raised his voice even more, *'to welcome our Angela back, and the month which bears twin moons!'* Then, leaning close to Angela's face he whispered, *'And an appropriate time for the two of us to go up to the mountains and meditate, together. There is much we must discuss.'*

★ ★ ★ ★

Towering *cumulus nimbus* clouds gathered in haughty presence covering Eastern Borneo's early morning sky in ominous, translucent forms, further delaying the appearance of July's first, full moon. Jonathan and Angela waited together in expectant, but reverent silence – their eyes locked on the heavens in eager anticipation as a rhapsody of platinum rays suddenly burst from behind the clouds, signaling the commencement of yet another, all-important cycle. Both fell into rehearsed routine, appealing to ancestral spirits for guidance and their blessings, the couple's resonating, harmonious chant carrying into the night, lost amongst soft breezes in the valley below.

When the ritual came to a close, they moved back into the cave's sacred surrounds, Angela sitting alongside her father on a *tikar* mat where, together, they broke their fast, eating a simple meal of berries and fruit, Jonathan then engaging his daughter in debate, discussing most pressing issues. They conversed by flickering candlelight, shadows dancing around the timeless cavern giving momentary life to carved shapes, etched into rock by ancestral hands, Jonathan revealing his concerns – Angela for the most part, listening to the wisdom of his experience and years.

'*...and, the worst is yet to come. It's now clearly apparent that we will be forced from our traditional lands to accommodate the transmigration process, one which is designed to dilute the Dayak presence, and one which can only be met with force. We can no longer stand back and do nothing while they bulldoze our mountains, destroying the soil, desecrating our sites, polluting our rivers where we fish and bathe. With the destruction of our forests, the roots of trees and plants will be gone, and invaluable information about natural medicines gathered by generations, will be lost forever. Our unique culture and language will eventually disappear altogether, perhaps even resulting in the extinction of our people.*'

'*If only these gold discoveries had not brought the outsiders here,*' she complained, bitterly. '*I still can't understand why the world places such great store in the metal.*'

'*The discovery has only accelerated the inevitable. Don't forget that the outsiders are determined to destroy our forests, as well.*'

'*But it was gold that brought them to our doorstep.*'

'*Yes, that's true. But we are also reminded that gold has also been an integral part of our own culture. For centuries our people have panned for nuggets in the rivers, we have worn it around our wrists, ankles and even attached it to our ears.*'

'*Why is it that this one metal can create such greed?*'

'*Gold is not the problem, Angela. It's what the yellow metal represents. It's value is in the power it generates for those who possess it.*'

'What can we do?' There was desperation in her voice. *'We don't have sophisticated weapons to fight the military.'*

'We'll avoid direct conflict with the TNI. Instead, we'll wage a war of terror against the trans-migrants. Without labor, their timber and mining camps will grind to a halt. Eventually, they will have no choice but to sit down and negotiate with us.'

'No choice?' Angela rejoined, alarmed. *'Papa, they could send their troops into our villages and kill us all!'*

'Not if we could bring the Dayak tribes together, united against our common enemies. A general uprising would see the end of Javanese domination. As you have suggested, world opinion would then force Jakarta to the negotiating table. The Mahakam River Dayaks have all agreed to support a world heritage listing of our forests and, with international support, this could be achieved. We would regain control over our destinies, and our lands and forests. Without access to these resources, the Javanese would withdraw.'

'How can we bring the Dayaks together?'

'That process has already commenced. Over the past months we have been in discussion with the others. There is strong support for this concept. We have received commitments from Dayak communities as far south as Banjarmasin, and from Sampit across to Amuntai. We plan to coordinate simultaneous attacks along the Kehayan River to Palangkaraya, which will draw the Javanese troops to the south, leaving the Mahakam communities a clear opportunity to rid the land of Madurese settlers. Make no mistake, my child, we are already at war, fighting for the survival of not just Dayak traditions and land, but our very existence.'

'But, Papa, Jakarta will surely send reinforcements?'

'When they do, we will retreat into the mountains. Remember, 'Gela, the Javanese fear the Dayak in battle, and we will strike terror into their hearts.' A sinister grin lined his face. *'They have no stomach for fighting in the jungle, you'll see!'*

'Surely there must be another way?' this, with a withering look.

'No, Angela,' he held her to console. *'We've exhausted all other avenues. Dayak representation in the Indonesian Parliament is virtually non-existent. The fundamental issue of Dayak community rights continues to be ignored, as have our appeals for logging and mining moratoriums to*

be imposed. Jakarta's elite send their scavengers across our lands stripping the forests, building wood processing and paper pulp factories, most of which thrive from illegal logging operations. You've seen the devastation visited upon other Dayak communities, further downstream? Close to three-quarters of our forests have been destroyed in one generation by logging operations and conversion for oil palm plantations. We have submitted evidence directly to the United Nations, requesting their intervention, but the influence of powerful Jakarta lobbyists whose very empires were built from profits generated at our expense, apparently extends even to the General Assembly. Unfortunately, 'Gela, because of the enormity of the wealth being stripped from mining and logging operations, Jakarta's rich and powerful will continue to act with impunity, as they have the President's blessing. We have been left with no alternative but to fight and, considering the forces we are up against, we have no choice but to strike them where they are weakest. If this requires that we attack and destroy Madurese migrant camps, then we must do so, and drive those who survive back across the Java Sea.'

'Our people are going to slaughter unarmed Madurese?' Angela asked, with incredulous stare.

'The Madurese have been arming in preparation of their own agenda.'

'Are you sure, Papa?' It was not her intention to challenge. *'How can you be certain?'*

'Reports of Javanese troops training militia groups have been filtering in for some months. We sent some of our young men downriver to the Madurese settlements. They confirmed the reports. We estimate that more than a thousand have been armed, and that clearly shows Jakarta's hand. We don't have a great deal of time to make our move. The longer we wait, the greater our casualties will be.'

'When?' Angela's mouth went dry, and she clenched her father's hand.

'With the next full moon,' Jonathan answered, solemnly. *'And, at that time, I want you here – away from the mining camp and by my side.'*

'The camp will be attacked?' she asked, with growing surprise.

'Yes. They have desecrated our most sacred site. We owe it to our ancestors.'

'There are foreigners at the camp,' she reminded.

'They will not be targeted. It's the Madurese we are after.'

'How can you ensure their safety?'

'The foreigners will come to no harm providing they don't interfere.'

'And if they do?'

Jonathan Dau's face became stern. *'Then they will die with the others.'*

'That would guarantee reprisals,' Angela warned.

'The Penehing will be ready.'

'If Jakarta sends troops, our losses could be high, Papa.'

'We are fighting for our very survival, 'Gela, and, for this, we should all be willing to die.'

With that one, all-embracing statement an uncontrollable shiver ran along Angela's spine and she was suddenly beset with dread and she asked, *'What if you were to be killed?'*

The chief responded with accustomed calm. *'If it is ordained by the spirits then that will be so.'*

Jonathan and Angela returned to their village built on stilts, their journey back down the mountain trail and through the forest conducted in unbroken silence, their thoughts burdened with what lay ahead.

★ ★ ★ ★

Jakarta – The Palace

General Sukirno returned the guards' salutes then followed a waiting aide into the residence under the Presidential Guard's suspicious eyes. Although evidence of the fifty-man team was not apparent, he knew that they were there – observing his every move, trained to shoot even high-ranking officers should their President, or his family come under threat. Charged with the task of safeguarding the Presidential household as well as state visitors, the Guard consisted of two, eight-hundred man forces, stationed in Central Jakarta's Tanah Abang district, within minutes by helicopter, should the need arise.

As Sukirno made his way through the formal setting, bodyguards dressed in civilian attire reminded the army General of the turbulent times that propelled the incumbent to power, when the country's military leadership was all but annihilated during an early morning communist sweep through this suburb. The former President, Soekarno, had survived six assassination attempts; the number that had failed during the current leader's tenure, one of the nation's best-kept secrets. And, a clear reflection of how loyal the sixteen hundred- strong, Presidential Guard remained had been clearly demonstrated in recent weeks, following the death of the First Lady. General Sukirno was aware of the claims that the President's neighbors reported having heard shots, following a heated exchange, the night the First Lady passed away. The Home Affairs Minister had moved quickly to squash the rumor; the Indonesian Press finding no substance to the suggestion that one of the sons had accidentally shot his ailing mother – the Presidential Guards on duty at the time adamant that the accusation was groundless.

Sukirno was escorted to a room towards the rear of the main house, where works by Indonesian masters, Affandi and Basoeki Abdullah hung, unappreciated, on the walls, the air of informality immediately placing the senior officer at ease.

'Thank you for coming, Pak 'Kirno,' the handsome Javanese youth greeted, waving the older man to a bright, *batik*-cushioned, rattan settee.

'Have you read the report?' the General asked, their relationship such, he knew that they could get straight down to the business at hand.

'Yes. Your people still agree with the data?'

'Well, copies filed with Mines and Energy support our own intelligence.' He lifted a glass of lukewarm herbal tea to his mouth, and sipped, then sampled the colorful, seaweed, jelly cakes placed at his disposal. *'It would seem that the Longdamai Sial project's current resource estimates, based on drilling results to date and future drilling targets, stands at twenty million ounces of gold. The reports clearly state that drilling has produced average grades of more than five grams per ton.'*

'Why didn't they establish a mine at the first site?'

'It would seem that the company has been collecting information for some years,' Sukirno revealed. *'You might recall how many of the oil companies cap the wells they have drilled once there is a discovery, and continue on until the entire field has been proven. The P.T. Kalimantan Gold team, which is now part of BGC, has followed a similar routine by the looks of things.*

This suggests that they have been quite clever, as their exploration license would collapse into an exploitation agreement under normal circumstances, the moment they commenced extraction. I believe that the first concession may be as rich in gold as the latest discovery, and that the foreigners are trying to outsmart the government by not disclosing all their findings.'

'What have they had to gain by waiting?'

'We're not sure. The consensus is, the Canadian company did not have enough capital to see its programs through, at the time their application was approved.'

'Then they misrepresented their capacity to develop the deposit's potential?'

'Many of the smaller foreign mining companies don't have the funds to complete their contracts. They do the initial work then broker off the projects to larger companies. It's common practice in the mining industry.'

'How can they do that without our approval?'

'Approval is normally given. Mines and Energy don't want to have projects stagnate over capital. It makes no difference which foreign group owns the rights once these are approved.'

'Then Dominion Mining and BGC are brokers?' the youth asked, surprised.

'Most mining companies tend to share projects to reduce their risk or to raise capital,' Sukirno explained.

'Why don't we just have someone buy the foreign company?'

'It would be far too complicated. That would involve purchasing shares from tens of thousands of investors and there would be no value in doing so.' Sukirno believed he understood what prompted the question as the other man's brother had recently acquired outright ownership of one of Europe's most prestigious sports' car companies, Lamborghini, in this manner.

'Have someone make an offer for their Indonesian operations!'

'They would most likely ask for an impossible sum.'

'But, isn't it true that they have yet to be granted an exploitation or development license?'

'That is correct,' General Sukirno agreed.

'I don't understand why there is a problem. Why not permit the contract to

expire and have the Ministry reassume rights over the area?'

'It is possible,' Sukirno hesitated, *'but this would raise considerable concern amongst the other foreign companies.'*

'Pak 'Kirno,' the President's son became impatient, *'does BGC have a final contract to develop a gold mine at Longdamai or not?'*

'No.'

'Then there should be no difficulty in assigning the rights to whomever the government wishes?'

General Sukirno squirmed uneasily, experience telling him that he must be careful now. *'There is always the international community to consider,'* he warned.

The President's son laughed loudly. *'And who cares what the international media has to say?'*

'It would be best to leave them with something.'

'We'll take their contribution into consideration.'

'There is also the question of relocating the local people,' Sukirno reminded.

'It was my understanding that there were no Dayaks on these sites.'

'That is also true,' the older man replied, *'but this would be an opportune time to relocate the nearer villages, whose people still claim traditional ownership over the areas which encompass the sites.'*

'Those living in timber concession areas?'

'Yes.'

'Is there a relocation scheme already in place?'

'It was sent to the President for his approval.'

'What else is required?'

The General pondered the question for some moments before responding. *'It would be desirable to have more troops in the area.'*

'Consider it done,' the President's son promised.

★ ★ ★ ★

In the days that followed, obsessed with lingering images of gold ingots leaving the country in the middle of the night, the President's son summoned Lim Swee Giok, determined to redirect this flow into Palace coffers. The Indonesian, Chinese *cukong* immediately responded, offering his offshore banking infrastructure as the vehicle to facilitate Baron Mining's acquisition of Borneo Gold Corporation's interests in the P.T. Kalimantan Gold's Longdamai concession.

Before the end of that month, when Indonesia's squeaky wheels of commerce had wobbled forward yet another turn and the major players in two continents remained quietly confident of their imminent windfall, Palace disharmony would thrust the magnitude of the Longdamai discovery upon the world stage, driving BGC's stock to unimaginable highs.

★ ★ ★ ★

Chapter Twenty

Los Angeles

Experience told Lim Swee Giok's son, James Salima that by mid-afternoon, the haze would turn reddish-brown, driving Los Angeles' rapidly growing population of asthmatics indoors. The Indonesian, Chinese financier had lived in California long enough to differentiate between smog and early morning fog, the blanket of moist, whitish haze severely curtailing his view as he gazed wistfully, towards the East.

When he and his brother, Denny had graduated from the University of California, both had been desperate to remain in the United States. Their father, Indonesia's foremost banker whose extraordinary wealth placed him amongst the most powerful entrepreneurs in Asia, had wanted his sons back in Jakarta to assist oversee his growing empire. James had sought the support of stepmother, Ruswita, who had intervened on their behalf, convincing Lim that James' suggestion to commence operations in the United States would be a strategic move for their family flagship, the Asian Pacific Commercial Bank. With the ageing *cukong's* blessing, the young men embarked on a search for an appropriate corporate vehicle suitable for the Salima family's American operations. This journey took them into Bluegrass Country where, in exchange for financial support for the governor's political campaigns, the Salima boys not only acquired a local banking license, but access to the White House. In James Salima's opinion, never had four hundred thousand dollars been better spent, their family network spreading across the United States and Canada, and back into Asia via Hong Kong, China, Taiwan and Japan. The extent of their empire had grown to include shipping, industry, all forms of financial services, property development, communications, and, more recently, mining.

James' thoughts turned to the complex negotiations at hand, and his whirlwind visits to Toronto and Dallas. Across the border, he had held discussions with the former Canadian Prime Minister, now Chairman of Baron Mining, then he had flown to Texas where he continued the dialogue under the alert eyes of Secret Service agents, as he walked through spacious, family ranch surrounds. Having secured tacit approval for the proposed corporate structure, James had returned to Los Angeles to finalize the relevant corporate arrangements, in anticipation of Baron Mining's unofficial acquisition of the East Kalimantan Contract of Work, over the area currently held indirectly by Borneo Gold Corporation.

The Salima family acted as trustees not only for elite Indonesian interests, but also Hong Kong, China, Taiwan and Singaporean groups. In effect, the Salima controlled Central Asia Pacific Bank's offices at 1912 Sunset Boulevard in Los Angeles, managed accounts for the majority of wealthy Chinese who dealt in North America, amongst their clients, Myanmar's drug barons and China's burgeoning, capitalist government officials.

And yet, in the years since he had first established the Salima family interests in the United States, James had never envisaged that, one day, he would be party to a deal of the magnitude that the Indonesian-Canadian proposal offered. Since first becoming aware of the massive find, the thought of participating in what would be the world's largest gold mine had preoccupied his thoughts to the point of obsession, until his father had finally given the green light to proceed with the facilitation process on behalf of the powerful, vested interest groups, on both sides of the Pacific. When he discovered that his family had somehow become the beneficiary of a small parcel of Borneo Gold Corporation's stock almost a decade before, this only added to his confidence that this enormous opportunity had been fated to fall into his hands.

Under the proposed arrangements to assume control over P. T. Kalimantan Gold's Longdamai discovery, the Indonesian Government would challenge the legitimacy of the BGC subsidiary's right to mine the concession area, citing misrepresentation at the time the original contractor, Dominion Mining, had applied for the exploration rights. The Ministry of Mines & Energy would also emphasize the fact that the local operating company, P.T. Kalimantan Gold had not concluded any formal arrangement with the government, to exploit/mine the area in question.

As this action would undoubtedly cause considerable concern within foreign investment circles, and generate negative, international press when BGC screamed foul, the Central Asia Pacific Bank would step forward as the newly appointed owner/operator, supported by its vast, capital reserves, and offer an adequate compensation package to BGC, one which would set well with the international investment community. And, in so doing, provide the desired buffer to protect both Indonesian interests, as well as those of Baron Mining, the latter to be appointed by CAP Bank as managers, once all rights had been effectively transferred to the new consortium. As for BGC, Salima expected an initial plunge in that company's perceived value when punters became aware of the Indonesian Government's challenge. However, there was no doubt in James Salima's mind that, by the time the dust had settled and Baron Mining's *de facto* control over the Longdamai deposit became public, both BGC and Baron's stock would have already risen dramatically, and it was his intention to position the CAP Bank in the market, to benefit from such movement. He waited with growing impatience for the Baron Mining representative, Phil Samuels to arrive, his mind filled with the prospect of millions in fees and profits which would be generated from strategic trading, of both the Borneo Gold Corporation and Baron Mining stocks, during the volatile transition of ownership.

Habit caused the prematurely balding banker to scratch his scalp as he further considered the rivalry amongst the Indonesian First Family siblings, and how their constant bickering had delivered the Longdamai opportunity to his Central Asia Pacific Bank. His father, Lim Swee Giok had patiently explained why Baron Mining had been selected to participate in the venture, over other international miners that had already established operations in the Republic. Many of those companies already enjoyed Palace sponsorship, precipitating fierce and intense competition amongst the President's offspring whenever new opportunities arose. James was aware that the Indonesian President encouraged the rivalry, and that the son now represented by the CAP Bank was vehemently opposed to sharing his future benefits from the Longdamai gold mines with any of the existing, Palace mining partners – including the multinational, Freeport. In short, he wanted it all for himself; and, with the President's blessing, together with CAP Bank's facilitation, it would appear that the Javanese youngster would have his way.

★ ★ ★ ★

Phil Samuels observed the Chinese-Indonesian's nonchalant flip of the wrist to demonstrate the insignificance of the potential problem.

'Jakarta will deal with the local tribes. Don't concern yourself further with this,' the confident banker assured.

'Baron Mining can't afford to have environmental lobbyists or human rights groups pointing the finger at us,' he warned. 'You would appreciate, James, that in the course of the next five years we have a considerable number of leases coming up for renegotiation in South America, Africa and parts of Asia. Be assured, any leverage we give the host governments will be used in those negotiations. Whatever needs to be done to ensure a non-hostile mining environment must be put into place before Baron Mining is identified with the Longdamai field.'

'I will pass this back to Jakarta,' James Salima promised. 'You can be confident that the Dayaks will not pose a threat to the mining operation. Jakarta has learned from the Freeport, Irian experience.'

'The Baron Mining Board doesn't want any bloodshed.'

'I will emphasize this point,' James said, although he had no intention of doing so.

'You have to explain that Baron wants the locals treated fairly. James, with two former heads of state closely associated with the Baron Board, this issue is extremely sensitive for us. We need an undertaking from Jakarta that the Dayak communities most likely to be impacted by the Longdamai operation will be accommodated peacefully – and, more importantly, fairly.'

'I'll make your position clear, Mister Samuels. Don't worry.'

'Then I can report back to my Board that their concerns will be addressed, as requested?'

'Yes,' James replied, 'after all, we don't want the Central Asia Pacific Bank's reputation tarnished, either.'

'Good,' Samuels rose, and placed his left hand on the younger man's shoulder. 'Then, in principle, I see no reason why we can't get this all wrapped up by the end of the month?'

'The CAP Bank will be ready,' James Salima affirmed, and with that undertaking, placed the lives of thousands of East Kalimantan Dayaks at risk.

★ ★ ★ ★

Jakarta

Having been left in reception for more than an hour to further ponder the urgency of their summons, the Borneo Gold Corporation executives remained apprehensively silent, in their intimidating surrounds. Although Alex Kremenchug had visited Indonesian government departments at one time or another, this was Christopher Fielding's first encounter with Indonesian officialdom, and at such an imposing level. Faxed communications had sent the two mining executives scurrying for flights to Indonesia, Kremenchug alerting Sharon Ducay by radio prior to departure, of the potential problem.

'It might be an idea for you to join us in Jakarta,' he had suggested.

'This is no time to be leaving the site,' she warned. 'Besides, Chris Fielding should be able to answer any of their technical questions.'

'Have you heard anything over there as to what they might want?'

'No,' Sharon replied, 'there's been nothing flow through from the Jakarta office. Didn't you call Mines and ask them what it's all about?'

'Of course I did,' Kremenchug snapped, 'I called the protocol section but they were very vague. Have you been having any on-site problems that we're not aware of?'

'No, nothing more than the usual,' she said, less than encouragingly.

Sensing she might be hiding something, Kremenchug pressed. 'Nothing at all?'

Deep in the Borneo jungle Sharon swatted a mosquito with the palm of her hand, ignoring the distraction. Over the past week there had been an increase in the number of Indonesian military at the camp. The officer in charge informed her that the build up was routine, and part of a general exercise planned for the area. Apart from that, the regular drilling and sampling program had continued uninterrupted and she had nothing to report.

'Well, we have a few more soldiers here than before but, I wouldn't read too much into that.'

'Can I talk to Eric, perhaps he can ask Subroto to make a few calls?'

'I sent him down to Samarinda. He won't be back until tomorrow. I could ask him then?'

Kremenchug considered this. 'Tell him that I'll be flying in with Fielding early Friday, arriving on Garuda via Hong Kong at nine. Get him to see if Subroto can shed any light on what's going on. If necessary, have Eric meet us upon arrival as I'm not overly excited about walking into this meeting, cold.'

'Fine, I'll send a message to Samarinda.'

'Okay, then, Sharon – I'll hook up with you from Jakarta once we've finished our appointment with the authorities.'

Kremenchug and Fielding had flown out together, both exhausted by the sixteen-hour haul from Vancouver to Hong Kong where they connected with a Garuda flight directly to the Sukarno-Hatta International Airport, which serviced the Indonesian capital. When the executives arrived, Eric Baird was nowhere to be seen, and so they decided to proceed directly to their Jakarta office, which they shared with P.T. Subroto & Associates.

The city's early morning, Friday traffic ground to a halt even before their taxi had reached the second tollgate, the journey placing them along a grid-locked Jalan General Sudirman, more than an hour later. Pressed for time, Kremenchug left the BGC President waiting in the cab while he hurried into the office building that housed their Jakarta office, to check on Baird. There, the staff informed him that Baird had been unable to return to the capital, as all flights to East Kalimantan had been cancelled due to heavy haze caused by forest fires. As Subroto was also absent, Kremenchug and Fielding had no choice but to proceed without the benefit of any briefing. With less than a few hours sleep under their belts, both men were severely jet-lagged when they arrived at the Ministry of Mines & Energy, where they discovered that their meeting had been re-scheduled, and the location mysteriously changed. They were then bundled into a Toyota LandCruiser and escorted to the revised venue, Kremenchug's uneasiness escalating when they entered the heavily guarded, parliamentary surrounds. They were taken through a building into an oval reception area, their footsteps echoing ominously as they were led across a highly polished, marble floor into a chamber. There the men were seated under an unsmiling portrait of the House Speaker, where they remained cooling their heels, while a steady flow of high-ranking, glassy-eyed military officers passed them by. A gold-leafed, printed plaque affixed to one door indicated that these were the offices of General Sukirno, Chairman, Steering Committee for Foreign Investment in Mining, the title alone sufficient to cause Fielding's stomach ulcer to flare.

When the BGC representatives *were* finally ushered into General Sukirno's office, they were met by an apologetic aide who offered coffee, explaining that the Chairman had gone to the mosque for prayers, and would return within the hour. Annoyed, Kremenchug leaned across and whispered to his companion, Fielding nodding in agreement that the delay was most likely deliberate.

* * * *

'Ah, gentlemen, you are already here?' General Sukirno swept into the lavish office and greeted the men cordially in their own language. 'I was not expecting you until mid-afternoon. Please, please,' he motioned for his visitors to be seated, then settled down behind his carved, crescent shaped, teak desk and, with clasped hands supporting his chin, looked over the top of his bifocals with eyebrows raised. Some moments lapsed before the General leaned back, removed his glasses, and tapped the frame against one hand as if searching for words to commence the discussion. Somewhere towards the rear of the room a grandfather clock beat the seconds, Fielding drawing a long, slow, deep breath as his need for oxygen grew.

'I take it that you represent the entire BGC Board?' Sukirno asked, suddenly, disturbingly composed – Fielding glancing at his associate to determine who should respond.

'Yes, General,' Kremenchug decided to lead. 'Chris is the company president, and I am a director. May I say that…'

'Then you are conversant with the terms of P.T. Kalimantan Gold's Contract of Work with respect to the Longdamai concessions?'

'Yes, indeed, General,' Kremenchug confirmed. 'Is there a problem with our contract?'

Sukirno look puzzled. 'Were you the company officers responsible for the original applications to obtain the concession areas?'

Kremenchug shot Fielding a signal for him to intercede. 'I was aware of the submission, General,' he said, 'but the submission was made by Dominion Mining. Perhaps Chris can respond?'

Fielding cleared his throat, nervously. 'How can I help, General?'

Sukirno's eyes appeared to narrow. 'You understand that I chair the Indonesian Parliamentary committee which oversees foreign investment in the mining sector?' Without waiting for their response, the influential figure continued. 'It has been brought to our attention, just recently, that some serious breaches have occurred in relation to submissions made on behalf of foreign applicants.' He paused, reached into a drawer, and extracted a file, dropping this heavily onto the desk, shaking his head as if disgusted with its contents. 'The committee is interested in determining whether BGC was aware that Dominion Mining had misled the Indonesian authorities as to its capacity to fund exploitation, in the event the exploration process was successful. It would seem that at the time Dominion Mining Incorporated was awarded the Kalimantan concessions and then established its operating company, P.T. Kalimantan Gold, the company's finances were inadequate to develop the project.'

Fielding's brow collapsed into deep, rippled furrows, with tiny beads of sweat gathered at the nape of his neck. 'What bearing could that possibly have on BGC?'

General Sukirno permitted disappointment to cloud his face. 'Obviously, my government has neither the authority nor the capacity to interfere in commercial transactions executed outside the Indonesian jurisdiction. The ownership of your companies, although of interest to us, remains your business, so to speak. Consequently, that P. T. Kalimantan Gold now appears to be some sort of subsidiary operation of BGC is not what concerns us here, today. That there is evidence of the original parent company, Dominion Mining falsifying statements made to the Mines & Energy Ministry in order to obtain general exploration rights is, however, of considerable concern. The members...'

'That's...absurd!' Kremenchug interjected, surprising the senior official. 'Dominion Mining is a reputable organization and is financially sound!'

'Then perhaps *that* company's directors would be able to offer an audited copy of Dominion's balance sheet for the period pertaining to the year it was awarded the Contract of Work?'

Both men knew that this was an unreasonable request, but one which, if pursued, could raise a number of embarrassing issues. Anxious to hear what else the Chairman had to say, Kremenchug regained his composure. 'I believe what is relevant, General, is that BGC has the capacity to develop the Longdamai discovery, and that all parties will enjoy a prosperous future together.'

'But BGC is not the recognized contractor to carry out such work,' Sukirno offered, filling the air with intrigue.

'I don't understand, General,' Kremenchug moved forward in his seat. 'How can there be any suggestion that BGC won't develop the Longdamai mine?'

'The Contract of Work stipulates that Dominion Mining Inc was awarded the right to explore the concession areas in question, through the locally created entity. It is my understanding that P.T. Kalimantan Gold has yet to submit a formal application to move to the next stage of the contractual process.'

Alarmed, Fielding sprang to his feet. 'What's really going on here?' He pushed Kremenchug's restraining arm away angrily, his tall, towering form glaring down at the Indonesian General. 'Are you telling us that BGC won't be awarded the rights to develop the Longdamai mine?'

General Sukirno looked up calmly, forcing a smile. 'I trust it won't be necessary for me to call the guards?' he attempted, lightly.

Kremenchug had also risen to his feet by this time, dragging Fielding back to his seat as he swore under his breath. 'Take it easy, Chris. Come on, sit down.'

Reluctantly, Fielding followed, color returning to his blood-drained face as anger subsided.

'If BGC's rights are ignored, there will be a mass exodus of foreign mining companies from Indonesia,' Fielding warned.

'You mean, P.T. Kalimantan Gold's rights, surely?' Sukirno allowed his smile to cool.

'Whatever!' the executive snapped, defiantly.

'I remind you, Mister Fielding, that we called this meeting to discuss what options might be available to us all, in determining the operating company's position with respect to the Longdamai concession.' Sukirno's fingers drummed the unopened file while he gathered his thoughts. 'Indonesia was built on consensus, gentlemen,' he forced another smile before adding, 'and compromise.' In untypical Javanese fashion, he stared the company president down, resisting the sneer that tempted the corners of his mouth. 'I suggest that you listen to what is on offer, gentlemen, before considering the alternatives. After all, P.T. Kalimantan Gold is yet to negotiate terms for exploitation of the Longdamai site. The Indonesian Government has received expressions of interest from a number of financially sound, mining houses offering finance and expertise and,' Sukirno hesitated, as if relishing the moment, 'the President has instructed the Minister to carefully examine these offers as to how they might impact on national interests.'

With the mention of the Indonesian First Family Kremenchug's chest fell heavily. He knew, from those few words encapsulated in the General's response, that the outcome was inevitable. They had seriously erred in not finalizing the secondary contracts guaranteeing them the right to mine before announcing their discovery. And, that error in judgment now jeopardized BGC's rights – and his own, elusive dream. Crushed by this realization he turned to Christopher Fielding. 'We need to talk.' Then, addressing the Chairman, 'General, may we have a few minutes?'

Sukirno rose. 'Of course, gentlemen, of course!' He touched a button hidden discreetly from view, and an aide entered. 'Show our visitors into the guest lounge,' he ordered, then returned to his seat, smugly confident that the BGC directors would acquiesce, and surrender control over the Longdamai field.

★ ★ ★ ★

The two executives were shown into an unoccupied room, the aide barely out of earshot when Fielding exploded.

'It's a goddamn outrage!' he all but shouted.

'Shh!' Kremenchug warned, finger to lips, 'keep it down, for Chrissakes!'

'Screw it, Alex!' he snapped, 'we should go straight from here to the Canadian Embassy!'

'Technically, they've got us by the balls,' Kremenchug slumped into a rattan chair.

'You're not seriously suggesting that we let these bastards walk away with our mine?' Fielding asked, disbelief spread across his face.

'No, I'm not suggesting anything of the kind.'

'They can't get away with it,' the BGC president wailed, 'the entire, fucking international mining community would blacklist them!'

Kremenchug crossed his arms and glared at his naïve associate. 'Including those companies vying for our rights?'

'We could take them to the International Court in the Hague,' Fielding insisted.

'And argue what?' Kremenchug challenged. 'That we failed to complete the necessary applications to move to the next phase of operations? Besides, this is not an issue between BGC and the Indonesian Government. The concession was awarded to P.T. Kalimantan Gold, a corporate entity created under their law.'

Fielding threw his hands in the air. 'We've been trying to finalize the paperwork for months. *You* know that!' He commenced pacing around the room. 'Couldn't we prove that they deliberately procrastinated – accuse them of orchestrating this mess to get control over the concession?'

'Chris, didn't you hear him say the First Family is now in on the hunt?'

Fielding came to a halt. 'Are you saying that the President's kids are behind this?'

Exasperated, Kremenchug unfolded his arms and pointed up at an unsmiling photograph on the opposite wall. 'They've obviously done their homework. We've screwed up, Chris. Now what we have to do is work out the best deal we can for BGC, or risk losing everything.'

'No, fuck it, Alex!' the company's president rejected 'We have to fight them on this. I say we take them to court and see what happens from there!'

Years of dealing in Indonesia had taught Kremenchug that, corporately speaking, such action would be suicidal as not only would

BGC have to deal with a corrupt judiciary, but the threat of having a Presidential Decree simply override any judgment which conflicted with the Palace's position.

'We couldn't win,' he responded, dejectedly. 'At the risk of being pedantic, Chris, they really have us over a barrel. The General knows it, Mines & Energy obviously believe this is the situation, and I think what they're saying is that we should go quietly and, if we do, they'll leave us with something.' Kremenchug suddenly frowned, wincing as bugs struck through his clothing where he sat in the louse-ridden chair. He jumped to his feet, scratching furiously around his crotch. 'What the...?' he looked down, disbelievingly, at the double-layered, infested seat. 'Let's go and ask the General what's on the table,' he suggested, 'and then take it from there?'

Reluctantly, Fielding agreed. 'You know that the shareholders are gonna have our guts over this?'

But Kremenchug had already left the room, his priority then to locate a washroom where he could drop his trousers, and dislodge whatever it was that continued to savage his buttocks, and groin.

★ ★ ★ ★

When the meeting reconvened, Kremenchug sat unhappily, inconspicuously dropping his hand from time to time to scratch the persistent, and painful itch, which, by now, had spread across his entire, lower torso.

'General, there was some mention of compromise?' Fielding muttered unhappily through partially clenched teeth.

'Well, the Indonesian Government only wishes to be fair. It is not my place to make BGC any official offer, you understand, but in the interests of achieving a mutually acceptable solution to your dilemma, I am prepared to offer you some suggestions, if you wish?'

The General's subtle approach did nothing to alleviate their despondency.

'Are you able to shed some light as to who the other players might be?' Fielding asked.

Sukirno suppressed a laugh. 'Not at this time,' he answered. 'But,

I can tell you that if you were to consider, say, some sort of internal arrangement which would accommodate all parties, then my government would be most supportive.'

'Such as?' Fielding pressed, abandoning any pretence that he was less than happy at BGC's interests being so brazenly hijacked.

'I'm sorry, it is not my place to say,' the Chairman replied, enigmatically.

'Then whose place is it, General, 'cause I'm getting the feeling that this is going nowhere?' Fielding said, frustration raising his ire. Then, directing his annoyance at his colleague he added, 'What am I missing here? I'm totally at a loss as to what's going on.' The company president ran a hand across worried brow. 'You're supposed to be the expert on local affairs. What the hell is he trying to say?'

Kremenchug resisted scratching further, anger also evident in his response. 'General, BGC was one of the first foreign mining companies to risk substantial capital on exploration in the Kalimantan areas. The company entered into agreements with your government in good faith. We need to know clearly, what it is that you are asking of us. At this point it would seem that you are suggesting that BGC, through its ownership of the operating company, P.T Kalimantan Gold, will only be given the development rights to the Longdamai discovery, conditional on some further arrangement being arrived at between our company, and others. If this is correct, we need to know who these parties are, in order that we might consider our position, and what the bottom line will be.' Unable to constrain himself further, Kremenchug's hand returned to scratching the penny-sized welts below his waist, while General Sukirno looked on in quiet amusement.

'It is only relevant that we establish here, today, your company's willingness to establish dialogue with other parties whose interests parallel those of my government's.'

'I'm sorry, General,' Fielding blurted, 'but can't we cut the crap and get right to it? How much will it cost us, say, for you to get this problem fixed?'

Blood flooded the Chairman's face and he blinked, stunned at the foreigner's impudence. He rose to his feet, angrily jabbing the button that summoned his aide.

'It would seem that our meeting is over,' he offered, tersely, 'I trust you understand that I will be recommending that the Ministry of Mines & Energy review any application made by P.T. Kalimantan Gold, to develop the Longdamai gold reserves. You may expect that any review will take into consideration the original applicant's submissions with respect to its financial capacity to develop the prospect, before any decision be made as to whether the company be even accepted as the general contractor to develop our country's natural resources.' The aide had entered, poised in his office doorway. 'See the visitors to their vehicle,' he ordered.

'But, General…!' Kremenchug pleaded, 'please be reasonable!'

The Chairman stood erect, the hushed atmosphere electric as he viewed Fielding, his glare traveling across until resting upon Kremenchug. 'Our business is finished, here, gentlemen,' he said, articulating each word slowly, then nodding at the officer to usher the pair outside.

★ ★ ★ ★

'Let's go directly to the embassy,' Fielding growled as they climbed into the Toyota Land Cruiser.

'No, we'd do better to go to the office and see if we can raise Eric by radio. Also, I think it's time we had a long talk to our erstwhile associate, Subroto. He's sure to have had advance warning of all of this, probably the reason he wasn't available before. He knew we were coming over and is obviously avoiding us. Now we know why.'

'I still believe we should make contact with our commercial counselor at the Canadian Embassy. Who knows, they might be able to shed some light on what's happening?'

'Wouldn't count on it,' Kremenchug's unenthusiastic response was a result of earlier dealings with the embassy Trade section, where he was unofficially considered, *persona non grata*. 'Besides, it's Friday. We're not going to get much done today.'

'We're to stay the weekend?' Fielding asked, with growing agitation.

'Tomorrow, at least,' Kremenchug announced, 'if we fail to get hold of Eric and Subroto by tomorrow afternoon, we should consider flying across to the site.'

'Why, what would be achieved by going to Longdamai. Surely our problem lies here, in Jakarta?'

Kremenchug pondered the point as he fidgeted with well-manicured nails. His suggestion that they fly to East Kalimantan had been made more out of desperation than logic. 'You're right, of course,' he agreed. 'Best we give Eric another try from the office now, and again tomorrow if we need to. Who knows, we might get lucky and collar Subroto while we're there?'

He gave the driver an address and, swept with fatigue from the long journey and the stressful meeting with General Sukirno, fell into a somber mood as they made their way through the traffic-snarled capital. Perplexed as to what recourse would be available to the Borneo Gold Corporation when its subsidiary, P.T. Kalimantan Gold, lost the right to mine the Longdamai deposit, Kremenchug's ulcer started to burn.

★ ★ ★ ★

'Ah, Mister Kremenchug!' Subroto clasped his visitor's hand then, in turn, Christopher Fielding's before revolving his huge frame and waddling back into the company office. 'You were fortunate to catch me here!' he smiled widely; Kremenchug uncomfortable with Subroto's unusually, warm reception. In the past, the two men had exchanged but few words – their mutual contempt for each other concealed under masks of necessary civility. Subroto's name had been added to the P.T. Kalimantan Gold Board when the company had first been formed, the suggestion at the time coming directly from the Ministry of Mines & Energy during the official signing of the Longdamai Contract of Work. At the time, Eric Baird had also actively promoted the idea, the appointment pleasing Baird's senior partner immensely. 'In fact, we were about to send a search party out looking for you!' his attempt at levity lost on the mentally bruised executives.

'We dropped by earlier in the day, but you weren't here,' Fielding complained.

'Did we have an appointment?' Subroto responded curtly. 'Friday is not a good day to be visiting, as you should well know.'

Still stung by General Sukirno's earlier treatment, the BGC President refused the admonishment. He took a step forward and pointed into Subroto's jowled face. 'Look, I've just about had enough of Indonesia and how you do business over here,' he started. Kremenchug was unable to prevent the boil-over as Fielding brushed him aside. 'We just flew twenty hours to learn that we're about to be screwed, and you're instructing us on business etiquette? Fuck you, and your manipulating associates. You can take this fucking country and shove it, as far as it takes to hurt.' Fielding turned, his face covered with rage. 'Fuck you, too, Alex,' he cussed, 'I should have known from the outset we'd end up like this!'

'Think you'd better leave,' Kremenchug's voice was cold. 'You're screwing up any chance we might have of recovering our position!'

'It's a little too late for that, don't you think?' Fielding's sarcasm-filled voice carried through the portioned office walls where anxious staff listened, mouths agape. Nobody had ever raised their voices to Bapak Subroto in this manner before.

Kremenchug seized Fielding's upper arm firmly. 'Let's go!' he snapped, pulling him towards the door. But the BGC President was not about to surrender that easily. Twisting away from Kremenchug's grasp, he half-raised his fists, defensively, Kremenchug caught off guard by the sudden movement. Tense moments passed before Fielding, sensing the recklessness of his actions lowered his arms, glared at both men, then stormed out of the office, his exit followed by astonished stares as he slammed the outer door behind, leaving half-muttered obscenities in his wake.

'I'm sorry,' was all Kremenchug could muster, lost as how he might recover the situation.

'He must apologize, not you!' a flabbergasted Subroto spluttered,

the words lost on the foreigner.

'We've had a bad day,' Kremenchug offered, weakly, his mind racing.

'He will never work in this country again!' Subroto threatened.

Kremenchug quickly realized that Subroto would not be easily pacified. He wanted to go after Fielding before the man did something *really* stupid, but abandoned that idea in favor of remaining there to appease their local director, on whom so much now depended.

'Again, I can only offer my apologies for his behavior,' he said, 'I will have him return and do so in person, once he has cooled down.'

With great difficulty, Subroto slowly regained some measure of his earlier composure – never, even during his days in the armed forces, had he been subjected to such vitriol. 'Your friend is a very ignorant man,' he said, the caustic comment doing nothing to allay Kremenchug's concerns that Fielding had pushed them all over the precipice, and that the situation may now be irrecoverable.

'May I sit down?' Kremenchug asked. Subroto, who now seemed to be lost in anther world, ignored the request. Awkward moments passed before the foreigner tried again. 'I'll come back tomorrow, if you'd prefer?' And then, '*Pak Subroto*?'

Subroto's eyes refocused as he was dragged back from dark depths, a place in his mind where Fielding was being considered for punishment. *'What?'* he asked.

Kremenchug repeated his suggestion. 'Would it be better if I came back later?'

Subroto's phone came alive – the abrupt signal snuffed by the man's pudgy hand as he grabbed the handset, growled then dropped the receiver back into its cradle, and went back to staring into space.

Kremenchug welcomed the interruption when it came, a concerned secretary appearing, half-hidden in the doorway to inform Subroto that the caller had insisted on speaking to him, directly. Kremenchug, unaware of what had transpired, remained standing, a sense of inadequacy eating away at his confidence while Subroto wafted on in his own dialect. When the conversation terminated,

Kremenchug was overwhelmed at the sudden change of demeanor that greeted him.

'Alex,' Subroto asked, almost pleasantly, 'in which hotel are you staying?'

'We booked into the Mandarin,' he answered, cautiously. 'But we haven't registered yet. We came directly from the airport.'

'Then you should find your friend and go there now,' Subroto advised. He then spoke into the office intercom and relayed a message via his secretary.

'But, Pak Subroto,' Kremenchug tried, 'I need to talk to you. Are you aware that the government intends reneging on our Contract of Work?'

'What does this mean, reneging?' Subroto queried.

'I mean, the Indonesian Government has decided not to sanction P. T. Kalimantan Gold right to work the Longdamai deposit.' Kremenchug waited, confused when the other shrugged his shoulders.

'It may not be as bad as it sounds,' Subroto suggested. 'That call was from the Ministry of Mines & Energy. Someone called Baron has been trying to contact you all day. I have informed the Ministry that you will be available in the Mandarin Hotel.'

'Did you say, Baron?' Kremenchug felt the chill return. 'Was it Baron Mining?'

Subroto shrugged again, feigning ignorance. 'It sounded something like that.'

'And they are going to phone us at our hotel?'

'Yes,' the Javanese confirmed, impatiently. 'So you will go there now?'

Suddenly, for Kremenchug, the pieces began to fall into place, overwhelmed by his own stupidity. He nodded, knowingly, at the betrayal, storming out of the Jakarta office, leaving the retired Air Force General to his own machinations.

⋆ ⋆ ⋆ ⋆

Subroto waited no more than a few minutes before calling General Sukirno at his parliamentary post.

'It's done,' he said, proudly. *'They are staying at the Mandarin Hotel.'*

'How did they behave?' The Chairman anticipated the response.

'Predictably,' Subroto answered, *'just as you said they would.'*

Sukirno chuckled. *'You've done well, Mas 'Broto.'*

Subroto replaced the telephone, delighted with his own performance, and the outcome. Before Fielding and Kremenchug had been summoned from Canada, he had been briefed, the stage set to drive the desperate BGC executives into his arms. That they would visit the Jakarta office was a forgone conclusion. He had avoided the office prior to the BGC executives' meeting with General Sukirno, positioning himself there later, in the knowledge that the mining executives would have nowhere else to go once they learned that their company stood to lose the rights to mine the Longdamai deposits. Although Christopher Fielding's near physical attack had been unexpected and he was, admittedly, shaken, the exchange had added credibility to the part Subroto had played.

Now it was up to Baron Mining to deliver.

* * * *

'Admit it, Alex,' the belligerence in Fielding's voice could be detected on the far side of the bar. 'You fucked up!' He was obnoxiously drunk – his aggressive behavior trying Kremenchug's already-frayed nerves to their limit.

'This is not time for recriminations, Chris,' Kremenchug tried. 'Let's just make the best of it, okay?'

'God, I'm getting shit-faced,' Fielding warned, 'haven't done anything like this since Caroline had me served.'

Kremenchug had heard Fielding's divorce story before and was loathe to listen to the morbid tale yet again. Having stormed out of their Jakarta office and caught a cab to the Mandarin Hotel, he was relieved to find that his luggage had arrived safely with Fielding. Kremenchug checked his associate's room, and found this empty then discovered Chris in the hotel bar throwing doubles down his throat at an alarming rate.

'Come on, Chris,' he tried, 'we've got to get ready for that call.' He continued to coax him away, conscious that the bar's mid-afternoon Friday throng was building, and that some would be associated with the mining industry. Fielding's voice carried, and Kremenchug did not want their situation compounded by industry gossip, resulting from something the BGC president might say in his current state of mind.

'I'm not interested,' Fielding's voice was beginning to slur and this worried Kremenchug. He glanced at the bar clock, concerned that they might miss the call, then remembered that no time had been established for the connection.

'Let's go up to the room and talk it through there?'

'There's not much point,' Fielding resisted.

'How about we freshen up, then come back down later?' Kremenchug caught the bartender's attention then requested the check. 'We'll take the call, listen to what they have to say, then decide on a course of action.'

Fielding turned and stared at his associate, questioningly. 'You really think we've still got a shot?'

'The game's not over yet,' Kremenchug said, unconvinced himself. He signed the tab and led the way to the lobby lifts, and to their adjoining suites, where they alerted the operator to their presence, then sat back and waited for the all important call.

By the time darkness had descended over the capital and no attempt had been made to phone their rooms, the two mining executives remained locked in limbo, the uncertainty of their situation driving Christopher Fielding dangerously to the edge. Three hours had passed – the repetitive CNN news broadcasts adding to their agitation as the pair continued to wait. Fielding had resisted drinking during the first two hours in preparation for the discussion with Baron, but when another guest had inadvertently phoned their room in error, Fielding broke his temporary fast, demolishing a variety of alcoholic drinks with punishing speed.

'Jesus, Alex,' Fielding staggered towards the once, well-stocked mini bar and ripped the top from a Jack Daniels miniature, emptying the contents directly into his mouth. He reached for another, twisting the cap with ease. 'Baron fucking Mining?'

'Chris,' Kremenchug warned, 'you've got to keep a clear head. Ease up, okay?'

'Why?' Fielding stumbled, regained his balance then eased himself onto the double bed. 'Once those mothers get their hands on our find, it'll be game over. You'll see.'

'Let's wait and see what they have to offer. The fact that they're willing to talk must mean something?'

Fielding sneered. 'Yeah, sure, they're gonna give us the world and all we have to do… is bend over and enjoy it.'

'We don't know that,' Kremenchug argued, but nothing was getting through.

'Half the fucking world… knows Baron Mining,' Fielding hiccupped then rolled his eyes. 'Shit!'

'Why don't you take a shower, Chris? We're going to need our wits about us when they call.'

'Don't think I'm up to it.' Fielding appeared to have reached some alcoholic plateau, where the effects were leveling off, and he was rapidly losing his taste for more.

'Okay, Chris, I'll take the call,' Kremenchug offered, relieved to some extent. 'But I need to have you clear minded. How about throwing yourself into the shower and I'll call room service for something to eat?'

Fielding frowned. 'Guess…you're right.' He rolled off the bed slowly and, with feet firmly on the carpeted floor, leaned forward with face in hands. 'Do you know that we haven't eaten since the flight?'

★ ★ ★ ★

When the connection was finally made around midnight, Fielding and Kremenchug were on the verge of calling it a day. Fielding had become sullenly quiet over the past hours of forced abstinence and, although his head was now reasonably clear, the late afternoon binge had left him with a debilitating headache. Kremenchug had been nibbling at the remains of an overcooked chicken when the shrill signal interrupted. He jumped up banging one knee, pushed the cluttered room service trolley to one side, and grabbed the phone.

'Yeah?' he spluttered.

'Phil Samuels – sorry to get you at this hour,' the voice apologized, 'is that Chris Fielding?'

'No, Phil, it's Alex Kremenchug. I have Chris here with me, but he's asked me to take your call if that's okay.' Kremenchug's mind went into overdrive, trying to recall where he had heard the name before.

'That's okay by me. You can listen to what I've got to say then, when you return to Canada we'll set up a meet to further the discussions.'

Kremenchug recognized Samuels' assumption that the BGC directors would do as they were instructed. 'What's the deal?' he asked, piqued at having the lesser hand, but straight to the point.

Samuels did not hesitate. 'For obvious reasons, this call will be limited to our registering an expression of interest in acquiring control over BGC's Indonesian operating company, P.T. Kalimantan Gold.'

'All of it?' Kremenchug's future collapsed into a chasm. They were to be left with nothing.

'That's not what I said,' Samuels replied. 'We have already been approached by the Indonesian Government to establish whether Baron Mining would throw its hat into the ring, so to speak. All we've done is indicated that we're interested. Seems to me that the next logical step is for you guys to sit down with us, and see how we can come to some arrangement while accommodating the locals.'

'You can't give me more than that?'

'Not over an open line,' Samuels refused.

'At least give us something to work on?'

'No,' the Canadian party responded, 'not until we can sit down with all parties around the same table. When are you returning?'

Kremenchug had already thought this through. 'We'll be back in Vancouver on Monday. Where do you want to meet?'

'Guess you'll have had enough flying by then so, how about I come over from Toronto on Tuesday, and meet you there?'

'Okay, thanks. Can you give me a minute?'

'Sure,' the caller agreed, Kremenchug holding a palm over the mouthpiece while he spoke briefly with Fielding. The other man nodded, held his hands as if in surrender, and Kremenchug returned to the phone.

'Okay, it's set. We'll wait for you at the BGC offices Tuesday morning.'

'Fine, I'll be there,' Samuels promised. 'And Alex,' he added, 'tell Fielding that there's to be nothing in the press about Baron until we give the green light. Agreed?'

'What about the Exchange, we're required to keep them posted?'

'No, there's no requirement, 'cause at this point in time we're only entering into informal discussions. The Indonesians want to keep the lid on this for as long as we can. I'll explain when we meet. See you next week.'

Kremenchug replaced the receiver. 'They obviously want to keep the negotiations quiet,' he relayed to Fielding. 'My guess is, that they'll screw us down to the boards and complete the deal before the competition gets wind of what's happening.' He turned to his fellow director and, for the first time in days, smiled. 'What do you say, Chris, that we beat the bushes to see what else is out there?'

Christopher Fielding stared at Kremenchug through glassy eyes. 'Aren't you forgetting that Baron's the preferred Indonesian player?'

'Sure, but what if we got into bed with, say, Freemont? They've already established a powerful position in this country, and would give Baron a run for their money.'

Fielding, already resigned to an outcome that would strip BGC of its main asset, just wanted to have their position resolved. 'If the Indonesians had wanted Freemont in the deal, they wouldn't have thrown Baron at us. I'm all for catching the first flight back to Canada and getting on with it, Alex. Let's not try to outguess everyone on this. Okay?'

'Only until we hear what's on offer.'

'Okay. But, we should inform Dominion Mining.'

Kremenchug had already considered this, but wanted to wait until Baron placed its offer on the table before contacting Sharon Ducay. When it was appropriate he would call her on the radio-phone from the Vancouver office. Whatever was ultimately decided, BGC would need Dominion's approval as the major stockholder before anything could proceed. Sharon's stranglehold on the company had prevented the directors from issuing further stock, effectively keeping the newly created, asset rich, billion dollar mining company, cash poor. The agreements that had been put in place when Dominion, as vendor, assigned all of its rights in the Indonesian operating company, P.T. Kalimantan Gold, stipulated that BGC could not issue any new stock until the escrow period had passed, at which time Sharon would be in a position to dispose of her holdings and move on, if she so desired.

With the discovery of the massive Longdamai field gold deposits, Kremenchug believed that Sharon should have long abandoned the original concept to launder her uncle's gold through the operation. He expected Sharon should be satisfied with the tens of millions their share of Dominion Mining's stock in BGC would generate, when the stock was finally released from escrow, and that moment was imminent.

* * * *

Philippines

General Narciso Dominguez's features froze, struck by the intensity of the pain, his fist seizing with the excruciating attack crumpling Sharon's most recent letter, and the *Indonesian Observer* newspaper clipping, into a ball. As the minutes passed and the severity of the onslaught lessened, the retired Filipino General managed to push himself upright, away from the desk, the back of his head striking the intricately carved crown on top of his chair. He cursed, loudly, calling for his manservant, whom he knew hovered outside the office. *'Take me... to... my quarters,'* he ordered, his voice barely a whisper.

Earlier, he had asked Alfredo to carry him to his study where, with gnarled, tortured hands, he penned a response to his beloved niece. He had then reread her letter written from the Indonesian goldfields, and the attached article, satisfied that Sharon would succeed.

Within moments, the faithful aide was at his side and half-carried the General's frail, emaciated body back to his bedroom, where he administered the tablets as prescribed. He gazed down at the withered form of the once powerful officer, the cancer now spreading at an alarming rate. *'Should I call the doctor?'*

'No...' Dominguez wheezed. *'He...will only...insist, on keeping me...alive.'* He closed his eyes – the pain, thankfully, subsiding as the powerful dosage took effect. *'You remember... your promise... Alfredo?'*

The loyal guardian's eyes filled with tears. *'Yes, General.'*

Dominguez's head rolled to one side and attempted a smile.

'A man... should be permitted... to die with dignity,' he said, the raspy comment barely audible in the solemn setting. *'Your... word...my old friend?'* Alfredo took his General's hand and held it as firmly as he dare.

'Are... you sure... General?' the words choked in Alfredo's throat.

A minute passed before Dominguez could muster the strength to answer. *'Yes,'* he said, then squeezed Alfredo's hands. *'It...is time...'* and the General rested his eyes. *'Please...fetch...it, now.'*

Alfredo released Dominguez's hand, rose to his full height, stared down at what was left of the man he had served for more years than either could remember, then left to carry out the dying general's final order.

Dominguez recognized the familiar sounds of Alfredo opening the locked gun cabinet, relieved that it would soon be over. Accepting that it was only a matter of days before the cancer killed him, the General had elected to die in his own time. Alfredo's shadow crossed the room as he returned with the revolver, placing the loaded handgun on the bedside table. He bent down and kissed Dominguez on both cheeks, streaming tears falling onto the General's pallid face. Then, without so much as another word he rose to full height, came to attention, saluted, and whispered, *'Go with God, General,'* then wheeled around and escaped before wobbly legs let him down.

General Narciso Dominguez grasped the weapon's handle, surprised at the weight of the gun. As he lay there contempiating the end to his life, his thoughts turned to his niece, Sharon, who had so clearly demonstrated that one could always count on the greed of others. The story of Marcos' gold had been around long enough to provide fertile ground for the never ending hordes of carpetbaggers and the Kremenchugs of this world. A wry smile twisted one side of his face as he recalled the speed at which that thief, Kremenchug and his associates had jumped at the opportunity to defraud others. The Indonesian newspaper had carried the story of how fiercely Palace interests had competed for control over the gold discovery, driving the value of his niece's holdings to incredible highs. Although, at first, he had not been convinced that what she planned was achievable, at least, now, he would leave this world assured that she would have a bountiful legacy of wealth, to guarantee her independence. She had cheated the cheaters! And, amused as this thought remained foremost in his mind, uncontrollable laughter built in his chest, the wheezy cackle noises gasping from his throat suddenly frozen in midair when he fired the gun.

★ ★ ★ ★

Vancouver

'I can't take an offer of only twenty percent to the shareholders.' Fielding's voice started to crack. Embarrassed, he reached for the water tumbler.

'It's the best we can do,' Salima shrugged. 'Look, the final offer's on the table and, if you reject it, we'll have a team sitting in Jakarta negotiating directly with the Jakarta authorities within seventy-two hours.'

Kremenchug and Fielding both glared at the man, annoyed that the threat was most likely true. Someone in Jakarta had wasted no time in leaking details of their visit, the Canadian Press clamoring for more information, immediately upon their return. Before that Monday's trading had closed, Borneo Gold Corporation stocks had halved, and were still falling at the bell. The directors had called the company lawyers who confirmed their worst expectations, that P.T. Kalimantan Gold had compromised its position by not finalizing its application to exploit the deposits discovered. The lawyers had also advised that, in all probability, they would not succeed in having the matter heard before an international tribunal, as P.T. Kalimantan Gold was an Indonesian legal entity, and therefore unlikely that the claim could be taken out of that country's jurisdiction.

The short interpretation being, they were screwed.

Kremenchug stole a glance towards the other end of the boardroom table where Phil Samuels sat quietly, the BGC director perplexed with Baron Mining's suggested role in the venture. When Samuels had arrived for the meeting, he'd surprised the BGC directors by announcing that he was present only in the capacity of observer, and at the request of the Commercial Asian Pacific Bank. He had then introduced James Salima and the banker's team, briefly explaining the history of Baron's association with the CAP group. Before passing the floor to the CAP President, Samuels went on to state that should the negotiations end on a positive note, Baron Mining would become the appointed operator responsible for developing the Longdamai mine.

The meeting had commenced badly with Fielding throwing down the gauntlet even before an offer had been made, followed by the bank president threatening to walk unless decorum was maintained. James Salima had then effectively taken control over the meeting, offering his bank's perception of how the situation had evolved, and what remedies might be available to the BGC group. Kremenchug had to admit that the Chinese-Indonesian's assessment was accurate, to the point where only insider information could have assisted with such detailed preparation. When Salima then opened the negotiations with a 'one-time' offer, the BGC executives knew, for certain, that they had lost the Longdamai mine. Fielding had not helped the situation, his less than diplomatic outburst requiring Kremenchug to arrange a brief adjournment, during which time he attempted to convince the BGC president that there were no other options left for them to consider.

'It doesn't really matter what we counter-offer,' he had explained, 'the bastards know they have us by the balls.'

'But, Jesus, Alex,' Fielding had agonized, 'twenty percent?'

'I know, Chris, I know,' Kremenchug had agreed. 'If we don't take the deal and the Indonesians assign the rights to someone else, we'll end up with nothing. The market's suspended trading of our stock until we address their demands for information. And, if you call and tell them that we have walked away from this offer, you may as well take all your own stock and options, and paper the fucking office with them – 'cause ten minutes after you make any such decision, the scrip will be worthless!'

★ ★ ★ ★

The meeting had been reconvened for mid-afternoon. When the Commercial Asian Pacific Bank president and his associates were seated, Fielding gave it one more try.

'Twenty-five percent, we recover all funds expended to date, and you have a deal.' The BGC president was reminded by Kremenchug's hand on his shoulder and added, 'Subject, of course, to shareholder approval.'

'The offer remains the same,' James Salima replied, stubbornly.

Alexander Kremenchug crossed his arms, then unlocked these, drew a handkerchief from his trousers' pocket and wiped a dry brow, unaware that a negotiation specialist with the other side made another mental note of his body language.

'It's nowhere near reasonable,' Christopher Fielding argued, 'we're miles apart and *that* distance is growing!'

'You've got less than a couple of million invested,' James Salima came back. 'We're offering to reimburse all of that, and still leave you with a handsome stake in the venture.'

'What, twenty percent?' Fielding scoffed. 'The last time I looked, BGC owned all of the stock!'

'Which could end up being worthless, if the Indonesian Mines & Energy Minister gets his way,' another implied, his team agreeing beforehand to repeatedly hammer this point.

'We still have the option of taking them to the courts,' Kremenchug rejoined the discussion, raising the issue of litigation once more.

'We've been down that path, already,' the banker reminded them, wearily. 'You'd lose.'

Fielding looked over at Kremenchug before his eyes swept the table, then fell to the floor. It was all over and they both knew it. In less than a week the value of the company's stock had plunged by more than a billion dollars. They were beaten. He lifted his gaze and nodded. 'Okay,' he sighed heavily, 'but it's still subject to shareholder approval.'

James Salima's face in no way reflected his pleasure. He thanked both Christopher Fielding and Alexander Kremenchug for their support, then went on to outline the conditions relating to their proposed acquisition of P.T. Kalimantan Gold, and the company's Longdamai gold deposits.

★ ★ ★ ★

Kremenchug had heard women swear before, but nothing that could match the invective that poured down the line from the Longdamai camp when Sharon Ducay learned the news. He had tried, desperately, to persuade her that not all was lost. Finally, having vented her anger, Sharon gradually cooled down.

'You should have come over to the site when you were in Jakarta. We might have been able to sort something out.'

'We couldn't get through.' Kremenchug had, in fact, tried.

'Did you talk to Baird?' Sharon challenged, suspicion evident in her tone.

'No, we…'

'Don't lie to me, Alexander Kremenchug!' her voice faded as atmospherics played with the rhythmic flow of voice through space, '…and if you think that I don't know you're playing some game…'

'I'm not, Sharon, listen, I've got some…'

'No, *you* listen, Alex,' she snapped harshly. 'I *know* you. This couldn't have happened unless you've done a deal with those bastards!' Her accusation hung heavily in the air – Kremenchug desperate to persuade her that not all was lost. He braced himself, deciding to drop the news of her uncle's death. Sharon, I'm sorry. There's more. They've been trying to contact you from Manila.'

'What?' he heard her voice drop a level.

'I'm afraid there's bad news. Can you hear me clearly?'

Their radio connection offered nothing but satellite hum, Kremenchug trying to imagine her standing in the Longdamai office – uncomfortable with having to inform her of Dominguez's death.

'Sharon?'

'My uncle?'

He braced himself, again. 'Yes, I'm very sorry. We had a call from Alfredo, just an hour ago.'

'He's dead?'

'Yes. The General passed away in his sleep.' Kremenchug had not been given the truth.

'I see,' was all she managed to say.

'You will want to be there, for the funeral?'

'Yes,' she said, emphatically and then, 'No,' which, moments later, was followed by a more measured tone and, 'I'm not sure.'

'Can I do anything for you, from here?'

'No.'

'Sharon, if there is…'

'His death doesn't change anything, Alex.'

Kremenchug expected that her judgment would be impaired by her loss. 'I'm sorry that you had to hear it all from me.'

This was followed by an uncomfortable delay. Then Sharon responded, and he could detect the sadness in her voice. 'I'm sorry for the outburst, Alex. I haven't got my head together, right now.'

Immediately, his confidence was restored. 'Let me know what you want to do about going to Manila, Sharon. I could meet you there?' The suggestion was greeted with mute response. He waited, hoping that she might be considering his offer. With General Dominguez dead, and the uncertainties relating to BGC's reduced position in the Indonesian gold mine, his attention turned to their original plan. She would still need his help to launder the General's gold. They could arrange another concession, perhaps in a different province, and put the project back on track.

'I can't leave the site,' she explained, 'and you should understand why.'

'Close the drilling down and go to Manila,' he urged, 'there's not much point in continuing now, anyway.'

'Give me a couple of hours to think it all through.'

'We're still going to make more money than either of us had envisaged, Sharon. Let's just count those blessings and agree that we've done well. Besides, we can still resurrect the original project.'

There was a distinct pause before he heard Sharon back on the line. 'You should have come over to the site when you were in Jakarta. We might have been able to sort something out.'

'We tried our best, Sharon, but everything got so fucked up over there, we just ran out of options.'

'What happens next?' She sounded emotionally drained.

'Nothing, unless Dominion Mining agrees.'

'You mean we can still block this raid?'

'Not really.'

'Then what are you saying?' she flared, Kremenchug moving quickly to soothe.

'It's Catch-22, Sharon. Dominion's acceptance is required otherwise the deal can't legally proceed. On the other hand, if you do block their offer, there's every chance we'll lose the mine anyway.'

'Will I have to come over?' she asked. Kremenchug sensing she was coming round.

'No, not if you can organize to have Dominion's directors courier their acceptance.'

Then, suddenly, she changed tack again. 'Alex, what are the BGC shares trading at?'

'They've virtually collapsed. Chris has to get down to the Exchange first thing tomorrow and do what he can to explain what's happening.'

'What are they trading at, Alex?' she pressed, annoyed.

'Five dollars,' he answered, weakly. This was greeted with another expletive, then resounding quiet. 'Sharon?'

'I'm still here.'

'Sharon, we're really sorry about the General.'

'Thanks, Alex.' And then, as if her uncle's passing was already a thing of the past, she asked, 'Alex, would you mind going over all of that again?'

'What, the offer?'

'Yes.'

Kremenchug shook his head at the woman's resilience. 'Wouldn't you prefer I called you back, say, in a couple of hours?'

'No. Let's get it over with, now. I could do with the distraction.'

'Are you certain you want to do this now?'

'I'm sure,' she assured him. 'And, Alex,' she continued, 'thanks for letting me know about my uncle.'

⋆ ⋆ ⋆ ⋆

Chapter Twenty-one

KALIMANTAN GOLD – LONGDAMAI SIAL

Sharon stood at the Mahakam River's edge, engrossed with the swirling eddy capturing leaves and small branches drawn into its path. Dragonflies dipped and hovered in never-ending, predacious pursuit, tantalizingly out of reach to the bulbous-eyed fish that stalked below the shifting, surface glare. Movement at her feet caught her attention, Sharon remaining perfectly still as she observed the cockroach's long, threadlike antennae emerge from under the timber planks, and test the air. Slowly, the shiny brown adult insect moved into full view, Sharon's swift stomp squashing the scavenger underfoot before it could flee. She scraped her boot against the jetty's timbers, kicking shattered remains through cracks, into the water.

Her uncle's death, although expected, could not have come at a more inopportune time. As Sharon could not communicate with Manila directly, she had solicited Kremenchug's assistance in relaying a message to Alfredo, to standby the telephone later in the day. She would take the chopper to Samarinda and speak to him from there, before catching the charter to Singapore, and then home to the Philippines via Hong Kong, to assist with the burial.

Although Sharon had earlier indicated to Kremenchug that she would not attend the funeral, she had changed her mind upon accepting that the hostile takeover was virtually a *fait accompli*. Now, with the shift in control, she knew that it was only a matter of time before the incoming shareholders discovered what had been done, and lay the blame directly at her feet. She would put all drilling on hold then fly to the Philippines to farewell her uncle, taking advantage of the visit to contact her nominee directors in the British Virgin Islands, and issue them with new instructions.

Dominion Mining's BGC stock had been released from escrow. Originally, she had planned to start selling these shares as soon as they became available. Now, she had to correct the timing. She recognized that, although BGC's stock value was down as a result of the unfavorable media questioning P.T. Kalimantan Gold's rights to the Longdamai discovery, this situation remained fluid. Sharon knew that once she had instructed her directors in Tortola to approve the 'farming-out' arrangements to the CAP Bank syndicate, and this information was released to the market, BGC's shares would recover some of their value, lost in that week. Sharon understood clearly, now, the path she must follow. She would revise her instructions to Dominion's nominee directors and, once the BGC stock had recovered, sell, then abandon the Longdamai site and disappear before the incoming operators restarted the drilling program – all of these latter actions integral to her original plan.

When Sharon first conceived the scheme she had no illusions of the resulting uproar, and the consequences, once the fraud had been discovered. Returning to the Philippines had never been her first option, as she had planned to relocate to any one of a multiple of destinations, such as the Cayman Islands or even Majorca. Armed with a projected treasury of twenty million dollars, she was confident that residency in such countries could easily be arranged, and that extradition may not necessarily become a serious threat. If trapped, she intended denying responsibility for the fabricated results, accusing Eric Baird and his accomplice, Alexander Kremenchug. After all, both had colorful histories – both were involved in business together prior to her appointment as operations manager, and both stood to gain substantially from salting the samples.

But, now, with the involvement of international bankers, she knew that this group would have the muscle and influence to dislodge her from wherever she might choose to hide. Money talks – and, she had no doubt that any host government threatened with losing CAP Bank's substantial revenue, or deposits, would not hesitate in surrendering her to the courts. No, she decided, there had to be a significant change to her original concept – so that when she did disappear, it would have to be *forever*.

Suddenly, Sharon looked up and squinted, her attention drawn by the familiar, chopping beat of rotors slicing through tropical air and recognized the TNI's military replacement Bell 205 'Huey' with its camouflaged arrangements. She remained standing, observing, as the helicopter landed heavily, then casually strolled towards the helipad as dust settled to greet the *Kopassus*, Special Forces pilot who had become so essential to her exit plan.

⋆ ⋆ ⋆ ⋆

Jakarta

'Stew, hi buddy!' Phil Samuels sounded in good cheer on the phone. 'How's that lady friend of yours – or have you already moved on?'

'Where are you, Sammy?' Campbell asked, ignoring the comment. Their friendship dated back to undergraduate days, when both studied geology at Washington State. In subsequent years, Phil 'Sammy' Samuels had been responsible for directing a considerable volume of mining consultancy work his way.

'Toronto,' came the reply.

'Coming over?'

'Sure, but not for another month or so.'

Campbell could hear the other man drawing, on what had to be a cigar. 'Those things will be the end of you, one day,' he said, lightheartedly.

Samuels laughed. 'You might be right.' Then, 'Say, Stew, got anything on at the moment?'

'Why, what's up?'

'Have something for you. That's if you're interested?'

'What's the job?'

'First, there's been no announcement, although that may be imminent, so you'll need to keep the lid on this until I personally give you clearance. Okay?'

Campbell's curiosity was immediately aroused. 'You know me, Sammy. All ears, no mouth,' he bantered.

'Stew,' Samuels' tone became serious. 'This is serious. If word leaks before the Board is ready…' he left the rest unsaid.

Campbell fell into step, acknowledging his friend's warning. 'Understood, Phil. What needs to be done?'

The distinctive sound of heavy exhaling preceded Samuels' response, Campbell visualizing his friend holding the phone in one hand, a Havana in the other. 'Baron is taking over the Longdamai operations,' Samuel imparted, leaving Stewart Campbell stunned. 'And I want you to get on site during the transition period to protect our interests. Do you want the work?'

Campbell's mind galloped at the offer. When drilling results from the Longdamai discovery had first been released, he had been amongst the most vociferous, of the many skeptics, in challenging the findings. However, when the test results had been verified by an internationally acceptable, analytical analysis laboratory *and* acclaimed by many amongst the world's finest mineral geologists as conceivably the greatest gold discovery ever to be made, he, too, became a believer. For Campbell, Baron's involvement merely confirmed what everyone in the industry already suspected – that the Longdamai site contained huge reserves of gold; so great, in fact, that some analysts were predicting the possibility of a collapse in world gold prices. Campbell considered the kudos in being associated with such an operation – being appointed, albeit, only in a temporary capacity, would do his reputation no harm. Still, something niggled at the back of his mind. Although Baron Mining enjoyed the reputation of being an adequate, corporate citizen in terms of environmental responsibility throughout its massive, multinational empire, over the years, he had observed that the mining giant rarely missed an opportunity to promote its public profile. 'Of course, Phil, who wouldn't be. But, why all the secrecy?' He heard Samuels conversing with someone in the background, surprised that he had not mentioned that others would be party to this conversation.

'When I say Baron's taking over the operation, Stew, I meant as operators. You'll hear it all soon enough once the company sends out a press release but, for the time being, you can assume that we'll be running things. A banking group that originates from over your way is leading the syndicate. You most probably know them. Their US-based banking arm is Commercial Asian Pacific. Does that ring any bells?'

'Sure does,' he answered, 'the Salima Family's offshore operations. It's huge.'

'That's one way of putting it,' Campbell could almost see the smile on the other man's face. 'You'll be answerable to me, Stew, but for the purposes of paperwork, the CAP boys are driving the engine. Okay?'

'Fine by me,' Campbell agreed, 'what's the brief?'

'Well, you'll need to get over to the site by the end of the week and establish yourself as Baron's onsite representative. Obviously, we want the transfer to go as smoothly as possible, as soon as the deal is finalized. P.T. Kalimantan Gold's ops manager is a Filipino. Name's Sharon Ducay.'

'I know. We've met,' Campbell did not elaborate. 'Doesn't she know, yet?'

'She'd be expecting something like this. The BGC board would have briefed her, by now.'

'Jesus, it'll be like walking into a hornets' nest. Will she be staying on?'

'No. But she doesn't know that yet. Guess she won't be too happy with your arrival. Keep it as cool as you can; Stew – there's big bucks riding on all of this.'

'She's going to be really pissed, Phil, I know. I would be, given that she's the one who discovered the deposit.'

'Can't be helped. We've got our own people with substantially more experience than she has. Besides, don't know if she's ever been engaged in any downstream operation. We're going to need production people – mining engineers, and the like. Sharon Ducay's done her bit. We'll talk to her once you're on site. Don't worry, Stew, we'll make sure she gets a reasonable payout.'

'Just seems like you're forgoing her local knowledge- she's got to be a great asset to have around.'

'Sorry, haven't made myself clear on that. Of course she'll need to remain until we get a full team on site, and that could take a couple of months. Kalimantan Gold still has Ducay under contract. Her final payout will be dependent on her remaining there until we can get things tidied up, and take over. Think you can handle that?'

'Doesn't sound like she has too much of a choice,' the Jakarta-based expatriate said, 'I'll need something in writing to take with me.'

'Fine, we'll have your authority sent tomorrow. There's not much we can do to empower you, Stew, until the announcements are all made. You're there as the Baron rep, nothing else. We can't give authority that is not yet ours to give. You'll be needed on site for around two, max three months. Does that fit your schedule?'

'That suits me fine, Phil.'

'Great. We'll pay double your usual rate seeing we're taking you out of circulation for so long.'

Campbell silently thanked his friend for bumping his fee, so generously. 'Seems fair,' he said, a grin spreading from ear to ear. Their conversation finished, Stewart Campbell remained in high spirits as he went about reorganizing his life to accommodate the contract, the thought of being reunited with Angela Dau at the Longdamai site, foremost in his mind.

The next day Stewart visited BGC's Jakarta offices where he asked to be patched through to the Mahakam River site. His request was granted. However, when he terminated the radiophone conversation with Angela, he was left deeply depressed with her unenthusiastic response.

★ ★ ★ ★

Hong Kong

'I'll need your signature on these as well, Miss Dau.' The manager for new accounts smiled admiringly at Sharon Ducay, impressed not by her elegant style, but with the size of the account. He had served his apprenticeship as an expatriate banker in a number of Asian capitals, and still never ceased to be amazed at the size of individual, private transactions that often exceeded the tens of millions of dollars. Although many of his colleagues who had worked in Singapore and Hong Kong frequently related stories of Indonesian citizens carrying suitcases filled with cash into their banks for deposit, the banker was smugly confident that none of his associates had ever opened a new account of this magnitude. His stocks would rise with management, and he could expect a most favorable review to be included in his annual assessment report. He looked on, admiring the new client's choice of clothes as the attractive, young Indonesian woman signed the remaining documents and declarations, then witnessed her signature on these forms.

'The transfer will be made within the month,' she smiled, seductively. Sharon wore a *jilbab*-styled headscarf over her head, the delicate material wrapped also around her neck and off one shoulder. And, with eyes hidden behind Christian Dior sunglasses, it was virtually impossible for the banker to distinguish between the woman sitting across the desk, and the face in the passport photograph.

The bank was required to report unusually large transactions as was required by international agreement, in an effort to stem the worldwide flow of laundered funds. Later in the day when senior management was made aware of the size of the pending transfer, the senior executive examined the bank's photocopy of Angela Dau's passport and Mines Department identification then merely shook his head. 'They're getting worse and worse,' he muttered under his breath and sanctioned the new account, assuming that the substantial transfer was just another case of funds being siphoned off by another corrupt Indonesian official. He believed, that if he and the other bankers were to report all such transactions to the authorities, the entire Hong Kong banking system would collapse.

★ ★ ★ ★

Longdamai Gold Site

When Angela first learned of Stewart Campbell's appointment, she was deeply troubled, and used all of persuasive powers to discourage him from accepting the position. When this failed, she even challenged his loyalty in accepting the position of caretaker to those who would ultimately continue with the desecration of the *Penehing-Dayak,* sacred site. Passionate when expressing her position, Angela accepted responsibility for the heated radiophone exchange that followed, accusing Stewart of compromising his principles. He had hung up, cutting her off in mid-sentence. Now Angela was anxious that she would be burdened with the responsibility of orchestrating for him to be away from the camp, when it came under attack.

Then there was the matter of how her own security had been compromised, Angela discovering that her passport and identification documents had been removed from her quarters – when this might have happened, a complete mystery to her. Although she could easily have these replaced, the violation had weighed heavily on her mind, added to which, she would now have to contend with Stewart's imminent arrival. With concerns compounding over the deteriorating security situation and the knowledge of her father's hostile intentions, Angela fell into a rare, and ugly mood.

★ ★ ★ ★

Philippines

Sharon had told Alfredo that there would be no wake, the ageing manservant relieved that they would be permitted to grieve alone.

Dressed in a long, black column dress, Sharon had attended her uncle's funeral, whispered a final farewell as the coffin moved slowly along the conveyor and through the velvet curtains into the crematorium, ignored the congregation that had gathered to offer their respects to Narciso Dominguez, then retreated under their astonished whispers, and stares. She had exited the Manila Memorial Park Cemetery as quickly as circumstances provided, then climbed into the Mercedes and urged Alfredo to hurry, concerned that she would miss her flight to the southern Philippines. Sharon gently raised the laced, net veil that had shrouded her pale features during the ceremony, removing the wide-brimmed hat cautiously so as not to disturb her hair, then discarded these accessories. She would finish changing at the airport before flying down to Cebu and onto Zamboanga on the southernmost coast, where Alfredo had arranged for her to meet with an expatriate boat captain, who had been known to her uncle.

She completed her business in Zamboanga and, in less than twenty-four hours Sharon returned to Manila, placed her calls to Dominion Mining's registered offices in the British Virgin Islands, and warned her nominees to expect revised, written instructions within that week.

Sharon briefed Alfredo again, then gave him a sealed, manila envelope containing her confidential papers and Angela's passport, kissed him affectionately and caught the next flight to Singapore, before boarding the direct service for Balikpapan, where the Kalimantan Gold charter helicopter was on standby to take her back to the site. Relieved, when she recognized the familiar face of the *Kopassus,* Special Forces pilot, Sharon flashed her widest smile and, an hour into their return flight to Longdamai, at her request the UH-1H, Iroquois put down in a clearing, and she laid the foundations for the most crucial part of her revised plan.

⋆ ⋆ ⋆ ⋆

Vancouver

Kremenchug's relief was immeasurable. In answering the Stock Exchange's query with respect to speculation that BGC had entered into formal negotiations with the Commercial Asian Pacific Banking group, Fielding had been obliged to reveal that there was, indeed, substance to the rumors. BGC's shares rose sharply on the back of that response, reaching fifteen dollars as the bell rang, ending trading for the day. When Fielding secured the CAP Bank's approval to issue a more formal release and posted this with the Exchange the following morning, BGC's shares climbed even further.

Although the company's stake in the Longdamai venture had been cut back to twenty percent of its original holding, stockbrokers traded frantically once it became known that Baron Mining would develop and operate the mine. Then, James Salima, the Commercial Asian Pacific Bank president released his own press statement, advising that his bank had no plans to take P.T. Kalimantan Gold public, and confirmed that the Longdamai gold reserves had been revised to a figure of sixty million ounces. The Chinese-Indonesian's Jakarta-based family had plundered the stock when it plummeted the month before, the not-so arms' length manipulation and insider trading creating a massive windfall for the Salima Family as a whole, netting more than half a billion dollars in profits. Realizing that their only access to this wealth was through the publicly listed, Borneo Gold Corporation, institutional investors commenced taking positions, driving the BGC stock through two hundred dollars before the week was out.

Kremenchug had tried to raise Sharon by radiophone as he wished to keep her appraised of the situation, keen to have her instruct Dominion Mining to commence offloading stock, so that he could realize on his share of their arrangement. But, for one reason or another, Sharon Ducay had refused to come to the phone. Now he could only imagine what might be going through her mind, bewildered as to why she even bothered to remain in Indonesia, as her personal wealth surely now exceeded some hundreds of millions of dollars.

★ ★ ★ ★

Jakarta
P.T. Subroto & Associates

Eric Baird's senior associate, Subroto sat quietly, considering the decision he had made as a result of his luncheon meeting with Brigadier General Sukirno – and the possible consequences for his niece's husband. He shifted his huge body around, favoring one side, the specially designed chair groaning under his tilted weight as an ominous explosion of air ripped from between his legs, and fell heavily into the room. Subroto waved his hand back and forth dispersing the invisible cloud, then tossed another handful of antacid tablets into his mouth, grinding these with determined motion as he visualized beating upon Baird's not-so-secret playmate, Mardidi.

General Sukirno had revealed details of the military's imminent move against what he termed, *'subversive elements within the Dayak communities'*, Subroto's informal briefing delivered by his former classmate as the latter was aware of Subroto's vested interests in the Mahakam mining areas. When asked if the Longdamai operation might come under threat, the General had suggested that the Longdamai operations would not be disrupted, but if Subroto could discreetly arrange for any of the company's expatriate staff to avoid further travel to the area over the coming weeks, then he should do so immediately. Subroto had been surprised when Sukirno explained the extent of the military buildup throughout the Mahakam area.

'The President wants the issue settled, once and for all,' Sukirno had whispered conspiratorially, *'and you know what that means! We've got both Kopassus and Kostrad troops ready to sweep the entire province, if necessary. The Palace is preparing the ground for a massive increase in trans-migrants to meet growing demands for plantation labor. The military operation is designed to pave the way for dozens of new settlements along the Mahakam, but with recent Dayak skirmishes, it's becoming increasingly difficult to get the migrants to settle anywhere in the province.'*

Subroto had returned to his offices and instructed the staff to get Baird on the radiophone, deciding this would be an opportune time to recall Pipi's husband and at least get *her* off his back. His niece's pestering calls complaining of Baird's extended absence and apparent false sentiment had to be addressed, and Subroto felt the timing appropriate, considering what he had just learned. When the Longdamai site operator innocently disclosed that the geologist had trekked off somewhere but his assistant, Mardidi was available, Subroto was filled with rage at the deceit. Then, as the overly spicy beef *rendang* he'd consumed during lunch revisited, sending sharp, stabbing pains across his chest, Subroto remained rock still, his only movement that of jowls opening cautiously to suck in shallow gasps of air until the pain gradually receded. Slowly, his hand edged to the desk and, with puffy fingers, managed to extract a sheet of antacid tablets from the well-stocked drawer, and stuff these into his mouth.

All too familiar with heartburn attacks, Subroto knew that relief would take some minutes and he used the time to reflect on his junior partner's betrayal. It was not Baird's sexual indiscretion that stung him so, but an irrational sense of betrayal that Eric Baird had continued his liaison with Mardidi, having given his word that the relationship had long been terminated. Mocked by their behavior, when he finally recovered from the excruciating attack, Air Vice Marshal (retired) Subroto made a call to General Praboyo's offices and arranged to meet with the *Kopassus,* Special Forces Commander, whose troops maintained a small contingent at the Longdamai site. Within twenty-four hours his unusual request had been relayed to the field, and immediately, Mardidi's future on this planet became very gray indeed.

★ ★ ★ ★

Chapter Twenty-two

LONGDAMAI GOLD SITE

Within days of Sharon's return to the Longdamai camp, Stewart Campbell arrived, his presence splitting the site management into two, distinct, hostile camps. An atmosphere of gloom enveloped the expatriates, Sharon refusing to accept Stewart's letter of appointment as an authority to remain on site – the belligerent expatriate drillers, and Eric Baird, immediately choosing sides, fueling the acrimonious scene.

★ ★ ★ ★

The tenants of the entire mining village came to a standstill to observe the altercation.

'If you're not going to pay them out, then why don't you tell them to pack up and return to Jakarta?' Campbell directed this to Sharon, now standing with hands on hips, her face filled with fire.

'That'll be for me to decide,' Sharon bristled.

'Seems to me that these guys are more trouble than they're worth,' he countered.

'I'm still the operations manager here. If you interfere, Stewart, you're off the site, letter or no letter from Baron!'

'Jesus, Sharon,' Campbell shook his head and turned to walk away.

'That's it?' she demanded, walking up and grabbing him by the arm. 'You come in here telling me how to run this operation, because you're the Baron Mining rep and think everyone has to bend over for you?'

Campbell winced as her nails dug into flesh, surprised at the strength in her grip. He pulled away, angry. 'I'm just offering what is obviously good advice.' He looked over in the direction of the Indonesian drillers. 'Screw it!' he snapped, 'they're your men – you go and deal with them.' He started towards the quarters that had been allocated to him upon arrival.

'Fuck you, Stewart Campbell!' he heard her call, her voice barely a whisper.

Incensed, he changed direction, deciding to do what he could about pacifying the drillers before they wrecked the plant and other expensive equipment.

⋆ ⋆ ⋆ ⋆

Angela stood observing Stewart and Sharon from a distance with growing curiosity, the pair acting more like an estranged couple, with their frequent confrontations, than she cared to perceive. Stewart's less than subtle handling of an altercation that had broken out earlier between the foreign and local drillers, seemed out of character, as was his ongoing feud with Sharon. Angela watched him stride purposefully away from the Filipino and was pricked with the possibility that the pair may have history.

The day before, still preoccupied with the dilemma of Stewart's presence on site, Angela had taken one of the company fiberglass powerboats and revisited her village, a journey she had not wished to make, unsure of what her father's reactions might be. There, she spent less than an hour in conference with the chief explaining for the first time, her relationship with Campbell – amazed with Jonathan Dau's seemingly, quiet acceptance that she had feelings for the man – and his indifference to the revelation that her beau was not only a foreigner, but one involved in the very industry which, at very least, was partially responsible for the devastation of their traditional lands.

'I knew from when you last visited,' her father disclosed.

'How?'

'Something you will learn, with time.'

'What if he refuses to come?' she had tried, *'will you abandon the attack?'*

'No!' the chief was emphatic, *'there is too much at stake.'*

'I cannot desert him,' Angela had challenged.

Jonathan Dau was prepared for his daughter's response. *'You say that he loves you?'*

'Yes.'

'And that you love him?'

'I am not entirely sure,' she replied.

'You cannot marry outside the Dayak spirit,' the chief had cautioned.

'I know.'

'You would give up your power, your future, your people for this man?'

'No,' Angela had not faltered, leaving her father satisfied.

'Bring him here. If he is the man you say, we shall hold a ceremony to initiate him into the Dayak brotherhood.'

Angela recalled her confusion. *'And this would resolve our differences?'*

Jonathan had then taken Angela by the hand. *'If he has the spirit, then we will accept him as one of us.'*

For one, ever so brief moment Angela's eyes were tempted with tears. Stoically, she held herself tall, bowed her head and said, *'I still have a great deal to learn from you, father.'*

Jonathan Dau's smile carried the mood. *'Tell Stewart Campbell that he must be here. If you ask, how could he possibly refuse?'* Angela had then returned to the Longdamai site under strict instructions to bring Stewart to the Longhouse village, no later than the day prior to the next, full moon.

Her eyes followed Campbell as he continued across the well-trodden path towards where the Indonesian drillers were billeted, and engage a number of the men there, in conversation. Angela's attention drifted back across the open field to Sharon, then back to Stewart, conscious of the unfamiliar stirrings inside when she observed the attractive Filipino's attention, locked in Campbell's direction.

★ ★ ★ ★

'No, I can't make payments on P.T. Kalimantan Gold's behalf,' Campbell responded. The Indonesian drillers were as apprehensive as their foreign counterparts, as to whether they would receive their overdue wages, and whether they would still have work once the company changed hands.

'But, Tuan, we haven't been paid for weeks!' an agitated worker complained.

The man's colleagues murmured their support. *'We were also promised bonuses,'* another contributed, *'and guaranteed work for at least six months.'*

Sharon Ducay had ceased all drilling, citing uncertainty regarding reimbursement of any operational expenses incurred during the transition period. Stewart had questioned her reasoning and appealed for Sharon to finalize the company's undertakings with its contractors. From experience, Stewart clearly understood the necessity of maintaining crews on site during such handover-takeover periods, alarmed at Sharon's dangerous precedent in refusing to meet existing obligations. He had pacified the expatriate drillers – convincing them that Baron Mining would guarantee their salaries, conditional that they remain on the site. However, when he made a similar offer to the local drillers, the mood had turned ugly, their spokesman demanding the company pay them out in full, inferring that the drilling rigs might be damaged, even destroyed, if their contracts were not honored.

Stewart commiserated with their predicament. These men were not paid the same, generous amounts received by their expatriate counterparts, and for wages to be overdue by even a few days, often created serious hardship for their families. *'I'll see if I can get the boss lady to change her mind,'* he promised.

'Tell her, Tuan, that we can't wait any longer.'

'Yeah,' one of the more recalcitrant types rose to his feet. *'Tell her that if we don't get our money, we'll go and talk to the machinery, instead.'*

The driller waved a heavy-duty spanner threateningly, in Campbell's face. The American reached out, angrily, grabbed the man's wrist and twisted it sharply until the tool fell from his grasp.

'If there's any damage to the rigs or the other equipment, there'll be no bonuses. That's the only guarantee I'll give you.' He released the driller's arm, annoyed that he had permitted his dispute with Sharon to provoke him into losing his temper with the men. He left the group muttering amongst themselves in their own dialect, less than satisfied with his own behavior.

Campbell's anger quickly subsided when he looked up and saw Angela standing in the near distance. He waved, and when she returned a half-hearted response, Stewart hesitated in his tracks, sensing that this might not be the right time to tell her his troubles.

★ ★ ★ ★

Eric Baird brushed the air, the lethargic gesture scattering less-persistent flies from the plate of greasy, fried rice – Baird cursed the number that remained, defiantly making their own meal of his food.

It was hot – the temperature unusually high for July. He raised a glass of boiled water to his mouth, and one of the flies camped on the lip of the tumbler caught by the sudden movement fell into the liquid, buzzing its way around in endless circles as Baird gazed on, mesmerized by the act. Harsh laughter from the far end of the canteen distracted and he glanced over, warily, at the expatriate drillers sitting there. One caught his attention and raised a finger – the peels of laughter that followed, signaling that he was the butt of the joke.

Mardidi entered the wall-less structure; in Baird's mind, his partner could not have picked a worse time, the raucous catcalls, derogatory remarks and exaggerated mock-kissing noises that greeted his arrival, demonstrative of the drillers' feelings towards them both. Fearing retaliation, Baird remained motionless in response, conscious of how volatile the drillers could be, particularly now future employment under the new management was in doubt.

'Why do they always pick on me?' Mardidi complained, taking a place alongside Baird. *'Can't you do something?'*

'Let it be,' Baird dropped his voice, and cupped a hand to his mouth for discretion. *'We'll be out of here, soon, once the new management team is in place.'*

'When?'

'Two months – maximum, three.' Christopher Fielding had informed Baird that Vancouver would not honor the bonus commitments unless he remained until the handover had been completed. As this amount was considerable, he had accepted the ultimatum, resigned to remaining on site to see it all through.

'Eric, can I go back to Jakarta and wait for you there?'

'No. I need you here, by my side.'

'But, there's nothing to do but sit around all day!'

'Stop complaining – you've never had it so good.'

'They're becoming even more hostile than before,' Mardidi's eyes flicked nervously in the direction of the drillers. *'I'm afraid.'*

'They won't start anything,' Baird said, less than convincingly. *'Campbell will keep them under control.'*

'And if he can't?'

'Let's just hope that he does.' Eric Baird then deliberately selected a point on the landscape, avoiding eye contact with the boisterous drillers. In the distance he could see Sharon Ducay standing, arms crossed, obviously in discussion with the Special Forces pilot whose team had assumed control over the charter flights, to and from the Longdamai operation.

★ ★ ★ ★

'I must see you!' the young, handsome officer's whispered entreaty was pumped with masculine urgency.

'We can't.' Sharon refrained from standing too close to the *Kopassus* Captain. *'There's much I have to think about.'*

'I will be discreet,' the pilot assured her, casting his eyes around the perimeter to see if they were being observed.

'No, I don't want you to come. Not unless you are sure you will go through with it,' she warned, turning and strolling away in nonchalant stride before the crest-fallen officer could respond.

'I'll do it!' he committed, with hoarse, raspy voice as she moved away. Then, glancing in all directions to see if he'd been overheard, waited for her response, but Sharon continued without looking back, pretending she'd not heard.

Returning to the solitude of her quarters, where she now spent increasingly more of her time avoiding the now daily confrontations with almost everyone in camp, she pondered her situation. She knew that her game was becoming increasingly dangerous, that the volatile mood evident amongst the drillers and laborers was more a result of their being idle than unpaid, and that this situation would already have become unmanageable without the *Kopassus* contingent's presence. Her decision to cease drilling the moment Stewart Campbell had set foot on site had been precautionary, to avoid the experienced geologist's possible intervention in the sample recovery process. Although discovery was inevitable, Sharon planned on disappearing well before the Baron management team assumed full control and reactivated the drilling program, the timing for her exit now only a matter of a week, if not days. Campbell's arrival had complicated her original plan, which now required serious adjustment to accommodate his presence, this delay contributing to her already, severely frayed nerves.

She looked around the Spartan quarters, her eyes falling to the narrow bed where her brief, teasing encounters with the *Kopassus* pilot guaranteed he would return for more, and the aluminum briefcase containing the remaining gold bars, recalling that the Captain's seduction had not been all that difficult. Had he not responded, Sharon was armed with an alternative plan, one that would have required a far more complicated and risky exit from the scene, and a dangerous riverboat accident that had considerably less guarantee of success.

She had decided on approaching the Javanese, *Kopassus* pilot when the Army had assumed control over the helicopter charter contract for the Longdamai project – the Captain had been appointed to fly the replacement, military chopper, a Bell 205. She had engaged the officer in conversations whenever the opportunity arose, flirting when not observed by others, and encouraging his attention with occasional innuendo. Confident she could have him at her feet, Sharon then deliberately avoided any further contact with the man, to test his appetite.

After her uncle's funeral, Sharon had returned from the Philippines to Samarinda, relieved to find Captain Subandi still on assignment to her operations – and waiting to fly her back to the camp. Without hesitation, she had climbed into the alternate pilot's seat, blatantly unbuttoning her blouse before even clearing the airport, then, with an alluring smile and partially exposed breasts, leant across and placed her hand on the pilot's thigh. The signals she sent were blatantly clear and, at Sharon's request, the pilot landed the chopper at a point approximately halfway to the mining camp, the Filipino beauty already undressed to the waist before the rotors came to rest. The Captain had leapt from the helicopter, scrambled through knee-high grass to the other side tearing skin from knuckles as he groped at the cockpit handle in his haste, and then stood there, trembling with excitement. Sharon climbed down into his outstretched arms, her breasts brushing his face as she clung to his neck, her intoxicating perfume too much for the inept and inexperienced Captain. They fell to the ground in passionate embrace, their bodies hidden by the tall grass, the pilot's eager fingers unable to dislodge Sharon's firmly buckled jodhpurs from around her hips.

She had planned the encounter well, smothering the man with hot, lustful kisses, driving her tongue deep into his mouth as she stroked his now exposed organ with one hand. Subandi had no chance. The warmth of her mouth and sensuous touch drove a tide of urgency from deep within his loins, and he lost control, spilling himself as he convulsed.

After that interlude, the rest had been relatively easy. Subandi exploited every possible opportunity to be alone with Sharon and, with each, subsequent rendezvous she still managed to avoid penetration, assuring the now totally infatuated flyer that his moment would surely come. Then, satisfied he would not betray her, Sharon concocted an elaborate story convincing the besotted officer to participate in her deadly game by promising him her elusive body, and a share in great wealth should he assist her execute what she portrayed as a simple, insurance fraud.

Sharon had explained her plan. As Chief Geologist, she had been insured against injury and loss of life – her beneficiary, an elderly cousin in the Philippines who would do anything for a modest share of the spoils. If Sharon were 'to die' whilst working for the company, there would be five million dollars for them to enjoy – but she needed someone she could trust – someone credible, whose report of her death would be accepted by the insurers. But, she had warned, the policy required that there be a corpse and had then suggested the idea that a body falling from any great height would be virtually unidentifiable upon impact and, consequently, her would-be-lover's complicity would be central to this plan.

When it became clear that the scheme involved the selection of a suitable substitute for Sharon's 'accidental death', she left the pussy-whipped Captain to consider this perplexing question, anxious that she not drive him away by revealing her own solution, before he had time to dwell on the alluring consequences of their future success together.

★ ★ ★ ★

Chapter Twenty-three

30TH JULY 1996
Kostrad (ARMY STRATEGIC FORCES RESERVES) FIELD HQ – UPPER MAHAKAM RIVER

The Indonesian Army's strength approached 250,000 and of this number, the Strategic Reserve, *Kostrad,* boasted twenty-seven thousand highly-trained soldiers, comprised of two infantry divisions and an independent airborne brigade based in Ujung Pandang, (formerly known as Makasar) in the Celebes, some five hundred kilometers across the straits to the east of Samarinda. Now, two of that brigade's battalions were spread across the vast, East Kalimantan province in further support for what had once been the 9th and 10th Joint Regional Defence Commands, *Kowilhan IX & X,* which covered the areas north and south of the Mahakam River. The additional forces had been positioned there under the direct control of the East Kalimantan *Kodam* (Army Territorial Command) in preparation for *Operasi Sapu Bersih* (Operation Clean Sweep).

Across the Java Sea, TNI hierarchy and Palace cronies in the national capital were fully aware that *'OSB'* was designed to clear the way for Bobby Djimanto (a.k.a. Tan Khu Sui), the timber baron, and the president's siblings to increase their presence in the Kalimantan provinces – some rumors even suggesting that the operation was designed to pave the way for a complete takeover of the fabulous gold discovery at Longdamai. That this major military activity coincided with the Dayak tribal groups coordinated move against transmigrant groups across the three, Indonesian Borneo provinces was, in every way, calamitously coincidental, would always remain an undisputed fact. The Armed Forces *(ABRI)* intelligence agency, *BIA (Badan Intelijen ABRI)* the military apparatus responsible for collecting, collating and distributing intelligence had, at that time, no inkling of an imminent, general uprising across the Dayak territories. Even *Kopassus,* which traditionally carried the responsibility for establishing networks within ethnic communities, failed to identify the move, the Special Forces agents totally oblivious to any Dayak conspiracy. The *Kostrad* commanders, all Javanese, understood their orders explicitly. The Dayak communities were to be 'relocated', their numbers culled, and the path cleared for increased numbers of Madurese and Javanese, Moslem settlers who would provide the necessary labor for timber, mining and oil plantation investments. The commanders accepted their roles unquestioningly – they had executed such orders across the archipelago, from Sabang to Merauke, in Aceh, Timor, Ambon and Irian Jaya, cruelly suppressing minority groups to maintain the great, colonial empire created by the Javanese.

At this time, airborne troops had already been dispatched from the Longbangun Field Headquarters by helicopter, to secure the isolated communities of Nahabuan, Batukelau, and Lasan, some of which located less than one hundred kilometers from the Malaysian -Indonesian, Borneo border.

But, it was the ominous presence of the nation's ubiquitous *Kopassus* Special Forces that clearly indicated the extent of Jakarta's commitment to dilute the Dayak population with an even greater infusion of Moslem migrants. Ten years before, when the Covert Warfare Forces Command regiment was renamed Special Forces, the para-commando, anti-terrorist and covert warfare force had already acquired a fearsome reputation. First formed to combat the Islamic, *Darul Islam/Tentara Islam Indonesia* (The Indonesian Islamic Forces) in the early 1950's, the command underwent significant structural and organizational change, its loyalty at times, questionable, until

General Suharto's bloody succession to power in 1966 when it became the second president's personal, covert executioners.

Amongst their first 'successes', was their participation in the 1975 invasion of East Timor. *Kopassus* had been involved from the very beginning, occupying Dili and securing the airport while marine and airborne forces swept through the former Portuguese colony. The Special Forces remained actively engaged throughout the brutal occupation, accused of many atrocities, and successful in their relentless pursuit of *Falintil* (National Liberation Armed Forces of East Timor) leaders. In 1978, after killing *Falintil's* leader Nicolau Lobato, they then hunted his successor relentlessly, finally capturing the Jesuit-trained, Jose Alexandre (a.k.a. Xanana) Gusmao, and incarcerating the freedom fighter in Jakarta.

In 1981, *Kopassus*' reputation received international attention when its Detachment 81, an anti-terrorist unit mounted an operation in Bangkok against aircraft hijackers who had forced an Indonesian domestic airliner to fly into Thailand. The *Kopassus* attack resulted in all but one of the hijackers being killed in the shootout, some observers later suggesting that a number of panic-driven passengers caught in the crossfire were incorrectly identified as hijackers, to cover their accidental deaths.

To the country's far west, in another separatist trouble spot, Aceh, *Kopassus* troops were responsible for mass graves containing thousands and, in the resource rich, most easterly province of West Irian, in what appeared to be a precursor of things to come for Kalimantan's indigenous people, these troops carried out a number of major operations against the OPM (Papuan Independence Organization). When attacks resulted in more than ten thousand refugees fleeing across the border, into New Guinea, a sigh of relief swept the boardrooms of those international, mining conglomerates which operated in the area.

Now, veterans of these *Kopassus* campaigns were once again preparing to implement a campaign of terror against another ethnic, minority group. They would attack the *Penehing* Dayak Longhouse community, whose chief was Jonathan Dau.

★ ★ ★ ★

Longdamai Mining Camp

Sharon had continued to avoid her lover-in-waiting, conscious what effect this would have on the man. Now, certain Subandi would accept whatever she proposed, Sharon waited for the Captain later in the night, to present the pilot with her demands. She had finally broken her silence with Vancouver by radiophone hookup, communicating with Christopher Fielding and Kremenchug on general matters, ensuring that they understood that she planned to vacate the site by helicopter, within the next days.

★ ★ ★ ★

With the blue moon almost upon them, Angela's relief was immense when Campbell finally succumbed, agreeing to accompany her to the Longhouse village only after days of constant urging to do so and, ironically, with the indirect support of the Indonesian military. Tempers were frayed, and the atmosphere within the mining camp had deteriorated even further with workers' hostility shifting from Sharon Ducay towards Campbell, when the end of the month approached with no clear determination as to their future. Angela accepted the possibility that the laborers might attempt to damage plant and other equipment once Campbell left the site, his justification for stubbornly refusing the invitation to visit her father. Perplexed by her situation, Angela was on the brink of revealing her father's plans to Campbell when the situation became even more complicated, with the arrival of more than fifty *Kostrad* airborne infantrymen who poured from choppers and, to the astonishment of all, immediately secured the area.

Stewart, Sharon and Angela were all summoned by the force's commander, and briefed on their presence. Although Angela doubted that the army's arrival would have gone unnoticed by Jonathan Dau's scouts, there was now an even greater urgency for her to return to the Longhouse to report what she had seen. Angela moved quickly, securing an undertaking from the commander that the laborers would be kept in check, and the company plant and equipment protected by his troops. However, Campbell remained obstinately set against leaving the project.

'*Now it's all set. We can go.*'

'*No, 'Angela, I'm sorry. It just doesn't feel right.*'

'*The soldiers will guard the site,*' Angela had all but pleaded.

'*I'm still responsible,*' Campbell argued, '*what if something happens while I'm off playing tourist?*'

'*What could possible happen with all these soldiers guarding the site?*'

'*Yeah, sure, 'Gela, and who's going to watch them?*'

'*Are you sure that's the real problem, Stewart. Could it be that you're intimidated by the thought of meeting my father?*'

'*Not at all,*' he replied, a little too hastily.

'*Stewart, this is very important for us, that we go. Now.*'

'*Why can't we postpone for a few days?*'

'*Because my father and the villagers are expecting us today...*' Angela caught Sharon Ducay moving in their direction. '*And they'd be very disappointed if you didn't materialize after all I've said. Come on, Stewart, it's time to meet my family. Besides, she's all but closed the operations down,*' Angela threw a glance in the Filipino's direction. '*Last chance, otherwise I'll leave you here with her.*'

The words had no sooner escaped Angela's mouth when Sharon was upon them, hands stuck despondently in pockets, the wide brimmed Akubra casting a shadow across her face as she stood facing Campbell, in confrontational pose.

'I'm putting you on notice, Stewart,' she announced, 'I've already informed Vancouver. I'm out of here as soon as transport becomes available.'

Campbell's body language identified with that of Sharon's. 'I thought you'd agreed to stay until the end of next month?'

'What for?' She threw a casual look at Angela. 'I've received confirmation that my bonuses have been paid, so as far as I'm concerned, it's now all yours.'

'When are you leaving?' he wanted to know.

'Boys playing soldiers over there have said that there'll be no charter flights for at least three, four days. After that, I'm gone.'

'Look, Sharon,' Campbell started to say, 'why not …'

'Stewart,' Angela made a point of checking her wrist. *'We're running out of time. Are you coming with me or not? You can discuss whatever it is you need to, when we return.'*

Surprised, Sharon picked up the conversation. 'Return?' She frowned at Angela. 'Where are you going?'

'Angela wants me to visit her Longhouse,' Campbell explained.

'My god, Stewart! Whatever for?'

Angela felt the colour drain from her face. *'Stewart?'*

'To meet Angela's father,' he replied.

'A day trip?'

'Probably overnight; I could come back tomorrow, but Angela wants to stay on for a few more days.'

'You're not concerned about leaving?' Sharon suppressed rising panic.

'Why?'

'As I said, if I can convince the pilot to leave earlier, I'm gone. I'm not going to spend one minute longer here than I have to.' Sharon could see uncertainty in Campbell's face, and pressed the point. 'If I do get a lift and something happens with both of us out of the camp, then you'll have to carry the can. Can't it wait?'

Campbell looked down at his mud-caked boots. 'Guess it could, at that.'

Angela, third party to this exchange crossed her arms, emulating the others. The three stood in awkward, funeral repose – the ensuing standoff uncomfortable for all.

'They'll be waiting for us, Stewart.' Angela moved to regain control.

'*What if I take you up there, drop in for a couple of hours, explain the situation, and arrange to return once we have everything here back under control?'*

'All right, let's go,' Angela consented, hastily, anything to get him out of harm's way. Once they were at the Longhouse she could concoct any number of reasons to prevent his immediate return.

'Not the most professional judgment you've ever made,' Sharon's plans were collapsing as they spoke. 'There's something going on around here, Stewart. Why do you think they're throwing so many troops into the area?'

'You were at the briefing,' Campbell's demeanor appeared less confident. 'The Commander said that they were beefing up their presence because of increased racial tensions throughout the province. The Indonesian government has a vested interest in ensuring that this site remains secure. To tell you the truth, I have no problems with their increased numbers. Why, what are you reading into their presence?' he asked, as Campbell sincerely respected her opinion.

With the Longdamai discovery, Sharon's reputation throughout the mining industry had become synonymous with those who had first found gold in California, Alaska and the Australian fields. She had ventured into Borneo's wilds, successfully completed drilling programs, established an operation that would lead to the development of the world's largest gold mine, and was now to leave the project. Campbell understood her bitterness, accepting that much of her animosity had been directed towards him as the Baron representative. However, her concerns were worth exploring, as she had been on the ground here, at Longdamai, much longer than he.

'Then you haven't given any thought to the possibility that the Indonesian government might be positioning troops to take over the entire operation?' she suggested, annoyed immediately with this desperate response.

Campbell stared at his fellow geologist, the absurdity of the comment twisting his mouth into a grin. 'Sour grapes, Sharon?'

'I guessed you'd think that.' Then, addressing Angela for the first time, 'Just seems a strange time for you to take time off, to play.'

Angela burned. 'What Stewart does is not your business!' she snapped, catching Sharon off guard. Continuing in English she said, 'Stewart, we *must* leave now!' Then, trembling only from inside, 'unless you feel more inclined to stay?'

Angela pivoted on one heel and started away, her eyes fixed on Mardidi in the distance, her heart pumping with a confusion of angst and jealousy.

'Angela, wait!' Campbell called, moving to follow.

'Stewart, you really shouldn't leave.' Sharon reached out, restraining him by the elbow. They remained facing each other as a distant memory carried the moment and he rested a hand on her shoulder.

'You're right. I'll be back in a couple of hours,' he agreed, 'Guess you'll still be here?'

'Most probably.' Sharon looked on unhappily as Campbell then followed Angela down the slope towards the jetty, where Mardidi waited patiently, having prepared their speedboat.

Unsuccessful in discouraging Campbell from taking Angela away, Sharon had hurried to her Captain, urging him to inform the *Kostrad* Commander of the pair's plans. But, by the time they had located the officer Campbell and Angela were well underway, with the latter behind the wheel. Mardidi unhooked the nylon ropes front and aft guiding the fiberglass hull away with one foot, waving when the twin, sixty horsepower engines roared into life and carried the couple upriver then, moments later, terrified as soldiers poured onto the jetty with weapons raised, watching the speedboat disappear around the first bend.

Angela refused to look back, her sixth sense warning her of the danger behind. That she abandoned Sharon Ducay, Eric Baird and others to an unknown fate, in no way pricked her conscience. In spite of her deep resentment towards all involved in the destruction of the *Penehing* sacred site, and other personal issues with the Filipino woman, prior to the military contingent's arrival Angela had seriously considered finding some excuse to also remove Sharon out of harm's way. Now, she no longer cared, believing this course of action would have been unnecessary, as the Dayaks would be unlikely to attack against such formidable odds.

★ ★ ★ ★

Baird sat quietly chewing on all he'd observed, mentally noting how quickly Mardidi had sprung to assist Angela Dau, yet again. The two had become increasingly friendly, and Baird was uncomfortable with the developing bond. He decided to warn Mardidi against spending too much time with the Dayak, his motives entirely jealousy-based, recognizing these for what they were.

★ ★ ★ ★

Sharon Ducay brushed the Captain's advances aside. *'You should have prevented her from leaving!'*

'She'll be back. We'll just have to wait.' Subandi tried to assuage her concerns but his voice lacked confidence.

'And if she doesn't return?'

'Then why can't we find someone else?'

Sharon swore under her breath. There *was* no one else – and this, her foolish lover would never come to know.

Subandi strode away angrily, his loins on fire, his mood fit to kill. Swinging towards the dedicated area reserved for the *Kopassus* contingent he noticed Mardidi returning to the Australian geologist's quarters, and was reminded of other unfinished business, a personal favor that had emanated from his headquarters, in Cijantung, outside Jakarta.

★ ★ ★ ★

Longhouse Village

Angela had idled the engines back as the river narrowed, guiding their powerboat through a passage covered by a continuous canopy of green, breaking again into full sunlight within sight of the falls. Almost entirely encircled by sheer drop-offs and walls, the Longhouse scene cast back through Kalimantan time. When the village first came into view Stewart Campbell could only stare in awe at the timeless setting, the cascading waterfall and river's reaches, the towering trees and lush, jungle growth smothering the land to water's edge to his left, the community fields and buildings stretched along the riverbanks, on his right. Directly ahead, Campbell could see children's arms thrashing through the water as they raced towards the Longhouse where excitement had been building in anticipation of Angela's arrival.

His companion eased the throttle back even further, directing their vessel towards eager hands as they glided to rest alongside the jetty, Stewart unable to comprehend the cacophonous, dialectal babble that greeted them. Then, the chief stepped forward and spoke to him in *Bahasa Indonesia*.

'Selamat datang,' the tall figure extended a welcoming hand, Stewart immediately recognizing Jonathan Dau from his daughter's photos. The chief wore a lightweight safari jacket, long trousers and sandals, his well-weathered features bearing the warmest of smiles as his powerful arms assisted the younger man ashore.

'Terima kasih, I am honored to be here,' Campbell returned the greeting, his feet barely touching the ground as he was whisked along a sturdy boardwalk towards the Longhouse proper. Villagers crowded, for most, their first glimpse of an outsider, the older children instantly curious, those younger, terrified to finally meet another human being in the flesh, who was white. No amount of satellite television had prepared them for Stewart's green eyes and pale complexion, his dark, brown hair and perfect smile. Toothless, betel-chewing, red-lipped women reached out to touch bare arms as he passed, and teenagers giggled effusively, recalling speculation of how well he might have been blessed. Campbell looked back over his shoulder, captured instantly by Angela's ear-to-ear smile and the warmth of their reception.

'They love you!' she called, but the words were lost amidst the excitement.

Without warning, an *orangutan* appeared and plunged, Angela laughing as Yuh-Yuh took possession of Campbell's right leg.

'This is Yuh-Yuh, Stewart,' she reached down and ran a hand over the ape's head. *'My father saved her from poachers.'*

'I thought Dayaks ate monkeys?' Stewart suggested, tongue in cheek.

'Yes, and missionaries too,' she responded, not entirely amused.

Campbell looked back over his shoulder when he heard the outboard engines roar into life. *'Where are they going with our boat?'*

'What?' Angela fell back amongst the crowding villagers to avoid a response, and was immediately whisked away.

'The speedboat!' he tried again, his voice drowned amongst the

determined reception committee. Angela waved, Campbell shrugged his shoulders and Jonathan Dau smiled, then led the American into the Longhouse where the elders officially welcomed him.

★ ★ ★ ★

Surreptitiously, Jonathan Dau continued to scrutinize Stewart, not unhappy with his first close encounter with the man he'd observed from thick, forest cover, over past weeks. That there was a very special bond between Angela and the foreigner was never in doubt. Jonathan had known for some time that his daughter had strong feelings for this man. What troubled the chieftain was the reciprocity and depth of Stewart Campbell's commitment to Angela, and whether he understood the demands to be made on her as a future leader of the *Penehing-Dayak.*

★ ★ ★ ★

Campbell remained courteous and attentive as Jonathan Dau led him through the Longhouse explaining customs and something of the *Penehing-Dayak* history. Angela followed – pleased that the men were bonding – warmed by Stewart's obvious sincerity and her father's apparent acceptance of their guest.

'...and this structure is built entirely on three-meter high, wooden poles as protection against flooding and wild animals.' Jonathan was pointing back towards the Longhouse village with timber-planked streets and footpaths. *'When I was a child, this area was still rich with game. Now...'* his voice trailed away as he led them through the rest of the village dwellings, which had been built apart from the Longhouse proper, to accommodate the villagers growing needs. They continued down a path to an area where women worked, plaiting dry, elongated *purun* leaves into mats and baskets. Campbell had seen the rush growing in marshy ground before, but had never observed the soft, pliant leafless stems being woven so skillfully, the more experienced village women's fingers moving with such speed, a basket materialized as he stood watching. Impressed, Campbell extracted a miniature Minolta from pocket and aimed the lens at the group, surprised

when the women shrieked and turned away in trepidation.

'I'm sorry, Stewart,' Angela stepped forward and re-pocketed the camera. *'The older people here are terrified of photographs. They are very superstitious. Many believe that, in the hands of an enemy, a photo could be used to make them ill, or cast spells.'*

'Black magic?' Campbell noticed that the women had all fallen silent.

'Yes, and the Penehing are susceptible to its ways.'

Campbell regretted the incident, wishing there was some other way he could capture this scene which contrasted so greatly with other ethnic groups he had visited in Indonesia. Here, many of the women wore tattoos, their ear lobes stretched by huge earrings dangling against prematurely aged skin, their hands calloused with toil and, as they squatted on splayed feet manipulating the *purun* into practical items of use, he was reminded of the multi-faceted society, that constituted the Indonesia people.

'Come!' Jonathan Dau continued leading Campbell along the river to a heavily foliaged area, stopping short of an ageless, *meranti* tree, and a gathering of young *Penehing* men. *'Wait over there,'* Jonathan pointed, indicating for Angela and Campbell to take their place, adjacent to the tree.

'What's happening?'

'It's a blessing ceremony, for the young men.' Angela fell short of revealing that the anointing ceremony, '*membayar hajat*' was aimed at summoning the spirits of ancestral warriors, to thank them for life and to strengthen these youngsters' resolve in the hours ahead. *'Under the Penehing belief, the spirits are an inseparable part of our daily lives. This is a ceremony to welcome the imminent, full moon.'* What Angela also failed to explain, was that her father, as spiritual leader, was preparing the way for ancestral warriors' spirits to enter these men in readiness for battle – encouraging them to practice *mengayau,* her people's frightening tradition of human decapitation, as they believed that *mengayau* strengthened one's powers, and would protect their community from evil spirits. Campbell continued on in ignorance as the group moved collectively into trance, unaware that

he, too, had fallen under the hypnotic spell that flowed past Jonathan Dau's lips.

Later, Stewart Campbell would recall nothing more up to the beginning of the mid-afternoon celebrations. By then, of course, he was resigned to remaining overnight at the Longhouse and, with the first nip of *tuak* under his belt, had required little encouragement to stay.

★ ★ ★ ★

The festivities had commenced with the slaughtering of a buffalo, five wild pigs, and dozens of chickens. An old, toothless woman had dipped her hand into the pig blood, then approached Campbell and smeared his brow with the sticky, darkened ooze, the air alive with the sound of gongs and drums beating as villagers danced around the miniature Longhouse shaped pyre, loaded with offerings. Tables had been removed from the Longhouse and placed outside, laden now with barbecued corn, steamed goldfish and suckling pig. Women then added deep-fried dishes of *bakwan, sukun* and jackfruit to the feast, Campbell sampling them all. *'Sacrificing a cow must be quite a significant event?'* Although lightheaded, he felt strangely refreshed.

'It is our belief that the greater the level of offering made, the more likely the powerful spirits would attend, and bestow their blessings on us all,' the chief explained.

Campbell leaned over and whispered into Angela's ear. *'I'm pleased I stayed. I'm really enjoying myself.'*

'You should pace yourself with that arak,' she warned, aware of the amount of *tuak* he had already consumed.

Following a wrap-around sunset, evening fell, and more than seven hundred sat down to the greatest feast the Longhouse had enjoyed since Jonathan Dau returned from his warring ways to become their spiritual leader. Wild pig and buffalo was stuffed into mouths, *tuak* poured for the women and Campbell as the young, village men quietly slipped into the night, to join others from neighboring, Longhouse communities. Soon, they would commence their attack on the string of Madurese and Javanese migrant settlements downriver, to coincide with others throughout the province.

The wind turned, filling the Longdamai sky with smoke particles from not-so-distant forest fires, the evening set in black until an eerie, bluish light appeared and spread across the setting's false tranquility. Calm descended upon the village as the moon's gibbous shape twisted and ballooned behind smoke-polluted skies, its ghost-like appearance unlike any these superstitious people had seen. In a more subdued atmosphere caused partly by the absence of the normally boisterous, young village men, toasts were called and challenges made, Stewart undeniably drunk from the *tuak* as the celebration to welcome the Blue Moon continued.

Not twenty kilometers downstream, the speedboat, which had earlier transported the American geologist to this idyllic setting, crept back into the Longdamai mining camp moorings, the heavy-throated engines stifled so as not to raise alarm. Anticipating Campbell's return, the boat's arrival was all but ignored as eight *Penehing* warriors slipped unseen from the vessel and easily overpowered the sleepy, *Kostrad* sentries, removing their heads with the skill of their ancestors, before laying their corpses in a line along the jetty, and continuing downstream.

Then, with an hour left to midnight, the wind shifted yet again exposing the moon in the fullness of its life, catching a legless Stewart Campbell staggering around unashamedly in the dirt as he tried to focus on the brilliant light. Dayak tribes in three provinces gazed up into the heavens and thanked their ancestral spirits for the sign, then simultaneously launched attacks against transmigrant camps, across half of Indonesian Borneo.

★ ★ ★ ★

Kopassus (Special Forces) Field HQ
Upper Mahakam River

The Indonesian Special Forces with its four, covert warfare battalions were trained in hijacking and kidnapping techniques, capturing and killing anti-government, separatist and opposition leadership, and mass executions of minority groups in support of Jakarta's insatiable demands, for a greater share of the country's resources. During the last decade tens of thousands had perished in oil and gas rich Aceh, resource rich Kalimantan, and Irian, most slaughtered by the military's covert killing machine, *Kopassus* with its complement of three thousand, five hundred men. Due to the nature of its covert activities, command of these forces was retained at the highest level by the TNI's most influential generals, namely, those closest to the President. These officers pursued a deliberate strategy of precipitating, even prolonging conflicts in order to promote their commercial interests and to justify their uniquely powerful position throughout the country.

Without the First Family's blessing, it was virtually impossible to conduct any meaningful business activity, anywhere in the Republic, and a commitment of between ten and twenty percent of one's activity was normally sufficient to feed the voracious, presidential appetites. However, as Palace sibling rivalry grew fuelling even greater acquisition of wealth, many state institutions and activities were monopolized, for the benefit of those who ruled this vast archipelago. By 1996, less than five families controlled Indonesia's economy, including banking and oil refineries, car assembly plants, textiles, the distribution of basic staples, cigarette production, shipping and an endless list of industrial plants. None of these *kongsi* could survive without the patronage of the President's family, some obliged to provide favored generals with substantial holdings in their activities, to suppress unionism, avoid taxes and, on occasion, send armed troops into factories to arrest the disgruntled. The high-profile timber baron, Bobby Djimanto (a.k.a. Tan Khu Sui), whose quest for total dominance of the timber industry often demanded *Kopassus'* occasional intervention in resolving issues, predominantly at the provincial level, their involvement, predictably, always leaving a trail of dead.

Often dressed as civilians, *Kopassus* agents would infiltrate communities and become agent provocateurs, destabilizing groups which hindered access to virgin forests, or whose villages were simply in the way of Djimanto's tractors and bulldozers. Soldiers would then be summoned to restore stability, the ensuing altercation achieving the required result for the timber tycoon's expanding interests. Entire villages would be relocated, the forest stripped, oil palm planted, migrant workers transported from Madura, Java and Bali, and the cycle continued, filling already overflowing Palace coffers at the expense of the indigenous peoples. *Kopassus'* deadly role was unlikely to reach the international community for even local military commanders were often unaware of any Special Forces' activities within their area of command, as the Western-trained, killing machine took its orders directly from the Palace. And, with media censorship similar to that imposed in countries such as China, Vietnam, Laos and former Soviet Union satellites, genocide was not a word contained in domestic, media vocabulary. Unfortunately for the Upper Mahakam Dayak communities, Bobby Djimanto's timber mills' ravenous needs required their virgin forests and, as there had been fierce resistance to further expansion of migrant settlements in the area, Palace interests required the active participation of *Kopassus* in resolving the problem.

Then, of course, there was the matter of the massive, Longdamai gold deposit. Baron Mining had reminded the authorities that it did not wish to be subjected to the same problems Freeport was having with the indigenous population in West Irian. Because Baron Mining would assume operational control and move to establish a mine within weeks, the Palace required the relocation of all Dayak communities within a radius of twenty kilometers, to remove the potential for conflict before infrastructure construction commenced – amongst these, Jonathan Dau's Longhouse village.

As the *Penehing-Dayak* chief's main body of young warriors proceeded along one tributary towards the Madurese settlement situated downstream from the Longdamai mining camp, one hundred, heavily armed veteran *Kopassus* soldiers silently traversed the parallel stream leading to the Longhouse, in preparation for their dawn attack. Their aim, to permanently remove the indigenous villagers from the area – and the commanding officer's interpretation of *Operation Clean Sweep* made no allowances for prisoners.

★ ★ ★ ★

Chapter Twenty-four

LONGHOUSE VILLAGE

Clouds blanketed easterly skies, further distorting the moon's ghostly image until it was erased, entirely, its disappearance bringing the ceremony to a close. Fires were extinguished, and weary villagers retired, the Longhouse community soon swallowed by the darkness of night as an unpredictable wind carrying haze from deep-seated, peat-land fires to the east, swept across the restive province. Burdened with the knowledge that some, if not many of the village youths would not return from their killing spree, Jonathan Dau continued through the early morning hours in prayer, communicating with the spirits, seeking their guidance and protection over the seventy-eight *Penehing* men who, within hours, would honor their ancestors in battle.

At the request of the other elders, the chief had reluctantly agreed not to lead the attack, offering this role to another, Udir – a proven warrior, and a childhood friend.

Drunk, Stewart Campbell had been assisted to the quarters prepared in anticipation of his visit, Jonathan confident that the American would be too ill to return to the Longdamai mining camp for at least another day. The chief frowned, deeply disappointed with the *Kostrad* troops' presence at the site, the strength of their numbers requiring a change in strategy, obliging Jonathan to postpone the planned assault on the small migrant, labor settlement there.

His orders had been explicit; the men who had commandeered Stewart's powerboat were instructed to wait for nightfall before entering the mining camp. They were not to engage the *Kostrad* troops, but send a signal to the Javanese soldiers that the Dayaks could slip in and out of their camp, unimpeded. The *Penehing* advance team's orders were to kill and decapitate perimeter guards, then move downstream to the main target. From experience, Jonathan understood the value of leaving headless bodies for the enemy to find, the gruesome sight never failing to unnerve, particularly at night. As for the Madurese laborers, for the moment they would remain unharmed, the chief expecting they would flee, once word of the Dayak attacks on other settlements reached their ears.

Perched high in the *meranti's* crown a hornbill cawed, Jonathan disturbed by its timing. He peered back from the solitude of his candle-lit surrounds towards the grayish, silhouetted Longhouse outline wondering how many mothers remained awake, fearful for their sons, and how many of the village wives would be widowed, before the day was done.

★ ★ ★ ★

Jonathan raised a smile for Angela when she drifted into his line of sight, Yuh-Yuh at her side. *'Can't sleep?'*

'*No. Haven't even tried. Thought I'd find you out here.*'

'You learned to recite your first prayers in this grotto.'

Angela glanced around the sacred place then knelt down beside her father, the furrows across his face exaggerated by the flickering light. *'How much longer?'* she asked, placing her hand on his.

The chief looked up at the starless sky. *'When dawn breaks.'*

'And the mining camp?' She had harbored concerns that her father's stubborn streak and fierce pride might have tempted an attack, in spite of the enemy's superior numbers.

'*We've sent them a message. They're safe…for the time being.*'

'I'm sorry, Papa,' she offered, inwardly relieved. And then, *'Poor*

Stewart, all that tuak, when it wasn't necessary!'

'He'll live. But that doesn't mean that you should return to the mining site – at least not yet. If the settlers don't abandon the camp within the week, we'll burn them out.'

'What about the soldiers? We're not equipped to take the fight to them.'

'Many will be ordered downriver to protect whatever's left of the settlements there. The scale of the exodus from transmigrant sites will keep the army preoccupied for weeks, if not months. Don't worry, Angela, our men will not have to face the army's firepower. If there's to be any slaughter, it won't be Penehing blood that is spilt.'

'What if there're reprisals?'

'Every Longhouse community has contingency plans, in the event they send their troops. But, we feel that this is unlikely. The Javanese have no taste for the jungle. Besides, their lines of supply would be difficult to maintain to such isolated outposts. They can't bring ships or landing barges this far up the river, and only helicopters can land. That severely restricts their capacity to mount any sustained operation against us. Don't worry. We've thought this all through, very thoroughly.'

'I know you have, Papa,' she repeated, *'I know you have.'*

'Come, I need coffee,' Jonathan rose to his feet, *'and it might be an idea to check on your man.'*

★ ★ ★ ★

Madurese Migrant Settlement

When dawn revisited the corrugated-roofed, shantytown settlement, buildings were already ablaze, the *Penehing* warriors moving to each dwelling armed with thirsty blades, slicing the air with deadly accuracy as families spilled into the open, confused that their village was under attack. Heads rolled from wheeling bodies, men, women and children alike, others lost hands or arms as they held these out in defence. A terrified migrant exited his home with such speed, his legs carried a headless torso well out into the street, before collapsing under a fountain of blood. None were spared, the indiscriminate slaughter continuing without resistance as the sword-wielding raiders slashed their way through the Madurese community, massacring hundreds within the first minutes. Children, lost in the confusion or abandoned by fleeing parents died where they stood, their screams cut short by the edge of cold blade, the carnage building as years of persecution drove the *Penehing* into an unimaginable, killing frenzy. The death toll climbed, the air filled with cries of *Hawawa…hu! Hawawa…hu!,* the traditional call used to further inflame the young warriors, all now convinced that they were possessed by *Nayau,* their ancestral spirits. One *Penehing* youth, a lad of no more than sixteen, sliced his victim across the chest and stomach with vicious blows, then followed the body as it fell to the ground spilling entrails onto the ground. He ripped out the man's heart, cupping one hand inside the gaping hole, then drank the Madurese migrant's blood. And, as the inflammatory cries of *Hawawa…hu! Hawaw…hu!* grew in crescendo, decapitated heads were taken and placed on sharp, bamboo poles and paraded through the burning village.

⋆ ⋆ ⋆ ⋆

Kopassus – Special Forces

'Keep it quiet!' the major hissed savagely. The raiding party glided through the forest channel, silently propelled by paddles when one of the forward oarsmen mistimed his stroke, drawing curses from others in the team. Crouched, the officer looked back over his shoulder at the shadowy line of rubber inflatables following closely behind, concerned that the currents had cost them time. They had covered the first twenty kilometers under tow, then paddled the remaining distance as quietly as their passage would permit, the mini-armada arriving within sight of the Longhouse with only minutes to spare. The major moved forward and whispered instructions to the Sergeant. *'We'll tie up over there.'* The men steered towards the riverbank, those behind acknowledging the officer's signal to follow. The covert warfare force landed alongside the grotto, secured all twenty dinghies, gathered their weapons and then split into des-

ignated teams for the final attack.

The major urged his troops to hurry as first light was imminent, and the element of surprise would soon be lost. Although *Kopassus* troops had a fearful reputation and the mere mention of their command sufficient to bring most to heel, he knew that the Dayak was not so easily intimidated, and only a fool would underestimate their determination and capacity to fight. It was therefore imperative to the success of this mission that his men strike before the alarm could be sounded and, this objective might have been achieved, had the village hounds not detected their scent.

★ ★ ★ ★

Hours had passed, and Stewart Campbell remained violently ill; the *tuak* and the spicy food had made for a dangerous cocktail. Stripped to his underpants, he staggered back from the primitive ablutions with water lapping across his unclad feet – knees threatening to collapse under his seriously weakened body, suffering the helplessness of the infirmed. His head continued to spin, his throat wretchedly dry – the nausea overwhelming and he convulsed, yet again. Another fierce, searing pain ripped into his gut and he winced with the hot, tearing signal, sweat leaking from every pour as he propped himself, preparing for the attack, the slippery, wooden boardwalk threatening to cast him into the river.

The pain came and went – his body bent in racked disorder as he gripped for a non-existent handrail and fell, his knees relaying messages of immeasurable pain to an already numbed brain. Campbell remained doubled in humble pose, a hand rescuing him from his predicament and he mustered remaining reserves, to drag himself upright.

'Here, let me help you,' Jonathan's voice seemed distant, Campbell accepting the strong hand dragging him to his feet. With tottering gait, and supported by the chief's arm wrapped around his waist, the American climbed back up into the Longhouse, and into Angela's care. Returning from the grotto, she had peeked into his cell-size accommodations, and discovered him missing. It was Jonathan who

had found Campbell in this debilitated state.

'Do you have anything… I can take?' He ground the words, the very thought of placing anything more in his mouth, threatened with rising bile.

'Why didn't you call for me earlier?' Angela admonished.

'It's not exactly something…I wanted to share.' They maneuvered him onto a bunk.

'Papa?' Angela looked to her father.

'I'll get something for him.' Jonathan then disappeared, to prepare a cure.

The room continued to spin, for Campbell – Angela waiting helplessly, at his side. When the chief reappeared, he carried a bowl mixed with ground *Salak,* and traditional herbs, surrendering the remedy to Angela who spoon-fed the concoction into Campbell's unwilling mouth, the patient grimacing with each swallow.

'You'll be all right, with some rest,' Jonathan assured, then returned to his own quarters, mindful of the hour. Throughout the Longhouse, families began to stir in preparation for the day, children left to sleep while mothers lit kerosene stoves and washed, before they would pray. Outside, village dogs began to bay – Jonathan Dau senses raised in alert, the possibility of wild game inadvertently wandering into the area, coming to mind. Then, with the distinctive squeal of an animal in pain reaching his ears, the chief's hand snapped a loaded weapon from the gun rack, checking the magazine as he moved cautiously outside.

Jonathan's eyes scanned the gray, early morning scene, lifting his chin and breathing deeply to test the air, a hand instinctively sliding along the weapon's stock as he sensed the presence of others – the howling, *kampung* dogs a sure sign that something was seriously amiss. He stood at the top of the wooden stairway and slowly panned the area with the muzzle of his rifle, his eyes narrowing when there was suggestion of movement – a finger curling inside the trigger guard, when he was certain. He called out, *'Who's out there?'* And then, *'Show yourself, I am armed!'* which was greeted with a hail of automatic fire, Jonathan throwing his body backwards as bullets ruptured the air, shattering timbers within centimeters of his head.

He returned fire; his rifle kicking as he shot into the area below, Jonathan shocked at the size of the attacking force. He heard someone scream out a command, and another hail of bullets punctured the longhouse structure forcing him to the floor. He rolled, quickly, rising on one knee and aiming directly at a point above and behind where he sighted muzzle fire. Jonathan squeezed the trigger, his aim true as the soldier in his sights spun in the air, the man's Steyr machinegun spraying deadly fire in all directions as he fell to the ground. Again, the attackers concentrated on Jonathan's position, a grenade falling short provided the chief with the opportunity to reposition. Something ripped through his leg and he knew he'd been hit. Instinctively, his hand fell to the wound but he could feel nothing. Another barked command brought momentary silence, but Jonathan knew that the soldiers would only be regrouping. Then, out of the corner of one eye he caught a glimpse of flaming torches twisting overhead as these were hurled through the air, and he cursed, emptying his magazine in the direction of those responsible. The troops returned his fire, and Jonathan knew he had to withdraw.

Somehow, he managed to drag himself upright and back inside the Longhouse where screaming women and children ran helplessly around, terrified, as *Kopassus,* 9 mm bullets tore through wooden walls and flesh. Villagers fell to the timber floors, wounded and dying, the unrelenting onslaught accounting for more than one hundred within the first minutes – all victims of the soldiers' Steyr Assault, machinegun fire.

Almost half of the remaining *Penehing* elders had managed to offer some resistance with their antiquated, conventional rifles, whilst others had bravely stood their ground, warding off their attackers with more primitive weaponry. Spears and arrows found their marks, the aging warriors' valiant efforts providing the opportunity for many of the women and children to escape.

This unexpected resistance and the mounting number of casualties stunned the *Kopassus* soldiers, their commander ordering his men to advance when the senior NCO fell dead at his feet. Moments later, a look of surprise spread across the Major's disbelieving face when a blowpipe found its mark, the poisonous tipped dart depriving him of life as he, too, slumped to the ground. At his side, a soldier struggling desperately to dislodge an arrow which had struck a comrade in the thigh, died standing, the accuracy of the spear cutting into his heart. And, whilst the greatly outnumbered, elderly group of *Penehing* continued to fight for time, more than half of the Longhouse families escaped along the river boardwalk, across the dangerously overladen suspension bridge, and into the jungle.

★ ★ ★ ★

Angela stared in shock as flimsy partitions disintegrated before their eyes exposing a scene exploding in chaos, and she screamed at Campbell to get up, shouting that the Longhouse had come under attack. Even in his weakened condition Campbell was able to stand, dress, and slip into field boots, Angela supporting some of his weight as they staggered out the rear of the building and down the congested, open stairway to the river's edge where the smell of cordite in the air hit them both with full force.

'Give him to us!' two middle-aged women grabbed the American by the arms and hurried him away. By now, their surrounds were enveloped with flames roaring through the Longhouse's dry roof, the outlying buildings also burning furiously as soldiers continued to spray the main building with automatic fire.

'I will catch up with you, later!' she called after Campbell's disappearing form, then ran back up into the Longhouse in search of her father, tearing through the burning structure as fast as her legs could carry her, colliding with a dividing wall as it fell, dragging her to the floor. Dazed, she climbed from under, stumbling forward, following the raised, wooden street that connected the many dwellings one to another, calling her father's name as she progressed. *'Papa! Papa!'* she screamed, panic rising as the far end of the Longhouse twisted, groaned ominously, then collapsed to one side, engulfed in flame. *'Papa! Where are you?'* Her voice was drowned amidst the roaring fire, another near miss from spraying bullets sending her facedown, momen-

tarily stunned as her head cracked savagely against hard timbers.

'Stay down!' she heard Jonathan Dau's choking voice, thickened smoke making it impossible for her to see. *'Stay where you are, Angela,'* her father yelled as loud as lungs would permit, his blurred image appearing as powerful hands took her by the shoulders. *'We have to get out, now!'* he ordered, flames threatening from every side. *'They won't be taking prisoners!'* Then, as an afterthought, *'Where's Stewart?'*

'He's gone with the others, into the forest.' Her eyes fell to the chief's bloodied leg. *'You're hurt?'*

'It's not that serious,' Jonathan took his daughter by the arm, *'now let's get the hell out of here!'*

As he shouted, another wall collapsed, exposing their position to the troops outside – barely a second passing before bullets rained down upon the pair. *'Go, Angela. Go!'* The chief screamed, leveling his rifle down at the enemy, he fired but two rounds before running out of ammunition then angrily discarded the weapon. Sweeping through the thatched-lined roof and bamboo supports, the raging fire had all but gutted half the Longhouse by this time. Favoring his wounded leg, Jonathan limped after Angela, ducking and weaving, climbing through burning debris as bullets whistled overhead, their escape effected when the village external fuel supply store suddenly exploded hurling bodies everywhere, adding substantially to the tally of *Kopassus,* already dead. Jonathan and Angela crawled out through the partially collapsed community hall, slipped down an embankment to the river's edge, then made their way along the length of the burning, wooden edifice in the direction of the waterfall. The chief tripped as he hobbled down the wooden pathway, and cursed.

'Here,' Angela offered an arm, *'let me help!'*

'No! For God's sake hurry, girl – get out while you can!'

★ ★ ★ ★

Stewart Campbell staggered across the unsteady suspension bridge with the structure swaying precariously underfoot – his hands firmly gripped to rope on either side as the village women urged him to hurry in their unintelligible tongue. Once across, they led him by the hand, Campbell slipping and sliding along the inclined path, his eyes refusing to leave the terrifying scene behind. By now, the Longhouse was an inferno of blazing timbers, rattan and bamboo, thatched sections adding to the immeasurable heat, a thick black plume billowing into the early morning sky causing him to stop and look back in dismay, for those still trapped inside.

'Hurry, hurry!' an older woman insisted, Campbell not recognizing the words. He stood transfixed as an explosion ripped through one end of the Longhouse, sending large sections of the raised village collapsing, in slow motion effect. Without further hesitation he turned, and started back towards the suspension bridge, overtaken within steps by determined, and surprisingly strong hands.

'No!' A villager gripped his wrist with vice-like claws, others coming to the elderly man's aid to prevent Campbell from suicidal form. *'You mustn't go back!'*

With more than a dozen hands holding him firmly, Campbell reluctantly surrendered, his heart sinking further when another explosion destroyed most of the remaining structure, the air filled with burning debris. The village women dragged him away, his misty eyes continuing to search the confused scene hoping to distinguish Angela from amongst the steady stream of others as they fled the devastation. Then, the carnage disappeared from view, shielded by thunderous spray when the jungle track, slippery with mud led into a cavernous route, behind the waterfall.

★ ★ ★ ★

Where the Longhouse community building had once stood proudly overlooking the river, only one section remained, the chief waving Angela away angrily as he searched through burning rubble like some desperate scavenger. *'Go!'* he pleaded, hoarsely. *'I'll catch up.'*

'What are you doing?' she cried in desperation, Jonathan scrounging for something under a collapsed wall. On the other side of the burning building, *Kopassus* troops continued to fire indiscriminately

into the blazing scene, their confidence restored in the absence of any response. The elders who had fought were now all dead to a man – their bodies incinerated in the Longhouse pyre.

'Got to find something to cut the ropes,' the chief muttered.

'Ropes?' she asked, bewildered.

'The crossing, Angela, we have to destroy the crossing!' he snapped, his face coming alive when fingers located a familiar piece. *'Help me!'* and without hesitation, Angela leapt forward and thrust her hands under the broken timbers, their combined strength lifting the solid piece, revealing the tool.

'Now, run!' he ordered, pushing Angela ahead, *'we don't have much time,'* both scurrying along the planked, river path, their escape hidden from view.

Waves of intense heat sucked the air dry of oxygen when the remaining structure imploded, scattering burning timber debris in all directions, a ten-meter crossbeam which had once rested directly above Jonathan's office was blown clear of the main building, destroying the community's satellite dish as it thudded to earth. For any who might have been trapped within the structure when it collapsed, the end would have been swift – the temperatures so extreme surrounding coconut trees exploded into flame, the resulting, running-crown-fire dancing across treetops through the island colony, until naturally contained. Jonathan fell as he made his way across the unsteady, rope-and-twine suspension bridge straddling the river, his voice lost against the waterfall's thunderous roar. Struggling to regain his feet, he wobbled to the other side, raised the axe and commenced hacking at the impossibly thick ropes.

'We have to destroy the bridge!'

'Papa, we don't have time. They're coming!' They had no weapons – defenseless against further attack.

'Come on, let go!' he cried out, in anguish, slicing furiously at an unforgiving rope he had so laboriously and meticulously tied to strengthen the bridge, only months before.

'They're coming, Papa!' Angela counted more than a dozen silhouetted shapes running towards the bridge. *'Leave it! We're too late!'*

But Jonathan Dau was driven by more than his desire to live. Hate burned through to his soul – he would have his revenge. The *Kopassus* soldiers were now dangerously close, clawing their way across the unsteady bridge, several aiming recklessly in their direction, firing from the hip. One fell into the river, the others grasping to regain balance when the manmade crossing started to yaw. Pumped with anger, Jonathan Dau swung the axe viscously, rope and twine giving, strand by strand, one side of the forty-meter structure swaying perilously in favor of the weakened side. Suddenly, a main support rope snapped, tipping the soldiers into the tricky currents.

'Papa,' Angela pointed across the river some two hundred meters at the remaining body of troops running in line, towards them.

'Hurry!' With arms locked around each other's waists for support, they moved as quickly as Jonathan's wound would permit, the axe dragged behind. The approaching soldiers opened fire, their accuracy hindered by the heavily foliaged, riverbank along which their quarry finally managed to escape.

The *Kopassus* soldiers were now without leadership, the remaining soldiers without appetite for any pursuit that would take them deeper into the Dayaks' natural habitat, where they could easily lose their heads. Comrades were assisted from the river, the severely demoralized unit gathering their dead and conducting one final sweep of the island community area, before returning to base.

★ ★ ★ ★

Longdamai Mining Camp

Baird had dispatched his assistant to see what the kafuffle was all about. The camp had come alive in a roar with the discovery of the soldier's bodies, and the realization of just how severely their security had been compromised. The Madurese section erupted, many attempting to abandon the site, their departure thwarted by over zealous *Kostrad* troopers who unhesitatingly aimed their weapons, threatening to shoot.

'Someone cut off their heads,' Mardidi was trembling uncontrollably,

'and left the bodies on the jetty!' He glanced around the quasi canteen, avoiding the expatriate drillers who were deeply engrossed in their own summations of events.

'How many?'

'Seemed like six, maybe seven.'

'Who did it, Dayaks?'

'There's no doubt about that. The laborers are clamoring for places on the longboats. It's bedlam over there.' Mardidi indicated the squalid quarters bunched on the far side of the camp.

'Has Campbell returned yet?'

'No.'

'Do you know if he took any communications with him?'

'Don't think so.'

'Where's Sharon?'

'Down at the jetty with the army commander.'

'Has he said what he's going to do?'

'I couldn't hear. The soldiers chased me away. Eric, don't you think we should leave?'

The situation was extremely hostile and Baird seriously considered the suggestion. Reluctant to go anywhere near the headless bodies, he pushed his unfinished breakfast to one side.

'I'll speak to Sharon as soon as she's finished down there.'

★ ★ ★ ★

Sharon stood with one hand on hip, another cupped protecting her mouth as she stared, disgusted, at the line of headless corpses, the severed necks smothered with swarms of persistent blowflies brazenly feasting on their congealed meal.

It seemed that her world was collapsing; Angela had not returned and Sharon's alternative plan was now unrealistic due to the hostilities along the Mahakam River. With no guarantee that Angela *would* return, Sharon needed full access to her pilot now, more than ever. Then, there was the problem with the *Kostrad* commander who had apparently received orders to reposition his troops to secure the migrant settlements, downstream – this resulting in her temporarily losing use of the helicopter.

Sharon had interrupted the Colonel while he was overseeing the removal of the headless bodies, the commander's anger at their deaths directed at her when she broached the subject of an evacuation.

'Miss Sharon, now is not the time,' he had warned. *'You can see that I have incurred casualties. Please, out of respect for these men?'*

'I don't think there is going to be a better time, Colonel. Please, give us back our transport so that we can move the foreigners out, if the situation deteriorates.'

'The Kopassus helicopter remains assigned under my orders.'

'What if we have injuries and require a medical evacuation?' she had argued.

'Then, if that situation arises, we'll get a chopper to you. Failing that, a fast boat.'

'That's not good enough, Colonel!'

'We are repositioning our forces,' the officer explained, his patience running thin. *'Security considerations must take priority!'*

'Who will guard the camp?'

'I'll leave enough men to see to that.'

Sharon was tempted to remind the *Kostrad* officer that the bodies lying at their feet had been guarding the site, and look what had happened to them. Wisely, she resisted. *'Then you don't agree that this would be an appropriate time for the expatriates to leave?'* she persisted, but the commander was adamant.

'We have our orders,' he repeated, annoyed at being challenged by a woman in front of his men, *'and these require that all of the company's employees remain here on site. It is far too dangerous to travel by longboat. We could not guarantee your safety.'*

'Then I need to use the radiophone,' Sharon insisted.

The commander looked at her suspiciously. *'There's a total blackout on all military movements. Who do you wish to call?'*

Sharon's mind raced. *'My boss overseas, he's expecting my call and if I don't make it, he'll get worried.'*

Pressed with far more important matters to resolve, the commander briefly considered her request, and agreed. He summoned an

NCO with a wave, and instructed the soldier to accompany Sharon. *'Keep it brief,'* he warned, *'and remember that all communications are being monitored.'*

Sharon then went directly to the operation's office where the radiophone was located, the NCO clearing her access with the guard. She contacted Jakarta and was connected to Vancouver, advising Kremenchug that her departure had been delayed, her enigmatic message dashing her partner's hopes for an early resolution to outstanding monetary concerns. And then, as requested, he dialed the number Sharon had given, and informed Alfredo of her delay.

★ ★ ★ ★

Longdamai Village Survivors

'How are you feeling?' Angela sat huddled with Campbell. He had been sleeping on a forest carpet of leaves and now ached all over.

'I'll make it,' he replied, listlessly.

'You've been asleep, for hours.'

'I should get back to the camp.' His voiced lacked conviction. He could see the chief's leg being packed with what looked like banana leaves wrapped in a makeshift bandage. *'What happened to your father?'*

'Shot in the thigh,' she answered, looking across the dim clearing to where Jonathan Dau's wound was being attended. *'It's not serious.'*

'Why did the army attack?' The two women charged with his safety had remained with Campbell when he could progress no further, Angela and Jonathan catching up with the stragglers, less than a kilometer from the Longhouse. Campbell's abdominal pains had lessened in intensity as he'd hauled his weary body to this place – his mouth now dry with thirst, and the nausea remained. It was not until Angela had caught up that he learned who was responsible for the raid, Campbell staggered when the chief suggested *Kopassus*. *'Will they follow us up here?'*

They had fled into the forest, reaching this temporary sanctuary after the most grueling trek, Campbell unable to keep pace with the main body of four hundred survivors, most of whom were women and children. Less than thirty *Penehing* men had managed to escape, none without serious injury, some now lying quietly with empty looks on their faces – others, oblivious to their final tide, with life gradually ebbing away.

'I don't know,' she replied, truthfully, wondering if the attack on her village could have been a pre-emptive strike – that, somehow, the military had learned of the Dayak plan to raze the migrant settlements, and acted accordingly.

'How long will the villagers remain here?' he asked. Light filtering through the canopy cast the meanest of glows across the clearing where the injured and wounded lay, beyond which, the movement of hundreds of villagers as they foraged for food, went virtually unseen.

'For as long as it takes.' Angela straightened her shoulders, back erect and chin high. There was a suggestion of arrogance in her demeanor.

Campbell detected the pride in her voice and asked, *'Do you want me to stay?'*

Angela cast him a fractious glance, then shook her head. *'No. There's nothing you can do here. As soon as the rest of the village men return, you should go.'*

Campbell looked at her quizzically. *'Return? Where did they go?'*

Angela's eyes dropped to the forest floor. *'There's no point in keeping it from you, Stewart. You'd learn the truth, anyway, the moment you set foot back in the mining camp.'*

'The truth about what?' he asked, curiosity aroused.

She sighed heavily. *'The young men, the warriors – they went downriver to disrupt the transmigrant settlement.'*

This response took some moments for him to digest, Campbell's reaction predictable. *'Disrupt?'* He rolled slightly, and propped on an elbow. *'What in the hell does that mean, disrupt?'*

'I knew you wouldn't understand.'

'They went on a raid?' this, with wild astonishment.

'Yes.'

He was stunned by her candor. *'And…and, you had foreknowledge of this?'*

'Yes.' Angela's face was devoid of expression.

'Which settlement?' he demanded, with growing alarm.

'Those downriver from the mining camp.'

An ominous, black cloud suddenly stretched itself along his horizon – Campbell tried to dislodge this by shaking his head. *'Those? They went to attack more than one?'*

'They're not alone.'

'What?' He stared in disbelief.

'I said they're not alone. The Penehing have joined with other Dayak communities, Stewart. They're not alone.'

Campbell's jaw dropped measurably, struck speechless by the magnitude of what she'd said. *'A general uprising?'*

'In three provinces.'

'Which ones?' he found himself asking – the enormity of her revelations still too difficult to comprehend.

'Central, Southern and Eastern Kalimantan.'

'But... why?' Campbell now spoke with difficulty, his throat parched with thirst.

'I guess they all decided, that they'd finally had enough.'

'And... this all started when?'

'Earlier today.'

'And you've known about all of this, since when?'

Angela's face masked her true feelings. *'Before you came to Longdamai.'*

'You've known for that long?' His voice all but cracked.

Angela cast a desperate glance across the clearing for support, back to Campbell, then nodded solemnly.

With this affirmation Campbell climbed unsteadily to his feet as blood drained from his face, returning instantly with a rush as he exploded into English with, 'I don't fucking believe it! Are you telling me that you knew all along that there was going to be a goddamn raid, and did nothing to prevent it?'

'Sit down, Stewart!' a voice cautioned from across the clearing, *'None of this is Angela's doing!'*

'What are you talking about?' Campbell retorted with equal spirit, not

registering that the chief had overheard *and* understood, every word.

'*I asked Angela to bring you here. Yes, she knew of our plans, but she has nothing to do with any of it. The truth is, she spoke against the action.*'

'*Then why am I here?*'

'*Because, initially, the mining camp was a target.*'

Again, Campbell exploded into English. 'Jesus, fucking Christ!' He glared at Angela. 'You were going to trash my operations, destroy the equipment, kill the people there? What happened?'

'*The army arrived. The mining site was removed from the list,*' this, with a disturbingly, serene calm.

'*And if they hadn't?*'

'*I would still have found a way to get you away from the site.*'

'*And I'm supposed to thank you for nearly getting me killed?*' Campbell shook his head in disgust. '*And what about the others?*'

Angela had steeled herself for this question. '*They weren't to be hurt.*'

'*How could you possibly have guaranteed that?*' his voice rose harshly, fueled with anger. '*You're all insane! What could you have possibly gained from attacking a foreign mining operation?*'

'*You mean the one that's destroyed a highly treasured, Penehing ancestral spiritual site?*' Angela retorted with venom.

'*My God, I don't know who you are anymore. This is madness, Angela!*'

'*No, it's war.*' Jonathan Dau again intervened.

'*But why?*' Confused, and weakened by his condition, Campbell's head started to swim. '*Why start a war... you can't win?*'

'*Because what happened to our village today, is but a precursor for what will happen to all Dayak communities.*'

'*You can't be certain of that.*' Campbell's eyes clashed with Jonathan's.

'*Look around you, Stewart. In just a few hours my people have been reduced to hiding in the forests, their homes destroyed, many within their families killed. This deliberate slaughter could in no way be retaliatory for what we had planned. It can only be coincidental that they chose to attack at this time. If you can consider this, then you must draw the conclusion that the army already had orders to wage war against us, the reasons obvious. We have become refugees in our own land. We have nothing to apologize for. I only wish we'd acted sooner.'*

Campbell inhaled deeply as he gathered his thoughts. Then, with the gesture of a disappointed teacher addressing a recalcitrant child, slowly shook his head. *'Surely you can't expect to win? Jakarta has enormous military resources.'* He paused for breath, more than affect. *'And, my bet is that they'll throw everything they've got at you!'*

'We accept this... and understand the price we must pay.'

'It's sheer madness.' Lost for words and physically incapable of further debate, Campbell could only shake his head at the insanity of it all. Jonathan Dau rose unsteadily, and Campbell could see that the chief's wound had been covered with strips torn from some woman's *sarong,* the temporary bandage high on his leg like some ridiculous garter.

'What if I told you that Kostrad army elements have been training militia units in all the settlements, for months? This activity was not confined to Javanese migrants, but Madurese as well. If Jakarta does not have a secret agenda, why would they be training such militia groups?'

'Perhaps to protect the migrants from raids?' Campbell threw back, sarcastically, and in the process lost his balance when his head began to spin, and he slumped to the ground. 'W*hat can you hope to achieve by wreaking such havoc?'*

The *Penehing* chief sat down again with his wounded leg extended, an arm over one knee as he eyed the American closely. *'The Dayak people want control over their economic resources and that includes timber, mineral resources and oil. We want the central government to cease its transmigration policy if for no other reason, than to prevent the further diluting of our ethnic purity. Our lands must be returned to us and with adequate compensation. Should these conditions be met, then the indigenous peoples of Kalimantan would be receptive to remaining within the Indonesian Republic.'*

Campbell believed the dream to be unrealistic – the *Dayaks* were up against a most formidable force. *'You can't win,'* was all he said.

'Stewart,' Angela was at his side, immediately, *'this is not your fight. As soon as the men return, we'll take you back to the camp.'* When she placed a hand on his crumpled shoulders, he brushed it away.

'Yeah...sure,' he said, sarcasm still dripping off his voice, *'if they*

haven't already...burned the place down.' He curled, dragging knees to his chest, and closed tired eyes.

Jonathan limped back across the clearing. *'They'll be back before nightfall.'*

'How could they possibly know where we are?' Campbell challenged, weakly.

The chief's face masked his contempt. 'W*hen they see what has happened to their Longhouse, they'll know where to find us.'*

'What are we going to do about food and water?' The American's tongue was dry; he needed water – food he could go without.

'The women are out gathering as we speak. Be patient.'

★ ★ ★ ★

Angela's deceit, and the ramifications of her disclosures continued to encumber Campbell's thoughts – bitter that nothing could ever be the same between them, again. That she had orchestrated to remove him from one dangerous situation, only to expose him to another, placing their relationship and his safety, in jeopardy. He recalled their conversation in Kuala Lumpur, haunted now by the nagging possibility that, even then, Angela might have known of the impending attacks. Overcome by fatigue, his eyes grew heavy, his breathing shallow and, as the consciousness slowly drained away, he drifted into troublesome sleep.

★ ★ ★ ★

Angela remained at Campbell's side, considering the exchange between the two men who occupied her life. She caught her father studying the American and rose, moving across to join the chief. *'I will take him back once he is rested.'*

Jonathan looked his daughter directly in the eye. *'Are you certain that you are making the correct choice of partners, 'Gela?'*

Angela glanced over at Campbell's prone form. *'To be honest, Papa, I'm no longer sure.'*

'Then you should not continue the relationship. Much has happened here today that will greatly influence our lives – and the future of the Penehing

people.' He pointed at the flesh wound to his thigh. *'This could have been serious.'* Jonathan reached out and placed a hand firmly on her shoulder. *'It is your destiny, that one day you will assume the role of leader, and priestess to your people, 'Gela. Do you think that Stewart really understands what sacrifices must be made?'*

'We've discussed it, Papa.'

'And what did he say to abandoning his Western lifestyle to live amongst the Penehing?'

'We didn't get that far.' A note of despondence crept into her voice. *'And I doubt if we ever will.'*

'You also must ask yourself, 'Gela, just how deeply you feel for this man. If you are in love with Stewart, then you should question whether that love is going to be enough to withstand time as I doubt if he has the capacity to commit to a life without the comforts he has grown accustomed to.'

'I understand, Papa.'

'Good. Think it through clearly. Because of who you are, when you marry, your partner in life must be just that.'

As they spoke, the object of their discussion cried out loudly in his sleep, the unmistakable words on his lips, calling Angela's name. She returned to his side and remained there for hours, gazing down at Campbell's handsome features, saddened that she would never know how it would feel to lie naked in his loving arms.

★ ★ ★ ★

BGC Offices – Vancouver

Kremenchug glanced at the desk calendar, mentally noting that in two days, it would be August. Buoyant, he remained in fine spirits in spite of Sharon Ducay's delay, having received an assurance that she would definitely depart Indonesia for Canada, within the week. Kremenchug leaned back in the executive chair and smiled smugly, his contentment linked to the imminent windfall, calculated to exceed forty million dollars – his share of the proceeds generated by the sale of Dominion Mining's BGC stock.

Kremenchug had monitored the movement of Dominion's BGC

holdings, aware that Sharon's nominee company had now all but liquidated its position in the Canadian miner over past days. Although BGC's stake in the Kalimantan goldfield had been reduced dramatically as a result of Baron Mining's indirect takeover, the value of the company's shares had recovered from their initial plunge, surpassing previous highs. Now, all he had to do was wait for Miss Ducay to return, at which time he would accompany his partner to the British Virgin Islands, where they would divide the spoils.

★ ★ ★ ★

Dayak-Penehing Camp

'Stewart, wake up!'

Disorientated, Campbell grunted, raised his head and squinted at Angela's blurred form sitting alongside. *'What...?'*

'You've been asleep, for hours.'

Campbell sat up slowly and rubbed life into his face, stubble triggering the deepest of frowns as the morning's events came flooding back.

'Here, drink this,' she held a half-coconut shell filled with water to his lips, Campbell drinking eagerly, then asking for more. Thirst quenched, he rubbed aching muscles to restore circulation, stretched, stifled a yawn and gazed around the setting, taking inventory, surprised to discover that they were alone. *'Where's everyone gone?'* he asked, rising slowly to his feet, peering into the thick undergrowth in search of movement.

'Up into the mountain; the soldiers are unlikely to follow them there.'

'When?'

'Two, three hours ago.'

'Why didn't you wake me?'

'Because we're not to follow.'

'Whose decision was that?'

'My father's.'

Campbell considered this, the mists of confusion clearing as he reasoned that the decision made sense. With the outbreak of hostilities along the Mahakam his absence from the mining operations would undoubtedly raise concerns, his continuing presence amongst the *Pencehing*, a liability. He had to return to the Longdamai camp, immediately.

'*I take it that you're to escort me back?*'

'*Yes.*'

'*Under the circumstances, don't you think that would be dangerous?*'

'*Why?*'

'*My God, Angela, with the entire Dayak population running around carving up the countryside, aren't you in the least concerned with the reception they might give you back in camp?*'

'*I'm a government official. I'm not in any danger. Besides, what have I done?*' What Angela couldn't explain is that she felt responsible for him. It would be unthinkable to expect that he should find his own way back. The man was physically drained. She would accept the risk associated with returning to the mining camp.

'*Well, to be practical, I sure as hell can't find my way back by myself. How are we going to do this?*'

'*We walk. If we start now, and providing you're up to it, we could be back before dark.*'

Campbell's chest fell. '*That's four, five hours!*'

'*There's no other way.*'

'*What about the village longboats? Is there a chance one might return soon?*'

'*My father didn't expect them back until tonight. But, that was before the Longhouse came under attack. Now we can't even be sure that the soldiers are not still there, lying in wait for them.*'

'*And the speedboat?*'

'*It's unlikely we'll see that again.*'

'*Okay, Angela,*' Campbell sighed heavily, '*then let's get underway.*'

★ ★ ★ ★

Throughout that bloody day, transmigrant settlements across three provinces were destroyed. Homes were incinerated, the makeshift towns nothing more than ash, cinder block and charred tin roofing once the bloodletting had passed. Temporary, government buildings were also torched and, wherever walls survived the onslaught, graffiti, most written in human blood, warned that the worst was still to come.

In the weeks that followed, communal graves would be needed to accommodate the six thousand Madurese and Javanese victims who had been slaughtered in three provinces, most unable to be identified as their heads were missing or their bodies brutally mutilated beyond recognition. And, when the international media became aware of these genocidal acts repercussions were immediate, and human rights organizations turned their attention to the problem area, and the atrocities being committed there.

The death toll of that one Jakarta-sanctioned military operation to destroy the *Penehing-Dayaks* exceeded two hundred and fifty villagers and thirty-seven *Kopassus* officers and men. Over the following days the army losses would escalate, the final count never revealed, some observers later claiming that at least two hundred *Kostrad* and *Kopassus* regulars had been killed by Dayak spears, bows and arrows, slingshots, blowguns and other unsophisticated weaponry, when the TNI foolishly attempted to take the fight into the jungle. Then, the President intervened, and as quickly as it had begun, the slaughter ceased.

★ ★ ★ ★

Chapter Twenty-five

Longdamai Mining Camp

Perimeter sentries spotted Stewart and Angela well before they entered the mining camp, the *Kostrad* army commander's curiosity aroused when he learned of their return, immediately refuting their claims that the Longhouse had been attacked by *Kopassus* elements. He glared angrily at the Dayak woman and took Campbell aside – Angela containing her resentment, when placed out of earshot.

'Why do they always blame others?' the officer complained, tilting his head in her direction. *'The Dayaks have been killing each other for centuries. No, what you saw was obviously an armed attack by another local, ethnic group. What purpose could possibly be served by the army killing its own citizens?'*

'Colonel, I was there. I witnessed the whole thing!' Campbell had insisted.

'You have already admitted that you were not well. Some food poisoning wasn't it?'

'Yes, that's true, but my judgment wasn't impaired by a bad stomach. The fact is, we were attacked with automatic weapons. It was definitely the army, Colonel and, as an American citizen, I can assure you that this won't end here.'

'Mister Stewart,' the commander had tried to placate, *'did you actually see these mythical soldiers yourself?'*

'No, I did not.'

'You didn't see anyone at all wearing uniforms?'

'No.'

'Can you tell me then, if you saw any of those who attacked the Longhouse?'

When Campbell was obliged to admit that he had been at the rear of the building and had not seen those who attacked, this drew a mirthless laugh. *'Then how can you make such outlandish accusations?'*

'I was there.'

'I'm sorry, Mister Stewart, but I must insist that you cease besmirching the army's name when, in fact, you not only did not see any TNI troops, but have absolutely no evidence that the attack was not carried out by neighboring tribes. These people adhere to the principle of 'payback'. I'm certain you will discover that the incident was the result of tribal rivalries. Now, come, let my medics have a look at you.'

Campbell ignored the offer. *'There are at least two hundred civilians, mainly women and children dead, back out there, Colonel. Come with me and I'll show you myself. There's sure to be thousands of spent rounds lying around. Surely that would be sufficient evidence in itself?'*

'Even these backward Dayaks have guns, Mister Stewart.'

'Sure, but not automatic machine guns, Colonel!'

'Again, how do you know that to be true?'

'As I said before, I was there. I heard the fire and I know what machine pistol fire sounds like.'

'You were a soldier?'

'No. But…'

'Mister Stewart,' the Colonel had taken him by the elbow and was steering him back towards the expatriate quarters, *'why don't you take a rest, and discuss this with me later?'*

'Then you refuse to go back with me? Colonel, there's an entire village lying in ruins with almost half of its inhabitants dead, not ten minutes by chopper from here. Please, take me there with you and I'll prove what I'm saying is true!'

The colonel threw his hands in the air. *'I don't have time for this. Captain Subandi?'* he turned to the waiting *Kopassus* helicopter pilot.

'Captain, are there any other Kopassus units in the area?'

Sharon Ducay's besotted pilot came to attention. *'No, Colonel, the nearest units would be in the provincial capital.'*

'Thank you, Captain,' the commander's face firmed, and he stared confrontationally into Campbell's eyes. *'That's the end of it, Mister Campbell. You can take it up with my superiors in Jakarta. Now, I'll have to go.'*

★ ★ ★ ★

Penehing in Hiding

Jonathan Dau scanned the slopes for signs of TNI troops, the vantage point a thousand meters above dense forest, and temporary home to five hundred of his fellow refugees. *'Udir,'* the chief grimaced when he bent down on his haunches beside the man who had led the attack against the Madurese settlement. *'Do you think they will come?'*

The other elder moved his feet, adjusted the automatic weapon hanging loosely at his side, a dark smile flooding his face as he tapped a full magazine. *'If they do, we'll be ready.'*

Jonathan admired his childhood friend's acquisition through the corner of an eye. Udir had come across the machine pistol amongst the village ruins, when he and the other *Penehing* men had returned to the Longhouse immediately following their raid. Discovering the carnage, they had moved their longboats further upstream where these remained, camouflaged, and under constant surveillance.

'They have the numbers to cause us great harm,' Jonathan reminded, *'we must avoid direct confrontation, at all costs.'* Once the community had regrouped and accounted for their number, it became evident that the male population they could draw upon if attacked, had been reduced to less than seventy-five – some as young as fourteen. Although barely into their teens, these youngsters were already skilled in the use of blowpipe and bow.

'What about those upstream?' Udir referred to the smaller and more isolated *Penehing* Longhouse communities which spotted the upper, Mahakam reaches.

'I have sent a runner, to see how they have fared.' Jonathan had assumed that all of the Upper-Mahakam Dayak tribes had come under attack. Deep in thought, both men then fell into silent camaraderie, their burden heavy as each maintained vigil against the TNI reprisal attack, which was certain to come.

★ ★ ★ ★

Immensely relieved with Angela's return, Sharon was determined not to let her out of sight again. She waited for Campbell's conversation with the commander to end, then wandered over as the helicopter lifted, carrying the Colonel downstream where he would rejoin the main body of his repositioned troops.

'Hi, welcome back. You missed the excitement.'

'You don't know the half of it,' Campbell answered moodily. 'What's been happening here?'

Sharon glanced at Angela. 'The locals paid us a visit.'

'Any damage to equipment?'

'No. They only got as far as the jetty.' She looked at Angela again. 'Left us quite a calling card, though – a string of decapitated corpses. Army corpses.'

Campbell's jaw tightened with this news, guessing this to be the reason behind the Colonel's reticence to discuss the village massacre. 'It hasn't been a particularly great twenty-four hours for anyone.'

'Well, at least the pair of you made it back in one piece.'

'Almost didn't.' Campbell looked like he was about to drop, that day had been so long he could not remember when it started.

'Sounds like you had a rough time out there?'

The American nodded. 'We're lucky to even be here.'

'What really happened?'

'The army attacked, burned the village to the ground – killed hundreds.'

Sharon was genuinely shocked. 'Why? Was it a reprisal for what was done here?'

'It's beyond me,' he said, his eyes following the chopper until it disappeared from view. 'What have you heard?'

Sharon looked at Angela. 'The word is that the locals have attacked the main settlement downriver. A group of Madurese came screaming into camp in a longboat just before noon. I couldn't understand what they were jabbering about, but they certainly got the laborers all worked up. The Colonel had a tough time convincing them not to go back to the settlement. That's where he's gone, you know.'

'How many men has he left here?' Campbell worried with the possibility of confrontation with the laborers.

'There's still a dozen or so watching over the site. Still, that's your problem from here on in, Stewart,' she announced, 'I'm out of here as soon as the Colonel gives us our chopper back.'

Campbell smothered a yawn. Exhausted from their recent ordeal, his body ached for sleep. 'And...what did he have to say about that?'

'We exchanged words,' Sharon forced a smile. 'He's undertaken to place it back at our disposal tomorrow. As soon as it's definite, I'm gone. Okay?'

Angela, who had remained silent up to this point, stepped in. *'Stewart, why don't you discuss this with Sharon later? You should get some rest.'*

Sharon's mind remained locked on the couple as they moved away, her thoughts now taunted with the possibility of Campbell's relationship with Angela interfering with the most crucial step in her scheme. When she had first conceived the idea the American was nowhere in the picture – Sharon satisfied at the time that when Angela 'went missing', her disappearance could have been explained away without any great difficulty. The mining camp had already achieved the reputation of having an unusually high number of fatalities amongst its workers.

After the pair disappeared from view she returned to her cabin in pensive mood, considering what else might be done to ensure that her exit was executed, according to plan. She slumped on the narrow bed, her eyes roaming the claustrophobic room registering that boxes and other personal affects were already packed, wondering if these would be shipped to the Philippines after her death – or rifled, with the best pieces stolen. Annoyed that she would have no control over this situation, Sharon decided to give it all away. Lazily, she tapped the locked aluminum case at her feet, reminded of the remaining half-kilo gold bars, and the two *Kopassus* soldiers her lover had recruited on their behalf.

Lying idly on the bunk, fantasizing about a future that included close to three hundred million dollars in her account, she fell asleep, waking an hour later with a start, to the sounds of the helicopter returning.

★ ★ ★ ★

'How did you manage it?' Sharon asked, with rising excitement, Subandi now in her arms.

'I convinced him that there was nothing he could do with the aircraft at night, and he agreed. But, he wants it back by first light.'

'That doesn't leave us much time!' Sharon's mood darkened. *'Can your men still do it on such short notice?'*

'No problem, they're used to working in the dark,' the *Kopassus* officer smirked.

'Then, all we have to do now is get that Dayak bitch away from the camp, without being seen.'

Sharon had never envisaged their exiting at night. It was imperative that she be seen climbing into the aircraft – the imagery essential to the credibility of what would happen next.

'Have her taken tonight. I'll make my departure when everyone's awake, and can see.'

'That's dangerous!' the pilot argued. *'The Colonel is expecting the aircraft back around that time.'*

'You can't do this for half a million dollars?' she pulled back, and commenced re-buttoning her blouse from the waist.

Subandi stared at her exposed breasts and his knees failed. Without further hesitation he reached out and tenderly cupped her in his eager hands. *'I'll tell the others,'* he promised, shaking uncontrollably when he felt the warmth of her hands fondling his crotch.

★ ★ ★ ★

Eric Baird whacked Mardidi playfully on the buttocks. *'Five, six days, and we'll be back in Jakarta.'*

'How can you be so sure?' His partner accepted the unexpected foreplay, reciprocating with an affectionate pinch.

'Well, we're finished here. Sharon's about to leave and that puts an end to my contractual obligations.' Baird ran a hand across Mardidi's shoulder, tickling him around the small of the back.

'When we return, what will you do about Pipi?'

'Do?' Baird's hot breath smelt like overly sweet honey against the side of his face. *'We'll not have to do anything.'*

'You will live with her?' Mardidi asked, praying this would never be the case.

'No,' Baird assured, his wandering hand moving over familiar ground, *'we won't be doing that.'*

'I love you, Eric,' Mardidi's unsolicited declaration was rewarded by Baird's assuming his customary position, followed almost immediately by a predictable grunt.

In the ensuing silence, they lay together, both engrossed in their own perspectives of how life after Longdamai would be. Baird reached across his lover's body – his fingers searching for the soft pack of clove cigarettes in discarded clothes at bedside. *'I love you too, Mardidi,'* he said, placing the *kretek* in his mouth – the younger man, accepting the signal, climbed out of the bunk and wrapped a sarong around his thin waist, then headed for the primitive, riverside ablution facilities, to scrub Baird absolutely clean from his body.

★ ★ ★ ★

As Campbell's stomach problems had persisted, one of the Madurese laborer's called upon his wife to administer crushed turmeric, the American geologist forcing the concoction down. Within the hour, the occasional cramps had all but disappeared, and he was feeling well enough to join Angela in the canteen. When he approached, she rose and started to move away.

'Stay and talk for a while. I'm feeling much better.'

'I was just going to my cabin.'

Movement across the site caught his eye and he tried to smile. *'Well, won't be long before we see the last of her,'* he indicated Sharon as she was spotted crossing towards the laborers' shanties. *'Can't say I won't be unhappy to see the back of her so we can get on with things around here.'*

Angela Dau's reaction to his idle comment was not what he'd expected. *'Will you really feel that way?'* Campbell surprised by her accusatory tone.

'What?'

'I said, are you sure you won't miss her being around?' She started to move away.

'What on earth are you suggesting?' Campbell was confused by her mood.

'*In the mountains – you talked in your sleep.*'

'*Why are you so angry?*'

'*I'm beyond angry!*'

'*I don't understand. What did I say?*'

'*You were dreaming about her. You called out her name.*'

'You've go to be joking?'

Angela stepped back – and he advanced to reassure. *'I only wish to know if your relationship with Sharon has ever been anything more than professional?'*

Campbell answered with a hollow laugh. *'How could you possibly think that?'*

'The way you both behave, the way you are always fighting. She occupies your dreams. Is it true?'

He tried to block her retreat, stepping between Angela and the adjacent table. *'Okay, we met at a conference years before she came to Indonesia.'* He leaned against the door. *'I don't understand why this is suddenly so important, now?'*

'Did you sleep with her?'

Campbell was completely nonplussed as to what might have triggered this reaction. *'What's this all about, Angela?'*

He moved closer, again she stepped away, and crossed her arms. *'Well, did you?'*

'Angela...' He advanced, arms outstretched.

Angela flared, stamping her foot heavily, the lightweight, timber floor cracking underfoot. *'Stewart, answer me!'*

Surprised by her sudden display of insecurity, Campbell's forehead crumpled to the brow. Unsure of what her reaction would be to a frank response, he lied. *'No, of course not.'*

Angela's foot lashed out, cracking his shin. *'Liar!'*

'For Chrissakes, Angela!' Campbell hissed through clenched teeth, the pain in his lower leg sending him limping to a bench. He dropped to the seat, raised the injured leg and tugged at his trousers to inspect the wound.

'Tomorrow, I'm returning to my people in the hills,' she announced. *'You don't belong here, Stewart Campbell!'* with which, she left.

'Wait, Angela. Wait!' He called, still in English, rising from the bench seat. He limped after her, but Angela was already gone, heading towards her cabin with purposeful stride. Campbell hopped back to the table, where he remained massaging the offended limb, cursing everything female in his life.

* * * *

Captain Subandi moved from the shadows where he had finished briefing the two, combat-experienced soldiers charged with the responsibility for delivering Angela to the designated pick-up point before morning, his attention now focused on Mardidi's movements towards the river. When the young Javanese disappeared from view, the *Kopassus* pilot followed.

Twenty minutes later, a terrified and disheveled Mardidi hurried back to Baird's quarters to change, taking care not to waken his partner as he climbed into work-clothes. Then, armed with the torchlight he'd been given, and carried by unsteady legs, he headed directly to Angela's quarters, as instructed. Halfway, he paused, leant against a coconut tree for support, clutched his stomach, and retched violently.

* * * *

Angela's face reflected her surprise. *'Did he give you his name?'* She had been deep in thought, contemplating Stewart Campbell when Mardidi had suddenly appeared, and relayed the message.

'*He says he's was sent by someone from your village.*'

'*My father?*' Angela, immediately concerned that the chief's wound might have worsened, was already on her feet. '*Where is he?*'

'*Hiding down at the jetty. He is afraid to show his face.*'

'*And the guards*?'

'*They're sitting over there, playing cards.*' He pointed, remembering what to say. Angela squinted, recognized the soldiers huddled together, and frowned.

'*You must hurry!*' Mardidi insisted, Angela hesitating as she searched his earnest face.

'*You'll come with me?*'

He knew he had no choice. '*Yes, of course,*' the words near choking in his mouth, '*but we must hurry!*'

'*Show me!*' Angela ordered, and Mardidi almost broke down and cried.

By torchlight, they followed the path down to the river, the camp's perimeter lights deliberately extinguished in this area earlier in the night, Angela Dau in no way suspecting the trap that waited her arrival. They walked onto the jetty, the sound of their footsteps carrying against the background of the Mahakam River's fast moving flow, Angela stiffening with the near sounds of a bird's woeful caw and wings flapping furiously, in flight.

'*Where is he?*' she asked with growing apprehension, sensing now that she might have erred in coming down to the river in the dark.

'*In the longboat,*' Mardidi centered the torch towards the end of the jetty where a number of narrow riverboats had been secured.

'*What...*' Caught by surprise, Angela's startled cry was muffled by the high pitched roar of an outboard engine coming to life as her legs were swept from beneath her body, when powerful hands reached from under the jetty, dragging her over the side. With her lungs filling with water, Angela screamed, kicking wildly at whoever was dragging her backwards through the river, a fierce blow to her head rendering her incapable of further resistance.

'Stop it, stop it, you're drowning her!' Mardidi pleaded, the *Kopassus* soldier ignoring his call, surrendering Angela's lower torso up to his accomplice, who was in the process of hauling her semi-conscious body into the longboat, when the hornbill attacked.

With the most terrifying caw, the bird struck, tearing flesh from the surprised trooper's face, the wounded solider immediately releasing his prisoner back into the water to defend himself. The man rose unsteadily, his balance momentarily lost as the bird dived again, his flailing arms unable to prevent the hornbill's razor sharp talons from lacerating skin, from wherever he was exposed. The bird's frenzied attack then turned on the second solider who had seized Angela's half-drowned form, and was dragging her back under the jetty. The soldier screamed for assistance, his wounded comrade coming to his aid wildly swinging a boat-pole through the air, by luck, striking the hornbill midair, sending it injured, back into the night.

The assault had lasted less than a few seconds; Mardidi frozen in his tracks while the two men returned to their task bundling Angela into the longboat. They tied her hands behind her back then rolled her over, face down.

'Get in!' one of the soldiers hissed.

'I don't want to go!' Mardidi shrieked, startled and turning to flee when he heard someone coming from behind. It was the pilot, Subandi.

'Get in the boat!' the Captain marched up and struck Mardidi savagely, the blow sending the light-framed Javanese crashing to the deck. The pilot stepped forward and kicked him for good measure, then reached down and dragged Baird's lover the remaining distance, by the hair. Whimpering, Mardidi took his position in the boat. The pilot then threw a plastic bag containing Sharon's clothes, and items of personal jewelry. *'When you get there, put her in these. Don't forget the rings – and the gold ankle-chain. Remember! Put them on the woman, not in your pockets. Screw it up and there'll be no bonus. And don't forget to cut her hair. Now, get moving!'* he snapped at his subordinates, adding in threatening voice, *'and make sure you're ready for me at 0630 hours.'*

The Yamaha engine roared into life, Subandi monitoring their departure until the longboat disappeared amongst the cover of darkness. Within the hour his men would have positioned themselves and their captive at the south end of the former island colony destroyed in the recent *Kopassus* raid. He had selected the devastated village to facilitate the next stage of Sharon's exit scene, reasoning that the possibility of detection would remain minimal, as the site had been abandoned. And, having reconnoitered the area and its surrounds from the air, the Captain had seen nothing even closely representing a threat that might jeopardize their plans. Angela Dau would be transported to her former home and held captive, until the time for her to die had arrived.

High above the rainforest's canopy a hornbill wavered in flight, the injury inflicted upon one wing during the attack forcing it to seek refuge until it could regain its strength. The bird dropped from the sky and came to rest in the tall *meranti* at the edge of the Longhouse island forest where restless spirits wandered through the sacred grotto, in the darkness of night.

★ ★ ★ ★

Penehing in Hiding

Shaman Jonathan Dau awoke in a bed of sweat, his heart thumping wildly, his right shoulder burning with pain, the dream of a hornbill falling from the sky, its image turning into that of Angela's before crashing to earth, all too real. He searched the heavens for further signs, examining the stars, touching the wind, but found nothing there. He turned to prayer, beseeching ancestral spirits to keep his daughter – and spiritual heir, safe from all harm. That this recurring dream had never been so clear, troubled him greatly – Jonathan now deeply concerned for his daughter's life. The chief summoned Udir, and confided in his friend. *'It was foolish of me to send her back to the mining camp. I can sense it in the air – she's in grave danger.'*

'Then we should go to her,' Udir recommended, *'we can leave now, if your leg is up to it.'*

The shaman checked the bandage. *'It will get me down to the river. We'll take four of the younger men in a longboat. The rest should remain here, just in case.'*

'How will you penetrate the mining camp, unseen?'

'We should tie up, short of the site. You and I would enter the area through this section,' Jonathan drew in the sandy loam with his finger, *'and the others can create a diversion here.'* He indicated the point with an X in the soil – this was the Madurese laborers' shanties. *'They'll set fire to the buildings then retreat to the longboat. We'll grab Angela and take her into the heavily-wooded area across here.'* Another X was drawn. *'We'll then cut through and regroup with the others where the longboat is moored.'*

'With your leg, we should allow two, perhaps three hours to get down to the river in the dark. The others can go ahead and prepare the boat, meet us on this side of the falls. Another thirty minutes, say, an hour to place us in position…' Udir paused, *'that would mean we'd be at Angela's door by around three, latest three-thirty. We could be in and out within fifteen minutes.'* Udir raised his eyebrows questioningly. *'We should leave now, Jonathan, if we are to get there in time for our men to create that distraction without being seen. Some of the Madurese will be around and about preparing for first prayers, and we wouldn't want them sounding the alarm. We don't have any recent intelligence, but we should assume that the camp is still heavily guarded.'*

'I agree. Wake the others, now. Tell them to gather their weapons. We'll leave immediately.'

★ ★ ★ ★

Mahakam Tributary

Angela's temples throbbed from the punishing blow; her badly bruised body slowly recovering from shock, now trembling with the chill of fear. Desperate, she attempted to untie her hands, but failed. *'Please, please don't do this!'* she pleaded — her entreaty lost amidst the powerful outboard's growl. She bent her knees and attempted to roll into an upright position, rewarded with another cruel blow, sending her unconscious.

Mardidi, eyes blurred with streaming tears dared not look back, his whimpering sobs only encouraging a cruel smile on the soldier's face, crouched behind.

'Far enough?' Mardidi heard the soldier ask, failing to recognize the imminent danger.

'Yeah, this is okay,' the man forward snorted, *'do the miserable little shit.'*

Mardidi heard these words and his eyes opened wide, the cold steel that slashed his throat preventing any scream. The killer heaved Mardidi's body over the side, dipped the blade in the river then wiped it against his side.

The vessel continued towards its destination, delivering its precious cargo to the designated site. There, the soldiers carried Angela's limp body up the muddy banks, dumped her on the ground, started a fire then settled down to fill in the hours under cover of the towering *meranti* tree.

★ ★ ★ ★

Longdamai Mining Camp

For Sharon, pumped with nervous energy and what amounted to a continuous adrenaline rush, sleep failed. She remained glued, impatiently monitoring the time, counting down the minutes before she could leave, frustration building when the hands on her watch appeared to slow. In six hours she would be on her way; after that, another three, perhaps four hours, and she would be sitting on the deck of the vessel that would take her home to the Philippines, where she would assume Angela Dau's persona, then fly to Hong Kong where her fortune from gold awaited.

★ ★ ★ ★

Chapter Twenty-six

LONGHOUSE VILLAGE ISLAND
0500 HOURS

When Angela regained consciousness she knew, immediately, where she was being held. Lying on her side she whispered ever so quietly, repeating words her father had articulated what now seemed so long ago, the rhythmic hum of her mantra carrying her into a trancelike state, and through the door of the spirit world. Unburdened by weightlessness Angela floated, and in her mind she parted with her physical being and, summoning her inner strength the novice priestess called upon the divine bird spirit to carry her away from the evil abode, unaware that her captors remained under the obdurate glare of the hornbill above.

★ ★ ★ ★

When Jonathan arrived at the cliff's edge where waterfall spray threw a fine mist into the air, one of the young *Penehing* men who had volunteered for the mission pointed excitedly downstream in the direction of the grotto.

'Soldiers,' he whispered, with a confirming nod in the dark.

'How many?' his chief demanded.

'*We'll know, soon. I've sent one of the men down to investigate.*'

'We could always go around the island?' Udir suggested.

'There may be more camped over there as well.' Jonathan clenched the other elder's arm. *'We can't spare the time to reconnoiter. We'll have to take them out.'*

'Where's the boat?' Udir asked.

'The other two have it out of sight. We had to bring it here under oar. Come, I'll take you.'

They followed the trail down the slope, disappearing behind the waterfall when they entered the natural cave, emerging on the lower side soaked with spray. The longboat was moored not meters from where the suspension bridge had once spanned the river, Jonathan and his group boarding quickly, then silently paddling across to where their Longhouse had stood proudly amongst the palms.

'There's Anton,' someone called in hushed voice. *'Anton, Anton, over here!'*

The young, *Penehing* scout spotted the others, running half-crouched to rejoin his group. *'There are only two of them.'* He paused, regaining his breath, *'and they have 'Gela.'*

'What! Are you sure?' this, from the shaman, gripping the youngster's shoulder firmly.

'Yes. It's definitely 'Gela. And, I saw Yuh-Yuh screaming around taking a fit!'

'Is 'Gela hurt?'

'She seems to be tied. Couldn't see too much more.'

'And the soldiers?'

'Armed. They look like they're waiting for others.'

'Why would they bring 'Gela back here?' Udir asked.

'They mean to kill her, that's for sure.'

'Then, what are they waiting for?' Udir glanced at the chief.

'Perhaps they've kidnapped her for ransom?' Jonathan, searching for answers, tried to fathom why his daughter had been brought back to her village grounds, reasoning that if they intended killing her, she would already be dead.

'What ransom could she possibly draw?' Udir, always pragmatic, asked.

Jonathan shook his head. *'If not for ransom, then for an exchange – they want me, and 'Gela could be the bait.'*

'You think it's a trap?'

'Would need more than two soldiers, if that were so.'

'There could be others, hidden out of sight?'

'Then we should determine that first. Udir, we'll split into two teams. We'll each take two men and sweep the forested area, to the rear. If there's nothing there, we'll regroup in the cover to the east of the grotto.'

Shadows in the night, the six *Penehing* men were swallowed by darkness as they merged with their surrounds, disappearing into the forested area that separated the river from fields. When it became apparent that the soldiers were acting alone, the *Penehing* moved to within meters of their enemy, having already discussed their next move. As they observed the scene, Angela's pet, Yuh-Yuh suddenly appeared and, with a terrifying cry, scrambled through the grotto to Angela's side where she remained, until a soldier came at her with a knife, and she fled.

Jonathan Dau had insisted that they take the men prisoners as he intended interrogating them to determine what lay behind his daughter's kidnapping. From his vantage point, he could clearly see Angela, her hands tied, his anger resolved to pride when she struggled to her feet, defiantly, and spat into the closest soldier's face.

'You filthy, Dayak bitch!'

Jonathan waved for the others to wait for his signal.

'Let's get those clothes off you now!' the other solider laughed loudly. He sprang to his feet, and opened the plastic bag containing Sharon's things. *'The Captain said nothing about not having a little fun. Get her undressed and we'll see what makes these people so special.'*

The first soldier knocked Angela to the ground, placed a boot on her chest, and started unbuckling his trousers, the other man chuckling with glee as he followed suit. With one trouser leg free and the other still wrapped around an obstinate gaiter, the man was unable to defend himself when Jonathan attacked, the *Penehing* subduing both men without effort. The chief's fingers worked quickly to release his daughter's hands, the others busily dealing with the soldiers. He lifted Angela to her feet and guided her towards the campfire, her face reflecting her obvious relief. Gently, touching her swollen jaw with calloused fingers he asked, *'How badly are you hurt?'*

Angela pulled away with the touch, before answering through the side of her mouth with great difficulty. *'Bruised. Sore. Angry. How did you know I was here?'*

'We didn't. We were on our way to the mining camp to bring you home.'

'Are these yours?' Udir passed the plastic bag he'd retrieved to Angela.

Disheveled, Angela straightened her clothes, before examining the contents, confused by what she found. *'What would they want these for?'* Then, when her fingers discovered the jewelry, she exclaimed, *'these are Sharon Ducay's. They probably stole them.'*

Udir was not convinced. *'Why would soldiers steal a woman's clothes?'*

'For their wives, perhaps girlfriends,' Angela pocketed the rings and ankle-bracelet, discarding the clothing when Sharon's image came to mind. *'Let's find out.'* Stepping over to where the soldiers were detained, both now on their knees, Angela deliberately reverted to the national language so that the prisoners would understand. *'Pak Udir, give me your sword. Let me be the one to remove their heads!'*

Roles reversed and resigned to his fate, the older and more experienced of the pair raised his head proudly and, with as much bravado as he could muster, growled through clenched teeth. *'You are the scum of Indonesia. One day, there'll be none of you filthy headhunters left. I won't be here to see it, but my children and their children will.'*

Alongside, his comrade in arms had started shaking, rocking backwards and forwards, reciting a prayer from the Koran. Jonathan Dau knew immediately which of the men would divulge the answers to his questions. He knelt in front of the weaker man. *'Tell me what I want to know, and I'll send you home to your family.'*

'Don't tell them anything!' the more senior man yelled, *'you're going to die, either way.'*

'I will keep my word,' the chief repeated. *'Tell me why you brought this woman here.'*

'It... was the Captain's idea,' the man choked on the words, his eyes opening wide when Udir leaned over and placed a shortened

sword on the ground.

'Shut up, you gutless fool!' his friend tried, *'they're going to kill you no matter what you say!'* There was a blow, and the offender fell forward, dead.

Jonathan placed his hand on the remaining soldier's shoulder to steady him, the gesture having the reverse effect as fear gripped the man's stomach, twisting intestines beyond his control and he soiled himself, his moan then turning to tears.

'I'll give you one more chance. Why did the Captain want her here?' Jonathan made great show of lifting the deadly blade, holding this for the prisoner to see.

'I don't want to die!' the younger man cried, between chest-racking sobs, *'Please... in the name of Allah The Merciful, oh my God... don't kill me...I beg of you...please don't kill me!'*

'Who is this Captain who gave you your orders?'

'The pilot...' the man answered, against a faint glint of hope he'd be spared.

'Which pilot?' Jonathan accentuated the annoyance in his voice.

The body of his comrade loosened his tongue. *'The Kopassus pilot – the one seconded to fly personnel at the mining camp.'*

'What were your orders?' Jonathan played with the blade.

'We were to bring her here,' he raised his head indicating Angela, *'and wait for the Captain to arrive.'*

'What then?'

'We were...' his eyes averted his captors' and he stared at the ground. *'We were to take her up in the helicopter... and make it look like an accident.'*

Behind, there was an audible gasp as these words fell upon Angela.

'But why?' Jonathan asked, intrigue drawing them closer.

'When they found her body... they'd think it was the other woman.'

'Which other woman?' Udir interrupted, confused with the explanation.

Jonathan shot a warning glance. *'I'll ask you again. Which other woman?'*

With tongue filling his mouth, the captive struggled to respond. Finally, between broken sobs, he said, *'The…Captain's… girlfriend.'*

'He's lying! None of this makes any sense,' Angela accused.

'Those clothes…' the prisoner hesitated, again, eyes rising to meet Angela's. *'The Captain wanted you to look like the Filipino woman.'*

Jonathan's face clouded, Angela stung by the implication.

'Can you tell us why?' they both started, simultaneously.

'The Filipino… promised us gold,' he whimpered.

'How much?' Angela's curiosity took charge. She wanted to know how much she was worth to Sharon, dead.

'A kilo, each.'

'And the pilot, how much was he to be paid?'

'I don't know,' he replied, truthfully, panic striking when Jonathan raised the blade threateningly. *'No, I swear, I don't know!'*

'If you were to kill this woman and make it seem like the Filipino was the one who died, what was planned for her?'

'The Captain is going to bring her here.'

'When?' Jonathan was trying to find the missing pieces to the puzzle. He still could not understand why the other woman had arranged for the identity swap.

'Soon,' the soldier revealed. *'Our orders were to have everything ready by 0630.'*

'And after you had killed this woman, what then?'

'The Captain would return here, pick up the Filipino, drop us off and fly to Samarinda. We were to return to the mining camp, as if nothing had happened.'

'Papa, this still doesn't make any sense!' Angela complained. *'How would they benefit by my death, and also Sharon Ducay's?'*

'Perhaps we're looking at this from the wrong perspective,' the shaman suggested. *'It isn't you who would be reported as dead, but the Filipino. What we have to look at, is how she would benefit by being dead.'*

'I don't understand, Papa.'

'At this moment, neither do I. What would the government do in the event of a foreign employee being killed?'

Angela rubbed her tired brow. *'I don't know what the requirements would be under the Foreign Investment Law. My mind is too confused to think.'*

'If this woman... Sharon?' he peered up and his daughter nodded. *'If Sharon dies, someone else benefits. But, if Sharon is only thought to be the one to die, then it's she who benefits. There can no other logical explanation.'*

'What should we do?'

'I don't know. Let me think.'

'What about him?' Udir asked, panic deepening in the soldier's belly – he sensed they were discussing his fate.

'Wait. He might still be useful.'

⋆ ⋆ ⋆ ⋆

Longdamai Mining Operations

A mood of restlessness permeated the camp. Campbell, still troubled by his recent near-death experience was amongst the first to rise when the Moslem laborers' dawn call to prayer sounded, depriving all others of sleep. He bathed, bucketing water over head and body, then dressed and wandered over to the mess in search of coffee, surprised to find Sharon Ducay already there.

'Can't sleep?' he sat down beside her.

'Just waiting for the others to come alive so I can bid everyone farewell.' Sharon deliberately projected herself as deeply depressed; it was part of the game.

'Farewell? What, now?'

'I have temporary use of the chopper. I'm leaving in another hour or so.'

'You're packed?'

'Ready to load,' Sharon's nervousness was not evident. Tired, from having not slept for days, her final exit from the scene was almost anti-climatic.

Campbell was shocked by her appearance. Her clothes had that crushed appearance of having been slept in. 'Are you okay?' he asked, genuinely concerned – it looked like she'd been crying.

Sharon sighed heavily, the actress in her taking charge now. She cast a despondent look around the camp then surrendered her hands to the air. 'No, I'm not okay.'

'What is it?'

Nestling chin on palm, her glum expression disguised the spark behind her eyes. 'It's nothing.'

'Can't be nothing,' he insisted. 'I know we haven't gotten along over the past weeks, but that was professional. Tell me, what's the problem?'

Sharon lowered her eyes and shook her head slowly. 'It's stupid.'

'So, okay, it's stupid. Still, might help if we talk about it.'

Misty-eyed, she lifted her chin. 'Guess I've been a right bitch, huh?'

Campbell smiled comfortingly. 'I've met worse.'

'Stewart,' she opened, following with well-rehearsed lines, 'have you ever wanted something so desperately that it completely consumes your life, everything you do, your thoughts from the moment you wake, until the day is finished? Then, when it's finally in your grasp it just slips away and there's nothing you can do to prevent what's happening? It's as if, suddenly, everything you've worked for has had no meaning, that you've been traveling down the wrong road all of your life and come to a dead end – left with nothing but a sense of failure?'

Since the takeover announcement, Campbell had regretted Baron's refusal to retain Sharon Ducay's services. At this precise moment, he felt deeply sympathetic towards her. Even though Longdamai was her discovery, it would be others who would benefit from the accolades and, with time, Sharon's name would be forgotten. 'I don't think any of us could begin to understand what you've been through – how you feel, particularly today. For what it's worth, Sharon, you go with my respect – for what you've achieved, here, and for the professional that you are. And, I'm sure that I'm not alone in expressing these sentiments.'

She touched the corners of her eyes with the cuff of a sleeve. 'Thank you, Stewart, that means a great deal to me.'

'Hey, look on the bright side,' he attempted lightly, 'by tomorrow you'll be sitting in a cozy tub with a drink in one hand thinking about your future, while we're still standing around concrete slabs throwing buckets of cold water over ourselves, one eye on the soap, the other on the lookout for snakes!'

Her pretense at a smile was superb; Campbell thought he saw her bottom lip tremble. 'Guess you're right. I'm being stupid.'

'Hey, Sharon,' he tried to grin, 'no one's ever gonna accuse *you* of that!'

She thanked him with another nod. 'Make sure you're standing there waving when I leave. Who knows, you might be the only one.'

'To tell you the truth, I wouldn't mind joining you, Sharon,' Campbell's remark causing her to choke on the coffee.

Sharon recovered from her coughing fit, moving quickly to prevent this possibility from eventuating. 'Well, if it were up to me, I wouldn't mind having you, Stewart,' she offered, sweetly, 'but, unfortunately, there's no space available.' Her mind raced. 'The Colonel wants the pilot to pick up some of his men and ferry them downriver.' On a roll, her confidence sliding up a gear, she continued with the fabrication. 'I'm lucky to have been given a ride. Besides, aren't you now locked in here until Baron restarts the drilling?'

'With what's happening, they're likely to put everything on hold until the locals are sorted.'

'You'll be okay,' she reached over and patted his hand patronizingly; the American failing to observe her missing rings. 'Anyway, you have your little woman to watch over you, don't you?' Smug, Sharon could not resist, wondering how Campbell would react if he knew what was actually on her mind.

Campbell let the sarcasm ride. He was not in the mood, especially so early in the day. 'Where do you go from here?'

'I don't have any immediate plans other than to get on that helicopter, go to Samarinda and catch the first flight out of this country.'

'Take my advice. Go home. Spend some time with your family. It usually works.'

Sharon couldn't believe her luck. Her face fell, her shoulders slumped, and she looked away, willing the tears to flow. 'I don't have any family. They're all gone.'

'Everyone?' Wishing he'd kept his suggestions to himself, Campbell felt the lead form in his stomach. 'You have no one at all?'

'My parents and the other children died in an aircraft accident. My uncle raised me. He passed away about the time you arrived here on site.'

Campbell now believed he understood the reason for her aggressive behavior from the moment he'd set foot in camp. His timing could not have been worse. She had been grieving and, to compound her loss, she had been formally advised of her termination as chief of operations and senior geologist. *No wonder she'd been pissed!* 'Jesus, Sharon, I'm sorry. Why didn't you say something?'

Sharon's demeanor assumed the persona of an abandoned urchin. She rose, found a handkerchief in her jodhpurs and commenced dabbing at eyes and nose. 'I'm going to spend some time alone,' and walked away towards her cabin, leaving Campbell convinced that she was, indeed, seriously depressed.

★ ★ ★ ★

'Have you seen Mardidi anywhere?' Baird, frantic that his partner might have fallen into the river, skidded into uncertainty.

'No, can't say that I have,' Campbell was now halfway through a combination of fried rice and eggs. 'Why, what's the problem?'

'It's just so out of character for him not to wake me in the morning,' Baird's eyes continued to search. 'Do you think he might be with Angela?'

'Could be,' Campbell was aware that Mardidi often spent time looking after her chores. 'Why not ask?'

Baird headed for Angela's cabin, Campbell still too tired to smile at the geologist's early morning antics, expecting that Mardidi and the Australian had another lover's tiff, and the young, Javanese lad was off in sulky silence, somewhere. With heavier concerns burdening his mind, Campbell revisited his relationship with Angela, confused with her recent and strangely erratic behavior.

★ ★ ★ ★

Word of Sharon's imminent departure swept the mining camp, many, delighted with the news. At precisely 0600 she surprised the Madurese laborers by dividing her remaining possessions amongst their women, then, her head covered with the familiar, wide-brimmed Akubra hat, she walked solemnly towards the *Kopassus* Airborne Iroquois helicopter, and boarded. Investigators would later note that the Filipino had given away even the most personal of items, adding to the speculation that she had climbed into the aircraft with every intention to jump.

Sitting alongside the pilot, Sharon Ducay gazed despondently from the cabin, an unseen hand stroking the Captain's thigh whilst the other waved dramatically at those she'd left behind. One of the expatriate drillers gave her the finger, which she ignored, blowing Stewart Campbell a kiss before turning away, with a white handkerchief to an eye.

The air churned and the engine whined – the helicopter rocked on its skids, dust driving the onlookers away. Suddenly, the machine rose and hovered with uncertainty, the rotors lifting the chopper a few meters off the ground as it turned towards the river, and commenced to climb.

Eric Baird followed the helicopter's ascent as it rose over the coconut palms, squinting into the sun when it turned east. Sullenly, he kicked at the ground, and swore. 'I'm going to have Mardidi's guts for garters. If he'd been here in time, we could have been on that flight.'

'You haven't found him yet?' Campbell didn't feel the need to explain that Mardidi's presence would have made little difference. Sharon had been explicitly clear – space had already been allocated to others, downstream.

'No. Stuffed if I know where the hell he could be. Checked Angela's cabin, he wasn't there.'

'Had she seen him at all?'

'Who, Angela? Hell no. She wasn't there either.'

Campbell felt the grip on his heart. 'Have you checked everywhere around the camp?'

'Everywhere except in the drillers' quarters. Do you think he might have gone over there?'

Campbell was not so certain. 'I'll ask.'

As an experienced hand, Campbell knew that in mining communities, nothing ever really went entirely unobserved. He spent the next hour talking to both the Indonesian and expatriate drillers, checked their accommodations, and walked through the galvanized iron-roofed dwellings that posed as housing for the Madurese laborers and their families. By eight o'clock, he had already arrived at the conclusion that Angela Dau had returned to her people and, for whatever reason, had taken Mardidi with her. They had been seen, together, making their way towards the jetty – and one of the longboats was now missing.

★ ★ ★ ★

Chapter Twenty-seven

LONGHOUSE VILLAGE ISLAND

Jonathan Dau cautioned the *Penehing* warrior. *'Undo the laces first!'* The younger man nodded, turning back to the task of removing the dead, *Kopassus* soldier's boots.

'Bring the other one over here.'

'Are you sure we can get away with this?' Angela asked. At first, she had been mystified by her father's instructions, watching with morbid curiosity as the dead soldier had been stripped of his camouflaged uniform, then with alarm when the chief dressed in the man's clothes.

'Of one thing I am certain, 'Gela. They intend for you to die. I don't understand what it is that makes this so important, but I do know that this Filipino woman, Sharon, is obviously responsible for your demise. We must be as clever as she.'

'I never liked her from the start.'

'If you'd trusted your intuition more, perhaps we wouldn't be here today?'

Angela quietly accepted the admonishment. *'What do you have planned for her?'*

'Some of that old Dutch justice – an eye for an eye.'

'You are going to kill her?' Angela was not really surprised.

'She's deserving of the same end she'd planned for you.'

'How?'

'Sharon will take your place on the helicopter.'

'How can we possibly arrange such a switch?'

'That's where he comes in.' She followed her father's eyes to the prisoner.

'What can I do to help?' Angela asked.

'Just stay out of sight; we'll do the rest.'

'How are you going to prevent the pilot from leaving the helicopter and following Sharon into the trees?'

'Udir will cover that – and, the other solider.'

'How?'

'He'll know that we'll be close by, with him in our sights. Look at him – he's terrified. Don't worry, 'Gela, he's the least of our concerns.'

'What's to stop him warning them? If he's that close to the helicopter, how could we prevent his signaling the pilot, and just climbing aboard?'

Her father's eyes twinkled. *'Let's see.'*

The soldier had been forced to his knees in front of the chief. *'My daughter thinks you will betray us.'*

Learning Angela's relationship to Jonathan, the man's eyes widened in terror. He looked from one to the other. *'No...no, Bapak, I will do whatever you ask!'*

'You must be sure that you will. Udir?' he summoned the other elder. *'Udir, I want you to kill this man without hesitation if he fails to do what I ask, when the helicopter lands.'*

'Happily,' Udir grunted.

The chief then raised a questioning brow in the prisoner's direction. *'You're familiar with that weapon?'* he asked, indicating Udir's machine pistol. The soldier nodded. *'Then you would know, that my friend here could cut you in half before you could take two steps?'* Again, the man nodded. *'What is your name?'*

'Amir,' the other answered.

'Well, Amir, unless you have a powerful desire to meet your prophet today, this is what you must do.'

'You will keep your word?' the prisoner asked, worriedly, wishing to remind Jonathan of his undertaking to send him home.

'Yes, I will keep my promise.'

'I have no wish to die. What is it that I must do?'

Confident that he now had a plan, Jonathan called upon his old friend. *'Udir, gather the others and I'll explain.'*

★ ★ ★ ★

Turbulence shook the Bell 205 as the aircraft descended, bringing the river island clearly into view. Captain Subandi had flown the Huey east from the mining camp suggesting for any who might have seen, that Samarinda was their destination. He then turned and followed a course which brought them to the general area where Angela was held captive. The helicopter dropped further, bringing the crescent shaped row of cliffs and waterfall to eye level, the pilot scanning the once picturesque setting for signs of movement. Sharon could see the blackened areas where buildings and forest had burned across more than half of the island, the fire's rampant destruction ending at the edge of recently tilled fields.

'Where are they?' She searched the scene below.

'There!' Subandi pointed, Sharon's eyes unable to identify the camouflaged soldiers amongst the unfamiliar terrain. *'Over there, at the edge of those trees.'*

Sharon spotted the solitary soldier and glanced apprehensively at the pilot. It was Amir. *'Where are the others?'*

He sneered. *'Agus is there. You just can't see him.'*

The solider was now waving, excitedly, indicating where the helicopter should land, the Captain guiding the '205 with experienced glove. Half crouched, Amir ran up to them and banged on the metal door as the machine settled, and Sharon unbuckled, removed the headset, then leaned across and kissed her man fully on the mouth. *'I love you!'* she lied, gathered her Akubra and a flask of water, then opened the cabin door.

'I'll keep the engine running while they fetch her,' Subandi yelled, *'make sure you remain out of sight until I get back!'*

'Good luck!' she called, easing her body down to the ground as the soldier squeezed past, and shouted up at the Captain, who shook his

head indicating he could not hear.

'She's escaped!' Amir shouted again.

'What?' The officer lifted the headset from one ear – saw Sharon turn and wave, then stand with hands on hips waiting for him to depart.

'The Dayak, she's gone!' Amir called even louder.

'What do you mean, she's gone?' Subandi yelled, his face creased with alarm.

The soldier climbed up into the cabin. *'We had her ready. One moment she was there, the next she wasn't!'* he shouted.

His superior's face clouded with anger then, with each exclamation, banged his fist fiercely against the metal panel alongside as he screamed, *'Shit! Shit! Shit!'* He ripped the headset completely away, and turned on the trooper, his voice spilling venom as his hand dropped to a holstered weapon. *'You useless bastards, you should both be shot!'*

The soldier reeled back. *'We'll get her back, Captain. It's only just happened. We'd caught a glimpse of her running through the forest towards the other side of the island.'*

'Tell her to remain where she is.' He jabbed a finger at Sharon. *'You get back with Agus and flush the bitch out. She's not about to break from cover. I'll meet you over on the other side of the wooded area. Now get cracking!'*

Subandi waited until Amir had returned to Sharon's side and relayed his instructions. He could not see the Filipino's face but, from the manner in which she tossed her hat to the ground and then stomped the Akubra, he knew she understood what had gone wrong. The helicopter lifted, the engine pitch changing immediately from a whining flutter to a chopping roar as it climbed to five hundred feet, and hovered.

★ ★ ★ ★

Sharon stamped her foot in frustration, angered by the soldiers' incompetent handling of their prisoner. It had all been going so perfectly – and now this! She bent down, dusted off her hat then stood with arms crossed, glaring into space. Something startled her from behind and she turned, her eyes opening wide with shock when the *Penehing* pounced, dragging her into the bushes before she could offer any resistance.

'Get her hat!' The Akubra had fallen to the ground. *'Now, get moving!'* she heard someone say. Sharon's cry for help choked dry in her throat as she tried to scream, now struggling desperately as the Dayak men dragged her even further into the island's minute, but densely vegetated forest.

'Where…where are you taking me?' she shouted, but was ignored by the men who rushed her through the thick undergrowth, her face and arms bearing the brunt of virgin bush. *'Please! Where are you taking me?'* she panicked, her long, painful cry lost on them all. Relentless, the *Penehing* men forged ahead, following a familiar trail through the sacred forest, conscious of the helicopter hovering above. Sharon tumbled, and they dragged her roughly to her feet, and when she deliberately dropped to the ground, deadweight, the men also took this in their stride. They scooped their captive up and lifted her onto their shoulders as one would a log, continuing with their mission until reaching the far side of the island. There they set her down, and the earth spun under her feet. She fell – someone grabbed her arms, and expertly tied her hands behind. She rolled to one side and peered up, splinters of light danced across her eyes, distorting her vision – and then heard someone call her name.

'Hello, Sharon.'

She recognized the voice, and was immediately confused. 'Is that you, Angela?'

'What did she say?' one of the *Penehing* asked, but was shushed by another.

'Angela?' Sharon's voice remained shaky. 'What do they want with me?'

'We don't have much time, Sharon,' Angela persevered in English. 'Why is it so important to have me killed?'

'Killed? Why would I want you killed?' She maintained the pretense – her confidence slipping to an all time low.

'It's too late, Sharon. We already know most of it.'

'Please, Angela, this is insane. Untie me!'

'Not until you tell me what I want to know.'

'I swear, I haven't a clue to what you're talking about!'

'Liar!' Jonathan bent down and hit the Filipino with a brutal, backhander.

Sharon felt the salty taste of blood in her mouth. Even though she recognized the hopelessness of the situation and was terrified of what they might do to her, she did not give up hope. 'I don't know what you've been told,' her mouth hurt, and she spoke with a quiet desperation. 'When you went missing, the army agreed to send a helicopter in search for you.'

'Stop it!' Angela kicked Sharon in the ribs, the pain instantly robbing the woman of breath. 'The soldier has already told us the plan, Sharon. What we want to know, is why?'

Swamped with pain, Sharon realized that her situation was perilous. Her only chance was to admit nothing, feign ignorance, and hope for the best. She groaned, opened her eyes, and struggled to speak. 'I'm…telling you…the truth.'

'Angela, we don't have time. The pilot will become suspicious if we don't show our faces.'

'On your feet, Sharon, it's time for you to go.'

'Go? You're… letting… me… go?' She lay on one side, hoping her hands would be untied.

'No, Sharon, you're going for a ride.' Angela paused, moving to within inches of the other woman's face, hate burning from deep inside. 'A helicopter ride!'

Sharon was dragged to her feet. Her knees buckled with the terrifying realization of what lay in store. 'No, Angela…! No… you can't! Angela, please!' And in desperation, 'Angela, I… have money…lots… and lots of money. I will share…it with you. Please, Angela, Please…' Her words finished mid-sentence, and suddenly she couldn't breathe – the gag wrapped tightly around the lower part of her face, also designed to disguise.

'Quickly, the jewelry!' She felt the rings pressed onto fingers, these now representing her engagement with death, and with the touch of metal against skin when the ankle-bracelet was affixed, she started to

shake uncontrollably.

'Amir, are you ready?' Jonathan Dau gripped their prisoner under the shoulder, Amir on the other side. She recognized the *Kopassus* insignia, and knew that this couldn't be right. Her panicked eyes darted from the shaman to Angela, then back again, searching for an answer.

'My father will see you on your way.' Angela paused. 'Goodbye, Sharon.'

Sharon's muffled plea brought no response. *'Put the hat on,'* she heard somebody say. Overhead, the impatient, chopping sounds of a helicopter on the move signaled it was time. Doubled in pain, and secured on either side by powerful hands, Sharon's unwilling body was half-carried, half-dragged, out onto the natural river-sandbank where they were spotted by the chopper pilot.

★ ★ ★ ★

Cursing his two men for Angela's escape, Subandi flew over the immediate area again, stymied as to what might have happened to them all. Not only had he lost visual contact with the soldiers and their prey, but Sharon Ducay as well. He concluded that she had joined in the chase, deciding to give his current position another five minutes and, if they failed to appear, he would return to the location where Sharon had disembarked, and wait for them there.

Subandi's grip on the cyclic control firmed as an abrupt wind change challenged the hovering helicopter, lateral stability maintained as he manipulated the collective and foot pedals to position the Huey directly above the deserted stretch of exposed, river sand. Droplets rolled down the pilot's brow momentarily blinding, and he cursed loudly, wiping sweat-stung eyes with the back of his torn flying suit as he struggled to identify movement through the thick, jungle canopy, fifty meters below. His alarm growing, the pilot permitted the chopper to drift as he continued to search for signs of his party, relief sweeping across his face when he spotted the men breaking from the dense jungle, dragging the woman he believed to be Angela Dau towards the narrow, treeless strip near the water's edge. Without hesitation, he decreased the main rotor's lift, the hasty descent resulting in his approaching passengers' near decapitation as whirling blades drove the placid, silicon-laden carpet below into a maelstrom of stinging, blinding river-sand.

Dressed in the dead soldier's uniform, Jonathan, assisted by Amir, dragged Sharon Ducay across the shallow water and onto the sandbank, the soft, dry surface tugging at their heavy boots, under an August sky. Subandi kept the approaching trio under surveillance, shaking his head when a gust from the helicopter blew the hat from their captive's head, and one of the soldiers chased after the Akubra, as it cart wheeled away.

Jonathan Dau used the organized distraction to drag Sharon closer to the chopper. He tightened his painful grip on her upper arm and turned her away from view, elbowing her savagely in the stomach to be sure. Amir gave up the chase, ran back to rejoin Jonathan, waving to his Captain when close enough to be identified. The officer raised a fist at the trooper, Amir glancing down nervously at Jonathan's sidearm which, unlike his own, was loaded.

'No tricks!' the Dayak chief warned, prepared for any play. *'Now help me lift her!'*

They reached the helicopter, bundled their captive into the rear compartment, and climbed inside. The pilot glanced back, acknowledged the chief's thumbs-up, lifted the aircraft into the air, then drove the Bell 205 to five thousand feet as he headed for the nearby timber concession, and the designated drop zone.

★ ★ ★ ★

Angela observed the shenanigans with dispassionate calm and, once the helicopter was lost from sight, signaled for one of the men to retrieve the wide-brimmed hat. Then, distasteful as she found it to be, Angela dressed in the clothes originally meant to be worn at her own death. She squeezed into the tight fitting jodhpurs and khaki jacket, then made her way back through the forest, to where she'd been instructed to wait.

★ ★ ★ ★

Fifteen minutes out, Sharon lay in desperate state, part of her silently screaming with the unfairness of it all, the rest consciously willing the pilot to do something – anything – that would save her. The solider who had betrayed them sat with head on knees, Sharon taking the opportunity to lash out, her heel striking Amir squarely on the side of his head as he sat quietly considering where the aluminum case containing his share of the gold bars might be. The soldier's head snapped to one side colliding with metal airframe. Blood poured from the wound, Amir's vision blurred, giving Sharon yet another opportunity to strike. She kicked out, again, her resistance brought to an end when Jonathan Dau pounced, and straddled her legs, opening the wound on his thigh. She summoned whatever strength remained and raised her head off the floor, her hate-filled eyes widening as the muffled words 'Fuck you!' formed in her mouth, her stifled rage unable to penetrate the choking gag.

The *Penehing* shaman bent forward until Sharon could smell his wild breath, panicking even more when he placed his mouth against her ear. 'Why do you want to die?' Sharon felt the heat of his body, his hand on her face, her nostrils filling with the stench of death. She clenched her eyes, but its presence lingered, Jonathan's fingers lifting the lower edge of the cloth enabling Sharon to answer. 'Tell me why my daughter was to die in your place, and your life will be spared.' And then, to be sure, he asked her again in *Bahasa Indonesia*.

Sharon heard the words, her desire to live unquestionable. Praying that she might survive this ordeal, she responded with amazing calm. 'I meant no… harm,' she gasped, her voice barely audible as the Bell 205 thumped along, Jonathan's ear pressed close to her mouth. 'My uncle died… and the Longdamai operation was taken over… by others… It seemed that I was to have nothing.' Jonathan's thumbs opened the gap even further – Sharon blinked, thankfully, and returned to character. 'The company… would pay millions in insurance… if I died while… under contract. It was the pilot's idea to use… Angela.' She coughed, and a cracked rib sent a fierce, stabbing pain through her chest. She gritted, sucking air through her teeth. Then, painfully, 'He was… to kill her… in my place.' Seizing the opportunity, she mentioned the gold. 'Please…please…don't… kill me! If you let…me go…I can give you…gold.'

Jonathan ignored her offer. 'This pilot is your partner?'

'Yes,' she struggled, again starting to choke. 'We…we were to…share… the benefits.'

Jonathan's lips moved back to her ear. 'And if you were the one to die?'

With the realization that she'd been tricked, Sharon choked with rage, venom twisting her once beautiful face into a grotesque mask. The chief tugged the gag back in place, his prisoner struggling with all her might to be free.

The helicopter chopped its way through light, clear-air turbulence – Sharon's head coming into contact with an extended harness bolt rising from the reinforced, plated floor. Feigning total surrender, she let her muscles go limp. Jonathan waited for a few minutes then, satisfied that she had completed her course and could now offer only minimum resistance, slid away, and regained his canvas seat.

The Bell dipped, shuddered, the turbulence cracking the back of her head against the floor and she came close to losing consciousness. Out of the corner of an eye she could see the bolt. And, with each movement of the helicopter as it bumped sluggishly along, she drew closer and closer until finally, she could feel it's firmness against her cheek. Sharon closed her eyes, her head following the aircraft's sway until the bolt was caught firmly, underneath the gag. Blood flowed down the hidden cheek, and she knew this would be her only chance to attract Subandi's attention. Sharon inhaled, deeply, through her nose, then with a snap of her head down and to her left, drove the bolt up through the flesh of her cheek, dangerously close to puncturing an eye. Leveraging the cloth loose from one side of her mouth, she screamed, *'Subandi! Help me! It's Sharon!'*

Jonathan reacted spontaneously and lunged, his hand groping at Sharon's bloody face, the once beautiful Filipino kicking and screaming for her very life until he hit her squarely on the jaw, and her body went limp. The gag was hurriedly removed, and her hands untied.

The pilot heard nothing of the commotion, of course. Even without headphones it was unlikely that Sharon's shrieks would have reached his ears. Subandi reached back from the cockpit and tapped against the half partition for attention. With the signal indicating that they were there, Jonathan opened the sliding hatch, and tossed her semi-conscious body into space. Watching as she tumbled earthwards towards the slashed and burned forest floor below, the shaman offered a prayer, thanking ancestral spirits for his daughter's delivery from the hands of this wretched woman, known as Sharon Ducay.

Captain Subandi had also followed 'Angela's' body falling as it disappeared through space, relieved that it was all over. He had never before participated in the senseless killing of women – even during his tours in East Timor. He stared down into the empty void unable to see the burnt plains below, suddenly filled with an unexplainable sense of loss. Then, with a philosophical shrug to counter his annoying attack of conscience, he turned the chopper back and retraced their steps, to collect Sharon. With more than adequate fuel reserves to continue onto Samarinda, Subandi would deliver Sharon to her rendezvous off the coast before noon – then return to the provincial capital to confirm 'her' tragic suicide. The pilot smiled, selecting the appropriate communications channel as he prepared to break the news of 'Sharon Ducay's' death, and minutes later he was relaying the somber story with convincing embellishment.

★ ★ ★ ★

The Bell 205's skids hit the ground hard, Subandi stretching his neck and snapping at the two troopers back in the main cabin even before the aircraft settled. *'Go and find her!'*

Amir saluted, '*Yes sir!'*, opened the sliding hatch and hit the ground running, Jonathan Dau, his head still covered with the regulation issue, wide-brimmed, camouflage bush hat followed – Captain Subandi still none the wiser that the second soldier was an imposter.

'Keep running!' the chief ordered, hard on Amir's heels. No sooner had they disappeared into the thick underbrush, than the *Penehing* chief called for him to halt. *'You have done well, Amir.'*

The *Kopassus* soldier removed his floppy hat and wiped an arm across his brow. *'What happens next?'* he asked, aware they were no longer alone.

Jonathan stepped away from Udir's line of sight. *'As promised, now we'll send you home.'*

Amir sighed, tensed muscles blessed with relief, the look of surprise grotesquely evident across his face when his head parted company with the rest of his body, and hit the ground with a sickening thud. Angela, who had never once witnessed a traditional execution stood locked by the bloody extravaganza as exposed jugular sprayed fountains of blood, everywhere.

'Place his body with the other one,' Jonathan ordered, *'then come with me.'*

★ ★ ★ ★

The pilot kept the Bell 205's, one-thousand-kilowatt Lycoming engine turning over, his impatience growing exponentially with each antagonizing minute.

They had flown over the river island, hovering whenever he caught a glimpse of movement, but the woman he had returned for was nowhere to be seen. The Captain checked his fuel – satisfied that he remained within acceptable limits, then settled back to wait for his men to reappear. Twenty minutes passed before Subandi accepted that something had gone terribly wrong, and he closed the chopper down, then waited. Another hour dragged slowly by – he climbed out of the '205 to relieve himself, somebody waving from amongst the trees finally caught his attention. Unlike their *Kostrad* counterparts who carried 9mm Beretta 92Fs in a shoulder holster, the elitist *Kopassus* flyers concealed their handguns. He reached down and checked the stainless steel, .45 caliber, 'DAO Backup' strapped to the inside of his leg, then walked slowly towards the tall figure standing at the forest's edge.

'Don't come any closer!' Jonathan Dau warned, now back in his own clothes. Suddenly, four others were at his side.

Dayaks! Subandi froze, a sickening feeling rising as his mind became congested with runaway fears. *Had they kidnapped his woman?*

'What do you want?' He found the courage to call.

'We just want to talk. Stay there and we'll approach.' Jonathan had reason to keep the pilot where he was.

'Who are you?' Subandi tried again, his feet slowly shuffling in the direction of the helicopter.

'Jonathan Dau, Chief of the Penehing and this is my land. Are you carrying a weapon?'

Subandi ignored the insolent man. Instead, he demanded, *'Where is the woman?'*

'The foreigner with skin like us?'

'Yes,' Subandi broke out into a sweat, ready to turn and run if they attacked.

'We are going to keep her hostage,' the chief lied.

'Hostage?' the pilot ceased his slow retreat. *At least she was still alive!*

'Yes.'

The Captain's mind started its slow descent into hell. *'Where are my men?'*

'We sent them home.'

Subandi guessed what this meant. *'They're dead?'*

'Yes,' followed the monosyllabic reply.

'Why?'

'Because they were Kopassus.' The shaman raised his hand and pointed towards where the Longhouse once stood. *'Kopassus attacked the Penehing.'*

The pilot calculated the distance to the chopper, and considered escape. Mentally, he counted off the time it would take to start the engine and get the bird airborne, and his shoulders slumped in defeat. Then he remembered Sharon's briefcase.

'Produce the woman and I'll give you gold!' he offered.

'How much gold?' the chief came back. Angela, out of sight but still within earshot, frowned. *What was her father playing at?*

'Two kilos,' Sharon's aluminum briefcase remained in '205's cabin. Her original plan called for Subandi to use the contents to pay off his men.

'That's not enough.'

The pilot was chilled by the cold dispassion displayed on the other man's face. *'That's all I have.'*

'You have it here?' Jonathan and the four *Penehing* started forward.

'In the aircraft.' Subandi knew the risk he was taking revealing that the gold was onboard. *'I'll get it for you.'*

'No, stay where you are,' the chief raised his voice, *'or my men will shoot!'*

The Captain glanced over his shoulder. It was obvious he was considering escape.

'Don't be foolish. Come, let's talk!' Jonathan said something to the others who remained standing where they were, while the chief advanced towards the pilot.

'Where have you taken the woman?' Subandi nervously stood his ground.

'*She is still here.*'

'*Show her to me!*'

'Not yet, first we talk.' Jonathan approached the *Kopassus* Captain. *'You can have the woman back if you pay the ransom.'*

Subandi's natural reaction was to threaten, as trained. Under any other circumstances he would have a hundred crack troops pouring over this area within hours. *'Dayaks don't kidnap for ransom,'* he challenged, *'why are you doing this?'*

Jonathan Dau stared the man down. *'Once, I was a pilot, like you. Now I am a kidnapper.'*

The Captain was unsure how to treat this man. *'You were a pilot?'*

The chief watched the other man's face. *'MIGs,'* then left the rest hanging.

Subandi eye's narrowed. *'What happened?'*

'*You don't want to talk anymore about your woman?*'

'*All I have is the gold.*'

'*It's not enough. We want a million dollars.*'

'What?' Subandi, staggered with the suggestion, *'Where would a pilot get a million dollars?'*

'I don't know,' Jonathan answered, solemnly. *'But that's what it's going to take to get your woman back.'*

'The amount's absurd!'

'Call it reparations, for what your corps has done to my people.'

'I don't have that sort of money – just the gold!'

Jonathan registered that the Captain had not refuted the accusation. His heart became stone. *'I'll give you three months – then she dies.'*

Subandi could not believe his ears. *Why wasn't this man listening? 'I need to take her with me now.'*

'No, she goes with us into the mountains; another precaution against your doing something stupid. When you have the money, come back here. My men will then contact you.'

'It's impossible. You're crazy to believe I can raise that sort of money!'

'You'll think of something.'

'Not on an air force salary – look, there has to be another way?'

'No.'

The pilot shook his head at the stupidity of this man. *'It's an impossible sum. Where would I get a million dollars?'*

'Perhaps from your girlfriend's family?'

Jonathan raised his fist and waved, Subandi removing his sunglasses for a clearer view into the shadowy forest. An older man appeared with his prisoner, at this distance the pilot was unable to see that it was Angela Dau, her hair tied away from the neck and hidden by the wide-brimmed hat. She was dressed in the familiar jodhpurs and sleeveless jacket and he immediately recognized the Akubra – his mind failing to question how this could be there. The pilot broke into a run, calling her name, Jonathan raising outstretched arms, blocking his path. *'Stop, or she dies now!'*

'Sharon?' Subandi yelled, his stomach churning when Udir appeared to handle his captive roughly, forcing her back behind the first line of trees. *'Where's he taking her?*

'You have to ask her family for the money.'

'How would I know if they have such an amount?'

'She has told us all.'

'About what?' The pilot feigned ignorance.

'About how you were to share the insurance.' It was obvious from the collapsed expression on Subandi's face that the chief had scored.

He continued with his fishing expedition. *'So, if you want her back, you will have to pay us, one million. I understand these things. It will take time before the insurance company pays, that is why we will give you three months. If you don't agree to our demands, we shall cut off her head.'*

Subandi gasped, his face turning white. *'I can't get the money without her help. I'm not sure what it is that I have to do!'*

'You will have to find a way.'

'Please. Let me talk to her, just for a moment?'

'No. Now you must leave.'

'You don't understand, I have to ask her what to do!'

'Contact her family in the Philippines,' Jonathan suggested.

'I cannot leave without talking to her. Please, I beg you.'

'If you want her, come back with the money.'

In desperation, *'I'll give you the gold I have in the aircraft if you just let me speak to her for a minute?'*

Jonathan's mouth turned into a cruel smile. *'I'm going to take that, anyway.'*

'You've got to let me speak to her!'

The *Penehing* chief continued to ignore his pleas. *'We require that you contact us at the end of each month. You are to come here, or send someone with a report on how it is all proceeding. If you miss the first month, we will remove her ears – the second month, her tongue. Who knows, we may even reconsider what to do if you miss the third month as well. We could always send her back to the authorities. Might be very embarrassing if you were required to explain how she came to be still alive, Captain?'*

Subandi knew he had lost – game, set, match. The Dayak had the woman he so desperately loved – and there was nothing he could do to remedy the situation. He raised his head and called out to the woman he'd just seen. *'Sharon, don't give up hope! I'll get them the money. Wherever you are, I'll find you!'* He waved, hoping she would see. A midmorning breeze gently tilted the Bell 205's main rotor blades as it passed, unseen. Beaten, the Javanese pilot faced Jonathan with surrender in his eyes. *'All right, you bastard – I'll do what you ask. I'll contact her family in Manila, and tell them the score.'* And then, threateningly, *'But, when I return, if Sharon has been harmed in any way…'*

'*Good,*' Dau interrupted, extremely pleased with himself. '*You know what is required. If you want her back in one piece, don't let us down. Now, I'll have that gold you spoke of.*'

★ ★ ★ ★

Without Sharon, Subandi decided there was no longer any justification for continuing his flight to Samarinda. However, in order to maintain credibility with respect to the 'accident', the pilot was still obliged to carry out the charade, deciding that everyone's interests could be best served should he return directly to the mining camp and submit his report from there. He climbed back into the cockpit and started the Bell's engine, his eyes locked on the man standing, watching him prepare for takeoff, their unspoken exchange filled with hate. The helicopter vibrated and shook, then lifted, wallowing momentarily, Subandi turning the aircraft recklessly, the tail rotor blades coming precariously close to where an unflinching Jonathan Dau stood. The chopper hovered and the engine pitch changed, the pilot's anger growing as he flew a circuitous route back to the Longdamai mining camp, where the fiasco had first been conceived – in the process, forgetting to alert the ship's crew off the Samarinda coastline that he wouldn't be delivering their precious cargo.

★ ★ ★ ★

Jonathan followed the helicopter until it disappeared from sight then signaled the others to follow. When Angela reached his side the chief handed her the aluminum case. '*We'll use this to buy food and clothes from neighboring communities, for our people. Come, we don't have much time.*' He led them along the riverbank to where so many of their fellow villagers had been slaughtered, the riverside scene smothered with knee-deep ash, burnt stumps all that was left of the once massive, timber structure. Carrion birds reluctantly abandoning their feast to take flight, circled patiently, high above the intruders – the suffocating smell of burnt flesh permeating the air causing Angela to tear a strip from Sharon's blouse, and cover her nose.

'*We will send another party down later, and they can gather anything which may still be of use.'*

Moving through the ashes in quiet introspection, stepping over unidentifiable remains, Angela relived the terror when the soldiers attacked and torched their home, the enormity of what had transpired chiseled into her mind with each charred body discovered.

'When we rebuild, will it be here? Angela viewed the devastation, once so filled with meaningful memories.

'That will be up to the council to decide. But first, we have dead to farewell.'

Angela understood that she would be expected to assist her father with these rites. *'Tell me what it is that you want me to do, Father.'*

Disturbed, the shaman glanced at his daughter standing amongst the ruins, her face blotted with tears. Before this, she had always called him *'Papa'* and, at that moment, Jonathan felt the weight of his mortality.

His body ached all over and the wound to his leg had started bleeding through the filthy bandage again. And, as far as the eye could see in one direction, there was nothing but ashes – and the bones of the two hundred plus who had perished.

★ ★ ★ ★

Off the Coast of Samarinda

The *M.V. Rager* lay off the East Kalimantan coast in a calm sea, the occasional slapping against the hull a reminder of the gigantic oil and gas vessels that plied the Makasar Straits. The ship's gaunt and bearded captain, Bartlett, leaned lazily up against the wheelhouse maintaining surveillance with a beer in one hand and 8 x 30DIF Nikon binoculars in the other. He finished the San Miguel and threw the crushed can forward into the open hold, adjusted the Nikon's focus then casually scanned the sky again, before returning to his maritime observations.

The small, coastal trader had sailed from the southern Filipino port city of Zamboanga on the Moro Gulf, southwest, along the northern reaches of the scattered Sulu Archipelago, before turning south and entering the Celebes Sea. At this point, the ship left the Philippines' territorial waters, and entered Indonesia, continuing on its five-day journey past Tarakan, Tanjungbatu and Talok. Three hundred miles south, the *Rager* had Southern Borneo's Tanjung Mangkalihat off the starboard side, and the towering summit of Sulawesi's Gunung Ogoamas, just fifty miles off port.

The mercenary ran a hand through thinned hair, leaned inside and listened to the communications' broadcast in the Indonesian language. Although it had been many years since the former ASIS operative and expatriate entrepreneur had reason to call upon his Indonesian language skills, the man, who in an earlier life had been known as Stephen Coleman never lost this asset. He switched to another frequency and concentrated on the military traffic. An hour passed then another. Bartlett squinted up at the midday sun, then went in search of another beer to pass the time while he waited for the helicopter carrying Sharon Ducay to arrive.

He scratched his scalp out of nervous habit, his nails following the scarred indentation on the side of his head – a souvenir of his past, left as a constant reminder of a friend who had treacherously betrayed him. Over the years Bartlett had in no way mellowed. He had killed, and on occasion, almost been killed. Now, his persona had evolved into borderline anchoritic, which more suited his lesser, gregarious needs.

As owner-operator of the vessel, he enjoyed contracts that required no other crew, these voyages often taking him to less salubrious ports throughout S.E Asia. Bartlett accepted charters to Vietnam's southernmost coastline where he would deliver contraband and sometimes take on those who wished to leave that perpetual communist regime, or even transport weapons to the Moro Liberation Front and other separatist groups. Apolitical to the core, Bartlett followed the dollar, many of his better paying deals originating with the CIA, or their allies in the area, which included the late General Narciso Dominguez.

Bartlett had first come into contact with the General years before when there was a need to mount an expedition to recover gold from a Philippines Air Force C130 which had crashed, killing Dominguez's brother. The aircraft had been on loan to the PAF from the USAF at the time, the tragic disaster leaving two hundred million dollars' worth of gold bars lost somewhere on the bottom of the South China Sea. The operation had not been successful, abandoned after six months, due to heightened activity in the target area when China, Vietnam, Malaysia and the Philippines saber-rattled over ownership of the Spratly Islands.

It had been General Dominguez's trusted aide, Alfredo, who had organized for Sharon's lightning visit to meet with him in Zamboanga. Once Bartlett had learned of the mission he had declined the lucrative offer citing his unwillingness to have any contact with the Indonesian military. Sharon had been persuasive, the advance of one hundred thousand dollars in gold bars was accepted and Bartlett went on standby, pending further instructions to be relayed via Alfredo.

Finally, when he received notification from Manila that Sharon's window of opportunity was imminent, he immediately set sail for East Kalimantan. Nearing his destination, he had avoided Bontang and Santan as these coastal towns were natural gas processing centers, dropping anchor several miles offshore from Muara Badak, on the northern tip of the mighty Mahakam's massive estuary system. As agreed, Bartlett then waited for the signal that Sharon was on her way, the helicopter pilot's report of 'her' tragic fall galvanizing the mercenary into a state of readiness. He lowered the rubber dinghy then remained alert, waiting for her to arrive, her failure to do so generating uneasiness in his gut.

The day wore on and the next passed without incident. Bartlett couldn't be absolutely certain that the report he had intercepted was, in fact, the signal he'd been waiting for and remained alert, monitoring further broadcasts throughout the day. That evening, as was his custom, Bartlett tuned into the BBC's international news broadcasts, which carried the news of Sharon's demise.

'And now, a report just in from our Canadian correspondent. A Baron Mining spokesperson had revealed that, today, Sharon Ducay, Chief Geologist for what has been mooted as possibly the world's largest gold discovery, has died. Miss Ducay, who was responsible for the Borneo Gold Corporation's multi-billion dollar discovery in the Indonesian, Borneo province of East Kalimantan, was reported as having fallen from a helicopter whilst traveling from the mining site, on the first leg of her journey home. Authorities are treating the incident as an accident. Today, the Borneo Gold Corporation's shares closed slightly lower with the announcement. On other news...'

Bartlett had expected this breaking story, as it was his responsibility to smuggle the 'dead' geologist out of Indonesia, and back to the Philippines. What he was not prepared for, however, was her failure to appear. He would wait with growing impatience for a further forty-eight hours then set sail for Zamboanga, leaving Sharon Ducay behind.

★ ★ ★ ★

Chapter Twenty-eight

Captain Subandi knew immediately upon sighting the *Kostrad* Colonel standing alongside Stewart Campbell, that his decision to return directly to the mining site had been wise. He jumped from the Bell-205, the rotors still turning sluggishly, and hurried towards his superior with every eye in camp glued to his arrival. Most, if not all of the Madurese and other workers had gathered, now staring at his helicopter, waiting to see if Sharon might still be alive. When she failed to appear, the workers turned their attention to the pilot.

'Is it true?' The Colonel craned his neck, peering in the direction of the Huey.

'Yes, sir, I'm sorry, it is.'

'How did it happen?'

'We were traveling along at around ninety-five knots and hit clear air turbulence. Miss Ducay had been off color and asked if we could land, I started to take her down when she unlocked the cabin hatch. Colonel, I swear, I thought she wanted to throw up. She jumped without warning. There was nothing I could do.'

'Where did this happen?'

The pilot had anticipated the question and unrolled the map in his left hand. *'Here. I took a quick run over the site, then reported the accident to base.'*

'Colonel, we have to retrieve her remains. There will be an inquiry.' Campbell stood grim-faced, with hands in pockets, still coming to terms with Sharon's demise.

'Captain, I want you to take Mister Stewart and a couple of men, and recover the foreigner's body.'

'Yes, sir,' Subandi had expected this would be required. *'I'll do it now,'* he agreed, with an appropriate suggestion of sadness to his voice.

Campbell spotted Baird standing alone under a tree and called out, 'Want to join us, Eric?' but this was greeted with a slow shaking of his head.

'I'll organize the men,' Subandi saluted the Colonel. *'We'll leave immediately,'* this, for Campbell's consumption.

'I'm ready.'

The Colonel reminded the pilot, as he was about to walk away. *'And Captain, don't forget the body bag.'*

★ ★ ★ ★

Campbell looked out in the direction of Bukit Batubrok, the unspeakable emptiness he then experienced by Sharon Ducay's death exacerbated by the knowledge that Angela Dau remained somewhere amongst those distant foothills. Bewildered by her sudden departure he decided to go in search of Angela once Sharon's body had been recovered, and put to rest.

The flight to where Sharon had met her demise did not take all that long and over the site and at five hundred feet, Stewart Campbell could see the *kampung* dogs gathered, enjoying their feast. He felt his stomach churn and the blood leave his face, but held on, forcing deep breaths into his lungs, preparing himself for the grisly find. They landed, Captain Subandi taking one of the trooper's rifles and shooting into the air, scattering the scavengers.

'That would be what's left of her,' the officer stepped slowly towards the ravaged and mutilated corpse. Campbell froze, felt faint, turned and staggered in another direction, gagging as he tried to escape the disgusting sight. *'Mister Campbell,'* Subandi called, cruelly, *'Do you*

want to identify the remains before my men put them into a body bag?'

The American knew that he should, but was in no way prepared for what lay there. He nodded, stepped back slowly, a handkerchief to his mouth as he approached what had once been a staggeringly, beautiful woman and was now nothing more than a crumpled, bloody mound of torn and pounded flesh. Again, he retched. Then, with his back to the scene, *'It's impossible to tell.'*

'What about the rings?' Although Subandi also struggled to overcome his own disgust at the gruesome mess, he was, nevertheless, enjoying the subterfuge and deceit of the game. *'You knew her better than any of us,'* he persisted, *'would you say that these are hers?'*

Campbell willed his eyes to look. The Captain was crouched, pointing with a stick at what once resembled a hand. *'I don't know,'* the American said, choking on bile, *'it could be.'*

'If not, who else could it be?' Subandi smirked to himself with the knowledge that Campbell had no idea that it was his girlfriend, Angela Dau, lying there. *'I don't have women jumping out of my aircraft every day of the week, Mister Campbell. What about these trousers she always wore, wouldn't you say that these are hers?'*

Again Campbell forced his eyes back, recognizing the remains of what had obviously been Sharon's familiar jodhpurs. One of the soldiers bent down, and recovered something from a piece of bone and flesh.

'Captain?' he held a bloody ankle-bracelet in the air.

Subandi raised the bracelet on the end of the stick, examining the piece. Satisfied, he lifted the bracelet for the foreigner to see. *'What do you think?'*

Campbell was close to fainting. *'I guess you're right,'* he muttered, then turned and retreated, making his way back to the helicopter, left with the haunting images of what lay behind.

The soldiers bundled what remains there were into a body bag and loaded their find. Campbell asked if he could sit forward, alongside the pilot, taking the very seat from which Sharon had supposedly fallen. They returned to the mining camp and, once on the ground, the American climbed down from the cockpit, and challenged Captain Subandi.

'What happened to the woman's personal effects?

The pilot raised his eyebrows. *'She didn't have any.'*

Campbell's muscles tightened with anger. *'When she left, Sharon was carrying a briefcase.'*

Subandi frowned. What with everything else cluttering his mind, he had overlooked this very important item. Had all gone according to plan, the briefcase would still be sitting in the cockpit, less the gold it contained.

'It must have fallen out as well.'

'You didn't see it happen?' Campbell's voice reflected scorn.

'No, I didn't. I was flying a helicopter in unstable conditions, a woman jumps to her death and you expect me to remember something as unimportant as…'

'Jumped? Did you say Sharon jumped?'

'That's not what I meant,' Subandi looked over Campbell's shoulders for help.

The *Kostrad* Colonel approached. *'Is that it?'* he demanded, observing soldiers unloading Sharon's remains.

Subandi saluted. *'Yes, Colonel.'*

'Mister Campbell, are you satisfied?'

The American locked eyes with the pilot. He knew the man was lying about the briefcase. Apart from personal diaries and correspondence, he doubted if there would have been anything of any real value inside. Since Sharon's departure that morning, he had learned of her generosity in dividing her personal effects amongst the poorer, Madurese women who lived and worked with the laborers. That there was now some suggestion that Sharon might have deliberately thrown herself out of the aircraft was of some concern, particularly as this might impact on Baron Mining's position with respect to the operation. However, as it was obvious that the Captain had stolen the briefcase and, as so little could be gained by pursuing the matter, Campbell decided to let it go. *'Terima kasih, Pak Kolonel,'* he answered, formally thanking the officer, *'with your permission I would like to use our radiophone facilities to talk to my office in Canada, so that they might contact the deceased's family in Manila?'*

'Boleh, silahkan,' the Colonel agreed. *'And if you require further use*

of the Captain's services, Mister Campbell, he will be here, on standby.'

'In that case, Colonel, I would like to start ferrying some of the expatriates from the site to Samarinda. They should be sent back to Jakarta if you have no objections?'

'The situation downriver is still volatile, but I can't see any further reason to keep them here. Will you be leaving as well?'

'Unfortunately, no – I still have unfinished business to attend to.'

★ ★ ★ ★

Vancouver

'Chris? It's Phil Samuels.'

Christopher Fielding peered through sleepy eyes at the bedside clock. It was past midnight, and he had been dozing, the call startling the CEO from his soporific state. 'Phil?' Fielding's brain struggled slowly into gear. 'God! Do you have any idea what time it is?'

'Chris, listen! I've some bad news for you.'

The BGC President immediately came alive. 'What's happened?'

'It's your Filipino geologist, Sharon Ducay. She's had an accident.'

'Accident?'

'Yes. Stewart Campbell, our guy on the ground over in Indonesia just called it in.'

'What happened?' Fielding was now wide-awake, his fingers fumbling with an unopened packet of cigarettes.

'She fell out of a chopper.'

'What?'

'It's true. Apparently she was on her way out, returning home to the Philippines or coming over to settle up with you guys when the chopper hit turbulence and she fell out, somehow.'

'Jesus!'

Samuels visualized Fielding shaking his head in disbelief. 'Sure is a first, Chris. How the fuck someone can simply fall out of a helicopter beats the shit outa me!'

'Are you sure?'

'Well, if it had been phoned in by anyone else but Campbell, I would've waited for further confirmation before calling. As far as I'm concerned, the man's completely reliable.'

'Shit!'

'Yeah, I know. It's a real bummer. Were you close?'

Fielding drew heavily on the cigarette then exhaled. It was only then that he noticed his hand was shaking. 'No, not really.'

'Sorry to be the one to break the news, Chris – will you inform her family?'

'Sure, thanks Phil, I'll go into the office and get some numbers now. Appreciate the call.'

* * * *

Alexander Kremenchug paced, wringing his hands. 'It's not possible!' he continued to rant, Christopher Fielding staring out the window into space, unaware of the arrangements in place between his fellow director and the late Sharon Ducay. 'God, we're screwed!'

'The company has no liability,' Fielding misunderstood, 'she was under contract. It's not our problem.'

'Jesus Christ! I'm not interested in any piddling insurance claim, Chris!'

'Knock it off, Alex. I was as fond of Sharon as you. And, I agree, we both owe her a great deal. If it hadn't been for...'

'Shut up, Chris!' Kremenchug snapped, 'you have no idea what I'm talking about.'

'Easy, Alex,' Fielding turned from the window, and the evening sky beyond. 'It's not going to make much difference to the stock.'

'Screw the stock!' Kremenchug ceased pacing, his breath short, overwhelmed by the gravity of Sharon's demise.

Fielding had called him at his hotel to break the news, Kremenchug agreeing to meet in the BGC offices to discuss the ramifications of Sharon's death. He had hurried down the quiet city street, his mind unable to accept the enormity of what this loss would mean to his pocket. Without her, he stood to lose tens of millions, his share of the proceeds generated from the sale of BGC stock. He felt faint.

'Any idea what time is in the Philippines?' Fielding had scribbled down some numbers while waiting for his associate to arrive.

Kremenchug ignored the question, refusing to come to terms with the fact that Sharon was gone. 'Are you absolutely sure there's been no mistake?'

'Samuels was sure. Says Campbell saw the body.'

'Campbell? Stewart Campbell?'

'Yes. Seems he's now on Baron's payroll.'

'Shit!'

'Look, Alex, someone has to inform her family in Manila. Do you want to make the call?'

Kremenchug was about to refuse when a thought came to mind. 'Don't think she's got anyone left, but I'll ring the old guy who took care of her uncle while he was alive. Jesus,' he shook his head, 'I spoke to Alfredo just a couple of days ago.'

'She had a sizeable bonus due.'

Kremenchug pounced, his hopes rising with another possibility. 'Did she leave any written instructions with the office?'

'A will?'

'Anything.'

'No, but you might ask that guy in Manila. If he was that close, he might be able to fill us in.' Fielding was beat, and ready to retire. 'Anyone else we should inform?'

Kremenchug was aware of Sharon's connections in the British Virgin Islands where she'd registered and operated Dominion Mining, but had no knowledge of the intricate arrangements the Filipino had put into place, to facilitate their original sham. 'I'll let the Dominion people know later. They're three hours ahead of us.'

'What about the press?'

'Fuck the press!'

'We've got to give them something.'

'You can handle that, I'm going back to the hotel.'

'When are you gonna phone Manila?'

Kremenchug's face was stone. 'As soon as I get to my room.'

★ ★ ★ ★

His first call from the hotel was to Jakarta, where he asked to be patched through to Longdamai, and Eric Baird.

'Campbell's report was forwarded by Baron. Is it true?'

'Can't believe she's dead.' Kremenchug could tell from the slur that Baird had started earlier than usual, his heart dropping with the confirmation.

'What the fuck happened?'

'She fell. It's as simple as that.'

'How can you fall out of a helicopter for Chrissakes?'

'Sharon could do anything she set her mind to.'

Kremenchug, thinking he detected an impish giggle, pulled the handset away from his ear and glared angrily into the receiver. 'Prick!' he shouted.

'Hey, Alex, we've started a wake over here.' Another giggle, then, 'Lighten up – there's nothing you can do. She's dead, and that's that.'

Kremenchug consciously breathed deeply to calm his nerves. He had known Baird for years and knew that yelling at the man had little affect. 'What's Campbell doing there?'

Baird smirked at the other end of the line. 'Who, Stewart? He's the Baron rep on site.'

'Shouldn't you be outa there by now?' Kremenchug's curiosity was now aroused.

'Yeah, but the place has grown on me so much, thought I might stay. Say, Alex, when can I have my money?'

'Fielding's responsible for fixing bonuses, not me,' Kremenchug responded, caustically.

'I meant my half of the three quarter mill from the sale of our shares.'

'We blew it.' Kremenchug, looking at a loss of tens of millions suddenly realized that the proceeds from selling the BGC shares he jointly owned with Baird, might now be the only liquidity left.

Stunned silence left the airwaves to occasional static as Eric Baird absorbed the import of what had been said. 'You blew it? What the fuck are you playing at, Alex?'

Kremenchug knew there was nothing more to be gained from

continuing this conversation. Baird could add nothing new to what he had already learned from Fielding. 'It's gone. We dropped it all selling the stock short before the announcement was made. None of us thought it would go up again.'

'All of it?'

'Yes, the lot,' he lied; something he did best.

This was followed by a pause so lengthy the Jakarta operator monitoring, terminated the connection thinking the two parties had finished their conversation. In Kalimantan, Eric Baird's blood-drained face reflected his shock, the effect instantly sobering – whilst in Vancouver, Alexander Kremenchug shrugged his shoulders thinking the geologist had hung up, and reciprocated by slamming the phone back into its cradle, closing yet another chapter in his unsavory life. He then decided to book on the first available flight to the Philippines.

* * * *

Longdamai Mining Camp

As the day progressed, Eric Baird continued his slide towards the depths of despair, obsessed with the reality that Mardidi had willingly left with Angela Dau, and refused to return. There had been no falling out, and neither had there been any sign that Mardidi had been unhappy with their relationship. Although devastated by Kremenchug's betrayal and the realization that money would now be tight, Baird believed he could still manage to survive, somehow – but, only if Mardidi were to remain an integral part of his life.

'You can evacuate with the others, if you want,' Campbell offered.

'Is there a problem if I stay?' Baird's disconsolate figure sat slumped outside his cabin. Campbell had found him sitting alone and, without seeking his approval, had joined the Australian, occupying what had been Mardidi's rattan chair.

'No, as far as I'm concerned, you can remain here until Baron sends in its own team to assume control.'

'What do you think really happened?' Baird asked, his voice slurred from the limited Bacardi stock he secretly maintained on site.

'Mardidi?'

'No, Sharon.'

'One of those freak accidents,' Campbell accepted the porcelain mug, sipped the rum, then frowned. 'Why, what's on your mind?'

Baird leaned back pushing the cane chair into an impossible position on two legs. 'Nothing. It's just that she had so much to live for. Why do you think she did it?'

Campbell glanced at Baird. 'Are you saying that you think she jumped?'

'There's enough evidence to suggest so.'

'Like what?'

'Well, for starters, she was severely depressed for days prior to her death. Her uncle had died, and she had just been given her marching orders. Shit, Stewart, we're both geologists. How would *you* feel if you were shafted the way she was?'

'Eric, I think Sharon Ducay was a much stronger person than you give her credit for. If she'd been a man, she would have had balls the size of a buffalo's. I don't know how much you knew about Sharon but, one thing I'm certain of, she didn't throw herself out of any aircraft.'

'Well, we're never gonna know.'

Campbell wanted to pursue this line of conversation. 'Furthermore, she had a whopping great bonus waiting for her in Canada. Why would she forgo that?'

Baird's interest was drawn. 'Do you know how much?'

Campbell thought for a moment before replying. 'Had to be at least two, three hundred thousand.'

'Shit!'

'Yeah, right! You see, it wouldn't have been in Sharon's interests not to return and take advantage of that much money.'

'That then leaves us with the accident theory.'

'It's not a theory, Eric. The pilot's account makes sense once you've removed the emotion. Freak accident? Sure. Suicide? No way.' Campbell then moved on. 'What's the latest on Mardidi?'

Baird reached down and grasped the bottle. He offered Campbell a top up but the American shook his head and placed his hand over his mug. 'Nothing. Seems he's done a runner.'

'Why?' Campbell was sincere. Although he was not overly fond of the Australian, he reluctantly admitted that Baird had produced some fine work out in the field, and that had it not been for his association with Alex Kremenchug, they might even have been on better terms.

Baird shrugged. 'That's the problem, I just don't know.' He looked slyly at his companion. 'Perhaps you could ask Angela, the next time you're speaking to her?'

Campbell snorted. 'Yeah, sure,' with which, Baird having touched a nerve, he changed his mind and held the mug out for another shot, the two then settling down for an afternoon together, their minds filled with the calamitous events of the past two days.

⋆ ⋆ ⋆ ⋆

Penehing Community

'Get away!' Angela threw a rock at a scavenging dog, missing the animal, hitting the twisted wreckage of the parabolic television dish. Together with others in their party, Jonathan and Angela had searched through knee-deep ashes throughout the day but, due to the intensity of the fire, none of the remains could be identified.

'Enough!' the chief called, tormented by his daughter's accusatory stares which had accompanied the discovery of bones of children.

'It is time to leave. We should get back to the others, before dark.'

'It's hard to believe that it's all gone,' Angela was gripped with sadness. *'Apart from this, we've lost everything.'* She indicated the aluminum case containing the two kilos of gold. *'What will we use for capital to rebuild?'*

Jonathan Dau dusted his powder-covered legs with a free hand. *'Why, the insurance money, what else?'*

'How can you be so confident that he will return?'

'Because he believes that we have the woman he loves.'

'I wish I could share your confidence, Father.'

Jonathan shot his daughter a stern look, the words that followed, prophetic. *'He'll come back, just wait and see.'*

'What will we do about the dead?' Angela remained subordinate; she would not question her father publicly, out of respect.

'We must return with all of our people and hold a ceremony to farewell their spirits. Then it will be for the remaining council of elders to decide whether our community resettles here, or we move on.'

Angela and her father continued to work through their grief without further comment, each immersed in their own thoughts – the chief, deeply troubled by his daughter's behavior, while Angela, having now accepted that there would be no place in her future for Stewart Campbell, felt desperately alone. With the enormity of the Longhouse carnage weighing heavily on their minds they climbed, wearily, back into the mountains, returning to the safety of their temporary village deep in the forest.

That night, Jonathan Dau summoned his people to discuss their options – and responsibilities to the dead. After the newly appointed council of elders' open debate, the entire *Longdamai-Penehing* community voted unanimously to return to what had been their home, for the greater part of the past century. They would rebuild the Longhouse further along the shore, the original site to become a shrine, the young men swearing to defend their people to the last man should they again come under attack. Pens would be rebuilt to contain wild pig and fowl, and new boats would be built to replace those destroyed. Materials such as bamboo, twine, palm and tall timbers, would be taken from traditional sources, and the fields replanted, Udir volunteering to go downstream to trade the gold bars for whatever food, clothing and seed could be found. They would become the *Penehing* of old, dependent on none but those of Dayak blood.

When the sun's rays appeared breathing life into the new day, Jonathan Dau again led his people in prayer, their chant calling upon ancestral spirits to give them strength to defeat their enemies, and to watch over them as they undertook the arduous trek back down through the foothills, to a new beginning. By mid-morning they had gathered near the falls, where the wounded were ferried across the river, the remainder swimming to the desecrated shore – all of this, under the watchful eye of the hornbill.

★ ★ ★ ★

Longdamai Mining Camp

A fire and brimstone sunset fell, the subdued quiet broken by the plaintive wail, *'Allah Akbar'* summoning the faithful to *Magrib* prayers reminded Campbell of the time, and he retreated to his cabin leaving the Australian geologist alone – inebriated, and in melancholic mood. Determined to expunge Mardidi and Kremenchug's betrayal from his mind, Baird continued to drink, demolishing most of a second bottle before collapsing, backwards, spilling over the rattan chair. He rose, staggered into his untidy accommodations and dropped to the unmade bunk, wallowing in his despair.

Blurred eyes fell on the framed photograph alongside the bed, the picture capturing some special moment of the two of them together, smiling, their arms locked around each other affectionately. He sat there staring through drunken stupor, reminded of those happier times. 'Why did you leave me, Mardidi?' he asked, reaching out with loving, but clumsy hands, knocking the frame to the floor. Startled, Baird stared down at the shattered memory, surrendering to a flood of angry tears. He rose, unsteadily, unable to contain his frustration and screamed, loudly, cursing Mardidi, then savagely stomped what remained of the memorabilia with his heel.

Outside, where Baird's screams carried to others in the camp, a group of drillers sniggered amongst themselves, aware of the rumor surrounding Mardidi and the *Penehing* woman, Angela Dau – raucous innuendo and facetious comments halting, with the distraction of the Bell 205's engine lifting Captain Subandi and what was believed to be Sharon Ducay's remains, into the air.

★ ★ ★ ★

Baron Mining – Toronto – Canada

Disquieted by Samuel's report, the multinational, mining conglomerate's chairman continued to listen intently.

'…furthermore, Campbell could have been killed in that raid.'

'What provoked the Indonesian Military into such action?'

'According to Campbell, the Dayaks claim that the attack was carried out by Indonesian Special Forces. Why, we'll never know.'

'Was he hurt?'

'Fortunately, no.'

'Well, at least that's something. Is there any connection between the village attack and the death of the Filipino woman?'

'None at all – she'd handed everything over to Campbell and was flying out when it happened.'

'And the Indonesian authorities confirm that it was accidental?'

'Yes. Sharon Ducay was extremely unlucky.'

'How much damage control do we need to initiate with respect to the instability in the province?'

'There's no doubt that the media will attempt to connect Baron with what's happening within our exploration area. The Indonesians have managed to keep a lid on what's happening, so far, but that won't last. We should be ready to respond when stories start to leak. Campbell says that the slaughter could run into the thousands and, with those sort of numbers, we could expect something to break at any time now.'

'When will we be ready to restart the drilling?'

'We're well ahead of schedule, two, perhaps three weeks. We've taken over the rigs operating under contract onsite, and our drillers are in Jakarta completing their paperwork. Once the army gives Campbell the green light, we could have them onsite and working, within a week.'

'Will Campbell stay after what's happened?'

'I'm working on that. We've arranged another hookup, tomorrow.'

'All right, Phil, I'll make the calls.'

Once Samuels had left the former Canadian Prime Minister's

office, the company chairman called his personal assistant and instructed her to place a number of international calls, amongst these, to the Indonesian First Family.

⋆ ⋆ ⋆ ⋆

Longdamai Mining Camp

'Tuan! Tuan, you are wanted over at communications.' Campbell heard someone call, breaking into his sleep. Groggy from the demands that had been made on his body over the past days he threw on some clothes, banged his field boots upside down against the solid bunk out of habit, finished dressing then hurried over to the radio hut.

'Is that Mister Campbell?' the Jakarta link-operator inquired. Once he acknowledged, she then patched the caller through, from Canada.

'Stew, is that you?'

Recognizing the familiar voice Campbell looked up at the wall clock, noting that it was past nine in the evening. He'd slept for less than three hours. 'Yes, Phil,' he confirmed, stifling a yawn. 'What's up?'

'Can you talk freely?' Samuels wished to know.

'More or less but whatever's said will most likely be monitored anyway.'

'Right, understood.' The line fell silent for some moments as both gathered their thoughts. 'Stew, we've decided to move the drilling program forward.'

Campbell indicated surprise. 'Sammy, this is not a particularly good time.'

'If you're referring to the troubles, Jakarta's given an assurance that this will be all resolved within days.'

'Sammy, listen to me. Unless you've got that directly from the horse's mouth, if you know what I mean, then I wouldn't count on anything much changing here.'

'Straight from Mount Olympus,' Samuels advised, the reference too abstruse for third parties listening, to understand. 'In view of which, Baron's keen to have you remain there while the drilling takes place.'

'I thought you'd decided to send in your own team?'

'We're still proceeding with the original program. The only change is that we're offering you the position of operations manager, until the drilling has been completed. How about it, Stew?'

Campbell didn't require time to even consider the offer. 'To be honest, Sammy, I don't want the job. I'm beat. Can't you get anyone else?'

'Our man's had a serious accident and we need to have someone there we can trust to do the job properly.'

'Why the rush?'

Again, there was a brief pause as Phil Samuels carefully selected words which would not be misconstrued in any way, without compromising the sensitivity of what needed to be said. He understood that, if their conversation was, indeed, being monitored, then he had to guard against the possibility of a leak to the media. 'Stew, we need to move quickly to verify previous data. As you know, it's standard procedure to conduct further drilling to prove up a site. Considering what has transpired over there during recent days, and I'm not referring to indigenous confrontations, the Board feels that it should move quickly to establish the veracity of all information originating from site activities, whilst still under a particular expatriate's guardianship. Do you follow?'

Campbell understood, annoyed that Sharon's untimely death had already started the rumor mills spinning. 'How bad is it?

The Canadian party responded with an audible sigh. 'Could damage the integrity of everything that's been achieved, to date.'

'What's the basis for comment?' he asked, guardedly.

'When has the media ever needed one?'

'Jesus, Phil,' Campbell felt in a bind. 'It's a big ask, even coming from you.'

Samuels forced laugh in no way comforted. 'Baron will demonstrate its gratitude, Stew. Come on, help an old friend out here?'

Campbell knew he had no choice but to agree. Phil Samuels had been extremely supportive over the years and, in this industry, when such markers were called, the debt had to be paid. 'Okay, Phil,' his voice faded, then recovered with the airwaves, 'I'll stay on until your man recovers. Agreed?'

'Agreed.'

Campbell considered the task ahead of him, and the methodology he would employ to substantiate Sharon Ducay's earlier results – results of such significance that he was now standing on what could conceivably be the world's largest gold deposit. 'I'll run a parallel program to what's already been done,' he suggested, 'and then I'm finished?'

'We don't require a duplicate program, just a dozen or so holes at random. We need to buy some time.'

'When will the new drillers get here?'

'They're in Jakarta as we speak. Should be there by the end of this week.'

'What about plant and equipment?'

'That's all been taken care of in Jakarta.'

'Sounds like you really don't need me at all, Sammy.'

'We've got powerful friends moving things along.'

Campbell now appreciated the comment regarding Mount Olympus, even more clearly, and was disappointed that Baron had climbed into bed with Palace interests. 'Let's hope they remain on side.'

'Okay, then, Stew. I'm pleased you've agreed to help out. Anything else for the time being?'

'Yes. I'll need bucket loads of cash here, quickly. The drillers and laborers haven't been paid and, with what's happened downstream, without fresh supplies and funds, it will all collapse.'

'Can you keep it together for another few days?'

'Won't be easy.'

'Good. I'll see to it that you get whatever's needed.'

Campbell had a sudden thought. 'I have *carte blanche* to hire and fire as I see fit?'

'Of course.'

'Okay, I'll get back to you with any other requests.'

'Say, Stew, almost forgot to ask. How are you and that gal of yours getting along?'

Campbell felt a knot tighten in his stomach. 'Not now, Sammy – not now.' With that, he hung up, wishing he had the appetite to eat.

Campbell strolled outside into the tropical night and looked up through the darkness into the starless sky, beset by a loneliness that only lovers can feel. He surveyed the camp looking for company – but there was no one there he cared to talk to, so he wandered across to the canteen and requested coffee. Lights in the expatriates' cabins suggested the drillers were most likely playing cards, and he considered going over to look in on the game, but dismissed this idea immediately it came to mind. He expected that Baird would be asleep, his thoughts then drifting to the Australian's companion, Mardidi, and why he had abandoned the camp, with Angela. Campbell remained deeply concerned for Angela and worried for her safety, even though Phil Samuels' advice indicated that Jakarta was moving to avoid further conflict in the area. He knew it would be foolhardy for him to attempt to find her in the mountains, deciding that Angela must return at some point in time, if not to settle things with him, then at least to communicate with her department.

* * * *

Jakarta
Indonesian Defence Headquarters (HANKAM)

The Army Chief of Staff looked weary. Days before, on 27th July, the capital had erupted in riots after his paramilitaries raided Megawati Sukarno's political headquarters. Sixty people had been taken away for interrogation, the Military's crackdown and intimidation campaign against NGOs gaining far too much attention from the international press – the main contributing factor behind the Palace's decision to revisit an earlier decision, which would have resulted in providing greater security for Javanese and Madurese settlers in Kalimantan.

Brigadier General Sukirno had remained reservedly composed throughout the briefing, aware that the decision to withdraw troops from the Kalimantan provinces would meet with derision. Major General Umar Sudopo, the Chief of Socio-Political Staff at Defence HQ, had attempted to allay the concerns of others present, the *Kopassus* Special Forces Commander, General Praboyo, the most vociferous in voicing his position.

'The decision is absurd! The Dayaks' challenge must be met with force.'

'The order came directly from Jalan Cendana.' When Sukirno spoke, the simple statement was designed to end debate. In his non-active status, he still wielded considerable power through Parliament, and a long-established network of powerful friends. Although General Sukirno considered Praboyo an upstart, he avoided alienating the man as he had the President's ear – and one of his daughters. When the decision had been made some months before, to increase military presence in Kalimantan, there had been no intelligence indicating that the Dayaks were planning insurrection. First and foremost, Sukirno's role was to protect Presidential interests. Subject to that, those of the military.

'This will be bad for morale,' Praboyo argued. Amongst his contemporaries, the *Kopassus* General was a clear winner because of his marriage into the First Family. He scowled at Sukirno for the inference that the President had deliberately bypassed him. Praboyo seethed, angered by Palace siblings' inept attempts to erode his power-base amongst the military hierarchy. Praboyo was young, ambitious, and determined to persevere until the President passed the mantel to him – what he perceived to be his natural ascension to the Presidency would be realized within the next few years. His father-in-law had already indicated that his promotion to Commander of *Kostrad,* the most senior military command position, was imminent, and for this reason he kept his own counsel, avoiding confrontation with his wife's billionaire brothers and sisters.

But, for the country's military leadership to initiate such conciliatory moves in favor of the Dayaks was too bitter a pill for Praboyo to swallow. In the recent skirmishes along the Upper Mahakam he had been severely embarrassed by the extent of *Kopassus* losses, and was determined to seek revenge, with or without the support of those present. As Commander of the Special Forces he could secretly mount an operation without necessarily seeking authority from any attending this meeting, including the Chief of Army Staff now sitting across the room. He had done so before, and knew that in the event his superiors did become aware of his actions, they would automatically assume that he had acted with the near-senile President's blessing. However, as the *Bapak*'s directive emphatically required a withdrawal of combat forces in the Kalimantan provinces, even Praboyo's hands were tied. Although it was not unusual for his Special Forces to be covertly deployed in areas under other commanders' operational control, the presence of *Kopassus* troops along the Mahakam was already known – such knowledge placing severe restrictions on whatever action he might contemplate against the Dayak tribes.

The Chief of Staff stepped in. *'The Army is not effecting a total withdrawal, 'Boyo. We will maintain a presence to provide security against further ethnic clashes, but the size of our forces will be reduced to accommodate the President's request. Special emissaries are already on their way to each of the provinces to seek an end to the attacks on transmigrant settlements. These representatives will be empowered to offer the President's assurances, that the military will not take any further reprisal action if the Dayaks agree to cease their activities immediately.'*

'And, if they don't?'

'Then we will obviously have to revisit those areas which refuse to compromise.'

'We were already close to resolving the problem. I still don't understand the sudden shift in policy.'

General Sukirno intervened. *'We should not look at this as something permanent, General. The President's concerns relate to an increase in international awareness with respect to the Mahakam River area and its local population. The Longdamai gold discovery has attracted considerable international attention over past days, and the President wants a hold placed on all military activity that might present our country in the wrong light. We must brace ourselves for a significant increase in the number of foreign journalists wishing to visit the Mahakam. The President does not want anything to interfere with either his*

Transmigrasi Program, or the development of Kalimantan's resources.'

'The Dayaks are already doing that,' Praboyo insisted.

'They have run their course. We believe that most will now return to their villages, satisfied with what they've accomplished.'

'How much time do we have?'

'Seven days.'

'Then, it's absolutely clear to all present?' this, from the Army Chief of Staff whose question appeared to be directed specifically at the arrogant General Praboyo. *''Boyo?'* The CAS insisted on his response.

'Kopassus troops will be out within the week.'

★ ★ ★ ★

Angered by the Army Chief of Staff's passing remark as he departed, Praboyo remained silent, planning his next move during the drive to *Kopassus* Headquarters in Cijantung. The remark may have been *'en passant'* but for the ambitious young General, being of educated Javanese stock, the comment cut him to the core. *'Ah, 'Boyo,'* he recalled the CAS taking him by the arm, *'are you familiar with the two legends in our (Javanese) culture relating to events pertaining to a man who marries the daughter of a king?'* Praboyo, already well versed in the literature had simply waited. *'According to the legend, the groom could be like 'Jaka Tigkir' who killed his father-in-law and established his own kingdom. Or, he had the choice of following the footsteps of 'Ageng Mangir' who, having attempted a number of coups against another sultan, ended up dead.'* Praboyo recalled wishing that it was the CAS who was dead when he then asked, *'Tell me, 'Boyo, which of these do you wish to be?'*

Praboyo knew that Jakarta's whispering classes often suggested that he maintained a private army to further consolidate his power, primarily because he often bypassed the chain of command to secure equipment for his Special Forces direction from foreign governments. He had become deeply involved with the U.S. forces when first attending training courses in Fort Benning and Fort Bragg earlier in his career. When Praboyo married into the First Family, the Americans had wasted no time in establishing rapport with the promising officer. He was invited to attend courses at Fort Benning and Fort Bragg in the U.S., to forge closer links between the Indonesian and American military.

He knew he'd have to move quickly to avoid discovery, which would require that any new operation would have to be mounted immediately, and given the appearance that it had been in effect for some time. Arriving at the Special Forces complex, the General went directly to the communications center and spoke to the commander responsible for the calamitous *Operation Clean Sweep*. He discussed the covert operation in detail, securing an undertaking that the mission would be completed within four days. By evening, commandos were already prepared and fully equipped for the lightning strike against the *Penehing,* the search and destroy mission designed not only to boost morale, but also to extract revenge. Now all that was left to do was to determine the position of their enemy. The officer in charge radioed for heli-support, and Captain Subandi was immediately reassigned to the combat unit.

Confident that the operation would go as planned, General Praboyo returned to observe the covert, 'Psy-Ops' training program provided by a special U.S. team that had been flown in from Special Operations Command-Pacific. The training had continued, uninterrupted, during the riots arising from the attack on Megawati's headquarters, just a few days before. General Praboyo then addressed another potential problem – what to do with the sixty or more members of Megawati's political movement he had incarcerated in the two clandestine, *Kopassus* detention centers in Cibubur and Bogor. Not even the Army Chief of Staff was aware of Praboyo's private 'jails'. He'd had no difficulty establishing his own slush fund, supported by Megawati opposition groups, the covert centers specifically designed for detaining and questioning dissidents that his men had abducted – or students who had simply 'disappeared'.

★ ★ ★ ★

Jakarta & Longdamai

Baird's partner, Subroto replaced the receiver and rubbed his hands together gleefully. The call had originated from General

Praboyo's offices in Cijantung, the General's personal aide apologizing for taking so long in responding to the AVM's request, the aide's call to confirm that the small matter Subroto had raised with the commander had now been resolved. The officer did not need to elaborate – Subroto knew immediately that the troublesome Mardidi was dead. He waddled into an adjacent room and instructed the operator to raise the Longdamai camp, and summon Eric Baird to the phone.

★ ★ ★ ★

The Australian geologist woke with a start, the banging on his cabin door setting off something similar in his head. He groaned, 'Go away!' but the head-splitting pounding persisted.

'Eric, it's Stewart. You've got a call.'

Baird responded with a string of muffled profanities.

'Eric, you'd better get up. It sounded important.'

'Can't. I'm as sick as a dog.'

'Come on, I'll walk you over. When you've finished I've got something to discuss.'

Moments passed, and Baird's unhappy face appeared under a crown of unkempt hair. 'Do you know… who it is?'

'Your chubby partner, Subroto.' Anyone who moved amongst the Jakarta expatriate mining community would have been aware of Baird's rotund benefactor.

'Shit,' another groan; 'he's the last person I need right now.'

'Let's get it over with, then. I really do have something important to talk to you about.'

Baird opened the door further, stretched then yawned, Campbell instantly wincing, much closer to the other man's breath than he cared to be.

'Give me a couple of minutes to get some gear on.'

Baird reappeared, disheveled, laces untied and dragging behind, his swollen eyes hidden behind shades. Recognizing the look on the American's face he attempted a smile, the two-day, reddish-tinged stubble on the lower end of his jaw adding to his decrepit demeanor.

'Okay, let's go and see what the bastard wants now.'

'On second thoughts, I'll wait for you over in the mess. Maybe you should consider eating something for a change.'

Baird squinted through the sunglasses. 'Yeah, guess you're right. I'll come over when I've finished with the call.' Reluctantly, he then continued over to the communications room, and accepted the headphones from the operator.

'It's Eric, Pak. Guess you've heard what's been happening over here?'

Subroto ignored Baird's question, going directly to the reason for his call. *'Pipi wants to know when you plan on returning.'*

Baird shuddered as an image of Subroto's niece occupied his mind. *'Soon, Pak, soon.'*

'I thought your contract was finished there?'

Baird was too tired to fence with his senior partner. *'It is. I'm just tidying up a few loose ends.'*

At the other end of the line the Javanese smiled. *Yes, and one of those won't be Mardidi's!* Tempted to raise the young man's name in their conversation, Subroto resisted doing so, eager now for Baird to return and get Pipi off his back. *'Don't leave it too long. We have some serious matters to discuss,'* he paused for effect, *'that relate to our partnership.'*

Baird was now fully awake. *'Our partnership?'*

'Yes, Eric. We've just received notice from the new operators, Baron Mining, that they will not be requiring our offices any further. This will mean that we will lose our main source of income.'

'I thought that might happen,' Baird said, unhappily.

'So, I wasn't going to raise this now, thought it might be better to wait until you get back.'

'Raise what, Pak?' Baird could feel a familiar knot growing in his gut.

'I'm going to retire, Eric.'

'What does that mean?' Panic gripped him again.

'It means I'll be closing the company down. I want you to return and finalize what is due to me from the BGC arrangements you promised to put into place.'

'But, Pak...!'

'No, no, Eric, best to leave the rest of our discussion until you return. Now, hurry back and we'll talk it all through,' with that, Subroto hung up leaving his junior partner numbed with shock. With Mardidi out of their hair, there was no reason for Baird not to return to Pipi and, with the company closed, his niece would have her wish, to accompany her husband to Australia.

⋆ ⋆ ⋆ ⋆

Baird had never considered the possibility of a future in Indonesia without the protection of his sponsor, AVM Subroto, and the companionship of his lover, Mardidi. Now, in the space of just two days, he had lost both. And, he expected that Subroto would hold him personally responsible for the monies Kremenchug had swindled. In a daze, he rose slowly to his feet and started to leave, the operator reminding him with a tap on the shoulder that he was still wearing the headphones. Baird stared at the man blankly, then in a pique of temper, threw them down angrily onto the console with a loud clunk. 'Stick them up your arse,' he snapped – the surprised technician reared back, the vitriol lost on the native speaker. Baird stormed out of the small building and stood in the open air, fuming, lost, bewildered by how quickly his life had changed, and the unfairness of it all. Without Mardidi, he had no wish to return to Jakarta – without Subroto, there would be no sponsorship. His world had imploded and he had nowhere to turn.

'Eric?' he heard his name called and looked in the direction of the mess. Spotting Campbell, he waved half-heartedly then made his way over, sitting down with the American as breakfast was served. 'First real meal for almost three days,' Campbell broke the silence. 'Are you going to eat?'

As if on cue, Baird's stomach growled and Campbell couldn't help but smile. 'Suppose I should.' He beckoned one of the staff and ordered toast and coffee.

'Bad news?'

'Something like that.'

'Tell me to mind my own business if you want, Eric, but you

should cut back on the sauce. You look like hell.'

Baird placed his head in his hands and leaned on the rickety table. 'It's just that lately, everything I touch seems to turn to shit.'

'Subroto?'

'Yep. Just told me that he's closing down the consultancy.'

'Did he tell you why?'

'Yeah, sure, Baron's getting its own offices.'

'And you don't have any other work?'

'Nah, been too preoccupied with what's been happening here.'

'You've had a good run,' Campbell inferred.

'I know. Maybe I should've got out when I had the chance.'

'Got any plans?'

'Don't know. Try and see if I can pick up something when I get back into Jakarta. There's plenty of work around, it's just not the sort of work I'd planned on doing at this stage in my life.'

Campbell watched the other man closely. 'What about Kremenchug, can't he get you something?'

Baird snorted. 'He's an arsehole of the first order. Bastard gypped me on our last deal. Half of the money due to me was earmarked for Subroto.'

'Ouch. I'm sorry to hear that.' Although he wasn't, Campbell felt obliged to say it anyway, pleased somewhat that Kremenchug was out of the picture, something he wished to ascertain before making Baird an offer. 'How would a couple of months working here with me, sit with you?'

Baird heard the words and stared in surprise, his hand holding coffee, frozen in time. 'Seriously?'

'Sure.' Campbell dug deep and found another smile. 'I was only offered the position by Baron last night. It wouldn't be long term, just enough to verify the last program's results, then we'd handover to another team.'

Baird sipped his coffee, contemplating the offer. Mardidi had to return, sometime, and when he did, Baird would be waiting. With a legitimate reason to remain onsite he could also delay the inevitable with Subroto – and Pipi. He screwed up his face with a twisted response, baring neglected, tobacco-stained teeth. 'If the offer's real, I'm interested.' His face cracked on one side as he attempted a grin. 'To be honest, at this particular moment in my life I don't give a shit about anything, much. But, if you want me to stay, I'll give it a go.' They both waited for their coffees to be topped up and the cook's assistant to move out of earshot, before continuing. Baird thought it worth the shot and asked, 'What am I gonna be paid?'

Campbell scrutinized the Australian across the eye-leveled rim of his mug. He needed to have someone qualified, onside, and onsite. This man's in-country experience was invaluable, his knowledge of the deposit's geology, second to none. 'Five hundred a day.'

Baird raised his eyebrows – a natural response. 'Laborer's pay!'

Campbell's laugh was natural. He leaned back and shook his head, 'Seven Fifty.'

'Make it a grand and you have a deal,' the Australian pushed, brazenly.

'Jesus, Eric, ten seconds ago you had nothing. Now you're bargaining?'

Now it was Baird who turned on the smile. 'You wouldn't have asked if you didn't need me.'

Campbell considered his options, then agreed. 'Okay, a thousand it is.'

'What are we gonna do about them?' Baird indicated the expatriate drillers sitting around lazily filling in time. Campbell looked over at the men, parked under a tarpaulin tied between two silent generators, playing cards.

'They'll be gone before you know it.'

Baird showed his surprise. 'What then?'

'Baron's drillers will be here in the next couple of days. Their superintendent will be carrying funds to pay this lot out, and cover anything outstanding to the laborers.'

'Supplies?'

'Essentials will be air freighted from Jakarta to Samarinda today. There'll be increased chopper support starting tomorrow. We'll have a couple of barges bring the rest upriver to the Tiong Ohang river station, and break the shipments down for the smaller longboats to carry the rest of the way.'

'All of this in less than a day? I'm impressed!'

'Baron's been mobilizing over the past month.' Campbell decided it wouldn't be smart to tell Baird too much – that Sharon's death had raised doubts as to the veracity of the find, and Baron was moving quickly to damage control.

'What do you have in mind for the drilling?'

'I thought we'd run a series of random holes parallel with what you guys have already drilled.'

Baird shrugged. 'That won't be a problem. The data's all here. We can start work whenever you're ready.'

'No time like the present – why don't you get some food into you first, then we'll meet in the office in, say, an hour?'

'Fine by me.'

'Okay.' Campbell extracted long legs from under the table and made to leave, hesitated, sitting sideways on the seat. 'Don't you think Angela and Mardidi's departure was just a little too spontaneous?'

Baird avoided the other man's eyes, staring into space. 'I'd wondered about that, too.'

'And Mardidi never mentioned anything at all about going off into the hills?'

'Not a syllable,' Baird said, sourly, recalling the events. 'Big day for everyone, huh?'

Campbell's mood toppled into darkness again. The morning before had started badly enough with the discovery that Angela had left. Sharon's death had then overshadowed everything else – the image of her bloody remains would be etched into his mind for the rest of his life. 'They took her body away to Samarinda, last night.'

'By chopper?'

'Yeah,' he confirmed, distracted by another, worrying thought. Sharon's briefcase would have contained her passport and other personal travel documents without which, Indonesian red tape would make it extremely difficult for the body to be transported back to the Philippines.

'She was really good at what she did,' Baird said, 'and tough.'

Campbell smiled sadly as memories triggered, and started to flow. 'Yes, she was all that, and more.'

'She took those bastards on single-handedly,' Baird looked over at the tough bunch of drillers, 'kicked one of them in the balls, she did.'

Campbell's slide into the past came to an abrupt halt. 'What?'

The Australian related the incident. 'Couple of them gave her a hard time back on the original site before we moved up here. After that, no one bothered her again.'

The reflection reminded Campbell to ask. 'Tell me, Eric, straight up. Why didn't she continue with the drilling there? What on earth encouraged her to suddenly pick up the entire operation and move it here when there was already sufficient evidence of a viable mine?'

Baird blinked with nervous alarm. 'Sharon could be bloody minded when she wanted to be.'

'But, based on the results one would have thought it would make more economic sense to establish a mine there, first?'

'One would have thought so, yes,' Baird agreed, evasively.

'Then why didn't she?'

Eric Baird faced Campbell. There was no longer any reason for him to conceal what had happened, Sharon was dead and he had lost out financially, in the end. 'The last holes drilled showed that the deposit was an isolated pocket. Sharon ceased drilling when she knew that the results would be detrimental to Dominion's offer to farm-out the property to BGC.'

'Jesus, Eric!'

'Yeah, I know. At the time Kremenchug seemed to be driving the deal, I just went along for the ride.'

'Then, how did it come about, that she selected this particular site for further drilling?' Campbell's intuition warned that the answer may be unpalatable, and he braced himself for the Australian geologist's response.

'I was commissioned to walk over the area some years back.'

'Go on,' the American urged.

Baird decided to let it all out, now unconcerned as Sharon's decision to drill here had been vindicated by the incredible results. 'This has to be off the record, okay?'

'Let's hear it first.'

'No, Stewart, I'll need your word, up front.'

Campbell was reluctant but something told him that whatever Baird was hiding, might be paramount to Baron's safe tenure over the mine. 'Okay, shoot.'

Baird then went into elaborate detail as to what happened during his first visit to the Longdamai site, the deaths of the two *Modang* river men, and how he had simply filed a 'general report' without really carrying out any investigation.

'After all, I knew more about the geology in the area than most, and Kremenchug was desperate to get his hands on something worthwhile, to acquire equity in the Canadian miners.'

'Then, how did Sharon come to move the operations here?'

'Ironically, Kremenchug encouraged Dominion Mining to take up the concession. That's how P.T. Kalimantan Gold was spawned.'

'But, you've just said that there was no original survey conducted. Why, then, would she want to start here?'

'There *was* a survey report,' Baird explained, 'it's just that it wasn't a survey of this site.'

Campbell's shock was evident. He sat stunned, the blood draining from his face. 'It was all a scam?'

Baird jumped to his own defence. 'No, it wasn't. That's the beauty of the whole thing. Don't you understand? Sharon's discovery was a sheer fluke!'

'Who else is aware of all this, Kremenchug?'

'No, Alex was not involved,' he said bitterly. 'Once Dominion Mining sold its position to BGC, the closest he came to any of this was to fill his pockets at everyone else's expense.'

'And you're telling me that the test-drilling was all above board?'

'Yes, would I still be here if it wasn't.'

'Are you sure?'

'Absolutely. You don't believe me?'

'Jesus, Eric, what can I say? You've just revealed that Sharon deliberately misled a public company to benefit her own associates, Dominion, then expect me to accept that this latest discovery is all its cracked up to be, with someone like Kremenchug involved?'

'I guarantee you, Stew, when we carry out the confirmation drilling, you'll be pleasantly surprised.'

'My gut tells me I'll be surprised, all right,' Campbell's sarcasm hurt, 'and it's going to be my name that will now be linked to whatever we find!'

'Hey, you can relax, Stew. Nothing's been dummied up here. I was around whenever sampling occurred and can assure you that the results are kosher.'

'There's only one way to find out,' Campbell argued, 'and I just hope that, for the both of us, those records haven't been compromised in any way.'

'Stop worrying.' Baird was annoyed at the other man's concern. 'They're okay. You'll see!'

★ ★ ★ ★

Chapter Twenty-nine

Kopassus (SPECIAL FORCES)

UPPER MAHAKAM RIVER

Captain Subandi was beside himself. Having flown what he believed to be Angela Dau's remains to Samarinda, he immediately requested leave, citing extreme family hardship. His intention, to visit the Philippines and establish his claim with the man Sharon called Alfredo, for when Sharon Ducay's insurers paid out. His request was ignored. And, adding to his chagrin, new orders were cut assigning him to the *Kopassus* forward position not twenty kilometers from the Longdamai mining camp – his mission, to fly armed reconnaissance to establish the whereabouts of the remaining Longdamai – *Penehing* villagers. Weapons were reinstalled, the pilot perplexed by the gravity of his predicament, wondering why so much in his life could had gone so seriously wrong.

Charged with this duty, Subandi deliberately avoided achieving the objective, realizing that any success would result in Sharon's capture – or worse, her death. He flew across the target area from early morning until midday, returning to the forward post to refuel. As the Bell 205, with its pintle-mounted machine guns skirted dangerously close to the forest canopy with its payload of fourteen, combat-experienced *Kopassus* troops in the main cabin, he prayed that the veteran sergeant sitting alongside was not as observant as he appeared.

Hovering at times close to four thousand feet, then dropping down to investigate river traffic, after hours of searching the thick jungle it became abundantly clear that pursuit from the air would be fruitless.

⋆ ⋆ ⋆ ⋆

Jonathan heard the helicopter's engine change pitch, immediately cranking his neck to search the sky. *'Nobody move!'* he yelled at the top of his lungs. *'Hold the children still! They might not see us if we don't move!'*

'Yuh-Yuh, quickly, come here!' Angela snapped her fingers and the *orangutan* sprang to her side, instantly wrapping her body around Angela's legs. Frozen in their tracks as the aircraft crisscrossed the forested end of the island, the villagers breathed a collective sigh of relief when the Bell 205 continued in a westerly direction towards Bukit Batubrok, and disappeared from view.

'It could be Sharon's pilot,' Jonathan signaled the villagers to continue sifting through the ashes.

Angela looked to her father, *'Why would he be back, this soon?'*

'Who knows? Perhaps he's had a change of heart. Maybe he wants to talk.' The chief called to Udir. *'Best be ready in case he returns. Post ten of the younger men with weapons, in the trees over there.'*

Udir knew what Jonathan intended. He chose men with carbines, ordering them to take positions on the cliff across the river, overlooking the area where their fellow villagers toiled.

'Should I change?' Sharon's clothes were now part of Angela's reduced wardrobe.

'Might be an idea, just in case.'

Angela unrolled the bundled possessions and did as her father suggested, Yuh-Yuh's inquisitive hands a constant challenge for Angela as she pulled and tugged on everything there. She reached out and waved a scolding finger in the ape's face. In response, the *orangutan* displayed a mouthful of teeth as if she didn't care, then snatched the Akubra, and dragged it away, one hand tilling the dirt behind.

'Damn it, Yuh-Yuh, bring that back!' But the *orangutan* wasn't interested, enjoying the tease. Angela returned to her task at hand, dismissing her playful friend with a flip of the hand – Yuh-Yuh,

offended by the signal, slunk off to sulk, hat in hand.

★ ★ ★ ★

Throughout the course of that morning the helicopter reappeared in the distance a number times and, with each threatening approach, the *Penehing*s repeated the earlier procedure, turning all movement to stone. Then, as the villagers emerged from shelter where they had been resting from the midday sun, the helicopter returned, its flight path taking the Huey directly over the waterfall, unannounced, catching all off guard.

When the Huey came into full view with weapons aimed in their direction, the chief knew they were trapped. *'Run for the river!'* he shouted, the staccato effect of bullets pumping through the air strangely distant, the earth exploding all around him as machineguns strafed the ground, terrifyingly real. *Penehing* men scrambled for their antiquated weapons then stood their ground firing up at the helicopter, while those positioned across the river released a barrage of fire at eye level, catching the pilot by surprise. Subandi's reflex action was instant. He stamped on the pedals controlling the tail rotor, rotating the aircraft on its axis. As he searched the cliffs for the enemy, simultaneously adjusting the cyclic and collective to maintain his position over the water, the sergeant sitting alongside screamed, slumping forward, yelling he'd been hit. Udir emptied his Steyr AUG Para submachine gun's thirty-round magazine in seconds, the 9mm bullets puncturing holes through the Huey's engine cowling, striking the Lycoming's intricate systems. There was a horrendous bang, followed by smoke belching from the Iroquois, Subandi automatically pushing the collective down, the relevant autorotation procedures flashing through his mind as he screamed *'Mayday, Mayday, this is Alfa Hotel, Charlie, Oscar, Oscar, we're going down, our position is...'*

'*It's hit!*' Udir screamed exuberantly, jumping up and down with childlike pleasure. Then, as Subandi lost control, Udir's jaw dropped, the Bell 205 sliding through the air towards where he stood on the river's edge, at an alarming rate. He watched in fascination as the Huey fell – then, at the last moment when it appeared the pilot might recover from the dive and the nose lifted, the aircraft collapsed back, crashing into the riverbank within meters of where he stood.

Jonathan hurried over to the mangled helicopter as quickly as his wound would permit, ordering his men to cease firing as injured commandos crawled from the wreckage – amongst these, the pilot. Udir raised his weapon and pointed the Steyr at the *Kopassus* soldiers. *'What are we going to do with them?'* he directed his question to Jonathan as the chief cautiously approached the smoking wreckage and checked inside where more than half the contingent lay dead or seriously injured. He turned on the pilot. *'Why did you bring them here to kill us?'* Then, to Udir, *'Collect their weapons. And get those as well.'* Jonathan pointed at the 7.62 mm, GPMG M-60 that protruded from the '205s main cabin.

Captain Subandi swayed groggily, blood pouring from a deep, forehead gash, his concussed brain disoriented from the brutal impact. When other *Penehing* arrived, the men moved quickly to disarm the surviving commandos who were then bound, and forced to their knees. Heads bowed, the prisoners started to shake, terrified to a man that they would be executed. The *Penehing* warriors turned their attention to the pilot but their chief raised his hand. *'Let him be!'* Jonathan Dau extracted a short bladed *golok* from its sheath, raised the machete menacingly in the air and approached. *'Did you think that you'd save your woman's life by attacking us?'*

Gripped with shock, his vision functioning in only one eye, Subandi failed to respond. As minutes wore on and the deep resonating hum filling his ears gradually abated, he remembered where he was, wiped his bloodied brow with the back of a forearm, and cursed his misfortune. Then, with head raised proudly he vilified the entire Dayak nation for good measure, and spat at the ground, to emphasize his disrespect.

The chief was unimpressed with this display of bravado. *'You are a fool, Captain. You have brought these men here, only to die. Why is it so important to Kopassus that they continue to target the Penehing and try to destroy my people?'*

'Go screw yourself!' came the insolent reply.

Jonathan nodded to the warrior closest to the prisoners. *'Kill the man on this end.'* The soldier selected for execution was unaware that he had been chosen to die, the man alongside fainting in terror seconds later as his comrade's head rolled along the ground and came to rest directly under his eyes. Once more, Jonathan addressed the pilot. *'You have four men left. I will ask you again. Why is Kopassus specifically targeting the Penehing?'*

Subandi had never felt this tired in his entire life. Drained by shock and the demands of past days he closed his eyes, drawing upon last reserves, grimacing with pain when reminded of his wound. The Captain breathed deeply – he knew this was the end. Calmly, he wiped his forehead again, inspected the smear on his suit, then glared at Dau and snarled, truculently, *'They come to kill because you are all savages, and deserve to die.'*

The chief's face clouded. *'You no longer care for the woman we captured?'*

At first, the question confused the pilot. Something niggled the back of his mind and he frowned heavily, ignoring the pain, desperately trying to recall what had been so important about this mission. He stared bewilderedly at the villagers who had gathered at the scene, his attention falling upon a young, Dayak woman who had appeared at the Penehing chief's side. Dau's hoarse, whispered command in the local dialect meant nothing to Subandi's ears, nor did he understand Angela's response that it no longer mattered, that the pilot had already seen her.

The Captain remained glued to Angela. There was a familiarity about the woman that remained annoyingly locked in his brain. He shuffled forward a few steps to get a closer look, Jonathan blocking his way. With amnesiac stare he searched for a clue, the jodhpurs finally causing the memory block to crumble. With recognition, came disbelief. Subandi staggered back with astonishment, shaking his head, refusing to accept what his eyes could see. *'No!'* he gasped, *'it can't be! You're dead!'*

'No, that would be Sharon Ducay.' Angela brushed the air, discouraging the *orangutan,* Yuh-Yuh, from tugging at her side for attention.

'No… it's… not possible!' Subandi stepped back, stumbling as he retreated in slow motion from the apparent hallucination. Then as the Captain's world continued to disintegrate, Yuh-Yuh, tired of being ignored, threw a tantrum and tossed the Akubra through the air, the hat falling directly at the pilot's feet. For moments Subandi stood staring down at the familiar item, then bent down and picked it up carefully, by the brim. Another piece fell into place as he felt the pit inside his stomach open even wider and he asked, *'Is she really dead?'*

Jonathan knew there was nothing left to be gained by maintaining the charade. His hopes for any share in the senior geologist's insurance had been dashed the moment the pilot had set eyes on Angela, and recognized her. *'Yes, she's dead.'*

'How?' he asked, groggily.

Jonathan Dau couldn't resist. *'That was the Filipino who was given the flying lesson.'*

Subandi flinched. *'You're lying, I saw my men…'* Then, when he saw the chief's chilling smile he shook his head disbelievingly. *'That's impossible…I watched her fall…'* A furtive look in Angela's direction confirmed that it was true. Dumbstruck, his mouth fell open, words unable to flow.

The chief pointed to Angela, and his voice acquired a serrated edge. *'It wasn't my daughter you thought you'd killed. It was the Filipino.'*

And then it dawned on the pilot. *'That was you in the back of the chopper?'* Jonathan merely shrugged.

'You killed Sharon?' Images of Sharon falling and her bloody remains flashed through his mind, Subandi slipping slowly to his knees sapped of all strength. He lifted his chin and glared at Jonathan Dau, his heart filled with rage, adrenalin driving him to do what happened next. He called out to his men in Javanese, encouraging their response, and in that moment of distraction he dropped his left hand behind his knees locating the brass zip that held the trouser leg firmly in place. He eased the ankle-zipper up slowly whilst calling again for the commandos to be brave, aware that Jonathan Dau had given the order, deliberately in *Bahasa Indonesia*, for the remaining prisoners to be executed. Amidst the cries of anguish and terror,

several *Penehing* warriors stepped forward, each lining up their victims of choice. And at the precise moment their fearsome blades cut through the air, Captain Subandi's right hand extracted the concealed .45 caliber AMT, pointed the weapon at Angela Dau, and fired with deadly aim.

The first of the five-chambered bullets narrowly missed Angela's head, Jonathan Dau lunging through the air, taking the next bullet in the chest. The pilot's finger squeezed the trigger again, but not before a warrior pounced, Subandi's brain then registering that the handgun had ceased firing. Bewildered, he glanced down – his arm had been severed and lay on the sand, fingers twitching, partly curled around the grip. He looked up, his face struck with surprise and, in that moment, a blade sliced through the air sending Captain Subandi to meet his *ajal* – the predestined time of death.

Angela, already at her father's side, examined the wound, shouting instructions for others to heed as she struggled to remain calm. *'Pak Udir, we must get him to a hospital!'*

'No... 'Gela... no...I must remain here.' Jonathan's pain was intense. He tried to lift his head to inspect the wound, but passed out with the pain.

'How bad is it, 'Gela?' Udir could only see the bullet's point of entry.

'Real bad,' she bit the inside of her lower lip, in angst. *'And we don't even have first aid.'*

'Should we take him to the mining camp?'

Angela's thoughts were running wild. *'I can't tell what damage has been done inside. I'm not sure what it is I should do!'* Then, *'Even if we did get him to the camp alive, the soldiers there would kill him!'*

One of the village women placed a wound cloth under her chief's head.

'What if I go to the foreigner who came with you and ask for his help?'

Angela had already been running this possibility through her mind. *'It will be just as dangerous for you to go there.'*

Udir jumped to his feet assuming control, and called to a number of men. *'Go and get the longboat. Quickly!'*

Jonathan moaned loudly, Angela looking on, fighting back the tears. She took his hand in hers and squeezed to let him know she was there. *'Papa...hold on, Papa. We're sending for help.'*

Udir had the villagers prepare a bamboo stretcher. Attended by loving hands, Jonathan slipped in and out of consciousness and, by the time the longboat had appeared, he had been carefully carried down to the grotto and placed in the shade. Angela remained at his side, talking to her father as the villagers stood their distance reciting their mournful chant, her feeling of helplessness growing with Jonathan's face and lips becoming increasingly pale, his skin cold and clammy as death cast the first of its finite spells.

'I will leave, now,' Udir let Angela know, *'but you must keep an eye out for more soldiers. They will come looking for their comrades.'*

'Then we should warn all the villagers to gather here, at the edge of the forest.'

'I will leave you in safe hands, 'Gela,' Udir promised, issuing orders for the men to remain hidden in the crescent shaped slopes across the river. He then jumped into the longboat and, together with four others, sped away at full throttle to seek help.

Angela sent one of the village women in search of the clothes she had worn earlier. No sooner had she changed when another army helicopter appeared, hovering cautiously over the other wreckage, assessing the terrain and examining the scene below before it slowly descended. Then, as the rescue team poured out of the second aircraft to investigate, Udir's well-positioned warriors opened fire with the 7.62 mm, GPMG M-60 appropriated from the wrecked chopper.

With nowhere to hide, the *Kopassus* rescue team was cut to pieces, their number slaughtered within minutes. Realizing that they had walked into a trap the pilot sent out an immediate distress call, reporting that they had come under attack, and had sustained heavy casualties. Then the radio went dead.

★ ★ ★ ★

Kopassus HQ – Cijantung

General Praboyo stormed from the communications center cursing the incompetent pilots responsible for flying the reconnaissance and rescue missions.

News of the disastrous mission had reached the *Kopassus* Commander during a luncheon organized by the United States Defense Attaché, in Praboyo's honor. By the time he had reached HQ, his staff had received confirmation that the entire reconnaissance team had been killed, and the last transmission from the rescue pilot suggested a similar demise for the recovery team. The General immediately issued instructions for the cessation of all covert activities in the Mahakam area, and a complete withdrawal of all units. No further rescue attempts were to be made, the Commander arrogantly pointing out to his staff that any *Kopassus* commando worth his salt, would make it back in due course.

Praboyo then instructed his deputy commander to send a signal to the Army Chief of Staff, advising that an airborne group of twenty-five *Kopassus* commandoes had been killed in a helicopter collision during demobilization ops in East Kalimantan. Satisfied that he would be able to apportion blame for this unnecessary loss when next in discussion with the President, Praboyo sauntered out to the motor pool and climbed into a purpose-built Jeep, a gift from the British arms industry. Then, with the air of a man who didn't have a care in the world, he drove himself to the suburb of Tebet, where the latest in a long line of conquests would provide that afternoon's interlude.

★ ★ ★ ★

Longdamai Mining Camp

Stewart Campbell completed the inventory check then handed the results to Eric Baird for comparison. 'Never thought I'd find myself out on site doing this crap again.'

Baird agreed. 'Yeah, but if the boss isn't seen doing these checks, it becomes an open invitation for the bastards to steal.'

Campbell heard the helicopter activity somewhere in the distance. 'Seems like their gearing up for something again.' He thought of Angela and her father, wondering how they were faring without much more than whatever clothes they had on their backs after their village had been attacked.

'Heard anything more on the chopper?' Baird asked.

'Had the drilling superintendent on hookup this morning. Says the replacement crew's already in Samarinda. Expects to have the first of his men ferried in by JetRanger later today.'

'Is the drill-boss coming in with the first group?'

'Yes, I asked him to, as he's carrying funds.'

'The pilot's gonna be busy.'

'Well, as he transports one group in, he can take as many back with him on the return flight. No point keeping the others hanging around. We don't want them filling the new crew's heads with all sorts of crap.'

'Good,' Baird glanced across to the other side of the camp. 'Can't say I'd be sorry to see *that* lot outa here.'

'I'll get them paid and on the chopper as soon as it arrives.'

'Hope there's enough to cover all the laborers. They're getting restless.'

'We'll fix them up at the same time.'

Baird was pleased that he had been included in the team. 'When do you expect to recommence drilling then?'

'We should have the bulk of our supplies within a few days, providing the longboats can now travel the Mahakam without hindrance. That would mean we'd be back drilling in, say, three to four days.'

'Word is, over in the Madura shelter, that the army has pulled out from the migrant camps.'

Campbell was reminded that the other geologist was even more fluent in the local language than he. 'I hadn't heard, but can't say it wasn't unexpected.'

'If the Dayaks hit those communities again, we can kiss goodbye any hopes of maintaining a labor force here.'

'I know, and that really concerns me. Indonesian politics at the best of times is difficult to get a handle on, but it would seem that the fighting has abated somewhat, at least for the time being.'

'If you can believe the Madurese, the count was in the thousands.'

'It's possible.' Campbell didn't feel like getting into that, and deftly changed the subject. 'Say, Eric, did Sharon ever discuss anything but work with you?'

Both men had agreed that mentioning the dead geologist should not be taboo. Although Baird had spent a reasonable amount of time working with the woman, their conversations never reached any personal plane. 'No, but I'm sure Mardidi did. He got along much better than me, with Sharon.' Before he could prevent the words from flowing, added, 'and Angela.'

Campbell cast the Australian an inquisitive look then let him be. They strolled back to the center of the camp, avoiding contact with the surly expatriates sitting bunched together, playing cards under a tree.

'Hey, look! Baird's got another boyfriend already.' The drillers' guffaws carried across the clearing.

Campbell was of two minds whether to confront the redneck crew, or let the crack pass. He paused, mid-stride and muttered under his breath, then turned and walked determinedly in their direction, leaving Baird behind.

The men were on their feet even before he arrived, their mood sour, confrontational, and Campbell knew instantly that they were spoiling for a fight. He strode up to the biggest man amongst them, Carl Patrick and drove his fist into the driller's abdomen, then punched the heavy-set man twice in the face, breaking his nose. He turned to Calvin Alderson and grabbed the man by the arm, twisting the driller's wrist before kneeing him savagely in the groin, Campbell now driven by days of pent up frustration and anger. Two of the drillers' mates joined the melee, Baird running as quickly as his legs would carry, screaming for them all to stop. Campbell fell heavily to the ground, got up, struck out again, and suffered a string of head-ringing blows, the fight continuing until the American started to weaken under the onslaught. One of the drillers roared with laughter when Baird arrived, and was still laughing heartily as the geologist picked up a length of quarter-inch rebar, and swung the steel length with style.

The first to be struck was Alderson, the meter-length rod of reinforced steel striking him across the back, and the overweight bully collapsed to the ground. Baird struck again, this time he aimed low, the sound of metal against shin a sure sign of breaking bone – the recipient driller screamed in agony.

'Okay, enough, back off!' Baird lunged at the others with the makeshift rapier, threatening with swordsman-like zeal, protecting Campbell as he pulled himself back up of the ground. 'Stew, are you okay?'

The American held his jaw, moving it from side to side to check, then rubbed bruised ribs. 'I'll be okay. And you?' he asked, as surprised as any that the normally docile and somewhat effeminate Baird had come to his aid.

'I'm fine.' Baird raised the rebar above his head. 'As for you assholes, you don't have much more time to go around here. I don't want any more of your crap – I'm sick of it. Okay?'

Alderson was hunched, holding his leg in pain, while Carl Patrick remained sitting on his backside holding a dirty T-shirt to his bloody nose. The others, so caught by surprise when Baird had entered the fray, immediately became subdued. Campbell dusted off, limping away to his cabin in search of the jar of Tiger Balm he always kept on hand whilst Baird, enjoying his elevated position to manhood status, strutted across to the canteen-mess, ordered coffee and laid the length of construction material on the bench for all to see.

★ ★ ★ ★

Udir had instructed his men to remain with the longboat while he covered the remaining distance, on foot. He passed through the perimeter area with the presence of a ghost, easily penetrating the army's slack security. Following Angela's instructions regarding the camp's layout, he was moving boldly towards the expatriate quarters, when the fight between the foreigners first broke out. The distraction worked in his favor, Udir managing to slip into Campbell's cabin, unseen, where he waited anxiously, praying that the American would find reason to return soon to his accommodations.

When Campbell did enter, Udir was standing totem-pole-still with a finger to his lips, the appearance of the *Penehing* elder in the room catching the camp boss totally off guard. 'Who…?'

Udir jumped straight in. *'Tuan, Angela sent me. Her father has been hurt!'*

Campbell's heart skipped a beat. *'What happened?'*

'The army, they attacked again.'

'And Jonathan?'

'Shot, in the chest.' Udir marked the point on his own body with a finger.

'Can he be moved?' Campbell started to think ahead. There would be no chopper availability until the new drilling crew arrived. By then, Jonathan Dau could easily have died.

'Angela says he shouldn't be moved. She asks that you come, now, with me, and bring any medical supplies you have.'

Campbell was aware of the substantive medical stores maintained onsite, as required by the mining industry. *'These won't be of much use without a doctor.'*

Udir stepped forward. *'Is there anyone here who would help?'*

Campbell's mind raced. He hadn't taken first aid training, something he now deeply regretted. *'I don't think so.'* And then, *'How did you get into the camp, unseen?'*

Udir was losing patience with Campbell. *'By longboat, of course! My men are waiting upriver. We don't have much time, Tuan. Please, can we go back now?'*

Campbell nodded. *'Wait here. I'll get the medical supplies.'* He left the Dayak elder and hurried across the open field towards the emergency storeroom, fumbling for the keys in his pocket as he went. He saw Baird sitting alone, eating, and shouted. 'Eric, need your help – now!'

Baird dropped his cutlery, grabbed the steel rod thinking that the drillers had started brawling again, and ran after the American, catching up at the storeroom entrance as Campbell unlocked the door and rushed inside.

'What's up?'

'Emergency. Angela's father's been shot.'

'The chief?'

'Yes. The army came back for whatever reason and he's taken

one in the chest.'

'Shit. Then I wouldn't bother hurrying, Stew. Chest wounds are usually fatal, even under the best conditions.'

'We've got to get him medical attention.'

'The chopper?'

'Won't get here fast enough.'

'What, then?'

'I'm gonna take whatever we have, over there now.' With this, he scoured the shelves cursing, unable to identify anything that might be of use.

Baird shook his head impatiently, grabbing items and throwing these into a small, cardboard box. 'You should take these, and some of those, and heaps of these bandages.' He continued to fill a box, clucking his tongue as he went.

Campbell stared in wonder at the other man. 'You know about this stuff?'

'Sure,' Baird continued searching the shelves, 'you learn a lot about self medication working out in the field.' He raised his eyebrows at the American and proffered the hastily produced first aid kit. 'What are you waiting for?'

Campbell knew he had no choice. 'Come with me, Eric, I don't know the first goddamn thing about any of this?'

Baird had anticipated the request. 'Okay, let's go.'

'You're sure?' Campbell had expected less.

'It's probably going to be safer with you than being left here, alone. Besides, I'll get the opportunity to talk to Mardidi, right?'

'One of us should be here for when the chopper arrives.'

'We've still got three, maybe four hours. That's enough time.'

They returned to Campbell's cabin – Udir with a knife raised when they entered unannounced, Baird petrified when confronted with the fierce looking elder and his intimidating *golok*. Campbell soothed both men, giving the *Penehing* a baseball hat for disguise. *'Here, wear this – it'll make you look like one of the local drillers. No one's going to pay you much attention if we all go together. Walk between us, and you won't be noticed.'*

They escorted Udir back through the camp, the smaller man's figure partially hidden by the American's larger frame. They cleared the camp perimeter without challenge then followed the elder as he guided them through the thick forest, to the longboat. No sooner had they climbed into the vessel when the powerful outboard roared into life, and they were on their way – Baird more apprehensive than he cared to let on – Campbell solemnly silent throughout the short voyage as he examined his own, mixed emotions for the woman who'd rejected his love – but who now called upon him in her hour of need.

★ ★ ★ ★

The Philippines

When Alexander Kremenchug's flight touched down at Ninoy Aquino International Airport, he understood why Pope John Paul kissed the tarmac upon arrival. His aircraft had caught the backend of a typhoon, the severe buffeting for most of the Eva Air flight from Taipei the worst he'd experienced in years. The mining entrepreneur had phoned from Vancouver, Alfredo confirming that he would be available to discuss Sharon's affairs. Kremenchug proceeded through immigration into the flight arrivals' baggage hall, zigzagging through the maze of trolleys blocking passage past the carousels, and surrendered his declaration to customs. Kremenchug was traveling light. The official waved him through with disinterest and, once he'd changed a few dollars into Pesos, he chartered a taxi and was on his way to the late General Dominguez's residence. The traffic appeared to be even more congested than he remembered, exacerbated by the heavy rain, the journey taking just under two hours.

★ ★ ★ ★

'*Mabuhay,* Mister Alex,' Alfredo greeted Kremenchug at the door dressed in sandals and light, casual clothes. He escorted his visitor to the late general's study on the second floor, Kremenchug surprised at the ease with which Alfredo assumed the role of host. Nothing had changed in the setting, the furniture, the pictures and other decorations – everything was exactly the same, as before.

Alfredo invited Kremenchug to sit, and poured coffee. 'I apologize for the weather. Even we Filipinos dislike too much rain. Have you booked into a hotel?'

'No. I can't stay long. My flight out leaves in about four hours.'

'I can understand your haste in wanting to leave. This is not a good time of the year to be visiting our beautiful country.'

Kremenchug was impatient to cut through the pleasantries. 'Maybe I can make it back some other time.' He went directly to the point. 'Alfredo…' he hesitated, 'may I call you Alfredo?'

The older man laughed pleasantly. 'Of course, of course, Mister Kremenchug.'

'Then you should just call me Alex.'

Another smile. 'Thank you… Alex.'

'Alfredo,' Kremenchug started again, 'I understand that this is a difficult time for you, but first let me say how deeply sorry I am with Sharon's tragic loss.'

Alfredo fell silent, acting out the part for which he'd been groomed. Kremenchug continued, 'As discussed over the phone, I come here today not only as Sharon's friend but also as a director of the Borneo Gold Corporation.' Alfredo knew that Kremenchug was watching his reactions closely. 'Alfredo, are you able to tell me anything about Sharon's private papers…such as correspondence with bankers in the British Virgin Islands, or anything which might relate to, say, Dominion Mining?'

Alfredo had expected Kremenchug's visit. Sharon had prepped him at the time of her uncle's funeral, in what to say, and do. His face became serious and he frowned, as if deep in thought. 'When you phoned, I went and examined all of Miss Sharon's private papers. There was nothing amongst these that relate to…where did you say?'

'British Virgin Islands – the place is called Road Town, on the island of Tortola,' Kremenchug prompted.

'Ah yes. I'm sorry, I did not write any of our conversation down.

I'm getting old and, unfortunately, forgetful…Road Town…Tortola?' he mused, '…no, Alex, I'm certain that there was nothing amongst her papers mentioning such a place.'

'Are you sure?' Kremenchug insisted, 'what about Dominion Mining?'

Alfredo continued with the game. 'Dominion…Dominion,' he moved his head slowly from side to side, 'no, I'm sorry, there was nothing about this company either.'

'But there *has* to be something!' Kremenchug's voice started to climb, 'It's just not possible that all her records have simply vanished into thin air.'

Alfredo appeared sympathetic. 'I agree, Alex. It does seem unusual.'

'Did she have a close friend, perhaps?' Kremenchug started to grab at straws, 'or a distant relative – anyone at all whom she might have entrusted with such documents?'

Alfredo responded as he had before, this time scratching the side of his head for effect. 'Apart from the General, I was the only other person who was close to Miss Sharon. We were like family, Alex.' At this point Alfredo lost his lines and paused, Kremenchug concerned that the old man might break into tears. Recovering his thoughts, Alfredo continued. 'Miss Sharon was like my own daughter. When she died…' his voice trailed off, the Filipino proud of his own performance.

Sharon had briefed him well. With her uncle gone, she had not hesitated in revealing what she planned, Alfredo's participation paramount to her success. The former solider had worshipped the General and, in return for his years of dedication and love for Narciso Dominguez, Sharon had promised to bequeath the mansion to him, the bequest to include a guaranteed income for the rest of his days. When news of her 'death' was relayed to him via Vancouver, Alfredo had acted the part of the loyal, grieving manservant. He knew to expect Kremenchug to come hunting for information, delighted with Sharon's intelligent assessment of the man's character, and the preparations she had so carefully put into place, to ensure her life in anonymity.

'Alfredo,' Kremenchug shuffled his shoes then lifted his eyes from the deep carpet. 'There is another matter I also wish to raise with you.'

'Please, Alex. You were a close friend of Sharon's. What can I do to help?'

Kremenchug cleared his throat nervously. 'It's about the General's gold.'

Alfredo had extreme difficulty in containing himself. Sharon had warned that this man was predictable. He responded with a confused face. 'I don't understand.'

Kremenchug tried again, his impatience rising, 'The gold in the cellar, Alfredo. You know, the gold Sharon and the General took me down to see!'

The aging Filipino appeared bewildered. 'Miss Sharon took what was left, moved after the General passed away.'

'Where to?' Kremenchug's spirits rose with this news.

'She didn't say.'

'You weren't around to assist?' Kremenchug asked suspiciously.

'There wasn't all that much left,' Alfredo was offended by the innuendo.

'But there was hundreds of millions!'

'No. What was stored in the cellar was all there was.'

'That can't be! Sharon said there was more than two hundred million!'

'I can assure you, Alex, if there ever was such an amount, it was definitely not stored here.'

'Then where?'

'I don't have the answer to that question. I would be happy to take you down to the cellar, to see for yourself?'

Kremenchug knew there was something dreadfully wrong with this picture. Sharon was professional with everything she embraced, yet she died without leaving any power of attorney, no will or any other documents suggesting that she had ever even existed. Kremenchug was convinced that Alfredo was lying to keep Sharon and her uncle's estate for himself. Confronted by this conclusion, Kremenchug realized that he had come to another dead end.

'I'll see myself out,' he rose, refused the outstretched hand, then stormed down the stairs and outside, never to return.

Alfredo stood with hands clasped behind, emulating his beloved General's frequent stance when peering through the study's windows, a broad smile holding his cheeks apart as he watched Kremenchug exit, the entrepreneur's slumped shoulders a sure sign of defeat.

★ ★ ★ ★

Former Longhouse Site

Campbell's first impression was that of a war zone. Torched earth and blackened stumps were all that remained of the once magnificent longhouse – the scarred scene a fitting backdrop to the helicopter wreckage strewn along the foreshore. By now, the soldiers' bodies had been removed, the heads secreted away by the younger men, the torsos dumped unceremoniously into the fast flowing tributary. Campbell recognized the military markings, noting that two choppers had gone down here. He returned Angela's wave as the longboat came to rest.

'Can you see Mardidi?' Baird asked anxiously.

'No, but I'm sure he's there somewhere.' Campbell left the Australian to bring the medical supplies, while he forded ashore and hurried to Angela's side.

'Thank you for coming, Stewart.' She placed a cheek against his, avoiding his lips. *'My father is over there, in the grotto.'*

Baird caught up, carrying the supplies. *'Sorry about your father, Angela. Hope this will help.'*

'Thank you Eric, we are all very grateful for your help.' She turned and led the way. *'He's been slipping in and out of consciousness. I don't know how long he's going to last.'*

'We'll do what we can,' Campbell's tone lacked confidence, not knowing what to expect. He had never seen a gunshot wound other than in photographs, and prepared himself for the worst. When they approached, Jonathan Dau lay quietly, his breathing shallow.

'Has he coughed up any blood?' Baird asked.

'Belum,' Angela answered, 'not yet', the word filled with ugly promise.

'His pulse is weak.' Baird's hands moved over the chief's body. *'Are there any other injuries?'*

'*No.*'

'The bullet didn't exit?' he asked, surprised.

'There's no other wound,' she explained.

Baird caught Campbell's attention, the exchange not lost on Angela.

'He's going to die, isn't he?'

Baird nodded. *'Unless we can airlift him to a hospital where they can operate, he's unlikely to last much longer, Angela. I'm sorry. Stewart?'*

'*We could take him back to the mining camp and wait for the first chopper. Can we move him?*'

'Better than leaving him here to die.' Baird had commenced cleaning around the wound.

'Angela, it's your decision. What do you want us to do?'

Angela fell into uncertainty. *'He won't go.'*

'*Look at him, Angela, he doesn't have any choice!*'

'Stew,' Baird interjected, 'why not have the chief picked up directly from here? That way he wouldn't have to be moved twice – lifted in an out of a bloody boat alone could kill the man.'

Campbell supported the suggestion. 'It makes sense. Once we get him airborne, they'd have him on an operating table in Samarinda within a couple of hours.' And then, to Angela, *'It's your call.'*

'*What if the pilot refuses to come?*'

'I'll see that he does.'

'*How long before you could get one here?*'

'There's a Bell JetRanger coming in with a new crew in a couple of hours.' He then addressed Baird. 'If you don't mind staying behind, Eric, I'll go back to camp and then return with the chopper when it arrives.'

'That's fine by me.'

'Angela, when your father regains consciousness, tell him what's happening.'

She looked down at her father then back at Campbell. *'Will you go to the hospital with him, please Stewart?'*

'You're not going?'

'I have to stay here with my people,' she placed her hand on his, her voice filled with sadness. *'It's how it must be.'*

Baird understood the Baron reps' problem. 'If you want, I can take care of things at the camp while you're away?'

Campbell knew he had no choice. *'Okay, I'll take your father to Samarinda. And as a precaution against the JetRanger coming in early and leaving us behind, I'd better get back.'*

Angela summoned Udir. *'Pak Udir, please take Mister Stewart back to the camp.'*

'Will I wait?' Udir asked.

'No.'

'Then, if Jonathan is in good hands and you don't need me right now, I should go upstream and buy supplies. Our people are hungry, 'Gela. I will take charge of the gold, as Jonathan requested.'

Campbell had not understood the *Penehing* communication, but it was clear to him that the aluminum case in Udir's hands had something to do with it. Angela's mind had been preoccupied with her father's demise, and when the elder held the case up for all to see, she realized the error immediately.

'Pak Udir, take that away. It will make them suspicious.'

'Isn't that Sharon Ducay's briefcase?' Campbell rose and walked over to the elder, reaching out to take the metal case in both hands. Udir resisted and, in the struggle, the briefcase fell to the ground, the Filipino airline sticker on the back of the case, apparent to all. Campbell glanced questioningly at Angela, who turned away. *'It is Sharon's! How in the hell did it get here?'*

'Now's not the time, Stewart. Please, let it be.' Angela could do nothing, now that Udir had given the game away.

'Where did you find it?' Campbell bent down on one knee to check the contents, whistling when he discovered the gold bars inside. 'Well, I'll be damned!'

Baird glanced over. 'What did you find?'

The American geologist held one of the gold bars for the others to see, then returned it to the case. He glanced through the personal papers, which included Sharon's passport and other credentials, his curiosity aroused even further when he opened a long, thin, cardboard container and found an industrial syringe inside. 'Now what in the world would Sharon have needed this for?'

Baird looked at the American, and the syringe in his hand. 'Is that what I think it is?'

Campbell held it out for him to see. 'Was she a diabetic or something?'

'I have no idea. What does it matter anyway, she's dead.'

'What is it?' Angela had no idea what they were talking about.

'I'm not sure. Now, do you wan to tell me where he got the case?'

'He found it – at the edge of the river.'

'Here?'

'Yes,' she lied. It was becoming less difficult.

'How?'

Angela Dau gave Campbell her back as she returned to tending her father. *'The case was in one of the helicopters that came to attack us.'*

Now Campbell was truly confounded. *'Was there a Captain Subandi amongst them by any chance?'*

'Yes. He was the one who shot my father.'

When Campbell had challenged the pilot with respect to Sharon Ducay's effects, he recalled the Captain denying any knowledge of the briefcase. Campbell had not pursued the issue, as it seemed irrelevant at the time. The question that now came to mind was, *how the case had suddenly reappeared, and why were there gold bars inside?*

Udir stood threateningly, his hand extended demanding the gold be returned. The American extracted Sharon's passport and placed this in his back pocket.

Baird glanced up from what he was doing, caught Angela's expression and then continued applying the dressing. He placed a piece of gauze over the wound, covered it with a pad of cotton wool and then applied adhesive strips to hold everything in place. He understood enough about first aid to know that if the chief lost much more blood, he would go into hemorrhagic shock. 'Stew, why don't we leave that to later?'

Angela smiled at Baird in gratitude. As for Campbell, she hoped that he could accept her explanation, as this would be as close as he would ever get to the truth. A chant she had learned as a child passed her lips, the rhythmic sounds not lost on those around – Baird silently applauding when the case containing gold bars and other damning evidence was surrendered to Udir without any further comment.

Somewhere above, recuperating in the canopy, a hornbill stirred.

★ ★ ★ ★

Jonathan Dau floated through a semi-comatose state, his mortal presence dependent on reaching the altered state of consciousness to survive. The *Penehing* shaman drew upon reserves of *tenaga-dalam,* the inner strength that supported life during this altered state of mind, and was able to draw upon the collective unconsciousness of those who had gathered at his side. He opened his eyes and called for Stewart Campbell.

'*I... want to speak... to this man... alone.*'

'Yes, Papa.' Angela took Baird by the arm and stepped away, leaving the American with her father.

The chief timed his words, so that each breath would carry them away. *'Do... you really love... my daughter?'*

Campbell took Dau by the hand. *'Yes.'*

A crooked smile appeared on the shaman's face. *'You... could have her... as your partner... if only you knew... how.'*

'You should rest. We can talk when you've recovered.'

Bloody spittle appeared on the *Penehing* chief's lips. *'Why can't... you understand?'* Jonathan lifted his head and blood dripped back into his damaged lung. *'It's... not Sharon who is...blind... she wants you...to commit...to, ...the...Penehing people.'*

Campbell leaned closer. *'Please, don't talk anymore. You must rest.'*

'I...am going...to die. You...must listen to me!'

Over Campbell's shoulder, Baird could see the spillage from Jonathan Dau's mouth and, not quite out of earshot, Angela's fingernails dug deep into her palms as she fought against tears.

'No more, Pak Jonathan, please!' Campbell pleaded.

'No...Stewart...you must listen. Angela truly...loves ...you. You must...be deserving...of her love...in her eyes. Help her.'

'Pak, you must rest. I am going to take you to the hospital in Samarinda.'

'No...Stewart Campbell...you cannot. Listen to me. I will soon...die. 'Gela will accept...you...if you give our people back...our land. Say it...now. Promise me...that you will...do this for 'Gela...and my people?'

Campbell took Jonathan Dau's hand and held it firmly, the warmth emanating from the *Penehing* leader creating an inner glow he would never, in this lifetime, be competent to describe. Compelled, Campbell gave his word. *'You have my promise.'*

Jonathan, satisfied, then collapsed into a coma.

Angela closed her eyes and changed the tempo of her chant, calling upon ancestral spirits to deliver her father from his peril, other villagers adding their voices until the grotto was alive with a melodic hum, one designed to comfort and ward off eternal sleep. Baird moved back from the chief's side, rose, and walked away, checking the hundreds of faces for Mardidi as the prayer softened to a whisper.

A gentle breeze touched the grotto, and a soft rustle of wind brushed the *meranti* tree's canopy high above, where a hornbill tested its damaged wing. The bird's caw fell upon the gathering and there was a hush, Angela accepting the ominous sign. *'The ancestral spirits are here to comfort. My father is in their hands now.'* She turned to Campbell and urged him to hurry. *'We may not have much time.'*

* * * *

Longdamai Mining Camp

When the Bell JetRanger arrived carrying members of the new drilling crew, Campbell immediately took the superintendent aside once he had introduced the members of his team.

'Look, I know this is big ask, but I need to have you do the best you can without me for awhile.'

'What's going on?'

'Local politics; there's a very popular tribal leader who will surely die without our help, and could possibly die even with it. I need to take the chopper over there and pick him up, fly the man to Samarinda, and remain with him for at least the next twenty-four hours. We would know by then whether he's going to make it or not and, either way, I'd be back on site by tomorrow night.'

'You don't need to ask my approval, you're the 'site-ops' manager.'

'I know that. It's just that I don't want you to get your nose out of joint because of something you weren't briefed about.'

The Canadian drill-boss placed his hands on his hips. 'I've got no problem with it providing it doesn't interfere with my getting the program restarted on time.'

'Good, thanks – oh, and there's one more thing – those guys are troublemakers of the first order.' Campbell indicated the outgoing drillers standing around, packed, ready to leave. 'I had planned on sending them back starting today but can't afford to have them onboard, causing trouble with the Medevac. Also, I wouldn't want them paid until I return. If they become troublesome, you won't mind keeping them in place?'

The superintendent's eyes narrowed. 'Not at all.'

Campbell spoke to the charter pilot, giving him instructions as to what was happening. Then, without further ado, he climbed aboard and directed the pilot to the Longhouse Island site, the journey taking less than ten minutes.

★ ★ ★ ★

Longhouse Island

'It was kind of you to come to help, Eric. Diperbanyak, terima kasih – I am deeply grateful.'

'I'm sorry that I can't do more.' They communicated in whispered tones whilst maintaining vigil at Jonathan Dau's side.

'Stewart will return soon. Hopefully, we'll be able to get him to a hospital

in time.'

Baird had been waiting for an appropriate moment to ask. *'Say, Angela, I know this may not be a good time but, what was behind Mardidi's leaving the mining camp with you the other night?'*

When Angela cast her mind back over the past four days she recalled that it was Mardidi who had enticed her down to the river. She threw Baird a condemning look. *'You think he left the camp with me?'*

It was now the Australian's turn to appear puzzled. *'You were seen going down to the moorings together. If he didn't leave with you, and he's not back in the camp, then where is he?'*

Angela realized that neither Eric nor Stewart were aware of events surrounding her kidnapping, and the subsequent attempt on her life – that Sharon's death was originally arranged as a sham, and the man who had killed the Filipino was, in fact, Jonathan Dau. The *Penehing* village had been destroyed and hundreds killed by *Kopassus* commandoes, her people attacked by helicopter gun-ships and, amongst all of this, she had forgone the love of another. For Angela, Baird's problem paled in significance when compared to what her fellow villagers had suffered over the past few days. The consequences of Mardidi's betrayal were immeasurable – Angela now firmly convinced that, by delivering her into the soldiers' hands he had set into train the disastrous events of the past twenty-four hours.

'I can assure you, I Eric, honestly don't know.' Angela's recollection of the conspiracy to murder her in Sharon's place remained vague. What had followed when she'd been seized, dragged through the water and into the longboat, was unclear. She had lost consciousness before Mardidi had been ordered into the vessel, and had not been witness to his death.

'All of his clothes and personal stuff are still back at camp,' Baird said quietly. *'He wouldn't have left all that behind if he hadn't planned on returning. It would seem that you were the last one to speak to him.'*

'I don't know what more I can say, Eric, other than...'

''Gela?'

Jonathan Dau opened his eyes and called his daughter's name.

Angela lovingly held his hands in hers. *'I'm still here, Papa. Please, don't talk.'*

''Gela... it's... time.'

'No, Papa! You must hold on! Please Papa!' She started to cry.

'Now...you...must be...strong...for the Penehing...people.'

'Please, Papa, please. Hold on just a little longer, they'll be back with the helicopter soon.'

The chief's last breath escaped, audibly, with the finality of death – Angela's lips quivered, her hands locked together with her father's as the villagers gathered by her side, hushed with grief.

★ ★ ★ ★

Baird rose, and walked slowly down to the river where he remained, cross-legged waiting for Campbell's return – privately questioning Angela's version of events with respect to Mardidi's disappearance. Her explanation had been far from convincing – Baird's naturally suspicious nature compelling him to believe that something calamitous had befallen Mardidi, and that Angela was somehow connected. For the first time since his lover's disappearance Baird was faced with the real possibility that Mardidi might be dead. With this chilling thought occupying his thoughts he looked skywards towards the sounds of an approaching helicopter, then climbed to his feet and moved out of harm's way.

★ ★ ★ ★

'We're too late?' Campbell was met as he climbed out of the chopper.

'You couldn't have done anything to save him.' Baird's demeanor was solemn, but not because of the shaman's passing. 'In a way, it's probably better that he died here and not on the way, if you know what I mean.'

Campbell sighed with exasperation. 'If only we'd been better equipped.'

'Well, we weren't. Can I get a lift back?'

The American was surprised with Baird's cold retort. 'When I'm ready,' he responded curtly then walked towards where Angela and others were in prayer.

'I'm so very sorry, Angela.' He had reached down and lifted her

gently, Angela placing her head upon his shoulder as she made her request.

'Stewart, everything we owned was destroyed in the fire. We can't prepare his body for the funeral. I feel so ashamed.'

'What do you need?'

Angela lifted her head and dabbed eyes with the back of a wrist. . *'It's our custom to cleanse the body before burial. We should anoint the remains with fragrances then place it in a white shroud. Look around you – we don't even have food let alone perfumes.'*

'Give me a list. I will get it for you.'

'Oh, Stewart, if only you would!'

'How much time do you have before...' he hesitated, *'before whatever comes next.'*

'My father was like a king to his people. The cleansing ritual must take place within the first day of his death.'

'You'll have to forgive me here, Angela, if I sound insensitive. It's just that I am totally ignorant as to what is required.' Campbell held her comfortingly. *'I guess none of us was prepared. Who would have thought...?'*

Angela stepped back wiping a deluge of tears as she fought to maintain control. *'Once the first ritual is over, he will lie in state until the end of the waning, crescent moon, the final farewell will coincide with the new moon.'*

Campbell immediately understood. They would need whatever traditional applications substituted for formaldehyde. *'I'll be back within a few hours. Now help me prepare that list.'*

★ ★ ★ ★

Campbell and Baird departed, leaving Angela with a promise that she would have her supplies.

'What's eating you?' Campbell had to raise his voice to be heard above the JetRanger's whine.

'Don't know what you mean.'

'Come on, Eric, you were walking around with your chin on the ground ever since I got back. What happened?'

'Nothing.'

'Okay, if that's how you want it, that's fine by me.'

They touched down back at the mining camp, Campbell going directly to the drilling superintendent. 'There's been a change of plans.'

'What happened?'

'Their chief died.'

'Will that impact on what we're doing here?'

'No, but I need to keep the chopper for another couple of hours. Also, I need to take whatever longboats we have, and load them with supplies.'

'What do you have in mind?'

'Well, the way I look at it, we've got a major public relations opportunity here to bring the locals back on side. We have sufficient stores and further supplies are on the way. I'm going to take as much as can be loaded into the longboats and send it upriver to the *Peneh-ing* settlement.'

'The Penny who?'

'The local Dayak tribe.'

'Not my position to say, but shouldn't you be clearing this with Toronto?'

'No, I'm taking full responsibility for this one on my own.'

'Okay, Stewart, how can I help?'

Campbell extended his hand. 'Thanks. I was counting on your support. I have to take the chopper further upstream and locate one of the other Dayak communities. While I'm gone, how about over-seeing the loading of supplies for me?'

'No problem – just point me in the right direction and you can consider it done.'

Campbell called out to Baird. 'Want to join me?'

The Australian shrugged his shoulders sullenly. 'Are you going back?'

The American waved a piece of paper. 'Later. Right now I need to fill these requests – could do with your help, Eric.'

Baird strolled over. 'What's on the list?'

'Stuff that we most likely won't find anywhere but in a Dayak village.'

'Okay,' Baird took the list and started reading. 'Yeah, you're right. You won't find most of that around here, even over in the Madurese quarter. Are you thinking of flying out to other villages in the area, cause, if you are, your gonna scare the bastards shitless arriving in a chopper?'

'We don't have enough time to take river transport. Besides, I've arranged to have whatever vessels are on standby, loaded with supplies.'

'I thought Udir was already on the river doing that?'

'He isn't aware of the chief's death.'

'Well, let's get on with it then,' and the two men set out in the helicopter again, catching up with Udir at the very first Longhouse along the way.

When they told him of the shaman's passing – the elder didn't express any surprise.

'*He knew he was dying – and so did I.*'

'*Then why did you leave when you did?*'

The *Penehing* looked Campbell straight in the eye. '*Because Jonathan would have wanted for Angela to assume his position of priest and, with my support, she will also become their new leader. They cannot survive on empty stomachs and these days will be difficult enough for 'Gela without having also to worry about such things. I will fill their bellies and then we will ask for them to vote for a new leader.*'

Tchick! Baird clucked and pulled a wry, contemptuous face, while Campbell simply shook his head. '*All right, let's fill this list and get Udir's supplies back to the villagers. Udir, do you feel like a ride in the helicopter?*'

The offer was declined, and once they had finished loading they left the elder behind, returning directly to the grieving, longhouse island community. When darkness fell, the last of the supplies ferried from the mining camp had already been stored and kerosene lanterns burned brightly, the *Penehing* women working throughout the night to prepare Jonathan Dau's body for the complex rituals that lay ahead.

★ ★ ★ ★

Chapter Thirty

THE *Penehing* CREMATION

Before the introduction of Christianity, Catholicism and Islam, all Dayak tribes embraced *Kaharingan,* a belief that ancestral spirits controlled life – and that these ancestors had originated from the Seventh Heaven and arrived on earth in the form of hornbills. According to legend, the hornbills then assumed human form, their numbers multiplying across the then borderless island of Borneo, spreading from Tantan Puruk Pamautan in the upper reaches of the Kahayan River to Tantan Liang Mangan Puruk Kaminting in the shadow of Mount Raya, across to Datah Tangkasiang in West Kalimantan's Malahui River region and, finally, in Puruk Kambang Tanah Siang towards the source of the Barito River.

When word of Jonathan Dau's death swept through the provinces with the speed of a raging forest fire, *Aoheng* and related *Penehing* communities along the greater Upper Mahakam River Dayaks were immediately galvanized into action. From Longbangun to Bukit Batubrok, and across to Nahabuan, Dayak men prepared longboats and gathered their guns and spears, while women, who expected the ceremony would bring them into contact with relatives from Lasan and Batukelau, packed additional food and prepared cloth for the farewell rituals. Then, as the news continued to spread to cities as far south as Palangkaraya and west to Pontianak, priests, chiefs, village councilmen and Longhouse foot-soldiers laid out their finest apparel, in readiness for the long journey to honor a most important man. There would be none who would not go to pay their respects to the *Penehing* leader, Jonathan Dau. This would be a farewell, fit for a Dayak King.

★ ★ ★ ★

Groomed by her father in Penehing customs and traditions as his heir and successor, it was only natural that Angela assume the role of chief priestess and officiate at Jonathan Dau's funeral. Angela believed unquestioningly, as had her *nenek-moyang,* her forefathers, that death signified the passing of one's soul to the spirit world. And, in a moment of quiet deliberation decided that it would be fitting for the funeral arrangements to be extended, to include all *Penehing* who had perished as a result of the attack on her Longhouse village. The announcement was greeted with great enthusiasm and approval, Angela's first act as shaman comforting those whom she would one day lead. That the lives of those lost would be celebrated together with their chief's passing, comforted young and old, and in their minds they visualized a great gathering of spirits to accompany their loved ones through this all-important passage.

But, first, the dead had to be purified before they could enter their other world, their spirits freed of ghosts or other unwanted spirits and liberated from all earthly desires. While a number of village women assisted Angela prepare Jonathan's body throughout the night, others collected remains gathered from the Longhouse ashes and placed these together, in a communal lot. Then, as the day following Jonathan's death came to a close, *madu pete,* the first stage of the ritual was undertaken.

Angela led the bathing ceremony to cleanse the spirits of the deceased in readiness for the 'final feast', when the spirits would be 'taken to dinner', the rite signifying a last farewell, simultaneously alleviating grief, and sorrow, amongst those left behind. Cleansed, the body was then treated with perfumes and the Dayak equivalent of formaldehyde, before being dressed, Angela arranging for men who had been charged with the responsibility of building a rattan, throne-like structure, to place the chief in regal pose. Jonathan Dau would remain sitting in this posture, treated by all as if still alive. Once the initial rites were completed, he would be carried to a thatched-roofed, timber hut constructed by the village men, the walls carved with pictures of tigers, dogs and dragons. There, he would remain, until the arrival of the new moon.

Traditionally, discourse regarding what belongings should accompany the deceased would have occurred. However, as all of Jonathan's material possessions had been destroyed in the great fire, Angela selected items from the list Campbell had filled, and placed these around her father's corpse in accordance with *Kaharingan* beliefs.

The setting was ready and already many guests had arrived, the second stage of the ceremony, *makan berawaq,* 'giving the dead their dinner', commenced. Custom dictated that only close family participate in this rite, and Angela invited her cousins to join with her in eating from the specially prepared tray covered with *tedung hiting* leaves, which had been placed beside the chief's head. Campbell had returned from the mining camp and spent the entire day – and had still not eaten, the memory of when he last ate at such a gathering still fresh in his mind, and he graciously retreated, electing to view the ceremony from afar – unprepared in every way for what was taking place.

Outside the grotto, and stretching along the river as far as he could see, bamboo, kerosene-fuelled flames flickered, providing light to the thousands that had already arrived to pay their respects. To Campbell, who had envisaged a ceremony filled with mourners in solemn role, the carnival atmosphere more resembled a festival than a funeral, for everywhere he looked food was being prepared in a mood that was far from somber. Plaited, *purun* mats covered with colorful fruit dotted the landscape, the air ripe with the pungent smell of *durian,* fried *tofu, tempeh* and *ubi kayu,* and freshly slaughtered pigs, goats, chickens and even monkeys were carefully skewered then placed over patiently fanned, deep charcoal fires. Fierce-faced Dayak elders, their heads adorned with precious and colorful feathers, mingled with their peers from neighboring tribes, the greater their import, the more pronounced their strut, Campbell engrossed in the ongoing spectacle. The hours passed, during which he avoided contact with Angela as she continued with her duties, the number of new arrivals already exceeding several thousand. Then, as if by telepathic command, the mass of visitors fell silent, the air electric with anticipation as the visitors became deathly quiet.

Campbell did not recognize Udir in his traditional costume, a chameleon, his body covered from shoulder to toe with feathers – his head, decorated with plumes. Jonathan's dearest friend had assumed the role of a family member, his function, to awaken the dead by calling out during the night. Udir took center stage and filled his lungs, the shrill piercing call he let forth sending shivers the length of Campbell's spine. He would discover that this ritual procedure would continue, four times each night, until the chief's body was transported to its final resting place.

Morning found Campbell asleep at the river's edge. Angela appeared, holding a cup of steaming coffee at his side. *'You don't have to remain here all the time, Stewart,'* she smiled, her face a radiant glow. *'It's is considered acceptable to come and go, and you have other responsibilities – as do I.'*

'Did you get any rest?' he asked.

'I'm not tired.'

'None at all?'

'My time to rest will come later in the day.'

'Is there anything else that you need?'

Angela smiled, and ran her hand across the stubble on his face. *'You've done so much already.'*

'I wish I could do more.' Campbell sipped the coffee. *'You must be very proud that your father has so many friends.'* While he slept, more than fifty more longboats had arrived, the river now incredibly congested with traffic.

'They will continue to come until the final day.'

Campbell climbed to his feet and stretched. *'Be careful, or this island will sink under their weight.'*

Angela surveyed the scene before them. There were more than three thousand now in attendance. *'They respected my father. He was a good man.'* She reached out and touched his cheek again. *'Even though you mightn't agree.'*

Campbell was immediately defensive. *'This past week has been a confusing time. And, you would have to agree that I haven't exactly seen the Penehing people in the best light.'*

'I overheard my father's words to you, Stewart. What will you do?'

He had already given considerable thought to the impossible commitment made to Jonathan on his deathbed. He was not so naïve as to expect he could successfully persuade Baron Mining to abandon Longdamai, and hoped that Angela would understand. *'I would be willing to try and move mountains for you, Angela, and I think you know that to be true. But, we have to be realistic. There is no way that a multinational mining company is just going to pack up and leave billions of dollars in gold behind.'*

'Then why did you give a dying man your word?' Angela had now stepped away and crossed her arms, her stance more defiant than he had ever seen.

'Because, your father was dying, 'Gela, and he deliberately put me on the spot.'

'Please don't call me 'Gela.'

'Okay, Angela, what if I just resign and leave?'

'Then who will stop them?'

Campbell didn't wish to argue further. It seemed that she had inherited her father's obstinate genes. *'Okay, Angela, I know this is a bad time. How about I come back and visit again, in a few days?'*

'Yes,' she agreed, *'that will be fine. Ask Udir to arrange to have someone take you back.'*

There was something else he had omitted telling Angela and, although this was not the most appropriate moment he could have chosen, nevertheless, Campbell felt that he had to be forthcoming with respect to what was happening at the mining site. *'They're going to recommence drilling, very soon.'*

'It doesn't come as any surprise.'

'Fine, Angela, just so you know and don't lay the blame on me.'

* * * *

Longdamai Sial Mining Operations

Campbell returned to the mining camp in time to observe the first of a series of new holes being commenced to verify earlier results. The replacement crew had settled in quickly, the old, having been paid out in full, were already history. Madurese laborers had received their outstanding wages and there was an air of normalcy surrounding the camp. The new drillers, working through ten-hour shifts, produced results at twice the speed of their predecessors.

From the outset, it had been established that the procedures for extracting and recovering samples for testing would, in every way, be identical to the methodology used under Sharon Ducay's supervision. However, in order to maintain the integrity of the results and place these beyond question, previous labs were not engaged – instead, Baron commissioned a Singapore-based analytical laboratory to conduct the fire assays. As earlier drill results indicated that the deposit lay between thirty-two and thirty-eight meters, samples were taken every one meter, and transported out by helicopter immediately to Samarinda, then onto the Singapore laboratory via the direct charter service. Wishing to maintain their newly established relationship with the multinational miner, the Singapore technicians worked to turn the results around, as requested by Baron Mining, within forty-eight hours. From the time the first hole had been drilled to the hour results were relayed to Toronto, the process had required only six days.

On the ninth day, when the results indicated beyond doubt that there was no evidence of any substantial gold showings present in the samples, the Baron Mining board collapsed in a collective, apoplectic fit. Within hours Phil Samuels was already winging his way to Singapore, where he would speak directly with the laboratory's management to establish whether it might have been possible that they might have erred. The Canadian, company director remained in the City of Lions for a further forty-eight hours until subsequent samples had also been assayed. Then he contacted the Baron Mining chairman and broke the bad news. As executives moved to damage control, family and close friends of the laboratory technicians commenced short-selling the conglomerate's stock. It would require another month's drilling before they could be certain but, by then, tens of thousands around the world would already know that they had been duped.

It was all over.

During that week Campbell attended the ongoing burial ceremonies as frequently as he could, traveling to and fro by longboat as the helicopter proved to be disruptive. Then, on the day before the new moon appeared and Stewart Campbell learned of the contradictory drilling results, he was confident that Jonathan Dau would have his wish.

★ ★ ★ ★

The Philippines

Alfredo stood staring out the window with the phone in his hand, wondering how Maria could still have the courage to confront the Doberman pincers. He observed that she carried the child on her hip while attending to the animals, reminding himself to raise this with the maid later. Alfredo had felt responsible for the attack Maria had sustained those years before, when the dogs had savaged her outside the servants' quarters. He turned his attention back to the conversation at hand. It was Bartlett – and the news was not good.

'I waited as per our agreement, Alfredo. She just didn't turn up.'

The late, General Narciso Dominguez's trusted lieutenant heaved a woeful sigh, recalling Sharon's penchant for discipline, and always getting it right. Also, he had no reason to doubt Bartlett, as the captain had long earned their trust. 'We must assume that something has happened to her.'

'Everything seemed to be going along fine. There was even a report on the BBC. There's no doubt that someone fell, or was thrown out of the chopper, the only question is, who?' The *M.V. Rager's* captain waved to the impatient hooker waiting at the far end of the bar, then turned his attention back to the matter at hand. He'd stash Sharon's advance of a hundred thousand in gold for a rainy day. 'What do you want me to do?'

Alfredo was struggling with uncertainty. 'Might be best if you remained on standby for a while, just in case.'

'Fine by me, Alfredo – you know how to get hold of me if there's anything new.'

Alfredo rang off then sat staring at the phone. It was so unlike Sharon to initiate changes to a plan without signaling such intent. For the first time since the scheme had been concocted, he became deeply troubled, and prepared to countenance the possibility that Sharon may have lost her life.

★ ★ ★ ★

Longhouse Island

Jonathan Dau's farewell ceremony continued with the waning moon. Each night, Udir repeated his shrill calls to waken the dead, while during the day, Angela maintained her demanding routine as the newly anointed, *Penehing* priestess. The crescent shaped sign had all but disappeared from the sky when the now twenty-thousand strong Dayak gathering again fell to a hush as young warriors lifted Jonathan's rattan and bamboo throne, and carried the dead shaman to the thatched-roofed hut built beside the river. They placed the chief in the center of the room together with an effigy carved in his likeness, then left the chief to commence his final journey. Angela followed, entering the small building and closing the door behind. In total darkness the priestess moved to exorcise her father's spirit by commencing the *muqaak tok* rites, reciting the mantra she had learned as a child. With carved dogs, tigers and dragons silent witnesses to the spiritual world she stomped her feet and called upon ancestors to gather and purify her father's soul, the ritual continuing until Angela, threatened with exhaustion, exited the hut carrying a small statue representing Jonathan Dau, and cast it into the river.

★ ★ ★ ★

Uncomfortable with the constant, and often hostile stares Stewart Campbell moved even further away from the crowded grotto. Something pulled at his trousers and he looked down to find Yuh-Yuh with outstretched arms, terrified by the strange events and hordes of unfamiliar faces. *'Don't tell me she's forgotten all about you, too?'* Campbell patted Yuh-Yuh on the head and the ape responded by offering the American a gift. At first, in the poor light, Campbell had no idea what it was that she held onto so possessively. *'Come on, Yuh-Yuh, what have you got there?'*

In one hand, Yuh-Yuh carried a very dirty and crumpled Akubra. Campbell led the *orangutan* towards a bamboo torch where he examined the find, straightening the broad-brimmed hat into some semblance of its original shape. Then, holding the evidence in his hands he looked over the heads of the crowd to where the sky was ablaze with fire, his mind dwelling on the nagging question as to how Sharon Ducay's unmistakable Akubra could possibly be there.

He had seen the Filipino board the helicopter – an hour later she was dead. When he'd looked inside the Bell 205 he was positive that he would have remembered seeing the briefcase, or her hat, had either been there.

★ ★ ★ ★

Udir stepped forward and handed Angela a flaming torch. She lifted it high for all to see – twenty thousand Dayaks watching with great expectation as the priestess called out again, beseeching the spirits to take their leader, and unite Jonathan Dau with his ancestors. She paused, offering a final, and private word for her father, threw the torch into the air and withdrew, the assembly roaring with delight as flames spread across the thatched roof and lit the sky. Within seconds, the methyl alcohol-laced timber building exploded into a ball of flame, Angela shielding her face from the intense heat as the structure imploded and, in one fleeting moment she caught a glimpse of her father, larger in death than he ever was in life staring blankly through the flames. Startled, she cried out *'Papa!'* – but the chief was already gone.

An hour passed before Campbell swallowed his concerns and rejoined the ceremony. Yuh-Yuh had accompanied the American, straddling his waist for only part of the way until, panicked by the fire, the *orangutan* dropped to the ground and fled, Akubra intact. By then, Campbell had arrived at the conclusion that the presence of both Sharon Ducay's hat and briefcase on the island had to be connected in some way with the helicopter pilot, Captain Subandi. And, as he was also dead, he doubted that the question would ever be resolved. He made his way through the thinning crowd to where Angela continued leading with prayer, amazed at her resilience, and so deeply moved by what she'd become.

When morning drifted across the Mahakam lifting night's dark veil, the fire was spent, and blood-red embers cooled, Angela scooped a handful of ashes from amongst the charred remains and, with somnambulant gait, drifted towards the river's edge. Morning's first rays blinked life across the landscape and the young priestess raised her head, the soft chant spilling from her lips to bless Jonathan Dau's ashes as she sprinkled his mortal remains over the Mahakam waters. The air moved, and Angela lifted her face to the heavens sighting a hornbill gliding silently, overhead, following the proceedings. With raised, open palms and a soft puff off the lips, Angela sent dust from the ashes floating skywards and, with a gesture of finality, washed her hands in the river, looked back into the sky, smiled, and blew the guardian hornbill a kiss.

★ ★ ★ ★

With the celebrations over, the main body of visitors gradually dispersed, leaving whatever they had brought for the ceremony to their impoverished, *Penehing* cousins. Udir had summoned the villagers to vote while the opportunity prevailed and, without exception, Angela Dau was accepted as her father's replacement, both spiritually, and as the Longhouse spokesperson. It would still require some years before she would be appointed chief. While women gathered bolts of cloth, utensils and tools, their men set to work building temporary shelters and pens for recently acquired livestock

– gifts from Dayak villages, both near and far – Angela and Stewart, now bidding farewell.

'You know that the Penehing will always be grateful for all you have done?'

Campbell held Angela's hands in his. *'It wasn't their gratitude I sought.'*

She lifted forward onto her toes and kissed him tenderly. *'Come back and visit, anytime. In the Penehing community, Stewart Campbell will always be welcome.'*

'Is there anything else that you need, anything I can help you with before I leave Longdamai?' He had already informed Baron of his intention to resign.

'You've already done so much.'

'How are you all going to survive?'

Angela swept an arm across the landscape. *'We will rebuild our Longhouse from forest timbers. Thanks to the generosity of the other communities, we will have sufficient food to carry us through until the first harvest. The gold will help us replace the generator and other essential items. What we really need is capital to build schools and hospitals, not just the Penehing, but for the entire Dayak nation. We remain abandoned by Jakarta and our resources plundered, Stewart. That's why I must stay with my people.'*

'At least work will cease on the Longdamai land.'

'There'll be others,' she reminded, *'and when they leave, there'll still be the scar.'*

'Baron Mining will want to re-drill most of the area, just to be sure.'

'How long will this take?'

'A month or two – three at the most.'

'Why did Sharon do it?' Angela knew only of the insurance fraud.

'We'll never know. My guess is she was somehow involved with Eric Baird's foreign partner – most likely selling shares.'

'Poor Eric,' there was so much she would never reveal to Campbell. *'What will he do?'*

'Expect he will fold his tent like the rest of us and find somewhere else to go.'

'You're not leaving Indonesia?'

'No, I'm not. But, I certainly could do with a break.'

They stood alongside the longboat that would take him back to the mining camp. Yuh-Yuh, seeing her favorite people side by side scampered across and threw long, hairy arms around their legs and hugged fiercely.

'Well, this is it,' he reached down and stroked Yuh-Yuh's crown. Campbell held Angela by the shoulders. *'If you need anything, just call.'*

'I will miss you, Stewart Campbell.' When their cheeks brushed – only Angela's remained dry.

An outboard engine roared into life and the American climbed onboard. Within moments they were underway and, as they neared the river bend and were about to disappear from view he turned, and waved a final goodbye.

★ ★ ★ ★

Road Town – Tortola – British Virgin Islands

'We have confirmation from the correspondent bank that the funds have been deposited as requested, Mister Daworth.'

Charles Daworth of the British Virgin Island law firm, Rankin, Daworth & Double adjusted his spectacles then continued reading the file. A clipping from the International Herald Tribune had been stapled to the inside cover, Sharon Ducay's photograph staring back mockingly, with a smile.

'Then, as of today, Dominion Mining Incorporated will no longer exist. Have you prepared the notices?'

The lawyer's secretary placed another file on his desk. 'I will start the company deregistration process, immediately you sign.'

Satisfied, Charles Daworth executed with a flourish of the wrist then handed both files to his most efficient assistant. 'One would think that Miss Ducay must have had a premonition moving her funds at the time that she did. Still, all the same, messy business that, falling out of a helicopter.'

'Was Miss Dau related to Miss Ducay?'

Daworth shook his head. 'I have no idea – I didn't inquire when

Miss Ducay set up the new accounts.'

'Do you think Miss Dau will be requiring our services?' the secretary asked, always hopeful for new business.

'I wouldn't think so,' Daworth said, already moving on to other matters. He looked up, surprised that she was still standing there. 'Don't dally, my dear, we've still a great deal of work to do.'

The secretary exited, returning to her workstation where she completed the mandatory filing to the BVI authorities. By mid-afternoon, following the path of so many other shelf companies whose beneficiaries had suddenly disappeared, Sharon Ducay's Dominion Mining Incorporated ceased to exist.

★ ★ ★ ★

Chapter Thirty-One

SEPTEMBER 1996

Eric Baird

Baird stood on the jetty surveying the deserted site recalling what it had been like when they'd first arrived. Gone were the coconut stands and towering trees that had encircled the original clearing – in their place, scarred landscape and bitter memories of what had once been mooted as the greatest gold fine in history. The camp had literally disappeared in less than a month. The shanty-styled Madurese dwellings had been burned to the ground along with the barrack-styled cabins that once housed mining staff, both acts of retribution by the departing and disillusioned labor force. The heli-rigs and other equipment had been repatriated first, followed by the drillers – the camp torched by the few remaining Madurese once they had searched the site for whatever might have been overlooked by management.

Baird had been surprised that Stewart Campbell had been amongst the first to leave. Baron Mining' executives, already convulsing from the leaks and a formidable, investigative press were eager for Baird to remain onsite, as he had been present during Sharon Ducay's tenure as senior geologist. Finally, when subsequent, randomly drilled holes substantiated earlier suspicions that samples had been tampered with, Baron pulled the plug and ordered an immediate demobilization. Following Mardidi's inexplicable disappearance, the exposure of drill test result tampering, the unexplainable attacks on the *Penehing* villagers and Sharon's questionable death, Baird suspected that his lover had somehow become innocently embroiled in one or more of these incidents, resulting in his death.

The Australian geologist returned to Jakarta and his rotund partner, retired AVM Subroto who, upon discovering that Alexander Kremenchug had turned his share of the BGC windfall into yet another disaster, suffered a severe stroke. The consultancy company, P.T. Subroto & Associates continued to function for less than a year before it closed. In the eyes of the mining industry, Baird's association with Sharon Ducay had left him professionally tainted and, upon cessation of activities at the Longdamai site, he failed to secure any further employment. His wife, Pipi lost interest once she discovered the true state of his financial affairs, and abandoned all hope that he might ever take her to Australia. They continued living separate lives – Eric Baird, living in the shadows of his own despair can now be found in an Indonesian shelter for the dispossessed, suffering from AIDS.

★ ★ ★ ★

General Praboyo

When James Salima, CEO of the Asian Pacific Commercial Bank learned that the Longdamai deposit was nothing short of a scam and informed his father, Lim Swee Giok, there was immense waling and gnashing of teeth amongst Palace sycophants as they bemoaned their paper losses. Bobby Djimanto (a.k.a. Tan Khu Sui) the timber and logging king, although not involved in the mining escapade, nevertheless took advantage of the situation to seek compensation for revenue lost as a result of the Kalimantan unrest. The First Family had been unusually embarrassed over their involvement in the Longdamai gold project further exacerbating existing sibling rivalry amongst the wealthy children. Concerned that family turbulence might prompt a settling of political scores, General Praboyo was promoted to Lieutenant General and assumed command of *Kostrad,* the Strategic Reserves.

Within the year, Indonesia's economy would falter, in another two, it would totally collapse. Under the malevolent General's stewardship, troops would clash with university students, shooting many in cold blood. Riots would erupt throughout the Republic, the situation would be further destabilized by Praboyo's Machiavellian attempts to turn the anti-government groundswell against the Chinese. *Kopassus* commandos who had served in the Mahakam operations would be deployed, dressed in civilian attire around the capital, with orders to target young Chinese women. Hundreds would be raped publicly in the streets, and many murdered. The Chinese would flee the country – the ensuing flight of capital crippling the nation economically, spiraling the world's largest Moslem population towards even greater turmoil.

With his sights on the Presidency, the ambitious and arrogant Praboyo would attempt a *coup d'etat*, and fail. Condemned by his ugly past, he would flee the country to live in selective self-exile, leaving a legacy that would result in the deaths of tens of thousands of his fellow countrymen.

★ ★ ★ ★

Kremenchug & Fielding

Disbelief spread from continent to continent, plunging gold stocks on world markets once it was revealed that the Longdamai prospect's incredible drilling results had been fabricated. Trading was suspended in all stocks associated with the former Borneo Gold Corporation asset, severely bruising James Salima's Asian Pacific Commercial Bank and Baron Mining's image. Stockholders screamed foul, accusing Christopher Fielding and Alexander Kremenchug of impropriety and fraud. The directors of BGC panicked, instructed their banks to move funds to offshore destinations, then quickly packed their bags before the Canadian Stock Exchange watchdogs could summon the executives.

In Vancouver, when the police finally got around to raiding the BGC offices, they found these deserted – with all the company's records destroyed, or removed. The BGC President, Fielding, followed his money to the Cayman Islands where he would remain safe from extradition. Fielding purchased a most magnificent villa and retired, content to live out his days in the style both his former wives had always wanted. Out of harm's reach, he ceased sending alimony.

As for Kremenchug, he knew it would be foolhardy to revisit Indonesia and, in consequence, gave the Republic a wide berth before finally returning to Perth in the spring. There, upon arrival, he was arrested as he cleared immigration and charged with fraud, the matter relating to his involvement in the Meekathara fiasco, of some years before. At the end of his trial, Kremenchug was incarcerated for five years amongst other fallen entrepreneurs, in the same prison as the disgraced Alan Bond.

★ ★ ★ ★

Stewart Campbell

After an extended sabbatical, the American geologist returned to Indonesia as the country moved to the brink of civil war, and a new president ascended to the throne. The country fell even deeper into recession as a result of its economic collapse, and foreign investment deserted the nation in favor of more viable destinations. The Republic's new leadership fumbled, and within months an even greater crisis confronted the mining industry, when autonomy was granted to provincial heads to negotiate directly with foreign investors. Overnight, existing gold mining operations were plagued with illegal miners occupying sites, and local communities preventing access to existing operators until excessive demands were met. Interest in Indonesian mining opportunities waned, but, in spite of political uncertainty and financial difficulty, Campbell still managed to survive.

When Campbell learned, with growing concern, how ethnic violence had again erupted throughout the Kalimantan provinces, he immediately suspected that Angela would be somehow involved. Often, he would lay awake at night in wistful mood, wondering what might have been had Captain Subandi not shot the shaman, Jonathan Dau. Stewart Campbell had written, but Angela had not replied. They would never be reunited, Campbell's lost love leaving an unfillable void.

★ ★ ★ ★

Angela Dau

Angela Dau's popularity increased amongst the *Penehing* and other Mahakam tribes, both as shaman and *Penehing* spokesperson. The Longhouse had been reconstructed along the riverbank adjacent to the grotto, the new complex incorporating classrooms for the children. A generator had been purchased and would be sent, stripped down to enable transportation, from Samarinda. There had not been sufficient funds to purchase a replacement parabolic dish and television – such luxuries would have to wait.

On the fortieth day following her father's cremation Angela had marked the occasion by celebrating *Hadui Taknaq*, a ceremony which commemorated the passing of the deceased's spirit to the world of spirits believed to congregate on the peak of Mount Batubrok. It would seem that even in afterlife, Jonathan Dau would continue to be influenced by the rising, full moon, which coincided with the occasion. Carrying gifts for the mountain repository, the young priestess had hoisted the *purun,* woven bag over one shoulder then followed her father's footsteps through the forest, climbing the slopes to the secluded caves where Jonathan Dau had presided over her indoctrination, six years before. There, she lit candles and unfolded the prayer mat, placing this on the ground. Then, as her father had done before her, Angela completed the ritual cleansing of her body and mind, stepped outside the cavern and offered her first prayer to the rising, full moon.

Soon, she could feel the effect of weightlessness as her induced state took hold, her body slowly lifting into the air and floating into timeless space. As she traveled through her mind, images of her father drifted by whispering encouragement, offering words of wisdom for Angela to abide, the journey lasting throughout the night.

Emerging from the trance Angela experienced an exhilaration she'd never felt before, the sensation one of final purification. With first light, she stood, refreshed, gazing down the slopes towards the Mahakam and over her realm, savoring the moment when a gentle morning breeze suddenly touched her cheeks. The priestess knew without having to search the sky, that her guardian spirit, the hornbill would be there, watching over her, as a mother does a child. Re-entering the cavern, she bent on knees facing the altar, and repeated her shaman oaths. When the ritual was finished, she rose and made her way through the disguised passage that connected to the inner sanctum, carrying candles in each hand.

Upon entering, light chased shadows across the cavern's walls and Angela was reminded of her first visit to this most secret place, and her reaction to the skeletal collection. As before, she cast her eyes along the gallery lined with human skulls, so carefully arranged in order by the generations of shamans that had preceded her. She placed the candles where these would cast the most effective light and, after careful deliberation removed the skull that had enjoyed Jonathan Dau's place of pride, resting atop of a pole. *'Sorry, Father, but he has to go,'* Angela said, lifting the skull and positioning it amongst the closest row, replacing her grandfather's prize with a trophy of her own, carried into the mountains inside the *purun* bag. Then, she stepped back to admire her work, brushing Captain Subandi's skull with the palm of her hand, Jonathan Dau's words reminding the priestess of her first encounter with the gruesome contents of this chamber.

'Why take another's head, Papa?' she recalled asking.

'Retribution, retaliation, revenge, honor, prestige...all of those things,' she remembered the chief answering. *'Nothing will change the way men feel towards each other. People will continue to kill each other. The manner in which they extract satisfaction is of no consequence. And, our actions are*

ordained by the spirits.'

Whereas Angela had once been shocked and saddened by her chief's disclosure that he continued with the practice of taking enemy heads, now she was a strong proponent of maintaining this custom as it represented an essential link to ancestral past, and acted as a powerful deterrent against outsiders. She had assumed charge over the collection and would not discourage its growth – providing trophies were not of Dayak blood.

In considering her responsibilities to her people, Angela accepted that her future would require that she marry – and that her partner be of pure, Dayak lineage. When the time arrived she would canvas other communities to identify an appropriate mate. As for Stewart Campbell, she deeply regretted that their relationship had advanced as far as it did – recognizing that it had been doomed to fail from the outset. Now, she could not even afford to have him as a friend.

Angela understood clearly that the road forward would be arduously long. First, the Kalimantan tribal groups would need to be united – and then, autonomy, if not independence, would no longer be out of the question. She would become a magnet for the other Dayak tribes. Then, the billions of revenues extracted by Jakarta from the resource rich provinces could be redirected to benefit Kalimantan's indigenous peoples – oil, gas, and fertilizer production -they would have it all!

Angela Dau had become her father – and her presence amongst the Dayak communities was creating a new dynamic. Blessed with Jonathan Dau's oratory skills and shrouded in shaman mystique, the priestess had become more than a *dukun* to the *Penehing* – many amongst the elders already recognizing her potential as a future voice of all the Dayak people. She became the leading proponent of the determination to infuse younger generations with the religious and cultural values that had molded their ancestors – and worked tirelessly towards encouraging dialogue amongst the indigenous, Borneo tribes so that one day, there might be a commonwealth of Dayak communities existing together, as one nation.

Angela Dau became a powerful force for the Dayak people, but remained incognizant of the enormous wealth held by a Hong Kong bank, in her name – the three hundred million dollars representing what might have been, the realization of Jonathan Dau's, and now her own impossible dream.

As for the desecrated ancestral Longdamai land, time would heal the scarred landscape when the jungle reclaimed the site, once again ensuring that the secret of Longdamai would remain intact. The real irony that this location had been so arbitrarily selected for drilling by Sharon Ducay, and failed, would be lost on the *Penehing*, and the world, forever. Had the Filipino Chief of Operations only instructed her crew to continue drilling further to a depth of another five meters, they would, in fact, have discovered a mountain of gold, even greater than that promoted by the falsified reports.

★ ★ ★ ★

Epilogue

Hong Kong – December 1996

'Maria!' Alfredo called, now breathless, struggling to keep up with the young, ebullient, Filipino woman. 'Be careful, these Hong Kong drivers don't care about pedestrians!'

Having crossed the busy Central intersection and narrowly missed being run over by one of the British colony's manic taxi drivers, Maria slowed, but not for long – squealing with delight as she propelled herself forward, propping in front of a window display. 'It's so beautiful! Please, please, Alfredo,' she begged with childish affectation, 'please buy this for me?'

Alfredo caught his breath, and peered into the store. 'Later.' He took her firmly by the wrist. 'It is time to go.' He squeezed, firmly. 'Do you remember what to say?'

Maria threw Alfredo a petulant look. 'And what if I forget?'

The aging Filipino flinched, then placed his hand behind the maid's back, steering her gently towards the bank. 'Think of your daughter, Maria. Just think of the child.'

★ ★ ★ ★

Months before, when the *M.V. Rager's* captain reported Sharon Ducay's failure to materialize off the Samarinda coast, Alfredo remained hopeful that Dominguez's niece was still alive. The Philippines Embassy in Jakarta had arranged for 'Sharon's' remains to be sent home to Manila where her body was cremated, as stipulated in Sharon's notes. Alfredo was aware that the ship's captain, Bartlett had limited knowledge of her plan and, apart from the helicopter pilot, there was no one else who knew that the real Sharon Ducay remained alive. But, the enigma of her disappearance rested heavily on his mind.

When long, slow, painful weeks dragged into months with still no word, Alfredo reluctantly accepted the worst, firmly convinced that had Sharon been alive, she would have contacted him. The *M.V. Rager* was no longer on standby and, with a constant barrage of journalists banging at the mansion's gates requesting interviews, sadly, Alfredo decided it was time to move on. He retrieved the sealed, manila envelopes from the cellar vault in search of some clue of her disappearance and, upon examining Sharon's documents, learned of the fortune sitting idly in the Hong Kong bank. Staggered by his discovery, Alfredo was then absolutely certain that she had met with foul play. With Sharon, and, he postulated, the woman whose identity she had intended to assume now both dead, Alfredo was then faced with the dilemma of finding someone to take their place. After considering this conundrum over a period of weeks, he determined that there were really only two prerequisites that person would have to meet. The first, she would have to pass inspection and, secondly, the woman would have to be someone he could control. He decided that the unmarried maid, Maria, with coaching and considerable makeover, could meet these requirements.

Alfredo had commenced work immediately and, by the end of November even he had been surprised with the results. Angela Dau's signature had been mastered and Maria's cosmetic transformation was adequate, in his opinion, for her to pass as the Indonesian woman. Maria's reward, the late General Dominguez's mansion Sharon had left to Alfredo, and a modest pension for life. And, as additional leverage, Maria's child would be left behind in the gardener's care to ensure that she complied.

* * * *

Smith, the newly promoted, assistant manager for new accounts smiled so widely his cheeks hurt, the ambitious banker aware that his predecessor's promotion had been linked to the opening of this Indonesian client's account. Perhaps, he hoped, Miss Angela Dau's visit would make more than just his day. The relative junior officer fussed as Maria took her place across the table, accepting her documentation with recently acquired flair. 'Thank you, Miss Dau.' He opened the passport, the photograph receiving less than a perfunctory check. 'That seems to be in order.' Then officiously, 'I believe you wish to open another account with us?'

Alfredo's ashen face recovered with the identification test being passed. He remained rock-still praying that weeks of rehearsals had placed Maria in good stead and, more importantly, that she did not forget her lines.

'Thank you, Mister Smith, yes. I wish to have funds transferred to the following accounts.' Alfredo wanted the funds out of Hong Kong before the colony's handover. He would ensure that the paper trail would disappear, and with it, all evidence that the wealth was now his.

The banker accepted the typed instructions and read these quickly, with lips and finger tracing the words. 'You wish to close the account?' he asked, disappointment evident in his scratchy voice once he totaled the amounts. Suddenly his day was not looking so good.

'Yes.' Maria sat posture perfect – then, smiling demurely, 'You do still have my money, don't you?'

Embarrassed, the expatriate banker coughed, rose, and unconsciously commenced wringing his hands. 'There is no problem, Madam. I will have the transfers seen to, personally.'

Alfredo's heart stopped pumping with Maria's impromptu deviation. He ground his teeth, a myriad of worry lines suddenly appearing above his cheeks. The banker gave the aging Filipino a curious look and for Alfredo, the landscape went suddenly blank.

'Call an ambulance!' the banker shouted, as the gray-headed figure slumped to the floor.

Maria knelt down and called his name. 'Alfredo?' But, the former aide did not respond. She felt for a pulse and, finding none, recognized the incredible window of opportunity that had come her way. She remained by Alfredo's side until bearers arrived and removed his body then returned, confidently, to her seat.

'You're not accompanying the gentlemen, Miss Dau?' Smith asked, surprised.

The maid glanced at the transfer forms in the banker's hand and, with a newfound confidence, acted out the play. 'Yes, but first I'd like to cancel those instructions, Mister Smith,' she said, with affected sigh, 'under the circumstances I think I'll just leave the funds in your bank after all. Well, perhaps not all of it. I will need a cash advance.' With which, the relieved officer tore the transaction orders in half, and set these aside for the shredder.

* * * *

Maria never went to the hospital where Alfredo had been pronounced dead on arrival – she went shopping, instead. Having filled a dozen suitcases with clothes and presents, she caught the next flight home to Manila. With her Gucci handbag stacked with dollars to see everything right, Maria was now far less concerned that the gardener might hurt Alexandria, her daughter from that one lustful night arranged two years before, at Mistress Sharon's request. Maria returned to the Philippines and paid off the gardener and, the following month, made application to migrate to the United States. Upon acceptance, she took Kremenchug's illegitimate child and moved to the United States. With the generous, monthly interest payments of one million dollars forwarded by the Hong Kong bank each month, Maria and Alexandria were, indeed, the most fortunate incidental beneficiaries of what had been Indonesian Gold.

* * * *

Postscript

That the Canadian mining company, BRE-X Minerals' Busang project in Kalimantan went from being 'the world's largest gold deposit' to the greatest gold and stock swindle, is now history – as is the death of the BRE-X Chief Geologist, a Filipino by the name of Michael de Guzman who 'fell' from a helicopter over a Borneo jungle, two months before the fraud was revealed. During the 1980s and 90s, there was, indeed, a gold rush into Indonesia, amongst the many bona fide operators, a plethora of the would-be-mining entrepreneurs originating from Australia and Canada whose machinations created a most distorted image of Indonesia's mining opportunities. As the owner of the only minerals analytical laboratory operating in Kalimantan during the initial rush for the precious, yellow metal, and the drilling company which carried out a substantial amount of investigative drilling along the East Kalimantan seaboard, I can assure the reader that there were some extremely contradictory press releases made by foreign exploration companies during that time.

★ ★ ★ ★

Dayaks are the predominant non-Muslim tenants of the island of Borneo. 'Dayak' is a generic term for Borneo's two hundred indigenous tribes whose traditional lands host one of the world's greatest rain forests and embraces the mighty Mahakam River system. Sadly, the Dayak culture in the (Indonesian) southern half of Borneo is vanishing under the overwhelmingly dominant Javanese, and Jakarta's poorly planned, transmigration policies. Today, more than three quarters of West Kalimantan's population live below the poverty line, encumbered by an unemployment rate in excess of forty percent. Marginalized, the Dayak people remain without political or economic influence as their lands continue to be plundered and their forests stripped, now fertile soil for growing dissent – their future mortgaged by Jakarta's powerful elite. In the twelve months following the close of this story, between Summer of 1997 and Spring of 1998, more than five million hectares of land was scorched across the province of East Kalimantan along the Mahakam River, once a gateway to promise – now a road to destruction.

Over the past fifteen years, there have been three major Dayak uprisings aimed at driving Javanese and Madurese migrants from Kalimantan. On each occasion, there were thousands of transmigrants slaughtered – the most recent, in 2001 when more than four thousand were killed, many amongst their number young children, whose decapitated bodies were stacked along roadsides for the international press to see. Unfortunately, the historical and ethnic imperatives which have led the Dayaks to resort to headhunting practices of old, remain misunderstood by their new colonial masters, the Javanese.

★ ★ ★ ★

Of all the birds in Borneo, the hornbill most readily stirs the imagination. The Dayaks remain deeply superstitious and consider the hornbill to be a descendent of the mythical bird-spirit, this belief originating from the mists of time when mankind was in chaos, and ancestors sought help from the Supreme Being. According to the legend, an eagle was dispatched – and rejected. The Supreme Being then assumed the shape of the eagle, returning to earth, copulating with a beautiful woman, creating the first shaman – the Son of Wisdom and female energy. Dayak warriors believe that, in battle, the spirit enters their body rendering them invisible, providing them with great speed and the capacity to fly. Today, the Dayak remains as superstitious as his forefathers, the village dukun, or shaman, often the most important member of the community.

★ ★ ★ ★

Some events, based on historical fact, have been shifted in time. Amongst these, the March 1960 MiG-15 attempt on Soekarno's life when an Indonesian MiG-15 pilot sympathetic to *Permesta* rebels strafed and rocketed the Presidential Palaces in Jakarta and Bogor. The pilot eventually ran out of fuel near the town of Garut in West Java, and crash-landed in the rice paddies. There were no casualties. However, the reference to the expatriate, Bell helicopter pilot being beheaded and his body cannibalized, is true. In 1971, I flew with Lee Archer of Commonwealth Aircraft Corporation, on the first successful, non-stop helicopter flight from Singapore to Jakarta in a Hughes 500. Three weeks before, our competitor, Bell had attempted the same crossing, incredibly running out of fuel short of the Java coast. Some months later, the same pilot attempted a flight across Kalimantan's forests, became disorientated in the haze and mist, hit the treetops and crashed into the jungle. He walked away from the accident only to be killed by Dayaks who had never seen a helicopter before.

★ ★ ★ ★

As for the references to Yashamita's Gold, this hoard did, in fact, exist. In the Philippines, during the closing months of World War II, several of Japan's highest-ranking imperial princes, under orders from the emperor's brother, Prince Chichibu, hid tons of looted gold bullion and other stolen treasure in caves and tunnels, for later recovery. This was the wealth of many Asian countries, accumulated by those dominions over thousands of years. Expert teams accompanying Japan's armed forces had systematically emptied treasuries, banks, and art galleries to build this hoard which was sealed, entombing the engineers to maintain the secret. Yamashita Tomoyuki escaped to Tokyo and later surrendered to the Americans. Former Filipino President, Marcos, is believed to have obtained part of his personal fortune from the hoard. In 1995 the Philippine Government recovered two metric tons of platinum (valued at US$500 million), from some of the caches.

The reference to (Danny) Dewanto Danusubroto, the Kosgoro President Komisaris is also true. I knew Danny well and, in fact, met with him in the Sahid Jaya Hotel the day before he was arrested for complicity in his mistress' murder. At that time, Danny was President Suharto's personal Palace aide. He was sentenced, and incarcerated for nine years.

★ ★ ★ ★

My fictitious character, AVM Subroto's story of the Australian Sabre jet incident when an ejection seat killed a farmer is accurate. In the early 1970s the Indonesian Air Force (AURI) accepted a squadron of Australian Sabre fighters and US – T33A trainers. Prior to this, AURI aircraft were predominantly from Soviet supply. The accident described over Java rice fields actually occurred. These Sabres were originally based in Malaysia. When finally recalled, the ageing aircraft were flown back to Australia, refueling at Tuban Airport in Bali in 1969. At that time, my Attaché, Group Captain Brackenridge flew to Bali to oversee this operation, sending me to the Indonesian Fleet Air Arm base in Djuanda, near Surabaya where I was present as the Embassy representative to assist facilitate the covert transit of our Mirage fighters northbound. The entire squadron landed, refueled and, apart from one near mishap, departed safely, in less than thirty minutes.

For months, we enjoyed the probing questions and speculation from our Soviet counterparts, as to how the Mirages managed to arrive in Butterworth, Malaysia. When this airfield was closed for repair and the squadron moved, temporarily to Singapore, the Commanding Officer was lost during a night training exercise. During a traumatizing week which required my hanging out the side of an RAF helicopter searching the Malacca Straits' communities for evidence of the disaster, an elderly, toothless woman on the island of Rangsang took me aside, and produced part of the officer's last remains, an ankle bone which she had secreted in an old, Bushell's tea bottle. A piece of the Mirage, showing the aircraft's number was also recovered. As for the antiquated Sabres, once refitted, the aircraft were gifted to AURI, within the framework of rapprochement, and future defence cooperation.

★ ★ ★ ★

It would be appropriate here, for me to acknowledge the help and support of others who have contributed to this three-year effort to produce, hopefully, an entertaining tale. In consequence, I wish to acknowledge and thank the following: Kal Muller, for the brilliant Dayak photo on the cover. Mario Cicivelli for the great cover artwork. Keith Cooley, for the full moon timetables. Danny Galbraith of Geodesy Information Center AUSLIG for direction on the moon's cycles and perspectives. Zaynab El-Fatah, for the precise Ramadan dates. Donald Lim, General Manager of the Hotel Equatorial in Kuala Lumpur for hotel layout confirmation and the wonderful stay. Eric Web, for his assistance with drilling, and assay procedures. Terry Bibo, for the wealth of information he has given and, finally, "Colonel Zack" for his weapons' advice and, more importantly, his lifetime support and friendship.

★ ★ ★ ★

In closing, I wish to state emphatically that I have the greatest respect for the Javanese and their culture, and am honored to enjoy so many close friendships with these fine people. This book is not meant to denigrate any of the many ethnic groups that make up the Republic of Indonesia – my second home.

Kerry B. Collison
Melbourne
Australia

Glossary

ABRI	*Angkatan Bersenjata Republik Indonesia* (Indonesia Armed Forces)
Aceh	Indonesia's most westerly province
Ada apa, sih?	What's going on?
Adjal	(the belief that) the hour of death is pre-destined
Aduh!	An exclamation – to complain, moan or groan.
'Aduh, dong,	
'Gue pasti basah!'	'Oh no, I'm sure to get wet!'
Ageng Mangir	A Javanese who plotted against his Sultan
Ajak	Invite
Ajikwa River	West Papuan river
Akubra	Wide brimmed, Australian 'outback' hat
Amok	To run amok
Ancol	Jakarta, coastal resort strip
Antara	Indonesia's main news service
Aoheng	One of the main *Dayak* tribes of Borneo
Apokayan River	Kalimantan river
Arak	Arrack, overproof liquor
ASEAN	Assoc. of S.E. Asian Nations (10 members)
Avtur	Also, A1 aviation fuel – refined kerosene.
Ayo	Come on, let's…
Babi	Pig

Bahasa	Language
Bahau	Borneo tribe
Baik	Good, okay
Bakin	Indonesian Coordinating, Intelligence Agency
Bakwan	Shredded carrot, cabbage, bean sprouts and shallots, mixed in batter.
Balikpapan	Major oil & gas town in East Kalimantan
Banci	Hermaphrodite – homosexual
Bangsa	People of…
Bangsa Moro	Filipino (Mindanao) secessionist movement
Bangsat	Asshole
Bapak	Father, (Sir) respectful form of address to older man
Barong Tagalog	Traditional, formal Filipino shirt
Bataks	Central to Northern Sumatran indigenes
Batik	Printed cloth
Belum	Not yet (leaves the word 'no' open)
Beringin	Banyan tree
Betawi	Original Jakarta area, pertaining to its inhabitants
BIA	Indonesian Intelligence Agency
Boleh juga!	Yes – (in agreement)
Boleh, silahkan	Please do…
Bubur	Porridge
Bugis	Celebes (Sulawesi) warrior-merchant sailors
Bukit	Hill or mountain
Bukit Batubrok	Mountain in the Upper-Mahakam area
Busang	Kalimantan tribe
Cakap amat	Very handsome
Comro	Mashed Cassava
Cukong	Chinese broker

DAO Backup	Double Action Only Backup – a secondary weapon often used by the prestigious Texas Rangers
Dayak	Majority indigenous groups of Borneo
Darul Islam/Tentara Islam Indonesia	Indonesian Moslem Army (subversive)
Diponegoro	Historical hero – Javanese Army Division
Dukun	Shaman – witch doctor – village healer
Durian	Melon-shaped, highly pungent, tropical fruit
Expats	Expatriates, foreigners
Falintil	Military arm of East Timor's Fretelin
Fossick	Australian mining slang for searching around a mine – also to scrummage for something
Ganjah	Marijuana
'Going twenty to the dozen'	Moving or doing something very fast
Golok	Machete
Gong	Half-metal drum used for announcements
Guru	Teacher, master
Hadui taknaq	Dayak ceremony celebrating one's passing
Hampatong	Dayak spiritual statues
Hari Raya Idulfitri	Moslem celebrations at the end of the *Ramadan* fast
Iban	Borneo tribe (Northern Borneo)
Immigrasi	Immigration
ITB	Institute of Technology, Bandung, West Java
Irian Jaya	West New Guinea or West Papua
Irian Barat	West New Guinea or West Papua
Jaka Tigkir	Javanese prince who murdered his father in law and then established his own kingdom

Jalan	Road or street
Jalan Cendana	The Suharto residence – also the name of the street
Jalan Asia Afrika	Bandung street
Jalan Dalam Kaum	Bandung street
Jalan Martadinata	Bandung street
Jalan Thamrin	Main protocol street in CBD Jakarta
Jalan Waringan	Street close to President's home in Menteng, Jakarta
Jali-jali	*Betwati* (Original Jakarta) song and verse
Jam karet	'rubber time'
Kaharingan	Dayak belief that ancestral spirits control life
Kain kebaya	Traditional sarong and blouse dress
Kalimantan	Indonesian Borneo
KalimantanTimur	East Indonesian Borneo Province
'Kami mau pulang'	'we want to go home'
Kampung	Village
Kappa 8	Japanese-Indonesian cooperative rocket program launch in 1964
Kartika 1	Indonesian Air Force first successful rocket launch in 1964 – as part of *Project Prima*
Kayan	Borneo tribe
Kehayan River	Kalimantan River
Kitab Suci	The Bible
Kodam	Designated military command area
Komisaris	Cross between a Soviet styled commissar and Western Secretary to the Board of Directors whose responsibility is to maintain a watching brief of the Board's activities and advise them and shareholders. (*President Komisaris – The senior Komisar)*
Kopassus	Indonesian Special Forces

Kopi, yo!	Let's get some coffee!
Kosgoro	A corporate entity, operating ostensibly as a 'cooperative' owned and controlled by the Indonesian Army, and presided over by the Secretary of State's personal assistant. *Kosgoro* formed many joint ventures, in industry, agriculture (pig farms in Java) and even nightclubs in Jakarta (LCC).
Kostrad	Indonesian Army Strategic Reserve Command
Kowilhan	Indonesian Territorial Command area
Krait	Deadly viper, normally with colourful bands
Kraton	Sultan of Jogyakarta's Palace
Kretek	Clove cigarette
Kupu-kupu	Butterfly
Ladang	Dry field such as for growing corn. Dayaks did not use the same irrigation systems as found in Java & Bali
Lasan	Village in the Upper-Mahakam area
Latihan	Exercise
Lechon	Filipino mini-feast with a roast pig
Lintah-darah	Leech, bloodsucker
Long Gelat	Kalimantan tribal area
Longboat	River vessel
Longhouse	Dayak traditional, community dwelling
Longbangun	Village on the Mahakam
Longdamai	Upper-Mahakam area near Bukit Batubrok
Longdamai Sial	River reaches located within Longdamai area
Losmen	Boarding house- backpackers' accommodations
Lumpia sariwa	Filipino dish

Maaf	Excuse me
Mabuhay	(ma-boo-high) has a variety of meanings amongst which are: Welcome, congratulations, thanks, etc
Madu pete	First stage of Dayak cremation
Madura	Island of East Java (densely populated)
Madurese	Inhabitants of Madura
Makanan kecil	finger food – snack
Makati	City of Makati is CBD Manila
Mandau	Traditional, Dayak sword used for executions
Mas	Friendly 'you' (male only)
Mengayau	The practice of headhunting
Meranti	Species of tree
Merauke	Indonesia's most easterly town
Modang	Lesser East Borneo (Kalimantan) tribe
Nayau	Ancestral spirits
Nenek moyang	Ancestors
NGO	Non-Governmental Organization
Oleh-oleh	Gifts, like souvenirs
OPM	West Papuan Separatist Movement (militant)
Operasi Sapu Bersih	Operation 'Clean Sweep'
Ot Danum	Kalimantan tribe
PAF	Philippines Air Force
Pak	Abbreviated form of *Bapak,* sir
Palapa Program	Indonesia's Satellite Programme
Pamekasan Baru	Madurese settlement on the Mahakam (fictitious)
Pancit	Filipino dish
Parahayangan Mts	Mountains surrounding Bandung in W. Java
Parang	Machete

Pasar Kota Kembang	Mall in the city of Bandung
Penehing	Upper Mahakam Dayak tribe
Perahu	Sailing boat, canoe
Permesta	*Piagam Perjuangan Semesta* 'Charter of Common Struggle' – Indonesian revolutionary forces which failed in their attempts to depose President Soekarno.
Pesut	Mahakam River freshwater dolphin
Pondok Indah	Elitist suburb south of Jakarta
Poofter	Slur for male homosexual, effeminate male (sometimes, just the odd man out)
Pork adobo	Filipino speciality dish
Pribumi	Indigene – son of the soil
Project Prima	Preliminary Scientific and Military Rocket Research and Development Project
P.T.	Abbreviated form of Limited Liability company.
P.T. Pindad	Indonesian Army weapons' factory.
Pulau Edam	Lighthouse Island – ten miles offshore Jakarta.
Pulutan	Filipino *hors d'ouvres* to go with the drinks
Purun	A rush
Ramadan	Fasting month leading to *Idulfitri* celebrations
Rellenong Manok	Filipino dish, de-boned chicken
Ringgit	Malaysian dollar
Robusta	Coffee type
Rokok	Cigarette
Rotan	Ratan, rattan
RPKAD	Indonesian Special Forces
Rupiah	Indonesian currency
Sabang	Indonesia's most westerly town
Salak	Fruit of a palm

Samarinda	Provincial capital of East Kalimantan
Sambal	Hot chilli paste
Sang Merah Putih	Indonesia's Red & White flag
Sate	Meat, food cooked on a stick
Saya tidak mengerti	I don't understand
Selamatan	Religious thanksgiving/meal
Selamat datang	Welcome
Selamat Siang	Hello, good day (1100 – 1500)
Selamat malam	Good evening.
Selamat pagi, non	Good morning, Miss.
Sialan!	Exclamation – Goddamn! – damn!
Selendang	Long, wide shawl worn over the shoulder
shabu-shabu	Crystal methamphetamine
Siliwangi	Central Javanese Military Command
'Stunned mullet'	Someone who does not seem to be 'with it' – confused
'Sudah kawin, tapi belum nikah'	Indonesian play on words. Been bedded but unmarried
Sukun	Breadfruit
Sulawesi	Celebes
Sumenep	Town on the island of Madura
Tagalog	Filipino language
Tanamur	Well known Jakarta disco bar founded by Fahmi and Ratna in 1971 – acronym for the street it is located on Tanah Abang Timur
Tempe	Fermented Soya bean cake
Tidak may terus	Don't want to continue
Tinolang Tahong	Filipino dish
Tokek	Large, colourful, loud, tropical lizards frequently referred to as geckos

Tofu	Soya bean cake
Tenaga dalam	Inner strength
Terima kasih	Thank you
Tidak mau terus	Do not want to continue
Tikar	Woven mat used for sleeping, praying
TNI	Indonesian Military
Tuak	Potent form of *arack*
Tuan	(Sir) Formal address
Tunjung	Kalimantan tribe
'Turd-burglar'	Crass term for male homosexual (also 'rear-gunner')
Ubi Kayu	Cassava
Ujung Pandang	New name for Makassar
Zamboanga	Southern Philippines port

Also from Sid Harta Publishers

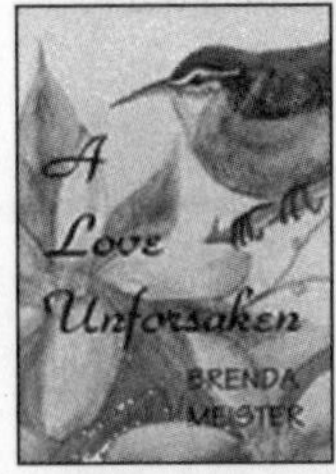

OTHER BEST SELLING SID HARTA TITLES CAN BE FOUND AT

http://www.sidharta.com.au
http://Anzac.sidharta.com

★★★

HAVE YOU WRITTEN A STORY?

http://www.publisher-guidelines.com
for manuscript guideline submissions

★★★

LOOKING FOR A PUBLISHER?

http://www.temple-house.com

New Releases...

Other best-selling titles by Kerry B. Collison

Readers are invited to visit our publishing websites at:

http://www.sidharta.com.au

http://www.publisher-guidelines.com/

http://temple-house.com/

Kerry B. Collison's home pages:

http://www.authorsden.com/visit/author.asp?AuthorID=2239

http://www.expat.or.id/sponsors/collison.html

http://clubs.yahoo.com/clubs/asianintelligencesresources

email: author@sidharta.com.au